HEATH SCIENCE CONNECTIONS 10

Jack L. Candido
Edward S. James
Ronald E. Phillips
Bryan D. Kaufman
Glen W. Wiley

HEATH

D.C. Heath Canada Ltd.

Design: Blair Kerrigan/Glyphics Inc.

Typesetting: Compeer Typographic Services Limited

Illustration: Acorn Technical Art Studio Inc./Peter Van Gulik

Communications Branch, Consumer and Corporate Affairs Canada has granted use of the National Symbol for Metric Conversion.

Canadian Cataloguing in Publication Data

Main entry under title:
Heath science connections 10

For use in Grade 10.
Includes index.
ISBN 0-669-95285-0

1. Science.   I. Candido, Jack L.

Q161.2.H43 1988   500   C87-095224-2

Printed and bound in Canada.   5 6   BP   93 92 91

The cover shows a sphere containing gases. When touched, a small lightning charge is given off.
Photo by Pete Turner/Image Bank

Acknowledgements

Many people contributed their ideas and services during the preparation of this book. We would like to thank the following people at D.C. Heath Canada: Ron Cornelius, editorial program manager, who assisted greatly in developing the final form and content of the book; Jean Bullard and Jane McNulty, editors, whose diligent and tireless efforts are in large part responsible for the finished product; Cathy McVicar, the copy editor, for her immaculate work; Stephanie Cox, production manager, along with Laura Jones, production editor, and Lana Kong for her work as a production editor and her invaluable editorial assistance; Sharon Kirsch for her editorial assistance; and finally Martin Goldberg, vice-president, who oversaw the project from its inception. We also extend our thanks to Helmut Weyerstrahs for overseeing the rough paste-up and Irma Ikonen for her meticulous final assembly; Peter Van Gulik and Acorn Illustration & Art Studio for their illustrations; Jane Affleck and Elaine Freedman for acquiring the photos and arranging photo sessions; and Birgitte Nielsen, the photographer. Our appreciation goes to journalist Judy Ross, who conducted the career interviews.

The authors also acknowledge the contributions of Eric Grace (Units 1, 2, and 3), John Freeman (Unit 5), and Douglas V. Lintula (Unit 7). Special thanks to Herb Deruyter for his assistance in developing Unit 2 and to Don Balcarras for assisting in the preparation of Unit 8.

The authors wish to acknowledge the patience and support of their families and friends, especially the following people to whom this book is dedicated: Lola, Leo, Joan, Ian, Paul, Tyler, and Corey; Jane, Scott, Claire, Jim, Marjorie, and Len; Paige, Shannon, Laurel, and Al; Walter and Dorothy. Thanks are also due to the students of Kitchener-Waterloo Collegiate and Vocational School, and of Eastwood Collegiate, Kitchener, who appear in photos throughout this book. We would also like to thank the interview subjects for having devoted their time and energy.

Finally, we would like to thank the numerous science educators who read parts of the manuscript and made many valuable suggestions. The aid of these people has made the book substantially better than it otherwise would have been. The reviewers were: John Pettit, Nels and Loretta Banting, Don Coukell, Paul Yamaguchi, Don Stephen, Norris Reynolds, Frank Mustoe, Robert Macnaughton, Cathy Mathews, Bruce Dureno, Randall Rose, Jan Unger, Paul Kraemer, Jim Moisse, Jeff Sage, Reg Friesen, Allan Craig, and Les Asselstine.

Table of Contents

Introduction

I Studying Science

What Is Science?

Today, more than ever, we are living in a scientific age. The products and ideas of science, both good and bad, surround us and affect our daily lives. It is difficult to know where science will take us in the future. However, there can be little doubt that, because of scientific advances, the world of tomorrow will be different from the world of today.

What is science, and why is it important? Put simply, **science is a way of gaining knowledge and understanding of our natural world**. The desire to know how or why something happens is the driving force behind all scientific inquiry. As science produces new knowledge, some people try to apply these findings to human and social problems. The use of scientific knowledge to make products designed to improve the quality of our lives is called **technology**.

In this century, we have made many scientific and technological advances of great benefit. We have discovered principles of nature that have allowed us to build computers to help us process information, to construct robots to do our work, and to explore space. Technological developments have helped us to grow better crops, to treat and prevent disease, and to create thousands of useful products, from sophisticated communications systems to powerful laundry detergents, to more fuel-efficient cars. Along with these benefits, however, have come widespread air and water pollution, abuse of the Earth's resources, and nuclear weapons.

Clearly, we cannot allow scientific development to proceed in an uncontrolled way. To do so would be irresponsible and could lead to disastrous consequences. But should only scientists, who are the most knowledgeable about their research, be involved in regulating scientific activity? The answer is no! Since much scientific research eventually has an impact on our lives, we must all be aware of the issues. The following section discusses how scientists make discoveries and solve problems.

The use of robots in auto assembly plants frees people to do more creative work.

The Scientific Approach

There is no magic formula for success in science, just as there is no guaranteed strategy for composing songs or painting pictures. What is important, rather, is the *approach* to problem-solving. In science, this means open-minded observation of the world around us, thinking about what we observe, making guesses to explain or predict phenomena, and then devising ways to test our guesses.

Many scientific discoveries have occurred by accident, sometimes in the course of investigating something else. In 1896, radioactivity was discovered when Henri Becquerel accidentally left a piece of uranium ore on a sealed photographic plate, and then found the film had been exposed despite its wrapping. Penicillin was discovered by Sir Alexander Fleming in 1928 when some bacteria in a laboratory became contaminated with mould and were killed. These accidents led to discoveries, however, because the scientists' minds were open and receptive to the clues provided.

Observation, Fact, and Scientific Law

Making careful observations is often the first step in scientific problem-solving. An **observation** is any information that is gathered through our senses. Everything we see, hear, taste, touch, or smell is an observation. If all observers agree about an observation, it is considered a **fact;** that is, an accepted truth, something that everyone regards as correct. While many observers may agree upon a certain fact, only a keen and informed observer can *verify* the fact by means of science.

A **scientific law** defines a relationship between observed facts. For example, the law of gravity states that bodies of matter attract each other: an arrow shot from a bow eventually falls to the Earth. Scientific laws describe natural events, but they do not explain them.

We often observe changes in temperature, colour, and many other characteristics, or properties, of matter. These observations are termed **qualitative** observations. Beyond merely observing such changes, we sometimes try to measure *how much* the temperature, the colour, or some other property has changed. Accurate temperature readings with a thermometer are more informative to a doctor than simply feeling patients' foreheads. Observations that answer the question "How much?" are termed **quantitative** observations.

Precise observations, both qualitative and quantitative, play a central role in science. Often, many observations must be made before a question can be answered. After making the necessary observations, we can examine them for possible patterns. This process is called interpretation, or **making inferences**. Sometimes, observations lead to questions that cannot be answered by further observations. It might then be necessary to find another way to solve the problem, that is, by designing an experiment.

Hypotheses and Experiments

Suppose that on the day following a class field trip to the zoo, many of the students became ill. The school principal called upon public health officials to find the cause of the illness.

The investigators began by making observations and gathering information. These actions led to several possible explanations for the illness. First, there might have been something wrong with the food the students had eaten. Second, there might have been something wrong with the water the students had drunk. Third, a person or an animal at the zoo could have communicated a disease to the students.

A possible answer or explanation for a problem is called a **hypothesis**. A good hypothesis is stated in a form that suggests a way to test the explanation. One such form is an "If...then" statement. In the case of the zoo excursion, one possible hypothesis could be, "If the water at the zoo were bad, then all the students who drank that water would have become ill". Can you state other hypotheses that might explain the students' illness?

Scientists try to formulate the most reasonable answers to their questions, and then look for evidence that supports or rejects these hypotheses. One way to find evidence and therefore to test a hypothesis is by conducting an experiment. In our case study, the investigators tried to determine which hypothesis explained the illness. They gathered information and made observations to test each hypothesis. They questioned the students in order to record what they had had to eat and drink, and which zoo animals they had visited. Those students who had not eaten the picnic lunch but had instead bought their food and drinks at the zoo did not become ill. Therefore, the investigators suspected the food or water in the picnic lunch, rather than a contagious disease transmitted by animals or humans. Experiments were carried out in a medical laboratory on samples of food and water. All the observations that the investigators and the medical testing laboratory recorded—that is, all the information collected in an experiment—are called **data**.

By systematically comparing pure food and water to the samples of food and water consumed at the zoo, each of the hypotheses could be tested in what scientists call **controlled experiments**. By comparing pure water with water from the zoo, investigators could find out if there were anything unusual in the latter. The pure water is called a **control**. If the zoo water were in any way different from the pure water, that difference could be the cause of the students' illness.

Controlled experiments permit scientists to test the effect of one experimental factor at a time, while all other factors remain constant. Scientists are therefore assured that any difference between the results of a control and an experiment must be due to the factor being tested.

The experimental factors being tested that can be changed are called **variables**. When collecting data, researchers are careful to change only one variable at a time. (This is what is meant by a "controlled" experiment.) The variable that is of interest, called the **independent variable**, is changed, and the effect on the outcome, or the **dependent variable**, is observed. All other variable quantities are not allowed to change. Performing a controlled experiment allows the investigator to discover whether or not a relationship exists between two variables. In our investigation, the independent variable is the food and water consumed by the students. The outcome, or dependent variable, is the illness suffered by the students who consumed the food and water.

The drinking water at the zoo proved to be pure. Thus, the hypothesis that water might have been the cause of the illness was discarded. This is a common occurrence in scientific experiments. The results obtained from an experiment do not always support the hypothesis. The aim in testing a hypothesis is not to *prove* the hypothesis, but to discover which facts are worth examining. The investigators therefore focused on another hypothesis. Tests showed that most of the food in the picnic lunch was also pure. However, bacteria were found in the egg salad sandwiches. Such bacteria can thrive when foods are not properly refrigerated, especially in warm weather. The investigators concluded that the bacteria in the sandwiches were the cause of the illness. They prepared a written report of the findings for the doctors, the school principal, and the media. Under proper medical care, all the stricken students recovered in a few days.

Scientific Theories and Models

Hypotheses are only tentative explanations for what is observed. They are working ideas that may change constantly to fit new experimental data. If many scientists test a hypothesis again and again, and always find that the experimental results support the hypothesis, then the hypothesis becomes widely accepted as a valid explanation. When a hypothesis explains many observations, leading to predictions that are consistently supported by experiments, it may eventually be termed a **scientific theory**. Developing a sound scientific theory usually requires careful analysis of the results of many experiments. Some important theories in science have been developed over hundreds of years, and are based on the work of many scientists.

A scientific theory can be changed if new evidence contradicts part of the theory. Often, theories are modified slightly to fit new evidence. Scientific evidence can support a hypothesis or a theory, but it cannot prove a theory.

One theory universally accepted by scientists today is the germ theory of disease, which was first suggested as a hypothesis only about a hundred years ago. Before this theory was established, people believed that illness was caused by evil spirits, by curses, or by sin.

When scientists began to use microscopes, however, they discovered that tiny living things — microorganisms — were everywhere, and they also noticed a connection between these microorganisms and disease. In the nineteenth century, Louis Pasteur hypothesized that microorganisms were the cause of disease, but few people accepted this hypothesis at first. However, as scientists conducted more and more experiments, recording more and more observations that supported Pasteur's hypothesis, it became a **theory** — the germ theory of disease.

Theories often take the form of **models**. Toy trains are models of real trains. Some toy trains are detailed scale models that run on tracks, stop at stations, and even sound like real trains. Others are simply painted blocks, on wheels, joined together, and pulled by a string. Models are simplified versions of reality; they omit many complex details, but they retain enough information to describe a phenomenon or a behaviour closely enough to be useful. Even though the resemblance can be remarkable, no one would confuse a model train with the real thing. Sometimes a model is a mental image, rather than an actual object or a group of objects.

Models and theories can be used to make predictions; they not only account for known facts, but they can also point to new ones. Experiments to verify the predicted facts are used to test theories and models. As new facts are discovered, theories and models are modified accordingly. Dalton's atomic model, for example, represented the atom as a small, indivisible particle not unlike a billiard ball. The discovery of electrical charge led to the Thomson "blueberry muffin" model of the atom, which took into account the existence of electrons. However, when Rutherford and other scientists discovered new facts about the atom, they had to abandon Thomson's model and to search for a better one. The modern model of the atom continues to be modified as new facts are discovered.

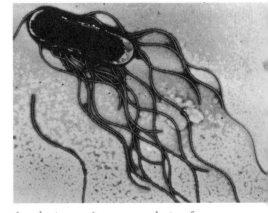

An electron microscope photo of *Salmonella* bacteria. If allowed to contaminate food, this microorganism can cause disease or death.

In summary, when scientists try to answer a question, they often follow certain steps, called the scientific approach. These are:

1. observing a phenomenon, behaviour, or event,
2. defining a problem or a question related to the observation(s),
3. making a hypothesis to explain the observation(s),
4. testing the hypothesis by means of further observations and/or a controlled experiment,
5. observing and recording the results of observations and experiments,
6. drawing conclusions based on the data,
7. reporting the final results, which either support or invalidate the hypothesis.

Such a list might imply that scientists follow these steps much like a recipe in a cookbook, but this is not so. The steps in the scientific approach are simply a good method of solving problems.

Study Questions

1. Explain the meaning of each of the terms printed in boldface in the Introduction.
2. Summarize the steps in the scientific approach.

II   Working Safely in the Laboratory
Laboratory Rules

The laboratory is a safe working place when everyone follows the rules. Below are some instructions for working in the lab.

1. The night before the lab, read over the assigned activity to make sure you understand it.
2. Wear an apron to protect your clothing. Do not bring coats, jackets, or caps into the lab.
3. Take note of the hazard symbols and caution notes shown in the margins of the text. Wear safety goggles: i) when heating substances, ii) when using chemicals, iii) any time when instructed to do so by your teacher or the text.
4. Be neat. If you spill something, inform your teacher.

5. When working, place your stool out of the way under the desk. Make a mental note of an escape route. You will know how to get out of the way quickly if an accident occurs.

6. When working in the lab, never taste anything and never bring in food or drink. Even chewing gum can be dangerous. Avoid touching chemicals with your hands. This will prevent you from accidentally transferring a poisonous substance from your hands to your mouth.

7. a) When heating substances, never point the test tube at yourself or a classmate. Point the tube along the length of the desk.

   b) If your experiment catches fire, stand back immediately. *Notify your teacher at once.* Then, think about ways to extinguish it, such as turning off the gas, smothering the fire with a glass plate, ceramic pad, etc.

8. Use only the chemicals you are directed to use. Check the label first to make sure you are using the right substance. If in doubt, ask your teacher. To avoid contamination, *do not return* used chemicals to the storage bottle.

9. If you spill an acid or another corrosive material:

   a) on your skin or in your eyes — flood the affected area constantly with water, and notify the teacher. Do not rub the area. Tell your teacher if you wear contact lenses.

   b) on your desk or on the floor — flood the area with water, and use plenty of paper towels to brush the spill into the sink or to mop it up. Use a mop to clean the floor.

   c) on your clothing — use lots of water and wipe with damp towels. Use a stain remover when you get home.

10. When finished an experiment, clean up and put away equipment *before* continuing to work on your report. Dispose of solid waste in the container specially provided (*not* in the sink). Empty liquids into the sink and wash them down with plenty of water, unless otherwise directed. Wipe the table top thoroughly.

11. Wash your hands with soap after an experiment. Even small amounts of chemicals may become irritating to the skin if left on for several hours. Washing your hands also prevents the possibility of contaminating any food you handle later on.

In all situations, act responsibly and carefully. Common sense will tell you why the lab is no place for carelessness or games. Be as concerned for your neighbours' safety as for your own.

Table 1: Hazard Symbols

Explosive
The materials or equipment used could explode under certain conditions.

Flammable
There is danger of the substance catching fire.

Toxic
The material is very poisonous.

Harmful
The material, while less toxic, is still dangerous.

Oxidizer
The substance may readily ignite and burn when in contact with other substances.

Corrosive
The substance may eat away at skin, clothing, or other material.

Irritant
The substance may irritate the skin, eyes, nose, or lungs.

Biological
There is danger of infection or poisoning from animals, plants, or microorganisms.

Radioactive
The substance is radioactive and gives off radiation.

Electrical
There is danger of electric shock.

Hazard Symbols

Hazard symbols and cautions are shown in the margin when they are considered important. The symbols are patterned after those used by the United Nations. Many of the hazard symbols shown here are used in this text.

The use of aprons and safety goggles is recommended when the following symbols appear.

apron   safety goggles

If no hazard symbol or caution is indicated for a particular activity, this does not mean that no risks are involved. Your teacher is responsible for the safety of the class as a whole, but you also have a responsibility to behave in an appropriate manner and to handle equipment safely in the lab. Always be alert to possible dangers when performing an activity.

Preventing Accidents

Most accidents that occur in the lab are caused by carelessness. The most common causes are:

1. Applying too much pressure to glassware — especially when inserting and removing glass tubing from rubber stoppers. Microscope glass slides and cover slips are also easily broken.
2. Handling hot equipment without proper care.
3. Using improper amounts or incorrect mixtures of chemicals.
4. Having messy and disorganized work spaces.
5. Indulging in inappropriate behaviour.

If an Accident Occurs

1. Report all accidents and injuries, however minor, to your teacher.
2. Report any cuts to your teacher for proper medical attention.
3. Run cold water over burns immediately. Allow the water to run over the burn for about five minutes.

4. If chemicals splash into your eyes, rinse them repeatedly with water for about five minutes. Your teacher may recommend further action.
5. If acid splashes on your skin, rinse the affected area with plenty of water. Your teacher may recommend further action.

Study Question

1. Identify the safety hazards depicted in the following illustration.

Environmental Interactions

What are your first impressions of the wilderness scene shown here? Despite its peaceful appearance, this marsh is a busy place. The browsing moose stirs up a feast for tiny underwater organisms that become food for young fish. The fish in turn become food for otters. Such activities are examples of environmental interactions.

The term **environment** refers to everything in an organism's surroundings. All organisms must interact with their environments for food and shelter. Human interactions, however, often cause damage and environmental problems that threaten our planet's ability to support us. The future of the Earth depends on our solving these problems and preventing new ones. Only by understanding the complexity of environmental interactions can long-term solutions be worked out.

In Unit I, you will explore the natural environment, study the interactions that maintain the balance of nature, and consider how human activities affect that balance.

Chapter 1   Basic Ecology

1.1   Classifying the Natural Environment
1.2   The Structure of Ecosystems
1.3   Ecosystems and Energy Pathways
1.4   Cycles of Matter

Chapter 2   Populations, Communities, and Biomes

2.1   Populations and How They Grow
2.2   Community Interactions
2.3   Biomes
2.4   Biomes and Natural Succession

Chapter 3   The Role of Humans in the Biosphere

3.1   The Human Impact Upon the Environment
3.2   Examining Environmental Issues

Chapter 1
Basic Ecology

Ecology is the science that studies the interactions of living things with each other and with their surroundings, both living and non-living. Like many scientific terms, the word ecology is formed from two Greek words: "oikos" meaning home, and "logos" meaning study. The home referred to is planet Earth.

Ecology is a branch of biology. The ancient Greek word "bios" means life, and biologists study living things. For example, a biologist might examine a spider to find out how it digests flies. Ecologists, however, study interactions. An ecologist might count and identify all the insects a spider eats to find out how many spiders and flies can live in one area.

Ecology has become an increasingly important science in recent years because our survival depends on understanding environmental interactions. In this chapter you will become better acquainted with the natural environment, learn the terms scientists use to describe it, and examine some of ecology's most fundamental ideas.

When you finish Chapter 1, you should be able to:

- identify both biotic (living) and abiotic (nonliving) components of the natural environment
- list and define the trophic (feeding) levels in a food chain
- discuss the relationships among ecosystems, food chains, food webs, and food pyramids
- explain how matter and energy are transferred and transported throughout the environment
- understand how nutrients such as carbon, water, and nitrogen are recycled from living things back to the abiotic environment
- consider how environmental problems such as bioconcentration upset the balance of nature

1.1 Classifying the Natural Environment

Whenever scientists are faced with large, complex collections of data, they classify the information to make it more manageable. Ecologists are no exception. They classify the Earth's environment into two categories: the **biotic** (living) environment and the **abiotic** (nonliving) environment.

Classify the biotic and abiotic components in each of these photos. What interactions are taking place?

Biotic and Abiotic Environments

The biotic environment consists of all living things: animals, plants, and microorganisms. The abiotic environment consists of nonliving components, such as air, water, minerals, climate, and the Sun's radiation.

All living things interact with the abiotic environment. When you inhale, for example, your body extracts oxygen from the air. When you exhale, you add carbon dioxide and water vapour to the abiotic environment. Whenever you drink, wash, bathe, or eliminate wastes, you are interacting with both the biotic and abiotic environments. When you eat, you are interacting with the biotic environment.

Figure 1-1. Classify the classroom environment in Figure 1-1 into biotic and abiotic categories. What interactions occur between the components in your lists?

Producers and Consumers

Ecologists classify the organisms of the biotic environment into two major groups: producers and consumers.

Producers manufacture food directly from the abiotic environment. All green plants are producers because, during photosynthesis, they make food from sunlight, water, and carbon dioxide. Producers are often called **autotrophs**, a term deriving from the ancient Greek words "auto" for self, and "trophos" for feeder. Examples of autotrophs include trees, grass, moss, and seaweed.

Consumers cannot manufacture food. Instead, they obtain nourishment from the biotic environment by consuming other organisms. For this reason they are often called **heterotrophs** (from the Greek "heteros", meaning other). Examples of heterotrophs are insects, fish, snails, and human beings. Because they must eat other organisms to live, these and all other animals are consumers.

Identify the autotrophs and heterotrophs in this photograph. What heterotroph(s) may be nearby?

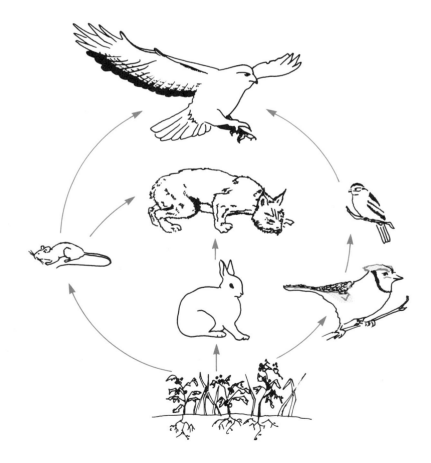

Figure 1-2. Pathways of food consumption in a Canadian woodland. Classify these organisms as autotrophs or heterotrophs.

This means that all animals are dependent on producers, either directly or indirectly. Plant-eaters such as the moose are directly dependent. Meat-eaters such as the spider are indirectly dependent, because all the food they eat can be traced back to green-plant producers. Other organisms, such as fungi, also depend on green plant producers.

In fact, the entire biotic environment depends on autotrophs. Without green plants to produce food from energy and materials in the abiotic environment, the consumers would soon go hungry.

Scavengers and Decomposers

Not all heterotrophs eat plants or other animals. Some play a vital role in the environment by obtaining their food from dead organisms. Once an organism dies, the materials in its dead body become part of the abiotic environment. If corpses were indestructible, our roads and yards would soon become carpeted with layers of dead plants and animal carcasses. Fortunately, nature provides some clean-up methods.

A **scavenger** is a consumer of dead organisms. Scavengers such as vultures and jackals do not usually kill their own food. Instead, they consume the meat of animals that have already died. Some scavengers, such as houseflies, deposit their eggs in dead animals. The meat becomes a food source for hatching larvae or maggots.

A **decomposer** is a consumer that breaks down the bodies of dead organisms and the waste products of living things. Decomposers carry out chemical decomposition. Through their actions, the large, complex molecules of living things are broken down into smaller, simpler molecules and are released into the environment.

What will happen to this zebra's bones after vultures have stripped the flesh from them?

How long do you think it will take this rotting tree trunk to disappear?

Bacteria, mushrooms, and other fungi all derive their nourishment by acting as decomposers.

Another breakdown process begins to occur even before scavengers and decomposers arrive on the scene. When death occurs, the organism's cells release chemicals that cause the body materials to disintegrate slowly. Whether a dead organism self-destructs in this way, is broken down by a decomposer, or is eaten by a scavenger, its body materials will eventually be returned to the air, soil, and water. Once they enter a plant through its roots or leaf pores, these materials rejoin the biotic environment.

Figure 1-3. Scavengers and decomposers link the biotic and abiotic environments.

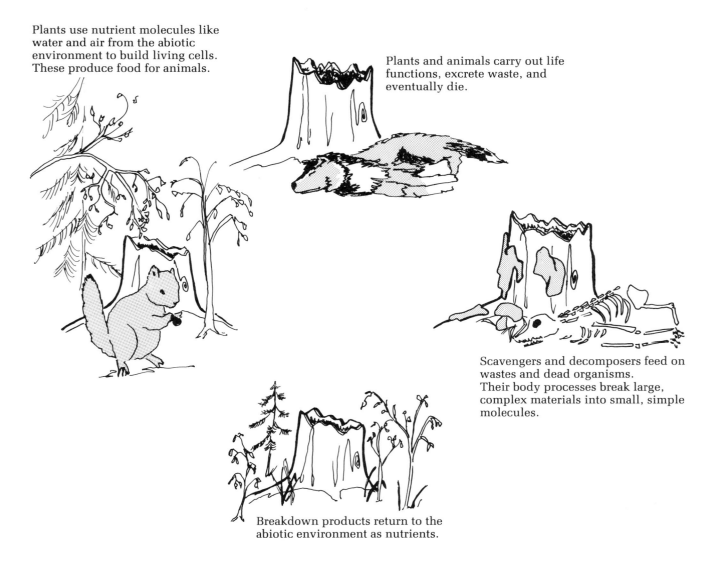

Plants use nutrient molecules like water and air from the abiotic environment to build living cells. These produce food for animals.

Plants and animals carry out life functions, excrete waste, and eventually die.

Scavengers and decomposers feed on wastes and dead organisms. Their body processes break large, complex materials into small, simple molecules.

Breakdown products return to the abiotic environment as nutrients.

Habitat and Niche

Although related, the terms "habitat" and "niche" have distinctly different meanings. A **habitat** is defined as the environmental space in which an organism lives, including other components of that space. For example, a bison's natural prairie habitat includes soil, air, inedible weeds, and insects, as well as the grasses it feeds on. Duckweed lives in a pond habitat that includes water as well as aquatic plants and animals.

Habitats vary in size. A caterpillar's habitat might be limited to just one part of an oak tree, while the habitat of a beluga whale might stretch across the Arctic Ocean.

Figure 1-4. Grass plants and bison occupy different niches in the same prairie habitat.

As bison breathe they exchange oxygen for carbon dioxide.

Bison are herd animals, roaming in search of more food when nearby grass is cropped.

Young or sick animals are eaten by wolves and coyotes. Dead animals provide food for vultures.

Bison are consumers of grass and other wild plants.

Bison provide nourishment for mosquitoes and fleas from their blood, and for flies and earthworms from their dung.

Grass leaves are food producers for bison and insects; they convert solar energy into food energy.

Grass roots penetrate soil, letting air in for microorganisms.

Grass leaves absorb carbon dioxide from the air and release oxygen.

The body wastes of bison are converted into nutrients by soil bacteria.

Soil microorganisms decompose dead vegetable matter and contribute to soil making.

The term **niche** refers to all the ways in which an organism interacts with its biotic and abiotic environments. A niche therefore includes both a habitat and an organism's role in its habitat. For example, the bison in Figure 1-4 shares the same habitat as the grass, but the two organisms have very different niches.

Ecology and Ecosystems

Everything scientists have learned about ecology suggests that all living things are part of one worldwide web, and that this living web is anchored to the nonliving world. The layer of our planet where living things exist and interact is called the **biosphere**. The biosphere can be classified into three major zones: the lithosphere, the hydrosphere, and the atmosphere.

The **lithosphere** is the solid portion of the Earth's surface. Consisting of soil, rock, and ice, it is home for countless organisms, such as millipedes, ferns, maple trees, and humans.

The **hydrosphere** is the layer of water that covers nearly three-quarters of the Earth's surface. It provides a habitat for numerous organisms, including dolphins, kelp, and green algae.

The **atmosphere** is the mass of air surrounding the Earth. As a habitat, it is less important than the other two zones, but it serves as a temporary "holding space" for organisms such as birds, insects, and airborne microorganisms.

Although smaller than the entire biosphere, each of these major zones is still too large for convenient study. Ecologists usually

Some consumers have complex relationships with producers. The pronuba moth, for example, interacts with the yucca plant in several ways. The yucca's nectar feeds the adult moth. The plant also serves as a habitat for the moth's eggs. The hungry larvae that hatch from the eggs feed on the contents of the plant's ovaries. The moth, in turn, carries pollen to and from neighbouring yucca plants.

Figure 1-5. The biosphere includes the lithosphere, hydrosphere, and the atmosphere.

atmosphere

lithosphere

hydrosphere

break down each zone into smaller units called ecosystems. An **ecosystem** is a unit of the biosphere in which organisms forming a distinct group interact with each other and with their environment.

The size of an ecosystem varies according to the objectives of the ecologist. One researcher might investigate an entire valley, while another observes a pond in the valley, and a third focuses on the microscopic organisms living in a drop on a single leaf. The study of ecosystems has no boundaries, so the story of ecology must include all of the many ecosystems on land and in the water.

Activity 1-1: A Survey of the Environment

Part A of this activity will be carried out in the classroom. The field exercise in Part B can be carried out in the school yard, a vacant lot, or a nearby park. Your teacher will show you how to use identification books to name the organisms you find in your study area.

Materials

magnifying glass	pencil
clip board	identification books
paper	

Part A: Examining Ecosystems

Procedure

Closely examine the four photographs on the next page, and then answer the discussion questions below.

Discussion

1. For photograph A (top left):
   a) identify the consumer(s) and producer(s).
   b) classify all components in the photograph as part of the abiotic environment or the biotic environment.
2. a) Which zones of the biosphere are shown in photograph B (top right)?
   b) Name as many components of each zone as possible.
3. a) Describe the habitat shown in photograph C (bottom left).
   b) Name the organisms that share this habitat.
   c) Classify each organism in photograph C as either an autotroph or a heterotroph.
4. Describe *completely* the niche occupied by the starfish in photograph D (bottom right).

A

B

C

D

5. a) Examine each photograph for evidence of scavengers or decomposers.
   b) If there is evidence, describe and explain it. If not, explain how you know that scavengers and decomposers probably do exist, even though you cannot see them.

6. Which of these photographs show an ecosystem? Explain.

Part B: Classifying the Environment — A Field Study
Procedure

1. Before leaving the classroom, make a copy of the following chart. Use it at the field site to record your observations.

Field observations at _____	Date: _____	Name: _____
List of components	Biotic	Abiotic
e.g., dandelion	X	
air		X

2. Classify everything in your assigned area as part of either the abiotic or the biotic environment.
3. Use the keys to identify as many components of the biotic environment as possible.

Discussion

1. Could the area you studied be considered an ecosystem? Explain.
2. a) To what extent is the field site studied by your class dependent on human care and maintenance?
   b) What would happen to this environment if there were no human influence?
3. Compare your observation chart with those of other class members.
   a) What part of the field site has the greatest variety in the biotic environment?
   b) What do you think are some reasons for this variety?
4. a) Did you observe any dead organisms in your field survey? If so, name them.
   b) Should dead organisms be classified as part of the biotic or abiotic environment? Explain.
5. a) In your field study, what evidence was there of decomposition and scavenging?
   b) If you saw any decomposers or scavengers, name them. If not, name some that might be present at times, and explain why you think so.

Study Questions

1. Define and give an example of each of the following: a) environment, b) biotic environment, c) abiotic environment.

2. a) Give an example to explain how the biotic environment depends on the abiotic environment.

   b) Use a diagram to explain how the abiotic environment depends on the biotic environment. (Hint: How are materials used by living things returned to the soil, air, or water?)

3. For each pair of terms below, explain first how the two terms are related, and then how they differ.

   a) biology and ecology
   b) producers and consumers
   c) scavengers and decomposers
   d) habitat and niche
   e) environment and ecosystem

4. Classify the following as heterotrophs or autotrophs.

   a) dandelion   c) potato beetle   e) moss
   b) cedar tree   d) distilled water   f) whooping crane

5. a) Define biosphere.
   b) List and define the three major parts of the biosphere.

6. The carcass of a road-killed animal disappears from a ditch over a four-month period. Name and explain each of the possible causes associated with this disappearance.

CHALLENGER

Choose a familiar tree native to Canada, and consult a reference book to identify the biotic and abiotic conditions that favour its growth. Try to find out whether or not your tree can thrive in large cities, and why.

This photo shows some common examples of biotic-abiotic interactions. How do all the different components of the scene (air, water, plants, and farmer) depend on one another?

1.2 The Structure of Ecosystems

Natural ecosystems usually include numerous organisms in a large area, and observing these ecosystems can be expensive and time-consuming. Student ecologists sometimes find it more convenient to set up an ecosystem in the classroom. Although they are small, model ecosystems have all the important features of larger, natural ecosystems.

Figure 1-6. A classroom ecosystem.

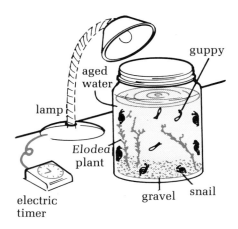

To "age" water, simply allow tap water to sit for 48 h to get rid of the chlorine dissolved in it.

CAUTION: Mount the lamp securely. Be sure it cannot be knocked over or swung closer to the jar.

Activity 1-2: A Classroom Ecosystem

In this activity, you will set up a miniature aquatic ecosystem for daily classroom observation.

Materials

large glass jar with screw-top lid

clean gravel

aged water

3 or 4 *Elodea* plants

lamp (40 W)
electric timer
3 guppies
6 snails

Procedure

1. Place 5 cm to 7 cm of clean gravel in a large glass jar.
2. Fill the jar with aged water almost to the top.
3. Add 3 or 4 *Elodea* plants.
4. Place a lamp with a 40 W light bulb approximately 5 cm to 10 cm from the jar.
5. Connect the lamp to an electric timer that will turn on the lamp for 12 h per day.
6. After three days, place the guppies and the snails in the jar.
7. After a week, seal the jar.
8. Answer the questions below once the ecosystem is established.

Discussion

1. Describe any food chain(s) established in this ecosystem.
2. Construct a diagram using arrows to show how each component in the model ecosystem interacts with every other component.
3. What do you think will happen to the model ecosystem if:
   a) the guppies reproduce?

b) the light bulb burns out over the weekend?

c) a 100 W light bulb is used instead?

d) the snails die?

4. Once the jar is sealed, can it be considered completely self-contained (that is, not dependent on any external factors)?

5. a) Draw a labelled diagram to show what gases are produced and consumed in the jar. Use arrows to show their locations and motions.

b) Is ''gas exchange'' a suitable term to describe the relationships shown in a)? Explain.

6. Could this classroom ecosystem operate just as successfully outdoors? Discuss.

Trophic Levels

In any ecosystem, interactions involve feeding habits. Thus, ecosystems are often described by classifying consumers according to their diet. Think about your own breakfast this morning. Was it all plant matter, such as cereal, bread, and jam? Or did you consume animal matter, such as bacon and eggs?

Consumers that eat both plant and animal material are called **omnivores**. Examples include pigs, black bears, and most humans. Animals that consume only plant material are called **herbivores** (e.g., cattle, sheep, and grasshoppers). Those that eat only animal material are called **carnivores** (e.g., foxes, sharks, and spiders).

Because a deer eats plants, it is classified as a herbivore.

Although a carnivore, the lion depends indirectly on plants eaten by gazelles and other African herbivores.

To classify consumers more precisely, ecologists use the concept of trophic level. A **trophic level** tells how directly a consumer interacts with the producers of its ecosystem. In the ecosystem shown in Figure 1-7, the grass plants are producers. The grasshopper, which eats grass directly, is a **primary consumer** because it feeds at the first trophic level above the producers. The frog that eats the grasshopper is a **secondary consumer** because it feeds at the second trophic level above the producers. The snake that eats the frog is a **tertiary consumer** because it feeds at the third trophic level. The owl that catches and eats the snake is considered a **quaternary consumer**. Animals that are not hunted for food by any other animal in the ecosystem are called top carnivores. The owl in this example is therefore a **top carnivore**.

Trophic levels can vary, depending on diet. A black bear eating berries is a primary consumer. When it eats fish, however, the bear is a secondary or a tertiary consumer.

Figure 1-7. Classifying consumers according to diet.

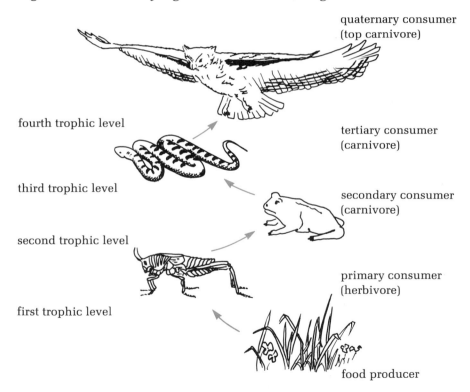

quaternary consumer
(top carnivore)

fourth trophic level

tertiary consumer
(carnivore)

third trophic level

secondary consumer
(carnivore)

second trophic level

primary consumer
(herbivore)

first trophic level

food producer

Food Chains and Food Webs

A **food chain** describes a feeding sequence in which each kind of organism eats the one below it in the chain. All food chains begin with a producer and include one or more consumers. For example, the grass-grasshopper-frog-snake-owl sequence just discussed is a food chain.

The organisms in a food chain are interdependent, and changes at any trophic level affect all other levels. Consider a food chain consisting of grass, rabbits, and foxes. A decrease in the number of rabbits (perhaps caused by human hunting) will affect both the foxes (which have less food) and the grass (which can grow without being eaten).

In most ecosystems, the interconnections between living things are more complex than those in a simple food chain. Most herbivores eat more than one kind of plant. A mouse, for example, eats seeds, leaves, and berries, depending on what is available. Most herbivores are eaten by more than one type of carnivore. The mouse is food for wolves, foxes, snakes, and owls.

Taken together, the interconnecting food chains of an ecosystem form what is called a **food web**. Identifying all the links in a food web increases our understanding of ecosystem complexity, and also increases our ability to predict the impact of human activities on the environment.

The fact that everything in an ecosystem is interconnected is not always appreciated when humans attempt to use the environment for their own purposes. For example, programs to eliminate wolves can cause changes in vegetation. Removing wolves permits deer herds to increase. This may lead to overbrowsing and hinder the growth of young trees, an important winter food. The ultimate result may be a reduced deer population.

Figure 1-8. A food web interconnects several different food chains.

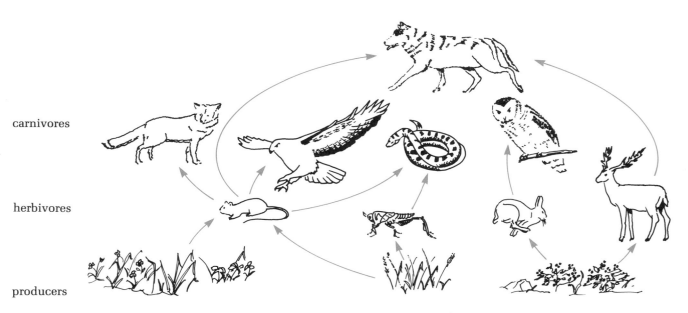

carnivores

herbivores

producers

Study Questions

1. Define and give an example of each of the following: a) herbivore, b) trophic level, c) food chain.

2. Why is a producer necessary in all food chains?

3. In a food chain, would you expect a greater number of:

   a) herbivores or carnivores? Explain.
   b) producers or consumers? Explain.

4. For each pair of terms below, explain first how the two terms are related, and then how they differ.

   a) omnivore and carnivore
   b) primary consumer and tertiary consumer
   c) food chain and food web

5. Consider the following organisms: berries, snake, grass, rabbit, frog, wolves, grain seeds, raccoons, owl, grasshopper, deer, hawk, trees, mouse, and shrubs.

   a) Construct three different food chains involving the organisms above. Identify the trophic level of each organism in these food chains.
   b) Construct a food web combining these three food chains. Make sure your food web includes a top carnivore. Add one if necessary.

6. Study the food web you constructed in 5b).

   a) How many different food chains exist? If there are more than the original three, explain how this happened.
   b) List the producers in the food web.
   c) List the herbivores.
   d) List the carnivores, and identify any top carnivores.

1.3 Ecosystems and Energy Pathways

All living things need energy to carry out their daily activities. Organisms such as animals, fungi, and bacteria get their energy by consuming food. With few exceptions, all food webs are based on green plant producers, which collect solar energy from the abiotic environment and convert it to chemical energy through photosynthesis. This chemical energy is stored in plant structures such as roots and seeds, where it is usually called food energy.

Food energy is used first of all by the plants themselves for their own life functions. Stored plant energy is transferred to animals when herbivores eat the plants. Energy stored in herbivores is trans-

ferred again when carnivores eat the plant-eaters. Thus, although the Sun is the ultimate source of energy for most living things on Earth, food is what carries that energy throughout every ecosystem. To trace the pathway of energy, we simply follow the food chain.

Food Pyramids

Food chains show how many transfers occur as energy moves through an ecosystem. They do not show the number of organisms involved at each level. Usually there are more animals that get eaten than animals that do the eating. There might be one fox to every hundred rabbits, but not one rabbit to every hundred foxes! Because the numbers are "bottom-heavy", ecologists often arrange food chains into **food pyramids**. There are three types of food pyramids.

A pyramid based on the number of organisms at each trophic level is called a **pyramid of numbers**. An example is shown in Figure 1-9. The pyramid of numbers is of limited value for investigating the pathway of energy through an ecosystem. For example,

The pyramid of numbers is ideal for studying how many organisms a given ecosystem can support. It is therefore used in population studies, which will be examined in Chapter 2.

Figure 1-9. A pyramid of numbers is a model of an ecosystem.

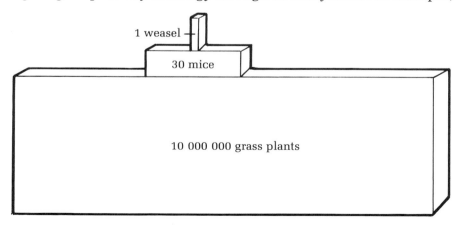

1 weasel

30 mice

10 000 000 grass plants

Figure 1-10. The pyramid of numbers does not show the quantity of food obtained by organisms. Quite clearly the mosquitoes do not consume an entire moose!

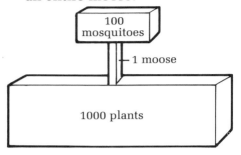

Figure 1-11. A pyramid of biomass for an aquatic ecosystem.

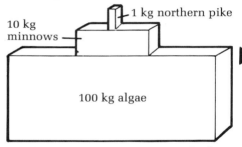

Figure 1-12. A pyramid of energy. Energy is measured in units called **kilojoules**. Since organisms consume other organisms for energy, an energy pyramid best represents the relationship between trophic levels.

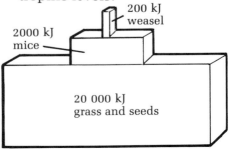

the moose-mosquito pyramid in Figure 1-10 looks top-heavy, because it does not reveal the mass of food at each level.

The second type of food pyramid is called a **pyramid of biomass**. It is based on the total mass of organisms at each trophic level. An example is shown in Figure 1-11. This model is also limited, because it does not consider the energy contributed by each organism in an ecosystem. For example, the energy content in 100 kg of algae is not equivalent to that in 100 kg of northern pike in the same lake.

The third type of food pyramid is called a **pyramid of energy**. The example in Figure 1-12 shows how much food energy is available at each trophic level in a particular ecosystem.

Of the three, a pyramid of numbers is easiest to construct, since data can be obtained simply by counting. A pyramid of biomass requires more effort by the ecologist, who must measure mass directly. A pyramid of energy is the most complex. The ecologist must carry out calculations involving numbers, masses, and energy content for each type of organism.

▶ **How to Prepare for a Field Trip**

1. Obtain a permission form from your teacher that contains the following information:
   - name of teacher conducting trip
   - educational purpose of trip
   - date of trip
   - method of transportation
   - school telephone number
   - location(s) to be visited
   - departure and return times
   - costs

2. Take the permission form home, get your parent or guardian to sign it, and return it to the school.

3. Provide your teacher with a telephone number where your parent or guardian can be reached in case of an emergency.

4. Advise your teacher of any medical problems or allergies that might affect your performance on the field trip.

5. With your teacher's help, make a list of the food, beverages, footwear, and clothing that you will need to bring.

6. With your teacher, discuss what scientific supplies your group will need, and work out a method of sharing responsibility for these materials.

Activity 1-3:   Gathering Data for Food Pyramids

In this field activity, you will collect data about trophic levels using two important ecological techniques: quadrat sampling and biomass sampling.

Materials

Part A

metre stick

8 stakes

string

measuring tape

hand lens

identification books

notebook

hand shovel

tweezers

Part B

4 collection jars

biomass sampler (2 L pail
    with both ends open)

hip waders

sieve net

identification books

notebook

tweezers

portable balance

medicine dropper

Part A: Quadrat Sampling of a Land Ecosystem

Procedure

1. Before leaving on the field trip, make a chart with the following headings in your notebook. Record all observations in this chart.

Quadrat Quarter	Plant Type	Number Found	Animal Type	Number Found

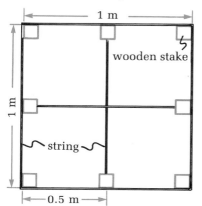

Figure 1-13. A quadrat sample divided into quarters.

2. When you reach the field site, your teacher will assign each group to a specific area. Randomly place a metre stick inside your area. Mark off a one square metre plot for study by tying string to stakes at each corner. This one square metre represents the **quadrat** being studied.

3. Section the quadrat area into quarters by tying string to stakes across the 0.5 m marks.

4. Identify the plants and animals in each quarter of the quadrat, using the identification books.

5. Working in one quarter at a time, use your hand shovel to remove a small portion of top soil. Look for and identify any living animals found in the soil.

Discussion

1. a) What is the dominant (most common) plant in your quadrat?
   b) What is the dominant animal?
2. a) Which type of food pyramid can be constructed from your data?
   b) Construct this type of food pyramid for your quadrat, using the dominant producer as the base.
   c) What problems did you encounter when constructing the pyramid?
   d) What additional information would make the pyramid in b) a better model of this ecosystem sample? Explain why.
3. Did abiotic conditions (e.g., soil, moisture, shade, humidity, etc.) vary in the quarters of your quadrat? Explain.
4. Compare your findings with those of other class members. How do the plants and animals in your quadrat differ from those in other quadrats? How do you account for this variation?
5. Approximately what percentage of the plants in your quadrat can be classified as weeds? Explain.

Part B: Biomass Sampling of a Water Ecosystem
Procedure

1. Before leaving on the field trip, make a chart with the following headings in your notebook. You will need it for step 8.

Trophic Level	Mass in grams

2. Label the collection jars as follows: "unsorted sample", "producers", "primary consumers", "other consumers".
3. Determine the volume of liquid the biomass sampler can hold and record this value in your notebook.
4. Place your biomass sampler at the bottom of a ditch, creek, or pond where the water is just deep enough to reach the top of the sampler.
5. If the water is too shallow to reach the top of the container, estimate the volume of water being sampled. (Figure 1-14 shows you how to do this.)
6. With a sieve net, gather all living things from inside the sampler and transfer them to the jar labelled "unsorted sample". To avoid disturbing either the sample or the surrounding envi-

Figure 1-14. The container is filled to the 40 cm level. It is 4/5 full, and contains only 4/5 x 5 L, or 4 L of pond water.

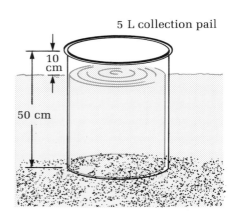

5 L collection pail

10 cm

50 cm

ronment, work one layer at a time. Remove the organisms from the top layer first, followed by the middle and bottom layers.

7. Use the identification books to name each type of organism found and determine its trophic level. Transfer all of the organisms from the same trophic level to the appropriate collection jar ("producers", "primary consumers", or "other consumers"), using the medicine dropper.

8. Using the portable balance, determine the mass of all of the organisms found at each trophic level and record the values in your chart.

9. Once step 8 is complete, return the organisms to the body of water from which they came.

10. Use the total mass of the organisms at each trophic level to construct a pyramid of biomass.

Discussion

1. a) What are some of the limitations of the method of determining mass for this activity?
   b) What are some of the limitations of the biomass sampling technique?

2. Suppose that you collected omnivores, such as a fairy shrimp. How would you incorporate their total mass into your pyramid of biomass?

3. Do you think your biomass sample studied is a fair representation of the entire ecosystem? Discuss.

4. a) Were there any tertiary consumers in the "other consumers" jar?
   b) Explain why tertiary consumers might be absent in many cases.

5. You were asked to determine the volume of liquid in your sample. Why is this volume significant? (Hint: What if some of the samples used in your class contained 20 L, while others contained only 10 L?)

How Energy Flows Through the Biosphere

The bottom-heavy shape of a pyramid of energy shows clearly that the energy content of organisms at upper trophic levels is always much less than at lower levels (see Figure 1-12). This happens because of energy losses at each level, beginning with the producers. Green plants cannot pass on all the food energy that they

In earlier studies, you learned that the process by which plants "burn" the food they make for themselves is called cell respiration. This process is discussed in more detail on page 27.

produce. Plants need to grow, take in nutrients, get rid of wastes, and exchange gases with the air. All of these life functions require energy, which plants obtain by "burning" their own food. Less than 10% of the solar energy collected by producers is available in the form of food energy for the consumers at the first trophic level.

Herbivores likewise use much of the food energy they consume for their own body functions. Grasshoppers, for example, use energy to find, eat, and digest plant food. Warm-blooded herbivores, such as rabbits, also require energy to keep warm. Only energy not needed for these purposes can be stored in the bodies of herbivores. Again, less than 10% of the energy taken in is available for consumers at the next trophic level.

Figure 1-15. Most of the energy transferred to each successive trophic level is converted into heat. Each successive trophic level receives less energy.

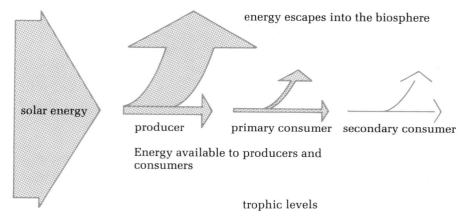

energy escapes into the biosphere

solar energy

producer   primary consumer   secondary consumer

Energy available to producers and consumers

trophic levels

Energy is transferred again and again as it passes through the biosphere from the plant producers to the top carnivores. With each transfer, more energy escapes to the external environment. Once it escapes, the energy cannot be reused or recycled. The continued existence of the biosphere depends, therefore, on a continual supply of solar energy.

Study Questions

1. Food chains, food webs, and food pyramids always start with a producer. Explain why this is necessary.

2. Explain the difference between a pyramid of numbers, a pyramid of biomass, and a pyramid of energy.

3. a) Usually, more organisms are found at lower trophic levels than at higher trophic levels. Explain why.
   b) Describe an exception to the statement made in a). In what type of pyramid could this exception cause confusion? Explain.

4. Sketch a food pyramid with three trophic levels, using labels to show how each level is classified.

5. Consider a food pyramid with five trophic levels.
   a) Discuss the energy efficiency of this food pyramid.
   b) At what trophic level would you expect to find the top carnivores? How would their numbers compare to those at the other levels? Explain.

6. A food pyramid is more than just another way to draw a food chain. Discuss this statement.

KAY McKEEVER— THE OWL LADY

Kay McKeever once rescued two small owls from a pet shop. Her interest turned into a consuming passion, and led her to establish a world-famous owl research foundation in Vineland Station, Ontario, and to become a leading expert on this important group of birds.

McKeever's story began in the 1960s. As word of her interest in owls grew, she was brought or sent more and more owls, and she had to build more and more cages to house them. Many owls were sent to her because they were injured. With the help of interested veterinarians, she discovered how to mend broken legs and wings, and how to rid a bird of parasites and infections. Often, birds were found half starved, and needed only a rest and some food. Whenever she could, McKeever released recovered owls into the wild. If they could not survive on their own, she kept them and encouraged them to breed, so that their offspring could replace them in the wild.

Although McKeever never went to university, she read as much as she could, kept notes, and carefully studied her birds. Many of her observations were unique, as not much is known about owl behaviour. She has managed to breed 9 different species of owls, in some cases defying experts who said it couldn't be done.

Over a hundred owl "patients" are now sent to the Owl Rehabilitation Research Foundation each year from all over North America, and half of them become well enough to be released back into the wild. Few of the more than 2000 birds brought to McKeever over the years were injured by natural means. Most were harmed by humans through gunshot wounds, traps, poison, or collision with cars, wires, or buildings.

For many years, McKeever and her husband spent their own money looking after the owls.

Then they began to receive donations and support from individuals and corporations, including the World Wildlife Fund. In 1975 they registered their Foundation as a charitable corporation, and now receive money from government agencies and universities. McKeever has written a manual on the care and rehabilitation of injured owls that has sold in 18 countries. In 1986 Kay McKeever received the Order of Canada for her contributions to conservation.

1.4 Cycles of Matter

The global environment includes many thousands of distinct materials. But all these materials are formed by the combination of fewer than one hundred different kinds of atoms. In both the biotic and abiotic environments, natural chemical reactions rearrange atoms to form new materials. Plants, for example, use atoms from the air and soil around them to build complex molecules of fat, protein, and carbohydrates such as starch, sugar, and cellulose. When the plants die and decompose, the molecules break down and the atoms are ready to be used again.

In earlier studies, you learned about the Law of Conservation of Mass, which states that matter cannot be created or destroyed, however much it is altered through chemical reactions. This means that all the living processes on Earth use and reuse the same supply of matter over and over again. Unlike energy, which is lost with use and must be constantly replaced by the Sun, the amount of matter on Earth is fixed.

Plant molecules are also decomposed by animals during the process of digestion. This breaks down large, complex molecules into simpler ones, which the animal can use.

Cycles of Nutrients

It is estimated that living things need about 20 different essential materials known as nutrients. **Nutrients** are the basic raw materials from which organisms manufacture everything needed to grow and to carry out other life functions. For example, cellulose is a complex material that gives plants their rigidity. Plants manufacture cellulose from carbon and water. The carbon and water are nutrients, because plants cannot manufacture them from simpler materials. The cellulose *can* be manufactured, so it is *not* a plant nutrient.

Nutrients are circulated from living things and back to the biotic environment again through nutrient cycles. These cycles involve a series of chemical or physical changes. The cycles take place in sequence, but there is no particular starting point. Several such cycles exist. The most important are those for the nutrients carbon, water, and nitrogen.

The Carbon Cycle

Most carbon in the abiotic environment is found in the form of carbon dioxide molecules in the atmosphere. However, numerous carbon-containing molecules occur in the biotic environment. Glucose, for example, is manufactured by green plants during photosynthesis, using carbon dioxide and water as raw materials. The following word equation describes photosynthesis.

Carbon-containing molecules in the biotic environment include carbohydrates such as glucose, starch, cellulose, fats, and proteins.

radiant energy + carbon dioxide + water $\longrightarrow$ glucose + oxygen

Figure 1-16. The carbon cycle.

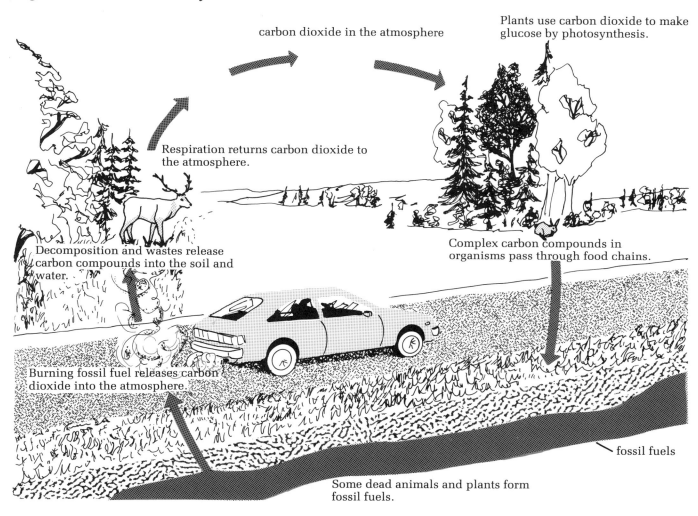

carbon dioxide in the atmosphere

Plants use carbon dioxide to make glucose by photosynthesis.

Respiration returns carbon dioxide to the atmosphere.

Decomposition and wastes release carbon compounds into the soil and water.

Complex carbon compounds in organisms pass through food chains.

Burning fossil fuel releases carbon dioxide into the atmosphere.

fossil fuels

Some dead animals and plants form fossil fuels.

Glucose is vitally important to living things because of the chemical energy stored in its molecules. Both plants and animals use glucose in a reaction called cell respiration that releases this energy. The following word equation describes cell respiration.

glucose + oxygen $\longrightarrow$ carbon dioxide + water + usable energy

The two processes, respiration and photosynthesis, are responsible for most recycling of carbon. Carbon dioxide is also released into the air when fuels are burned for heat and transportation. Living things release larger carbon-containing molecules into the abiotic environment through their body wastes, and through decomposition after death.

All carbon-containing molecules found in the carbon cycle contain oxygen as well. This cycle plays an important role, therefore, in circulating oxygen through the environment. Respiration ensures that carbon dioxide is always available for plants. Photosynthesis ensures that the oxygen needed by both plants and animals is always available.

The Water Cycle

Water would circulate through the environment even without living things (see Figure 1-17). However, living things increase the number of routes through which water can pass. Animals drink surface water, while plants absorb ground water and use it for photosynthesis. Living things return water to the environment through respiration, transpiration, and excretion.

Figure 1-17. The water cycle.

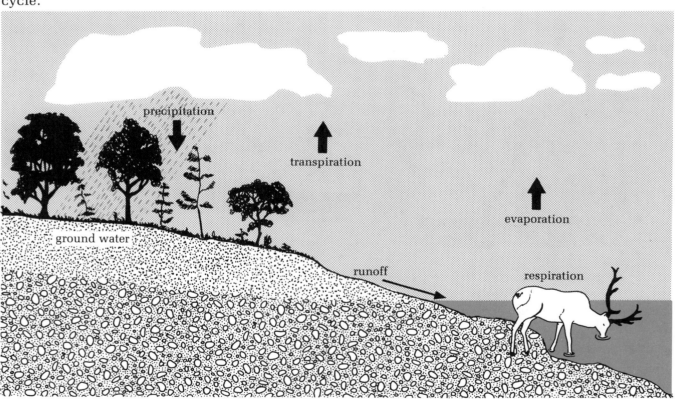

The Nitrogen Cycle

Every time you take a breath of air, 78% of the gas you inhale is nitrogen. Exhaled air contains an equal percentage of unchanged nitrogen gas. This exchange suggests that nitrogen is not used by living things, but a close look at Figure 1-18 reveals its importance.

Both plants and animals require nitrogen atoms as nutrients, but neither can use nitrogen gas directly. Animals get the nitrogen they need by consuming plant protein. To manufacture this protein, the plants require nitrogen compounds called **nitrates**. This is the only form of nitrogen that plants can absorb.

Three routes through the nitrogen cycle lead to nitrate formation.

1. Lightning may form nitrate compounds from nitrogen and oxygen in the air.
2. Soil contains nitrogen-fixing bacteria, which convert gaseous nitrogen into nitrates.

Figure 1-18. The nitrogen cycle.

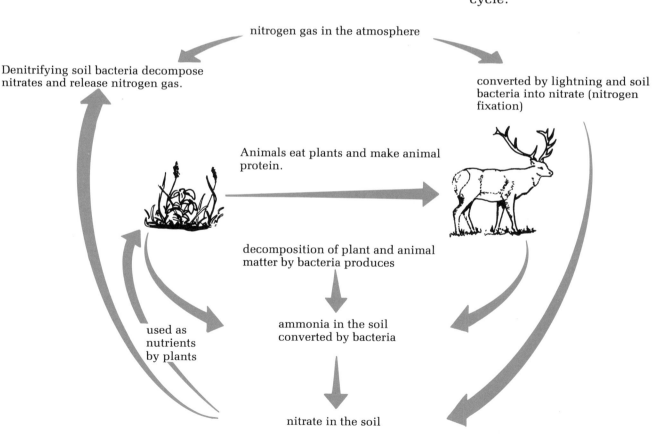

nitrogen gas in the atmosphere

Denitrifying soil bacteria decompose nitrates and release nitrogen gas.

converted by lightning and soil bacteria into nitrate (nitrogen fixation)

Animals eat plants and make animal protein.

decomposition of plant and animal matter by bacteria produces

used as nutrients by plants

ammonia in the soil converted by bacteria

nitrate in the soil

3. Some green plants, such as clover, harbour another kind of nitrogen-fixing bacteria in nodules on their roots. These bacteria form nitrates that enter the soil, as well as directly into the plant itself.

Nitrogen gas may return to the atmosphere by either of two routes.

1. Denitrifying soil bacteria may decompose soil nitrates and release nitrogen gas.

2. The second route involves three steps. As dead organisms and animal wastes decompose, they release a nitrogen-containing gas called ammonia. Bacteria (different from any mentioned so far) convert ammonia to an intermediate nitrite compound. Then, yet another kind of bacteria acts on the nitrites to form nitrate.

Activity 1-4:   Litter Analysis

The decomposition of dead plants and animals plays an important part in both the carbon and nitrogen cycles. Dead organisms that accumulate on top of the soil are known as the **litter layer**. In this activity, you will learn an important technique for separating (or analyzing) mixtures containing very small organisms.

Figure 1-19.   A Berlese funnel separates living organisms from the litter layer.

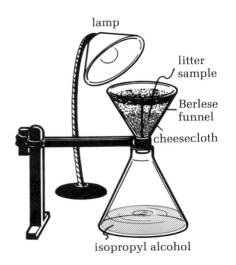

lamp

litter sample

Berlese funnel

cheesecloth

isopropyl alcohol

Materials

collection containers	lamp with a 25 W light bulb
Berlese funnel	identification books
isopropyl alcohol	cheesecloth
hand trowel	flask

Procedure

1. Collect several samples of litter from different locations using the same size container in each case. Label each litter sample to identify the collection site.

2. Set up a Berlese funnel as shown in Figure 1-19 for each sample to be analyzed. Add 10 mL-15 mL of isopropyl alcohol to the collection apparatus.

3. Place a litter sample in each funnel. Allow 48 h for separation to occur.

4. Identify the organisms found in the flask of alcohol.

5. Make a chart with the headings below in your notebook, and use it to record your findings.

Collection Site	Organisms Found	Numbers Found

6. Your teacher will put a class data chart on the chalkboard. Record your results in this chart.

Discussion

1. In the Berlese funnel, what is the function of:
   a) the light source?
   b) the alcohol?
2. a) Which sites yielded the greatest number of organisms? the greatest variety? Try to explain why.
   b) What were the two most dominant organisms in the litter samples?
3. a) Explain why you would expect the rate of decomposition of litter to vary from season to season.
   b) What season would be most favourable for litter decomposition? Explain.
4. During the winter, a blanket of snow is removed from a small area and the litter is collected. A sample of this litter is placed in a Berlese funnel. What results would you expect? Explain.
5. What is the final result of litter decomposition? Why is this important to soil fertility?

Other Nutrient Cycles

Living things cannot survive on carbon, water, and nitrogen alone. Many other substances are needed to make the chemical compounds essential for life. One such substance is the element phosphorus, which all organisms need to release energy from food. Phosphorus atoms are also used to grow shells and bones.

Phosphorus atoms, however, are easily trapped in the abiotic environment. Piles of shells and animal bones, and large accumulations of sea bird droppings all contain phosphorus that has been taken out of circulation. Such materials may take years to decompose naturally. Until they do, the phosphorus they contain is unavailable to the living world.

Figure 1-20. The phosphorus cycle.

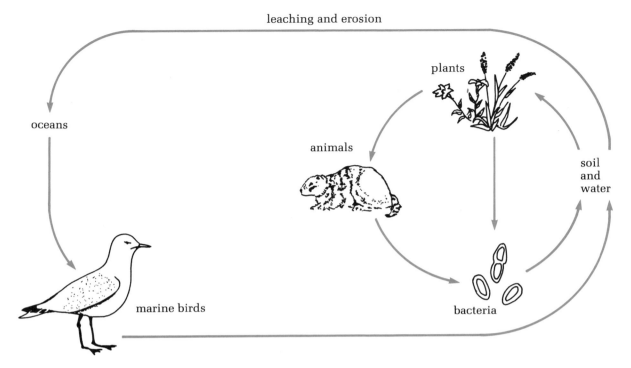

For this reason, the phosphorus cycle is often described as incomplete. Other elements with incomplete cycles include calcium (also needed for shell and bone), iron (needed for blood), and magnesium (needed to form the pigment chlorophyll in green plants).

Bioconcentration

All living things have the natural ability to process a wide variety of materials from the natural environment. Some materials serve as food, while others are harmless and simply pass through unused. For example, bears swallow chokecherries whole for the sake of the nourishing flesh. The pits, which cannot be digested, pass away harmlessly when the bear defecates.

Unfortunately, the environment now contains manufactured materials that are neither useful nor harmless. These include **bio-cides:** poisonous chemicals used to eliminate or control pests such as insects and weeds.

Biocides introduce entirely new chemical compounds into food webs. The target organism weakens and dies because its body can neither break down the biocide nor eliminate it as waste. But the effect of the biocide does not stop there. The biocide molecules pass intact up the food pyramid, into the bodies of consumers. Organisms at the highest trophic levels accumulate concentrated amounts of biocides from the many smaller organisms they consume.

Thus, a poison intended for grasshoppers can also weaken or kill a top carnivore. You might think the death of the owl in Figure 1-21 would be the end of the line for the biocide, but this is not the case. All the original biocide is still intact in the carcass, waiting to accumulate in scavengers and decomposers.

The Balance of Nature

The story of ecology is a story of interactions. In most cases, the natural environment can recover quickly from natural interactions. For example, a moose may eat many marsh plants, but they will grow back, nourished by nature's own cycles. Deer weakened by age or disease may be eaten by wolves or coyotes, but the reduction in herd size is both temporary and beneficial. It ensures enough food for the rest of the herd through the winter, and improves the likelihood of healthy fawns in the spring. Taken together, such interactions result in what is often called the **balance of nature**.

Many environmental problems result when human interactions disturb the balance of nature, resulting in totally unexpected consequences, such as bioconcentration.

Study Questions

1. a) Define nutrient.
   b) Name three nutrients that circulate through the environment in complete cycles. Explain why these cycles are considered complete.
   c) Name three nutrients that follow an incomplete cycle. Explain why these cycles are considered incomplete.
2. Explain how cell respiration and photosynthesis make the carbon cycle possible.
3. a) What type of organism(s) play(s) the most important role in the carbon cycle? Explain.
   b) What type of organism(s) play(s) the most important role in the nitrogen cycle? Explain.
   c) What factor plays the most important role in the water cycle? Explain.

Figure 1-21. A pyramid showing bioconcentration. All the biocide introduced at the first trophic level is passed up to the top carnivore.

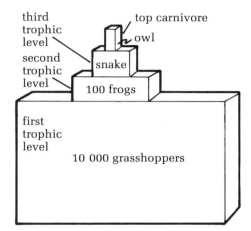

This human-made fish ladder helps salmon to swim upstream to their spawning grounds. What consequences might this human interference have on the balance of nature?

4. Cold winter weather slows down the nitrogen, carbon, and water cycles. Explain.

5. Name some human activities that interfere with: a) the carbon cycle, b) the nitrogen cycle, c) the water cycle.

6. a) What is a biocide?
   b) How does the movement of a biocide through the biotic environment differ from nutrient cycles?

HOW CAN EATING VEGETABLES HELP FEED THE WORLD?

At each ascending step of a food chain, the amount of energy available to the level above grows smaller. In other words, there is more food energy at the base of a food chain—in plants—than there is higher up the chain—in animals. This reasoning has led some people to argue that one way of increasing the food supply for a hungry world is to cut down on meat-eating and to use more agricultural land for crop production. A given area planted with crops, if eaten directly, can feed many more people than the same area used to raise animals for human consumption.

Scientists can calculate the amount of energy in any particular food and how much food energy the average person needs to stay alive and healthy—about 9200 J a day. (Food energy is measured in joules.) By measuring the energy value contained in all the plants on Earth, and

dividing it by 9200, they arrive at a figure of six hundred thousand million. In other words, the Earth can produce enough food to support this many people, if only edible plants are grown. Suppose the plants were fed to cattle, instead of people. The plant energy would become cattle energy, with a net loss of energy available to human consumers. In theory, the human population that could survive on this carnivorous diet would be only one-tenth the size of a vegetarian population.

Could this land be used more efficiently to produce food for people?

Although the scenario and the maximum figures presented above are somewhat artificial, the principle is sound. Loss of energy in an ecosystem means that there are always fewer carnivores than herbivores, and fewer herbivores than plants. Plants, in fact, make up 99%, by mass, of all life on Earth. Without this broad base for the pyramid of life, which traps its energy from the Sun, there would be no animals at all.

Meet a Biologist— Jacqueline Dixon

Jacqueline works for Ducks Unlimited Canada, a private, non-profit organization whose goal is to preserve, restore, develop, and maintain waterfowl breeding habitats in Canada. Jacqueline is currently completing her thesis for a Master's degree in biology.

Q. WHEN DID YOU DECIDE TO BECOME A BIOLOGIST?
A. When I finished Grade 10, I knew that I wanted to get a job in this field. At university in Winnipeg, my emphasis was on ecology. After I did a research project involving ducks, I knew I wanted to go into waterfowl.

Q. HOW DID YOU GET YOUR JOB AT DUCKS UNLIMITED?
A. I first got a summer job with the organization. I was hired along with seven other undergraduate students to work on a marsh ecology research project at the Delta Waterfowl and Wetlands Research Station, located on Lake Manitoba. This is one of the top research stations in North America. It was a very stimulating experience.

Q. WHAT IS THE GOAL OF DUCKS UNLIMITED?
A. Our goal is to secure wetland habitat for the future. Wetlands are threatened by development and drainage, among other things.

Q. WHAT DOES YOUR JOB INVOLVE?
A. I'm in charge of the small marsh program. I try to secure small wetlands—ranging from 2 to 8 ha—for a Ducks Unlimited project. We sign agreements with private landowners that allow us to restore and preserve marshlands on their property. To do this we have to be able to control the water levels by building a small earth dam with a control structure on the property.

Q. HOW DO YOU FIND THESE PROPERTIES?
A. First I go to the Ministry of Natural Resources aerial photography library. I study topographic map sheets and aerial photos, looking for wetland areas that are well-contained and have an outlet where a dam could be built. I make up a master list of sites and drive around the countryside to see them. Usually, people haven't heard of us, but once I explain what we do most are very receptive.

Q. HOW MANY PROPERTIES END UP BEING DEVELOPED?
A. About 12 to 15%. Some are rejected because they're too costly to build on, others because the landowners turn us down.

Q. HOW SUCCESSFUL HAS THE PROJECT BEEN?
A. Across Canada we have over 3000 projects that we control. This represents about 4000 landowners who are cooperating with us.

Q. WHAT DO YOU LIKE BEST ABOUT YOUR JOB?
A. Being outdoors. During the summer I look at sites and meet the landowners. In a way, I'm like a salesperson, selling the idea of wetland conservation. Sometimes it's hard work, but I like the challenge.

Q. WHAT DO YOU DO AFTER THE SUMMER?
A. I continue negotiating with landowners. I meet with our engineer and surveyor who also look at the sites to see if they can be managed.

Q. DO YOU HAVE ANY ADVICE FOR STUDENTS INTERESTED IN WORKING IN THIS FIELD?
A. At university, attend any seminars or speeches given by people from different ecology organizations. It's a great way to meet people doing research in areas you're interested in, and to get job contacts. My key connections came from one of these talks. I went to a lecture given by someone from Ducks Unlimited. That led to the summer job, and started me on the path to where I am today.

Review Questions

A: Knowledge

1. a) Define environment and environmental interaction.
   b) Explain how these terms relate to ecology.

2. Classify the following as biotic or abiotic components of the environment. In each case, justify your classification.
   a) pond water   d) soil
   b) plant seeds   e) soil organisms
   c) fossils

3. Consider the following list: grass, grasshopper, grass snake, seaweed, starfish, salmon.
   a) Classify these organisms as autotrophs or heterotrophs.
   b) Classify them as producers or consumers.
   c) Explain the relationship between your answers to a) and b).

4. a) Are decomposers autotrophs or heterotrophs? Explain.
   b) Are scavengers producers or consumers? Explain.
   c) Why is it essential for all ecosystems to have scavengers and decomposers?

5. a) Is a dead organism part of the biotic environment or the abiotic environment? Explain.
   b) List the steps involved in the breakdown of a dead organism.
   c) Explain the importance of this breakdown process to living things.

6. a) Define habitat and niche.
   b) Use an example to explain how a habitat differs from a niche.

7. a) Explain the meaning of biosphere.
   b) Name and describe the major zones into which the biosphere is classified.
   c) How do these zones differ from ecosystems?

8. a) Define ecosystem and give an example.
   b) Why would you expect to find green plants in every ecosystem?
   c) How would the number of green plants in an ecosystem compare to the number of other organisms? Explain.

9. a) Construct a food chain based on the following organisms: cricket, frog, grass, hawk, snake.
   b) Identify the producer(s) in this food chain and classify any consumer(s) according to trophic level.

10. a) Construct a food web by adding the following organisms to the food chain in question 9: deer, grasshopper, lynx, plant seeds, rabbit, skunk, weasel.
    b) Identify all herbivores, omnivores, carnivores, and top carnivores in this food web.

11. a) Define food chain, food web, and food pyramid.
    b) Explain how each item in a) can serve as an ecosystem model.
    c) Explain why ecologists need so many different kinds of ecosystem models.

12. a) How do ecologists trace the pathway of energy through the biosphere? Explain.
    b) What happens to the amount of energy as it passes through the biosphere? Explain.
    c) Explain why the biosphere does not run out of energy.

13. a) What is a nutrient? Give three examples.
    b) What happens to the amount of a nutrient as it passes through the biosphere? Explain.
    c) Explain why the biosphere does not run out of nutrients.

14. a) Describe the role of cell respiration and photosynthesis in the carbon cycle.
    b) What other essential material is recycled through these two processes? Explain why this is important.

15. a) Describe the role of decomposers in nutrient cycles.
    b) In which nutrient cycle are decomposers most important? Explain.

B: Application

16. A student sits down to a meal of broiled salmon, a baked potato, and a glass of milk. What is the student's trophic level for each food item? (Salmon are carnivores.)

17. a) A Venus flytrap is an "insectivorous" plant. What do you think this term means?
    b) What niche does this plant occupy? Explain.
    c) Where would it fit on a food pyramid?

18. a) Compare the pathway of energy through the biosphere with the pathways of nutrients and biocides.
    b) Like energy and nutrients, biocides are carried through the living world by food. Explain why the outcome is so different.

19. Do zoos maintain niches or habitats for the occupants? Explain.

20. a) Describe an incomplete nutrient cycle.
    b) What environmental problems may result from such cycles?
    c) What can be done to compensate for an incomplete nutrient cycle?

21. Explain what would happen to an ecosystem with an excess number of top carnivores.

22. a) On journeys into space, astronauts must take along everything they need. List some of these needs.
    b) In what way(s) does a space vehicle resemble the biosphere it leaves behind?
    c) In what way(s) does the space vehicle differ from the biosphere?

C: Problem Solving

23. Wolves are carnivores. Explain how placing a bounty on wolves may cause a significant loss in vegetation.

24. The Earth could support a much larger human population if everyone became a vegetarian. Explain what is meant by this statement.

25. Humans have a tendency to alter the environment to suit themselves. What possible environmental consequences might result from:
    a) burying metal containers of insecticides?
    b) placing a large dam across a river to create a swimming area?
    c) eliminating rats at a local dump by poisoning the garbage?
    d) building roads through a wilderness park?

Try This

1. **Trophic Levels at the Supermarket**
   In the supermarket, identify three food products based on producers, three based on primary consumers, and three based on secondary consumers. Determine the price per serving for each. Is your trophic level for these foods related to their cost?

2. **An Aquarium Experiment**
   Set up three small aquaria (5 L-10 L), using a water heater to maintain one at a temperature of 20°C, one at 25°C, and one at 30°C. Once the temperature is steady, place the same types of fish and plants in each aquarium. Note the effects of different temperatures on plant growth and fish activity.

Chapter 2
Populations, Communities, and Biomes

The biosphere consists of individual organisms interacting with their environments. As a result, ecologists seldom focus on individuals but look at plants and animals as part of a total picture. A deer at the forest's edge is part of a community that includes maple trees, ferns, forest-floor decomposers, wolves, and other deer belonging to the same herd or population.

Ecologists often investigate an ecosystem by breaking it down into populations and communities. Focusing on these smaller groupings makes it easier to understand environmental interactions. In this chapter, you will examine how populations grow and how they interact with other populations in their community. You will also learn how populations, communities, and ecosystems relate to the larger ecological unit called a biome.

When you finish Chapter 2, you should be able to:

- define and list the characteristics of a population

- discuss factors affecting population growth, and the four processes that change the size of a population

- explain the various ways in which populations interact with each other
- define a biome and explain how it relates to communities, populations, and ecosystems
- discuss two types of natural succession in a community

2.1 Populations and How They Grow

A **population** consists of all the individuals of the same kind, or species, that live in a given area. A **species** consists of organisms so similar that they can mate and produce fertile offspring. When discussing a particular population, ecologists identify its species, its location, and when it lived there. For example, an investigator might study the population of white-tailed deer in Algonquin Park during 1980.

Often, population density is of more interest than the actual number of individuals in a population. **Population density** is defined as the number of individuals per unit of space. For example, if 1200 deer spend a winter in a 200 km² area of northern Ontario, the population density is:

$$\frac{1200}{200} = 6 \, \text{deer/km}^2$$

Variations in population density within a particular habitat are described in terms of **population distribution**. For example, a map of the population distribution of deer across Ontario may show herds of animals clustered at locations where there is more food, while other areas have no deer at all. The population density also changes from winter to summer as herds spread out.

The concept of species is extremely useful to biologists in their study of living things. Species and other groupings of similar organisms are discussed in more detail in Chapter 4.

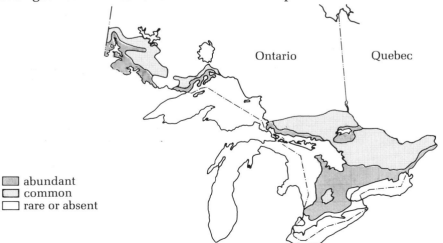

Ontario

Quebec

- ▨ abundant
- ☐ common
- ☐ rare or absent

Figure 2-1. A map showing the distribution of the white-tailed deer population in Ontario.

Under ideal conditions this mouse may produce 60 offspring or more in a year.

Removing wolves from an ecosystem by hunting or trapping has had an unexpected effect. In eastern Canada, reduction in wolf populations has enabled coyotes to immigrate into what used to be wolf habitats. The newly established coyote populations occupy the same ecological niche as the wolves, and are thriving in their new environment.

How do you think wolves might immigrate to an island? What might prompt a wolf to undertake such a journey? Why might one wolf leave the island?

How Populations Change Size

Although many environmental factors affect population growth, only four processes can change the size of a population: births, deaths, immigration, and emigration.

1. **Births** add new individuals to a population. In some species, births can increase population size rapidly. For example, a single female mouse may produce a litter of four or five babies every 30 d.

2. **Deaths** remove individuals from a population. Most mouse offspring will be caught and eaten long before they die of old age.

3. **Immigration** occurs when new individuals move into a habitat. For example, the construction of grain elevators might lead to immigration of mice.

4. **Emigration** occurs when some individuals of a population leave their ecosystem for a new habitat. During floods, mice may emigrate from grain elevators to higher ground.

The **growth rate** of a population tells how much its size has changed in one year, and is expressed as a percentage.

$$\text{growth rate} = \frac{\text{births} - \text{deaths} + \text{immigration} - \text{emigration}}{\text{initial population number}} \times 100$$
$$= \underline{\quad} \%$$

Example

Using the following data for a population of 16 wolves living on an island, calculate the growth rate of this population.

Births = 7   Immigration = 2
Deaths = 4   Emigration = 1

Solution

Substitute the given data into the growth rate formula, as shown.

$$\text{growth rate} = \frac{7 - 4 + 2 - 1}{16} \times 100$$
$$= \frac{4}{16} \times 100$$
$$= 25\%$$

If births and immigration balance deaths and emigration, the population size will not change and the growth rate will be 0%. This condition is sometimes called **zero population growth**. If deaths and emigration exceed births and immigration, the population will decline and the growth rate will be negative. A population can increase only if births and immigration exceed deaths and emigration. This condition results in a positive value for population growth.

Growth rate can also be expressed in terms of **doubling time**. This is the time it takes for a population to double in size. For example, a population with a growth rate of 1% will have a doubling time of 70 years. A growth rate of 2% will double a population in 35 years. Calculating doubling time helps ecologists see how quickly a population is likely to outgrow its present habitat.

A Model for Population Growth

Imagine that a population of ten starlings (five mating pairs) is blown to the shores of a remote island. There are no competitors for the abundant food on the island, and no carnivores capable of catching birds. How will the starling population grow under these ideal conditions?

If we assume an average of six eggs per nest hatch, then after the first year there will be 30 offspring and ten adults. During the second breeding season there will be 20 mating pairs, and 120 offspring will be produced. After five years, the island's starling population will exceed 10 000, if no birds die of old age or disease. (See Table 2-1.)

Doubling time is a concept often used in human population studies. Canada's doubling time is 70 years, which is brief compared to Great Britain's 200 years. Because of improved sanitation and medical treatment, the doubling time in some underdeveloped countries is less than 25 years, which is considered disturbingly short. By the time today's infants grow up to be parents, underdeveloped countries will find it increasingly difficult to feed their populations unless something is done to alter this trend.

Table 2-1: Population data for imaginary starling population*

Years on Island	Number of Adults	Number of Offspring (Mating Pairs × 6)	Total Population
0	10	none until end of first year	10
1	10	5 × 6 = 30	40
2	40	20 × 6 = 120	160
3	160	80 × 6 = 480	640
4	640	320 × 6 = 1920	2560
5	2560	1280 × 6 = 7680	10 240

*These data assume equal numbers of males and females.

Figure 2-2. Population explosion of starlings.

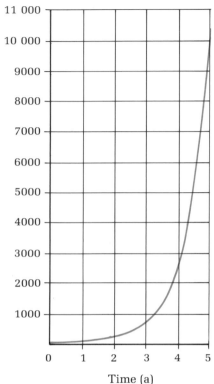

Total population

Time (a)

Figure 2-2 shows these data in the form of a graph with a steeply inclined curve. Growth this rapid is often called a **population explosion**.

For a real population in a real environment, uncontrolled growth is unlikely. Numerous environmental factors, such as the food supply, the space available, competition with other species, natural enemies, disease, and emigration all limit population growth.

Activity 2-1: The Growth of a Real Population

In this activity, you will compare the growth of a fruit fly population with the starling model above. Fruit flies are used because they reproduce rapidly, and because a large population can live in a very small space.

Materials

Drosophila (4 mating pairs)	glass plate (10 cm × 10 cm)
Drosophila medium	grease pencil
2 vials (10 cm)	anaesthetic
2 vial covers	camel hair brush
plastic mesh (6 cm × 6 cm)	

Procedure

1. Label two vials A and B.
2. Half-fill vial A with dry *Drosophila* medium. Add enough water so that the medium is moistened but not saturated.
3. Fill vial B one-third full of dry *Drosophila* medium. Add water to moisten.
4. Place plastic mesh above the medium in vials A and B for the adult flies to crawl on.
5. Place two mating pairs of *Drosophila* in *each* vial and add the covers.
6. After 3 to 4 d, with your teacher's help, use the anaesthetic to put the flies to sleep. Carefully pour them onto the glass plates and quickly count them using the camel hair brush.
7. After determining the population number for each vial, carefully place the flies back in the vials when they begin to show signs of movement.

Scientists often manipulate the genetic information in fruit flies to study the effects of change on a population. These red-eyed flies are the genetically engineered offspring of a brown-eyed fly.

8. Draw a chart like the one below. Repeat steps 6 and 7, and record the population number every second day for two weeks, or until both cultures die out.

Date	Population Number Vial A	Population Number Vial B
(Starting date)	4	4

9. From the population data in your chart, draw a graph using the axes shown in Figure 2-3.

Discussion

1. What evidence do you observe of a life cycle for the *Drosophila*? Show stages of this life cycle in a labelled diagram.
2. Population growth in small organisms often produces extremely large numbers. How could you estimate numbers of fruit flies without counting the entire population?
3. Which of the four basic processes (births, deaths, immigration, and emigration) affect(s) the size of the population in these cultures? Explain.
4. What is the most important factor limiting population growth in this experiment? Explain.
5. Discuss how and why your data might differ if you had used:
   a) larger vials,
   b) more *Drosophila* medium in the vials,
   c) more mating pairs.

Figure 2-3.

Number of fruit flies

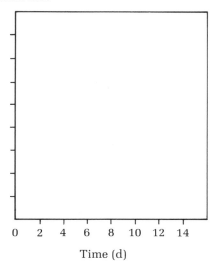

Time (d)

Environmental Factors Affecting Population Growth

Figure 2-4 shows the growth of a typical animal population. A slow initial increase is followed by a period of rapid growth. This rapid growth is similar to that of the imaginary starling population in Figure 2-2. In a real population, however, the growth rate eventually declines to zero, and population size stabilizes.

This pattern of change in a natural population occurs because of environmental factors affecting growth. These factors include the food and water supply, available living space, climate, competition, predators, and disease.

Figure 2-4. The typical growth curve for an animal population is S-shaped.

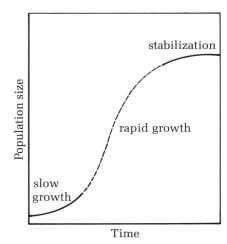

How might a snow-free winter affect the population of arctic hares? How might it affect a population of wolves in the same area?

Figure 2-5.

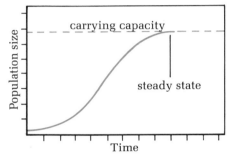

Figure 2-6. The graph illustrates a **steady state** in the human population of an Ontario village. Despite minor fluctuations, the population hovers around 1400. What would account for the small variations?

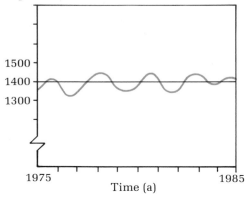

An abundance of both food and water results in more births and thus a growth in population. Scarcity of either food or water results in fewer births, weak individuals, more disease, and more deaths.

All populations need space in which to grow. If space is limited, and emigration cannot occur, the population may be unable to grow, even when there is plenty of food. In laboratory studies of mice kept in crowded cages, deaths from disease were greater, and females bore fewer live young compared to mice in the wild.

Climate also affects population size. For example, an extremely cold winter with deep snow can prevent animals such as moose from foraging for food. The moose population may therefore decline. A mild winter produces the opposite effect.

On the other hand, hibernating insects need a cold winter in order to survive till spring. A mild spell can bring them out of their hiding places, then if it turns cold again they die from exposure.

The factors described so far relate to the abiotic environment. Population size is also influenced by interactions with other populations in the biotic environment. These interactions are discussed in the next section.

Carrying Capacity and Steady State

The interaction of all the environmental factors mentioned above determines the **carrying capacity** of an ecosystem. Ecologists define this as the maximum number of organisms an area can support without harming the environment. As a population approaches carrying capacity, various environmental interactions occur to slow its growth. Diseases and stress from overcrowding result in more deaths and fewer births. The population reaches a stable level somewhat below the maximum predicted value.

This stable level is often referred to as **steady state**. Steady state occurs when a population is in equilibrium, gaining and losing individuals at the same rate. In most cases, an undisturbed population will maintain a steady state for a long time.

Study Questions

1. Explain the difference between population density and population distribution.

2. a) List the four basic processes that can change the size of a population.

b) List two environmental factors that can cause a population to grow and two that can cause it to decline.

3. Define immigration and emigration. Explain how each affects population size.

4. An animal population of 50 has no immigration or emigration, 3 births, and 4 deaths in one year. What is the percentage growth rate of this population?

5. Populations of animals newly introduced to an ecosystem often show uncontrolled population growth in the early stages.
   a) Explain why this occurs.
   b) What eventually happens to the size of such a population?

6. Explain the difference between:
   a) growth rate and doubling time
   b) carrying capacity and steady state

7. In 1967, the population of a village suddenly shot up from 900 to 1500 and remained roughly at that level for the next 20 years.
   a) What might account for this sudden increase?
   b) What does the new population figure of 1500 represent?

CHALLENGER

Biological control of a population species means that a population species is being used to control the number of another population species. Find some examples of biological control programs that have been successful and some that have been failures.

2.2 Community Interactions

An ecosystem consists of many organisms living together in the same abiotic environment. All of the living things in an ecosystem make up its **community**. A single community may include many different populations. Since all the populations in a community must share the natural resources of the ecosystem, numerous interactions occur among different species. All such interactions are examples of **symbiosis**. Symbiosis is a relationship in which two organisms live together in close association. There are three basic types of symbiotic relationships.

1. **Mutualism**. This is a symbiotic relationship in which both organisms benefit. The interaction between legume plants and nitrogen-fixing bacteria is an example of mutualism. The plants benefit from the nitrates produced by the bacteria. The bacteria obtain carbohydrates and other food materials from the plants.

Some mutualistic organisms are even more closely linked. For example, the lichen in the photograph appears to be a single plant-like organism. However, each lichen is actually a combination of two organisms: a fungus and a photosynthetic partner, usually a green alga.

Mutualism enables the two species in this lichen to colonize the bark of a tree.

Commensalism helps these orchids to obtain the energy and materials they need, without leaving the tree they are growing on.

What other populations might compete with this weasel?

Both fungus and algae benefit from this association. The blue-green alga carries out photosynthesis to provide food for both itself and the fungus. The fungus attaches the algae to a surface and prevents the algae from drying out. Because the lichen combines both a heterotroph and an autotroph, it can live where few other organisms could exist. Lichens thrive on the bark of trees, and are the first living things to grow on newly exposed, bare rock.

2. **Commensalism**. This is a one-sided relationship which is beneficial to one organism and neutral to the other. For example, orchids have a commensal relationship with the trees they attach themselves to. In this interaction, the orchid gains better access to sunlight for photosynthesis, and obtains water that collects in the fork of the branch where it grows. The orchid's growth does not damage or in any way affect the tree.

3. **Parasitism**. A **parasite** is an organism that obtains its nutrients from the tissues of another living organism, called the **host**. Parasites seldom kill their hosts, but they often cause a weakened or diseased condition. This type of symbiotic relationship is called **parasitism**. One organism benefits, while the other is harmed but usually not killed. Parasites such as fleas on a dog live externally to the host, while the tapeworm in the dog's intestinal tract lives internally.

Competition

Often two populations in the same community depend on the same resources. For example, elk and deer need similar food. In most ecosystems, food resources are limited. The two populations may therefore interact in a way that affects their growth and perhaps even their survival. This type of relationship is called **competition**.

When two species in the same ecosystem compete for food, both species are harmed. The presence of deer means less food for the elk. The presence of elk means less food for the deer. In addition, the two populations compete for living space.

Competition can also occur among members of the same species. During a food shortage, for example, older, younger, and weaker deer will get a smaller share.

Activity 2-2: Plant Competition

Individuals of the same or different plant species often compete for resources such as food, water, oxygen, and space. In this activity, you will study competition for space.

Materials

12 radish seeds	12 peat pots
12 bean seeds	labels or tags for peat pots
germination tray	potting soil
paper towels	metric ruler

Procedure

1. Soak 12 radish seeds and 12 bean seeds in wet paper towelling, and keep them moist until they sprout. (See Figure 2-7.)

2. Label three sets of peat pots as follows: A-1, A-2, A-3, A-4; B-1, B-2, B-3, B-4; and C-1, C-2, C-3, C-4.

3. When the seeds in the towelling have germinated, plant the seedlings in the peat pots filled with potting soil, as outlined in steps 4 to 6.

4. Plant one radish seedling in each of pots A-1, A-2, A-3, and A-4.

5. Plant one bean seedling in each of pots B-1, B-2, B-3, and B-4.

6. Plant one radish seedling *and* one bean seedling in each of pots C-1, C-2, C-3, and C-4.

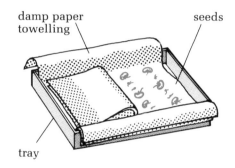

Figure 2-7. A germination tray.

damp paper towelling — seeds — tray

Figure 2-8.

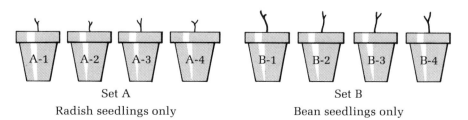

Set A	Set B	Set C
Radish seedlings only	Bean seedlings only	Both radish and bean seedlings

7. During the next two weeks, keep all twelve peat pots at the same temperature, and give them the same amount of water and light.

8. Make four blank copies of the chart below, titled as follows: "Radish plants of set A", "Bean plants of set B", "Radish plants of set C", and "Bean plants of set C". Do not copy the sample values shown in the example below.

Example

Chart of Growth Data for: *Radish Plants of Set A*

	Daily Height Measurement				Total of Daily Heights	Total Growth for Set A	Average Daily Growth per Plant
	A-1	A-2	A-3	A-4	(A1 + A2 + A3 + A4)	(Day 2 Total − Day 1 Total)	(Divide Total Growth by 4)
Day 1	1.2 cm	1.3 cm	1.1 cm	1.0 cm	4.6 cm		
Day 2	1.9 cm	1.8 cm	1.8 cm	1.6 cm	7.1 cm	7.1 − 4.6 = 2.5 cm	2.5 ÷ 4 = 0.6 cm
Etc.							

Figure 2-9. Plot the growth of Set A in pen and Set C in pencil.

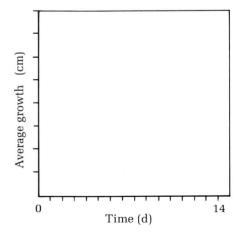

9. Each day, measure the height of the plants and record the values in your charts. Calculate the average daily growth for each as shown in the example.

10. Plot the average daily growth rates per radish plant for both set A and set C on a graph similar to the one in Figure 2-9. Plot the average daily growth rates for both sets of bean plants on a second graph.

Discussion

1. How do the average growth rates for the plants in set C differ from those in sets A and B?

2. Which set of radish plants grew better? Identify the limiting factor affecting the set with poorer growth, and explain this factor.

3. Repeat question 1 and 2 for the bean plants.

4. What is the purpose of the A and B sets of plants in the experiment?

5. In set C, is one plant species dominant? If so, how is this dominance shown?

6. a) What variable was tested in this experiment? Explain.
   b) What other variables could be tested, and how?

Predation and Population Cycles

A more direct type of population interaction is that of **predation**, which is a relationship in which one species benefits while the other dies. A predator is a consumer that actively pursues other animals as a food source. The animal consumed is the prey. For example, predators such as owls consume prey such as mice or young rabbits.

The chameleon preys on insects, which it captures on the sticky end of its long tongue.

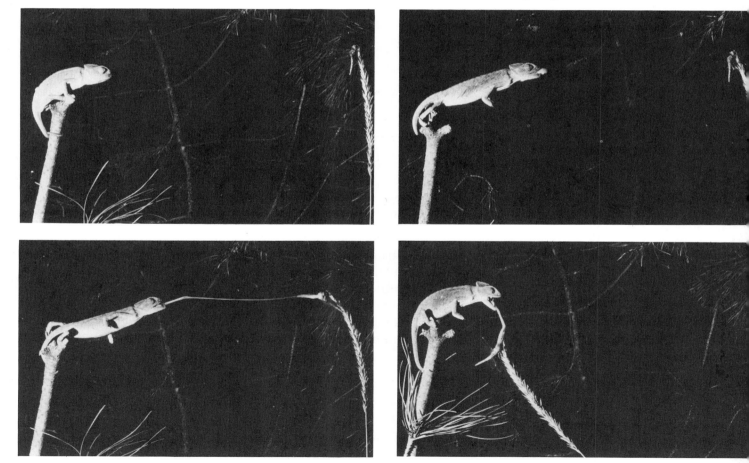

Predator-prey interactions sometimes cause population cycles of the kind shown in Figure 2-10. During each cycle, the total population increases to a maximum and then drops sharply to a minimum. The resulting pattern of peaks and troughs tends to repeat itself over time.

For the Canadian lynx, the interval between peaks is about 9.7 years. The snowshoe hare is a primary food source for the lynx, and Figure 2-10 shows that the hare exhibits a population cycle with a similar interval between peaks. Clearly, the two curves are related, but they do not completely coincide. The lynx population reaches its peak a year or two later than does the hare population. The trough in the lynx curve also occurs some time after the trough for the hares.

Figure 2-10. The population cycles of the Canadian lynx and the snowshoe hare over a 90-year period.

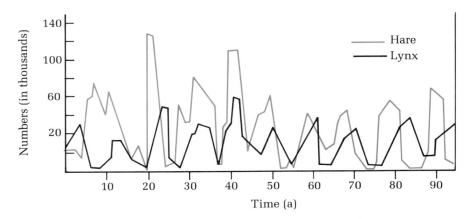

Community Structure

Because there are so many different interactions within a community, its structure can be described in many different ways. (See Figure 2-11.) Populations in a community can be classified according to symbiotic relationships. Each species can also be classified as a producer or a consumer, and populations can be organized into food chains, food webs, and food pyramids. Ecologists use the description or classification that best suits their needs.

Study Questions

1. a) Explain the difference between a community and an ecosystem.
   b) Is a community interaction different from an environmental interaction? Explain.

Figure 2-11. Three ways to classify populations within the same community.

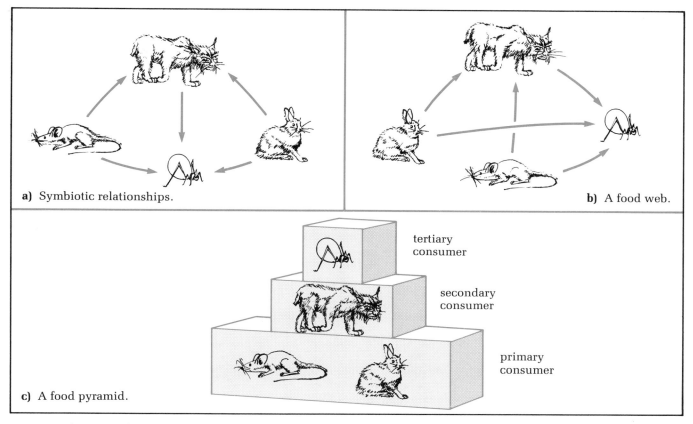

a) Symbiotic relationships.

b) A food web.

c) A food pyramid.

tertiary consumer

secondary consumer

primary consumer

2. a) Define symbiosis.
   b) List three kinds of symbiosis.
   c) For each kind of symbiosis, write a definition and provide an example.

3. In nature, the number of prey must always exceed the number of predators. Explain.

4. In some cases, a parasite might be a primary consumer; in other cases, it might be a tertiary consumer. Explain with examples.

5. Use symbiotic interactions to classify the following population relationships.
   a) humans and pet dogs
   b) dairy farmers and cows
   c) mink ranchers and mink
   d) gardeners and garden carrot plants

Explain the basis for each of your answers.

TERRITORIALITY

All living things need a certain amount of space in which to live, find food, and reproduce. Some animals, especially birds, reptiles, and mammals, defend their living spaces against others of their own species by a particular type of behaviour called **territorial behaviour**.

Many birds, for example, establish territories in the spring to ensure enough space in which to find food to rear their young. Typically, a male bird will establish a territory and defend it against other males by singing loudly at the boundaries of the territory, and chasing away other males that venture near. Females are attracted to males that command territory. A pair of birds will mate and may defend the area together. Birds that do not manage to defend a territory will not breed. In this way, territorial behaviour ensures that the population is limited to a number that can be supported by the available resources.

Animals that keep territories must have ways of announcing where the territory begins and ends. Birds do this by singing. Some monkeys, such as the howler monkeys of South America, signal their territories by making loud howling noises every morning. Male fiddler

crabs display their territories by waving one large, brightly coloured claw in the air. This behaviour warns other males not to approach, and attracts females at the same time. Many mammals mark their territories by depositing urine, feces, or a strong-smelling musk from a special gland. Wolves, for example, leave their scent in urine on tree trunks or rocks at the borders of their territories so that other wolves can tell that the area is already occupied.

Animals generally manage to establish and defend a territory

Wolves establish their territory by scent-marking — urinating on trees and other markers at boundary points. This plays an important part in the distribution of wolf populations.

through behavioural displays or signs alone. If the population density is high, however, there may be more intense competition for space or mates, and territories may have to be defended by fighting. Some scientists have argued that humans also display territorial behaviour. From your experience, do you think there is evidence for this idea?

2.3 Biomes

A **biome** is a large geographical area with a similar climate through-out the area and a dominant type of natural vegetation. Biomes are named according to this dominant vegetation. For example, the boreal coniferous forest is named after its dominant conifer trees. Certain abiotic factors such as temperature, rainfall, and soil con-ditions influence what types of plants dominate a biome. In turn, the plants influence what kind of animals live in the biome.

Biomes tend to be made up of many similar ecosystems, each having its own community comprising populations of many dif-ferent species. A biome has more or less well-defined limits or boundaries, determined by global climate patterns. In Figure 2-12, the biosphere has been subdivided into six terrestrial biomes.

Figure 2-12. A guide to the major biomes of the world.

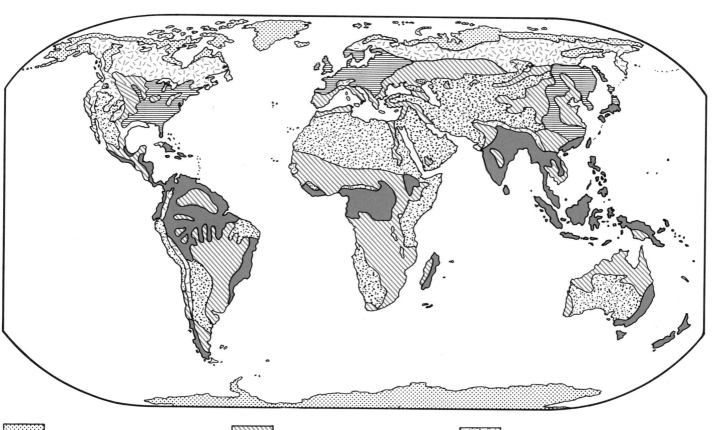

Tundra and Ice	
Boreal Coniferous Forest	
Grasslands	
Temperate Deciduous Forest	
Desert	
Tropical Rain Forest	

Biomes of North America

Figure 2-13 shows the six major biomes of North America: tundra, boreal coniferous forest, grasslands, temperate deciduous forest, desert, and tropical rain forest.

1. **Tundra**. This biome occurs in arctic regions where the subsoil is frozen. The layer of permanently frozen ground is called permafrost.

   The cold climate in this biome allows only two months of the year for plant growth in a shallow layer of defrosted topsoil. The dominant plant vegetation on the tundra includes lichens, mosses, herbs, and low-growing woody plants.

2. **Boreal Coniferous Forest**. The boreal forest biome covers almost 50% of Canada's land area. The dominant coniferous trees in this biome are black spruce and white spruce. Trees at the biome's northern edge are stunted by poor growing conditions. This northern belt is called the **taiga**.

3. **Grasslands**. The southern part of Canada's prairie provinces and the central United States consist of grasslands. Most grasslands have thick, fertile soil ideal for agricultural activities. As in all biomes, the dominant natural vegetation can only be seen where humans have not planted gardens and crops.

The tundra's short growing season and shallow soil limit the maximum sizes and variety of its plant populations.

Boreal coniferous forest covers most of Ontario.

Tall grass species grow in the moister parts of the grassland biomes.

Figure 2-13. Biomes of North America.

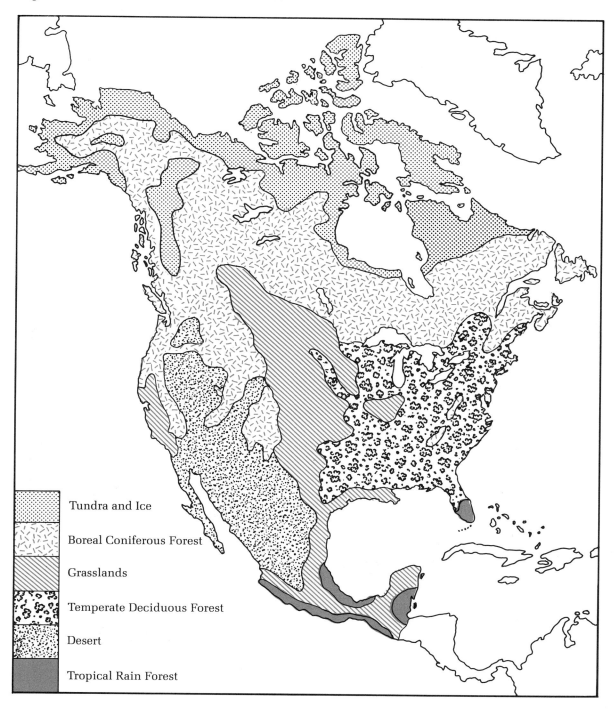

Tundra and Ice

Boreal Coniferous Forest

Grasslands

Temperate Deciduous Forest

Desert

Tropical Rain Forest

Do You Know?

As human populations expand in poor countries near the equator, tropical rain forest is being cut down and cultivated to make room for farms and homes. Ecologists around the world are concerned that many plant and animal species may disappear as a result. At best, it will take hundreds of years for these forests to grow back, and at worst, they may never recover.

4. **Temperate Deciduous Forest**. This biome is located in the southern parts of eastern Canada (including Ontario) and throughout the northeastern United States. The major deciduous trees in this biome are oak, maple, beech, and hickory.

5. **Deserts**. This biome is characterized by low rainfall and daily temperature extremes. Desert covers much of the southwestern United States. The major types of desert vegetation are cactus and sagebrush. Small, desertlike regions exist in western Canada, but none is large enough to be called a biome.

6. **Tropical Rain Forest**. The tropical rain forest biome is located near the equator. It has the most uniform conditions of any terrestrial biome. Temperature varies little and rainfall is frequent. The dominant plants in this biome are broad-leafed evergreen trees.

Of all biomes, the tropical rain forest has the greatest diversity of living things.

The appearance of the temperate deciduous forest changes from season to season.

Although daytime summer temperatures may exceed 45°C, desert vegetation is well suited to conserve precious water.

Most residents of the tropical rain forest live in the canopy, high above the forest floor.

Activity 2-3:   A Report on a Canadian Biome

In this activity, you will research a Canadian biome. Present your report in the form of a poster, essay, or short talk, with guidance from your teacher. Information about biomes can be obtained from libraries and government agencies. In your research, include both abiotic and biotic components of the biome you have selected. The biotic aspects should include ecosystems, communities, and populations of both plants and animals in the biome.

Do You Know?
Mountains provide an opportunity to observe several biomes in a relatively small area. Increasing cold at higher elevations results in ever-changing vegetation up the mountainside. Near a mountain's snow line, plants are similar to those on the tundra. Often, one side of a mountain receives much more precipitation than the other, which also affects plant life.

Aquatic Ecosystems

Nearly three-quarters of the Earth's surface is covered by water. Fresh water is normally considered part of the terrestrial biome in which it is located. Bodies of fresh water, such as lakes, rivers, and ponds, play a vital role in the interactions within biomes.

This lake represents a freshwater aquatic ecosystem.

Approximately 98% of Earth's water is salty, and most salt water is in the oceans. Oceans are subdivided into zones, according to depth.

The **intertidal zone** is the shoreline area that is covered by water at high tide and exposed at low tide. Barnacles, mussels, and red and brown algae are abundant in this zone.

The **littoral zone** lies along the shore, and includes all shallow water to a depth of 200 m. Because light can penetrate to the ocean floor, a wide variety of organisms inhabit this zone. Various types of algae, sea cucumbers, shellfish, and fish make up the biotic community in the littoral zone.

In the **open ocean zone**, the water is deep, and light cannot penetrate to the ocean floor. Porpoises, whales, and larger fish, including sharks, inhabit this zone, as well as numerous tiny plants and animals called plankton which drift in the surface waters.

Whether water is fresh or salt, aquatic ecosystems interact with all of the Earth's biomes. Natural cycles circulate water throughout the biosphere. Oxygen gas, produced mainly by plant plankton in the ocean, is carried by atmospheric currents for use by heterotrophs in the terrestrial biomes. Fish and other food sources from aquatic ecosystems may be used by terrestrial inhabitants. Thus, food chains, food webs, and food pyramids in terrestrial communities are interconnected with aquatic ecosystems.

Figure 2-14. The three zones of the Earth's oceans.

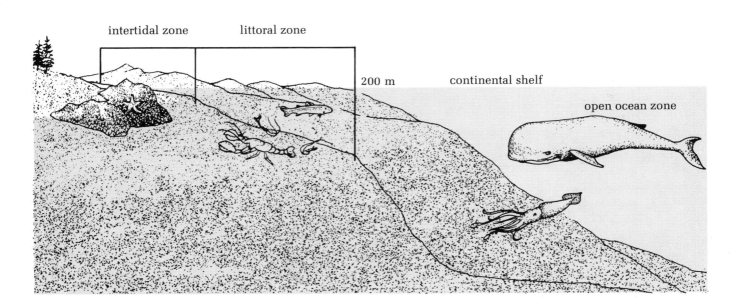

intertidal zone   littoral zone

200 m   continental shelf

open ocean zone

Study Questions

1. Explain the difference between the biosphere and a biome.
2. Explain how ecosystems, communities, and biomes are related.
3. Which biome(s) is (are) located:
   a) in the province of Ontario?
   b) in Canada?
4. List and describe the six major biomes of North America.
5. a) What determines the name and the classification of a biome?
   b) Why are biomes not named according to the animals that live in each one?
6. The salt-water part of the hydrosphere can be subdivided into zones. List these zones and describe one characteristic of each.

2.4 Biomes and Natural Succession

Today's biomes are the result of a sequence of change that occurred when ecosystems were altered by the organisms living within them. Organisms may change conditions in an area so drastically that they can no longer survive there. For example, the white birch often acts as a "nurse" tree for young spruces, which thrive in its shade. The birch itself must have bright sun. As the spruces grow taller and cast their shade, the birches die from lack of light. Eventually, the stand of white birch will be replaced, or succeeded, by a stand of spruce. This example describes a single step in a much longer process called **natural succession**.

Natural succession is a predictable sequence of change in an ecosystem's biotic community. Stages of natural succession are identified according to the dominant autotrophs, since the types of animals in an ecosystem depend on food available. In the example above, birds and insects dependent on white birches for food will move elsewhere when spruce trees take over. There are two major types of natural succession: primary and secondary.

Primary Succession

Imagine a newly formed volcanic island, or a surface scraped clean by a retreating glacier. Given enough time, even bare rock eventually becomes populated with living things through **primary succession**. The term "primary" is used because this population develops only where no organisms have lived before.

In a climate such as northern Ontario's, primary succession often

Not all lichens produce acids, but those that do produce them have a competitive edge in colonizing bare rock surfaces.

begins with the lichen, a true pioneer. The first lichens arrive in the form of tiny reproductive structures blown into cracks and crevices in rock by the wind. Lichens take hold by producing acids that break rock into small particles. Over centuries, these particles mix with fragments of decayed lichen to form a thin layer of soil. At this point, the lichens have changed their ecosystem so much that conditions are more suitable for mosses. Gradually, mosses replace or succeed the lichens, and build up more soil. As more centuries pass, grass plants succeed the mosses, shrubs succeed the grass, and trees such as aspen and birch succeed the shrubs. Each plant community helps to prepare soil conditions for a fairly permanent boreal forest of spruces and firs.

In any ecosystem, the final stage of succession is called the **climax**. The plants present at that stage are called the **climax community**. In the example above, the climax community is a boreal forest. This is also the name of the biome in which the forest grows, for biomes are often named after the dominant plants of the climax community.

Although it may take thousands of years to develop, a climax community tends to be very stable. For example, once a boreal forest is established, it may thrive with very little change for hundreds or thousands of years. Even when individual plants die, they are replaced with others like themselves.

The type of climax community produced depends on climate. Primary succession will always ultimately produce boreal forest in a climate like northern Ontario's. A climate such as southern Ontario's will produce a deciduous forest, while hot, wet conditions result in a tropical rain forest.

The clean new rock surface scraped bare by this glacier will soon become covered by lichens, beginning the first stage in the process of succession of living things.

In another part of Glacier Bay, where glaciers passed over centuries ago, succession has gradually given rise to a community of spruce trees.

Figure 2-15. Primary succession from rock occurring in a climate such as northern Ontario's over a period of thousands of years.

climax community — coniferous forest

intermediate stage — deciduous forest

shrub growth

grass plant growth and soil development

moss-covered rocks and stones

lichen-covered rock

bare rock

Secondary Succession

Climax communities last a long time only if nothing occurs to disrupt them. Disruptive events are common, however. Some, such as floods, volcanic eruptions, and many fires, are natural. Others, such as cutting, clearing, draining, and some fires, result from human activities. The sequence of changes in plant life after a disruptive event is called **secondary succession**. Table 2-2 compares primary and secondary succession. Although some details differ, both types of succession lead eventually to identical climax communities if uninterrupted.

Some events, especially those caused by humans, may be overwhelmingly frequent or disruptive. In such cases, the new succession may never lead to the original type of climax community.

Table 2-2: A Comparison of Primary Succession and Secondary Succession

Primary Succession	Secondary Succession
occurs where no previous biotic community exists	occurs after disruption of existing biotic community
predictable, orderly plant sequence starting with pioneer autotrophs	predictable orderly plant sequence starting with seed plants
slow — thousands of years	fast — one or two centuries
leads to stable climax community; details depend on climate	leads to stable climax community identical to that for primary succession

When dissolved in water, ashes form an alkaline solution. Alkalis, also known as bases, are the chemical opposites of acids. Alkalis affect plant growth just as much as acid rain.

Consider a boreal forest destroyed by fire. Within months, secondary succession begins to establish a new biotic community. Because soil is already present, plants can grow from seeds blown in by the wind. At first, only sun-loving plants such as fireweed can sprout in the ash-covered soil. Soon, however, these plants are succeeded by grasses, small shrubs, and eventually by a climax community of spruces and firs. These tree species also dominated the original climax community.

The precise sequence of secondary succession depends on the nature of the disruptive event. (See Figure 2-16.) The sequence of plant growth after a fire, for example, differs from that following a logging operation. In time, however, all succession sequences normally lead to the same type of climax community.

Figure 2-16. Secondary succession following various disruptive events. Compare the climax community produced by secondary succession with that produced by primary succession.

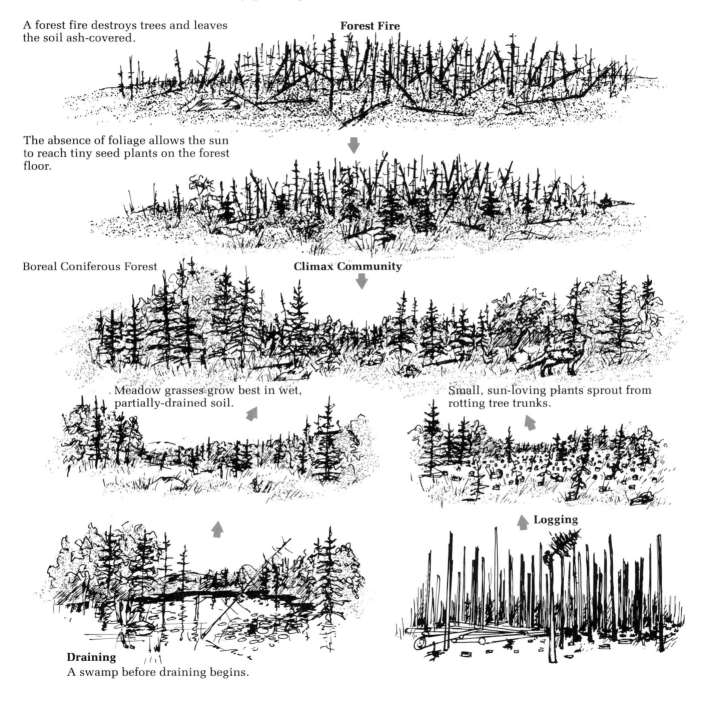

A forest fire destroys trees and leaves the soil ash-covered.

Forest Fire

The absence of foliage allows the sun to reach tiny seed plants on the forest floor.

Boreal Coniferous Forest

Climax Community

Meadow grasses grow best in wet, partially-drained soil.

Small, sun-loving plants sprout from rotting tree trunks.

Logging

Draining
A swamp before draining begins.

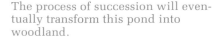
The process of succession will eventually transform this pond into woodland.

The photograph shows how succession occurs at the edge of a pond. Gradually, debris from shoreline vegetation forms enough soil for meadow plants. Slowly these plants are succeeded by shrubs and later on by trees. Meanwhile, succession at the new shore line establishes more soil, and the pond continues to fill in. A walk away from the pond's edge would reveal many stages of succession within a short distance.

Activity 2-4: A Succession Survey

Ontario has many bogs, ponds, marshes, swamps, and small lakes where stages of succession can be observed. In this activity, surveying wetland succession will enable you to see stages that occur many decades or centuries apart. The most important equipment for this survey is proper footwear.

Your teacher may divide the class into two or three large groups so that data can be gathered on more than one succession line. If this is done, each group should follow the procedure independently.

Materials

notebook	measuring tape
pencil	coloured markers (e.g, surveyor's tape)
stakes	
mallet	identification keys
string (at least 200 m)	

Procedure

1. In your notebook, draw a straight line right across the page. Label it "water's edge" at one end.

2. Test the shore line for ground firm enough to drive in a stake. Tie one end of the string to the stake.

3. With your classmates, walk away from the water until you either run out of string or reach the largest kind of plant surrounding the water (e.g., trees).

4. As you walk, unwind the string to mark your path. Look for changes in the types of vegetation. Measure the distance from the water of each distinctly new zone, and tie a coloured marker to the string to show where each new zone begins.

5. The straight line in your notebook represents the string. Use this line to map the zones, labelling each one with a brief description.

6. Break into smaller groups, each group representing one of the zones you identified, if possible. Each group will be responsible for a quadrat survey of its zone.

7. In the quadrat survey, try to identify the dominant type of plant, and describe any animals you observe.

Discussion

1. Combine the findings of all the groups to label a large-scale map of the area surveyed. What evidence do you find of succession?

2. Is the sequence observed an example of primary or secondary succession? Explain.

3. What changes do you expect to occur at the present water's edge? Explain.

4. Explain why you probably did not see a true picture of the animal life in the area surveyed.

5. What kind of animals do you think might normally live in each zone? in the pond itself? Explain.

Study Questions

1. a) Define natural succession, and give an example.
   b) Briefly describe two types of natural succession.

2. Explain why lichens are referred to as pioneers.

3. A fire has burned all the plants in a grassland ecosystem. When new plants grow, will they be the result of primary or secondary succession? Discuss.

4. Provide an example to explain how plant succession influences animal populations in the same ecosystem.

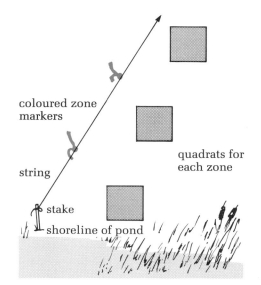

Figure 2-17. Carry out a quadrat survey for one of the zones identified by your class.

coloured zone markers

quadrats for each zone

string

stake

shoreline of pond

5. a) What is a climax community? Give an example.
   b) List some natural and humanmade events that could destroy a climax community.
   c) What will be the eventual outcome of such disruptive events?

6. a) A farmer clears a woodlot and plants turnip seeds. Explain why this is not an example of natural succession.
   b) What type of event is being described in a)?
   c) Explain how natural succession could occur in the turnip field if it was abandoned by the farmer. Identify the succession as primary or secondary.

SAVING WETLANDS

Wetlands are areas covered by shallow water most of the year. Ecologists classify wetlands according to the dominant vegetation. Marshes are dominated by grassy plants such as cattails. Swamps have trees such as cedar and willow. Bogs contain floating mats of acid-loving plants such as sphagnum moss. Fens have floating mats of alkaline-loving plants such as sedges.

To nature lovers, a wetland is a place to watch migrating birds; to children, it is a source of tadpoles. For many people, however, a wetland is a nuisance. Southern Ontario has already lost three-quarters of its wetland areas by draining, filling, and conversion to farmland. Recent studies, however, show that wetlands are far from being unimportant and unproductive.

Wetlands are ecologically important because of their role in

Ontario's Holland Marsh was drained to provide an area suitable for market gardening.

the water cycle. They catch and store rainfall, releasing it gradually into surrounding land and waterways. This activity filters out pollutants, helps to control flooding, and prevents soil erosion.

Wetlands are also a valuable resource that contribute $300 million to Ontario's economy each year. Wetland products include wood, fur from muskrats and beavers, and wild rice. Wetlands also attract tourist dollars, because of their serene beauty, and their role as a habitat

for waterfowl and sport fish.

Now that the benefits of wetlands are better understood, provincial authorities in Ontario have ordered a complete inventory of the remaining wetlands. This study will take several years to complete, and will provide data on the economic, biological, social, and hydrological value of each wetland.

Science-Related Career

Meet a Government Employee — Irene Bowman

Irene is the non-game program coordinator for the Ontario Ministry of Natural Resources in the Wildlife Branch.

Q. HAVE YOU ALWAYS BEEN INTERESTED IN PLANT AND ANIMAL LIFE?
A. I was a born naturalist. I can remember as early as age 9 reading about all kinds of wildlife. I later went into biology at university.

Q. HOW DOES THE GOVERNMENT IDENTIFY SPECIES AT RISK?
A. Ontario belongs to the Committee on the Status of Endangered Wildlife in Canada. It's a federal-provincial committee with representatives from all provinces and territories as well as non-government organizations interested in wildlife conservation. Before we can decide how to help or manage a species we have to get background information by conducting field studies and by writing a status report. The report is reviewed by the Committee, which then assigns the species to the appropriate status — rare, threatened, endangered, or not in any of these categories. Then we determine what management action to take.

Q. WHAT'S AN EXAMPLE OF THE TYPE OF MANAGEMENT ACTION YOU MIGHT TAKE?
A. One project that many people are familiar with is our ongoing work involving peregrine falcons. The eastern race of the peregrine is endangered throughout North America as a result of DDT poisoning, which causes eggshell thinning. Many government agencies in Canada and the United States are releasing captive-bred peregrines to help increase numbers that are breeding in the wild. The peregrine plays an important role in nature's food web, and its decline gave advance warning about a serious environmental problem.

Q. WHAT WAS DONE TO SAVE THE PEREGRINE FALCON?
A. The use of DDT was restricted almost twenty years ago in the United States and Canada, but it's still widely used in Central and South American countries where peregrines spend the winter. We worked with other groups to release peregrines in several Ontario locations. In Toronto, we released them from the roofs of downtown office buildings. We monitored them until they migrated south for the winter.

Q. WHAT ARE THE MOST REWARDING ASPECTS OF YOUR WORK?
A. The opportunity to work with a wide variety of animals and plants is rewarding in itself. But one project, involving the protection of a large great blue heron colony, was especially important to me. I worked with many people in the Ministry and other government agencies to help protect a heronry on Great Manitou Island in Lake Nipissing. It is now managed as a nature reserve.

Q. ARE THERE MANY JOBS IN THIS FIELD?
A. There has always been a shortage of good jobs in this field — most are still on a contract basis.

Q. HOW CAN STUDENTS BECOME INVOLVED ?
A. Most provinces have naturalist clubs that welcome young members. Some museums also have nature activities for children and teenagers. When I was a student, I worked as a volunteer in a museum department. It's a great way to find out if you're really interested in the field — and it can be useful for job contacts later on. There are also lots of books and field guides about wildlife that interested students can read. Most important of all are hobbies such as birdwatching and plant identification that give students the opportunity to make their own observations about nature.

Review Questions

A: Knowledge

1. a) Define population as it is used in ecology, and give an example.
   b) Define community as it is used in ecology, and give an example.

2. Explain how population distribution differs from population density.

3. Explain why an extremely dense population is harmful to the environment.

4. For each of the following pairs of terms, explain how the two are alike, and how they differ:
   a) population growth and population explosion
   b) community and ecosystem
   c) biome and ecosystem
   d) tundra and desert
   e) carrying capacity and steady state

5. List three ways ecologists use to describe community structure. Explain why three ways are needed.

6. List the four processes that can change the size of a population. Give an example of each.

7. List six environmental factors that can affect population growth. Explain what effect each factor has.

8. a) Name three North American biomes that occur in Ontario, and briefly describe each.
   b) On what basis are biomes classified?
   c) What factor plays the most important role in determining the nature of a biome?

9. a) Compare how the taiga and tundra biomes differ in biotic and abiotic conditions.
   b) Which biome has a greater diversity of living things?
   c) Why is there such a difference between the two biomes?

10. The term biome usually refers to a terrestrial area. What equivalent term is used for aquatic areas? Give an example.

11. a) Define symbiosis.
    b) List four types of symbiosis and give an example of each.

12. The birth rate of prey must always exceed the birth rate of predators. Explain the reason for the difference.

13. All living things in the environment compete directly or indirectly. Discuss this statement.

14. a) Explain the meaning of natural succession and give an example.
    b) Name and describe the final stage to which all succession pathways eventually lead.

15. a) Describe the pathway of primary succession.
    b) Under what circumstances does primary succession occur?

16. a) Describe the pathway of secondary succession.
    b) List three circumstances that might lead to secondary succession and explain why.

B: Application

17. Briefly discuss the population density and distribution of humans in Canada and the province of Ontario.

18. a) Give an example of mutualism involving humans and some other species. Explain the role played by the humans and by the other species.
    b) Repeat a) for commensalism and parasitism.

19. The human digestive tract contains bacteria that produce important vitamins. What symbiotic relationship does this illustrate? Explain.

20. Agriculture and forestry represent symbiotic relationships between plants and human beings. Identify the kind of symbiosis referred to. Give reasons for your answer.

21. Animals that live in dark, moist environments like caves often exhibit structural characteristics such as lack of skin pigment, blindness, and extra antennae. Explain how these features might have developed. Are they examples of adaptations? Explain.

22. Human beings compete with every other living thing on Earth. Explain.

23. What advantage(s) does a predator such as a coyote (which hunts and eats many other animal species) have over one that preys exclusively on a single type of organism?

C: Problem Solving

24. On January 1, a small rural town had 1400 inhabitants. During that year, there were eight births and fourteen deaths. Ten townspeople left for the city, but 24 city people moved into the town. Calculate the growth rate of the town's population (to one decimal place).

25. Give the general name for all the environmental interactions described below, and then give a specific name for each.
    a) a dog's coat becomes covered with burrs
    b) a deserted meadowlark nest is taken over by a pregnant mouse
    c) a marathoner develops athlete's foot

26. a) What is the density of the rabbit population in a wilderness area of 100 m by 200 m with a population of 400 rabbits?
    b) How could the same population seem to have a density of one rabbit per square metre?

27. a) Study the population cycles of the lynx and the snowshoe hare in Figure 2-10. How would these two cycles affect the grass population, the primary source of food for the hare?
    b) What effect would the answer to a) have on the lynx and hare population cycles?

28. Find a vacant lot in your area and observe how it has gone back to nature.
    a) What evidence is there of succession?
    b) Predict what this vacant lot will look like in 100 years from now if left undisturbed.
    c) Does your answer to b) describe a climax community? Explain.
    d) Are the changes in b) an example of primary or secondary succession? Explain.

Try This

Death and Density

Go to your school library and find out the population size and surface area of the five largest cities in Canada. Calculate the density of each city in square kilometres. Find out the number of homicides in each of these major cities for a given year. Does population density relate in any way to homicides? Discuss your findings.

Block-cut harvesting of trees has a less harmful impact on the environment than the system of clear-cutting huge areas.

Chapter 3
The Role of Humans in the Biosphere

So far in this unit, we have studied the biosphere as if humans played almost no part in it. In fact, humans have the same relationships with the environment as do all other living things. Like other organisms, humans must obtain energy and materials from the surrounding environment. Unlike most other organisms, however, humans can manipulate and transform the environment on a massive scale. We are the most abundant and widespread large animal on Earth, and our impact on the environment has created many difficult problems. These will affect the future not only of the human species but of the planet as a whole.

When you finish Chapter 3, you should be able to:

- discuss how humans use major natural resources
- describe the impact of humans on the environment
- apply the principles of ecology to environmental problems
- recognize the effects of bias, emotion, and prejudice in discussions of environmental issues
- describe how humans can help maintain a productive natural environment

3.1 The Human Impact Upon the Environment

All humans depend on the environment for survival. Directly or indirectly, the natural environment provides us with energy, food, and materials for clothing and buildings. The materials and energy that we take from the environment are called **natural resources**. These include plants and animals, minerals, water, air, and soil. In obtaining and using these natural resources, humans interact with both the biotic and the abiotic environments.

The human impact on the environment caused by our use of natural resources depends on several factors.

1. *The kind of resource consumed.* Some natural resources, such as rain, wind, sunshine, and soil, are widespread and are not reduced much when used. Other resources, such as petroleum, diamonds, and hardwood trees, are not widespread. Unless they are properly managed, resources such as these can become depleted or exhausted.

2. *The technology used to obtain and process the resource.* Natural resources can be used in many different ways. Petroleum, for example, can be used as fuel in a car or manufactured into plastics. Water can be exploited by digging a well or by building a massive dam. Fish can be caught with a rod or by a trawler equipped with sonar. In these examples, how does the type of technology used affect both the resource and the environment? What types of technology produce the most waste products and side-effects?

3. *The amount of resource consumed per person.* There are great differences in the quantities of natural resources used in different parts of the world. A typical inhabitant of Switzerland, for example, consumes 40 times as much of the world's resources as a person living in Somalia in East Africa. Canada uses more energy per person than any other nation. People in richer countries demand

A giant rotating digger helps explore a new energy source in the Alberta tar sands. Will human demand eventually use up this natural resource?

and consume larger amounts of natural resources per person than do people in poor countries, and have a proportionately larger impact on the environment.

4. *The total amount of the resource consumed.* This factor depends on the amount consumed by each individual and on the total number of people in the world. As the human population grows, the demand for every kind of natural resource also grows.

Using Canada's Natural Resources

Canadians are fortunate in having a large land area, a small population, and abundant vegetation, water, wildlife, and minerals. This does not mean that Canada is free of environmental problems, however. We will look at each Canadian resource in terms of both its value to humans and its ecological significance.

1. Land Canada is the second-largest country in the world, with an area of nearly ten million square kilometres. Canada's land is a valuable resource providing space for homes and other buildings, farming, recreation, roads, and railways. In terms of human use, not all land is equal. Mountains and tundra, for example, cannot be used for farming or extensive building. Most land, however, can be used in several different ways, and there may be conflicts over which use is best.

Large areas in Canada previously covered with forests have been cleared and used for farmland. A great deal of this farmland is now being converted to suburbs, shopping malls, and highways. In these construction projects, wetlands are often drained and sometimes eliminated from the environment. Formerly considered useless, wetlands are now recognized as important to the water cycle and as valuable habitats for wildfowl.

2. Soil The material covering most of the land differs from place to place across Canada. In the arctic tundra, thin soils lie over permanently frozen ground called **permafrost**. In early summer, arctic soils become water-logged. The soils under most forest land are acidic and unsuited to farming. In the plains bordering the Great Lakes and the St. Lawrence, soils are fertile and produce a wide range of crops. Extending from Winnipeg to Edmonton, prairie soils are black, thick, and rich.

Soil provides an environment for both wild and cultivated plants. About 6% of Canada's land area is used for agriculture, and about 80% of this farmland is in the prairie provinces of Alberta,

Building Highway 401, Toronto. Note the surrounding farmland that has since become part of metropolitan Toronto.

Saskatchewan, and Manitoba. Agricultural activities account for more than 25% of Canada's economy, and Canada is one of the world's few exporters of wheat.

The intensive cultivation of prairie soils for food production demands a high use of energy in the form of agricultural equipment, as well as the use of artificial fertilizers and pesticides. Without proper care soils can lose their fertility, and can be destroyed through erosion by wind and water. Agricultural practices can also pollute the soil and surrounding waterways.

3. Forests About 44% of Canada's land area is covered with forests. The northern coniferous forest of spruce, fir, and pine is one of the largest in the world, sweeping across the country in a broad band. The eastern forests are a mixture of coniferous and deciduous trees, such as maple, beech, pine, and hemlock. The western forests, which receive heavy rainfall, include dense stands of immense trees such as red cedar, Douglas fir, and redwoods.

Forests are complex and important parts of the natural environment. They cycle significant amounts of water and atmospheric gases, stabilize soils, and provide homes for a wide variety of animal life.

About two-thirds of Canada's forested land is harvested regularly for pulpwood or lumber, and forestry is directly and indirectly responsible for 10% of Canadian jobs. Northern forest trees are ideal for pulpwood, while western forest hardwoods provide construction lumber.

The destruction of forests—through cutting without replanting, forest fires, flooding from dam projects, diseases, or acid rain—leads to a loss of habitat for many animals. Loss of forest land can also affect climate through changes in the water cycle, and this can lead to soil erosion.

4. Lakes and rivers Thousands of lakes and rivers cover almost 8% of Canada's land surface, providing one of the best supplies of fresh water in the world.

Fresh water is used for drinking and sanitation, in industrial processes and in agriculture. Most large cities are built near a river or lake. Canada's early trade and transportation routes followed waterways, and the Great Lakes and the St. Lawrence River are still important routes for shipping bulk products such as wheat. Running water is an important energy resource, used to produce hydroelectricity. Humans use both rivers and lakes for commercial and recreational fishing.

The total mass of organisms living in the soil of a pasture is much greater than the mass of a herd of cattle grazing in the pasture.

Modern tree-harvesting machines can do in minutes what used to take hours or days.

Do You Know?
The longest river in Canada is the Mackenzie in the Northwest Territories. It extends 4241 km and drains nearly 2 000 000 km² of land.

In many countries short of water, only bottled water can be drunk. In Canada we take for granted that fresh, drinkable water will come from taps whenever we want it. In some areas of southern Ontario this may not last much longer.

A coastal settlement in Belleoran, Newfoundland.

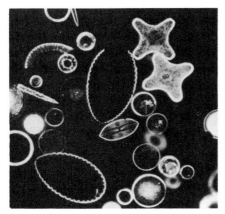

A large proportion of the phytoplankton in warm seas is made up of a species of dinoflagellates.

Some uses of water in Canada are destructive. Wastes from industry, agriculture, and domestic sewage are still dumped into rivers and lakes, and waterways receive other toxic chemicals in the forms of land run-off and acid rain.

5. Oceans and shorelines   Canada has coasts on three of the world's five oceans: the Atlantic, the Pacific, and the Arctic. Even the inland provinces of Ontario and Manitoba have a salt-water coast on Hudson Bay.

Oceans form the largest ecosystem on Earth. The most productive ocean areas are in the surface waters and the shallower waters off the coast. Here, where additional nutrients come from rivers and eroding land, and where sunlight can penetrate the waters and produce algal growth, large shoals of fish and marine mammals such as whales and seals are found. Sea birds, too, feed in these waters, while the shores are home to numerous crabs and molluscs.

Over one million tonnes of fish and crustaceans are caught in Canada annually, including cod, herring, and lobster on the Atlantic coast, and hake, salmon, and sole on the Pacific coast.

Drifting near the ocean surface, small floating plants called **phytoplankton** are the base of many ocean food chains. Because of their vast numbers, phytoplankton carry out most of the photosynthesis on Earth, and contribute significantly to the level of atmospheric oxygen. Pollution of the sea, such as oil spills, can harm these plants, with serious consequences. Marine life is also threatened by overfishing and overhunting, which have caused a decline in populations of fish, whales, seals, and turtles.

6. Wildlife

Each biome across Canada has its own characteristic flora and fauna. The tundra is the simplest ecosystem, with the least diversity of wildlife. Forests, estuaries, and wetlands, however, include many different types of plants and animals. Many species of birds migrate over large areas of Canada, breeding in the north and flying south for the winter.

When hunted extensively for furs, Canada's wildlife once supported a large part of the economy. With the decline of trapping, wildlife is now an important resource for the tourist industry. However, hunting, human disturbance, pollution, disease, and habitat loss have greatly reduced wildlife populations in many areas of Canada. Unrestricted hunting and settlement have caused the extinction of species such as the passenger pigeon. Others such as the wild turkey and the blue whale are near extinction.

7. Beneath the biosphere

Canada is rich in mineral resources that lie beneath the land surface and are usually extracted by mining. The most important minerals include copper, nickel, lead, zinc, molybdenum, silver, and gold. Canada also produces 25% of the world's supply of asbestos and 40% of its potash.

Some underground resources, such as coal, gas, and oil, are direct sources of energy. Petroleum and coal can also be used as raw materials in the manufacture of plastics and other synthetics. Metals and precious stones are used in industrial processes, and in the manufacture of goods such as jewellery and insulation, while nonprecious rock is used in the construction of roads and buildings.

The extraction and use of resources from beneath the ground can cause environmental problems when overlying soil and vegetation, along with the animals that depend on them, are removed. Also, the heavy machinery used in mining consumes a great deal of energy, and the processing of ores causes pollution.

A graveyard exhibit at the Bronx Zoo in New York tells visitors about the many species made extinct by human activities.

Nickel ore is carried from mine to mill at the Inco Ltd. operation at Copper Cliffs, Ontario.

8. Energy resources Canada is richer in sources of energy than any other country, and produces surpluses of energy for export. The most important energy sources are fossil fuels (oil, gas, and coal), running water (hydroelectricity), and uranium (nuclear energy). Winds and tides are also potential sources of energy.

Extracting and using all this energy poses a great threat to the environment. Hydroelectric projects, oil refineries, drilling rigs, gas pipelines, the burning of coal, and nuclear reactors — all are environmentally damaging activities. These activities create environmental problems even when functioning properly, but the consequences of an accident, such as an oil spill or a reactor breakdown, can be disastrous.

Pollution and Environmental Stress

The environment is stressed by many natural factors, such as floods, drought, heat waves, earthquakes, glaciation, volcanic eruptions, and disease. These events cause stress because they change the environmental conditions, and the ecosystems must adjust to these changes. In extreme cases, environmental changes can lead to the disappearance of entire habitats.

Human activities, especially the extraction of minerals and use of energy, also create environmental stress. With the development of powerful technologies, human changes to the environment can now be as great as or greater than those caused by natural events. Consider the impact of building a large dam, for example. The reservoir created by the dam floods vast areas of land, alters river courses and drainage patterns, changes the numbers and types of

These two photos show the site of the LG 4 Dam of the James Bay Hydro-Electric project in Quebec, before it was started (left) and after completion (right). What changes have been made to the surrounding land? How do you think this affects the environment?

plants and animals, both on land and in the water, affects the local climate, displaces local communities, and can destroy historical artifacts.

The impact of dam-building on the environment does not end around the dam site. The energy produced by the dam is channeled through power lines to distant towns and cities, where it provides electricity for activities such as manufacturing and industrial processing. The massive and concentrated use of energy in and near cities is great enough to alter the local climate — for example, through the heat given off from buildings. By-products of energy use such as exhaust fumes and industrial wastes pollute air, water, and soil.

The environmental stress caused by pollution can have short- or long-term effects, depending on the type and magnitude of the activity. The dumping of raw untreated sewage into a river, for example, has an immediate impact on many organisms in the river's food web. Eventually, the populations of aquatic organisms may adjust to the increased nutrients in the sewage. However, if the volume of sewage increases beyond the ability of the river ecosystem to tolerate it, many of the river's organisms will die or move elsewhere. Unless the input of sewage is reduced, the river's ecosystem will be changed permanently, from one with a balance of fish, molluscs, crustaceans, insects, and plants, to one consisting mostly of microorganisms such as bacteria.

Pollutants can damage the environment not only at the immediate site where they are produced but also in areas far from the source. Pollutants are spread through living mechanisms, such as food chains and migrating animals. They are also carried through the abiotic environment by wind, rain, and waterways. Toxic chemicals have been traced in pathways around the globe, and have been found in the remotest parts of the ocean and in antarctic animals.

Both ecosystems and individual organisms have a range of tolerance to stress. Some ecosystems are more vulnerable than others because they have fewer species of organisms, and hence their ability to change is limited. The Arctic, for example, is a harsh and stressful environment to which relatively few species are adapted. A threat to any one species in such a simple ecosystem is a threat to all. The larger numbers of organisms and food webs in a forest ecosystem provide more ways of adjusting to environmental change.

Some living things adjust to a changing environment by moving away. However, areas remote from human interference are increas-

Canada has built some of the world's largest dams, mostly for the production of hydroelectricity.

Mixing different chemical pollutants to form new combinations has caused a serious pollution problem in Canada and other industrialized nations. Sulphur and nitrogen oxides are released into the air from smelters, coal-fired electricity plants, and car exhausts. These gases mix in the air and dissolve in moisture to produce secondary products, including sulphuric and nitric acid. These acids enter the water cycle, falling from the air as acid rain and passing into streams, rivers, and lakes. It has been estimated that 43% of the two million lakes in Ontario and Quebec have received moderate to high levels of acid rain, with resulting damage to their ecosystems.

ingly rare. In the long term, organisms and ecosystems adjust to environmental changes. Organisms capable of living in the new environment survive better than those that cannot, and their populations increase.

The Impact of Human Population Density

Most of the students reading this book live in a town or city within 350 km of Canada's southern border. Although Canada has 7% of the world's land and only 0.5% of the world's population, we live as though we were short of space. Thirty per cent of Canadians, for example, live in one of three metropolitan areas — Toronto, Montreal, or Vancouver. The population density of Toronto, Canada's largest city, is fifty thousand people per square kilometre, a density greater than that of New York, Los Angeles, or London. Concentration of the population into high-density areas can have a devastating impact on the environment.

Most large cities are built close to a good supply of fresh water and fertile land. As cities grow and spread into suburbs, some agricultural land is converted into housing and roadways. Concentrated industrial activity in or near the city often produces wastes that pollute the air and water and damage nearby crops and farmland. In many cities, it is becoming difficult to dispose of the domestic waste produced by a large population. Nobody wants to live near a garbage dump, so waste is trucked further and further from the city, or is incinerated. Both these activities require extra energy and create more pollution.

People's physical needs are essentially for space, shelter, food, employment, and recreation. Not only was population density and distribution different 60 years ago, but so was technology, the supply of goods, and demand on the part of individuals. Because people are now concentrated in areas of high density separate from farmland, food supplies must be trucked daily into cities. People enjoy city life and its employment opportunities, but they also like peace and privacy, so many people live in suburbs and commute to work daily. People and goods moving constantly on routes to and from population centres cause increased congestion, energy consumption, and pollution.

Another result of highly concentrated populations has been the loss of space for wild plants and animals near centres of human activity. Areas of natural vegetation in cities are an increasingly rare and irreplaceable part of the environment. They remind people that humans cannot survive in a world of concrete alone.

The phenomenon of population concentration in large cities in Canada is relatively new. In 1931 about 30% of Canadians lived on farms. By 1981, rural inhabitants had dropped to less than 5% of the population.

Activity 3-1: Human Population Growth—A Case Study

What has happened in Canada is also happening around the world, as people move from the countryside to cities, and cities grow beyond their capacity to meet the population's needs. In this activity, you will trace the growth of the Earth's human population, and consider the impact of this growth on the global environment.

Materials

100 sheets of continuous (fanfold) computer paper	pencil
masking tape	ruler (30 cm)
	marking pen

Part A: Graphing Population Growth

So extraordinary is the shape of the human population growth curve that you must follow an unusual method to chart it. The class will be divided into groups that will carry out this activity in a large area, such as a hall or a gymnasium.

Procedure

1. Tape one end of the computer paper to the floor, and mark it as shown in Figure 3-1. Your graph begins in the year 8000 B.C., when the Earth's human population was about five million.

Figure 3-1.

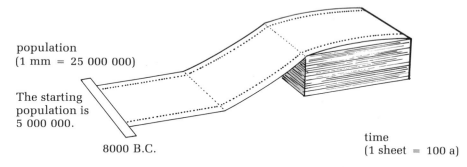

population
(1 mm = 25 000 000)

The starting population is 5 000 000.

8000 B.C.

time
(1 sheet = 100 a)

2. Note that the perforations serve as markers on the horizontal axis, indicating time. Each sheet of paper represents one century. Unfold and lay flat the first 40 sheets from the stack of paper, taping them to the floor. Label the year 4000 B.C. on the appropriate perforation of sheet 40.

3. Mark the population level (see Table 3-1), using 1 mm to represent twenty-five million people on the vertical scale.

Table 3-1: Human Population Growth

Date	Population (millions)
8000 B.C.	5
4000 B.C.	85
117 B.C.	200
1650	545
1832	1000
1939	2000
1960	3000
1975	4000
1986	5000

4. Continue laying out the paper until you reach sheet 79. The left side of this sheet represents 200 B.C. and the right side 100 B.C. Locate and label the year 117 B.C., and mark the appropriate population. (See Table 3-1.)

5. On the right-hand side of sheet 80, make a heavy vertical mark to show the transition from B.C. to A.D.

6. Unfold the rest of the sheets and tape them down. Label each century from the birth of Christ, and refer to Table 3-1 to mark the population levels.

7. Use a marking pen and a ruler to join the plotted points showing population levels with a smooth line.

Discussion

1. In what way(s) does the shape of your graph resemble that of the growth pattern for a typical animal population? (See Figure 2-4 on page 43.) How does your graph differ?

2. a) In what stage of typical population growth is the human population at present?
   b) What normally happens to an animal population after this stage?
   c) Is there any indication of this occurrence on your graph?
   d) Do you think b) will eventually happen? Explain, supporting your argument with what you have learned about animal populations.

3. a) How long did it take for Earth's population to double from one thousand million to two thousand million? How long to double from two thousand million to four thousand million?
   b) By what year do you think the Earth's population will reach ten thousand million? Explain.

4. a) What four basic factors affect population size?
   b) Which of these factors has been most influential in the growth of the human population in this century? Explain.
   c) Which factor do you think is most likely to control the size of the human population in the future? Explain.

Part B: Carrying Capacity — A Matter of Opinion

Scientists cannot easily answer the question of how many people the Earth will ultimately support. The answer depends on the human demand for resources, on the climate, and on the terrain. Besides the question of absolute numbers, there is also the question of the quality of life. More people in a world that cannot expand will mean less of everything for everybody. Read the following article on carrying capacity, and then form small groups to discuss the questions based on the article. Briefly report your group's responses to the class.

Case Study

Scientific estimates of how many people the world can support range from fifty thousand million to two hundred thousand million or more. Scientists arrive at these figures by measuring the human needs for space, energy, and food, as well as the rate of population growth. At the present rate of increase, population density will reach about 11 people per square metre over the Earth's entire land surface in only 650 years! Clearly, the Earth's population must reach a maximum well before there is standing room only, if for no other reason than to save some land for growing food.

Speculations about the Earth's carrying capacity lead back to a fundamental principle: the limiting factor. The limiting factor is whatever essential resource is in shortest supply. This factor limits population growth, no matter how abundant other resources might be. If there is an abundant supply of food, space, shelter, and energy, for example, but only a small supply of fresh water, then the water supply alone will determine the size of the population. When the demand for water exceeds the supply, the resource will gradually shrink and the population will shrink with it. The limiting factor for human populations differs from one part of the world to another.

Scientists cannot agree on ultimate numbers, because they cannot agree on what constitutes a satisfactory quality of human life. It is physically impossible for everyone in the world to enjoy the same standard of living that we enjoy in Canada today. There are not enough trees in the world to make enough paper to supply everyone with a daily copy of a newspaper, for example. The question that scientists cannot answer is: how much would people be prepared to give up in order to support a larger population competing for a fixed amount of resources?

Discussion

1. How does nature regulate the size of other animal populations? Is the human population regulated in this way at present? Do you think it is likely to be? Explain.

2. Some people argue that only underdeveloped countries like Ethiopia should try to control their populations. To whom is this argument likely to seem attractive? Is it a reasonable idea?

3. Some people think that all humans on Earth have the right to adequate food and shelter. They believe that affluent nations like Canada should share their wealth with fellow humans in underdeveloped countries. Do you agree? Consider the effect such aid could have on population growth.

4. Some people think that affluent nations like Canada should stop using resources so much, especially energy. This would leave more resources for people elsewhere who do not have enough. How might this plan affect world population growth?

5. Form a list of proposals for regulating human population growth so that it levels off at ten thousand million by 2050 A.D.
   a) Which of these proposals would be acceptable in Canada? Worldwide?
   b) Are any of your proposals completely unacceptable? Explain.

Extinction and Endangered Species

A serious problem posed by an expanding human population is the loss of habitats for wild plants and animals. Loss of space, combined with hunting, pollution, disease, and disturbance, have threatened many species with extinction. Although the extermination of species is a natural process that has taken place since the beginning of life on Earth, the number of species now threatened is far above the normal rate. The massive disruption of entire ecosystems caused by the loss of species diversity could make the ecosystems with which humans interact more vulnerable to destruction.

A **vulnerable species** is one whose numbers are decreasing and which is threatened with further reduction in population. An **endangered species** is one with a population so reduced in numbers that the species is in immediate danger of becoming extinct. Organisms that no longer exist in the wild are classified as extinct. Sometimes only a few specimens of species extinct in the wild survive in captivity in zoos and parks.

The Bengal tiger is an endangered species, reduced in numbers by hunting and destruction of its forest habitat.

Study Questions

1. What are the major natural resources found in Canada's:
   a) land and soil?
   b) forests?
   c) lakes and rivers?

2. Explain how Canada's land and water resources have shaped the pattern of human settlement in this country.

3. List five jobs that depend on Canada's natural resources.

4. Explain why human impact on the natural environment has increased greatly in the last 50 years.

5. What is the difference between an endangered species and an extinct species? Give an example of each.

ENDANGERED SPECIES: CAN HUMANS HELP?

The endangered cheetah has a low fertility because of excessive inbreeding.

Although human activity has caused many species to become endangered or extinct, humans can also help rare species to recover from impending extinction. In Canada, for example, the whooping crane population has been boosted by a combination of strict hunting laws, habitat preservation, and captive breeding programs. In the 1960s, extensive hunting and loss of habitat had reduced the population of this bird to only 43. A cooperative Canadian-American breeding program has doubled the whooping crane population, which is now over 100.

Although whooping cranes often lay two eggs, they rarely rear more than one chick. Beginning in the 1960s, a "spare" egg was taken from each nest and incubated in captivity. Some breeding programs have used the closely related sandhill crane to hatch and rear whooping crane chicks and to teach them how to survive in the wild. Despite these efforts, the whooping crane's long-term survival in the wild is still uncertain.

The African cheetah is another species threatened by habitat loss, but recent evidence shows that its numbers may have declined even without human interference. Scientific studies have shown that wild cheetahs have a low reproductive rate and high infant mortality. All cheetahs are very closely related, and the population has developed genetic defects as a result of excessive inbreeding. Some scientists believe that cheetahs came close to extinction long ago, and only a few individuals survived. The modern cheetahs descended from these few have inherited the problem of low fertility.

The small degree of genetic variation between individuals leaves this species extremely vulnerable to changes in the environment. A disease affecting one cheetah, for example, could rapidly become an epidemic wiping out an entire population, because the resistance to disease of all the animals would be equally low. New techniques of studying genes, and experimental breeding between captive cheetahs from different zoos, may enable scientists to help the cheetah win its struggle for survival.

3.2 Examining Environmental Issues

Different people view the environment in different ways. Consider a wilderness park near a major city. For some people, the park is a quiet area where they can walk, canoe, ski, and watch or photograph wildlife. Other people see the park as a place to hunt or fish. Wilderness parks often contain minerals and trees that some individuals would like to exploit. Tourist-related businesses entice large numbers of visitors to wilderness parks, while ecologists value parks as places where they can observe natural processes free from human influence. Interests in the environment sometimes conflict. The debate over the best use of the environment grows more critical as the human population increases and wilderness areas shrink.

The impact of environmental issues on the public depends on the level of awareness. Public awareness is usually aroused through campaigns, demonstrations, advertising, news, reports, and lobbying. These techniques can cause a significant shift in viewpoint. Thirty years ago, most people considered wolves dangerous animals which should be shot on sight. A bounty was paid to hunters who killed wolves, and anyone who defended the wolf was considered eccentric. Then a popular book entitled *Never Cry Wolf* by Canadian author Farley Mowat convinced many readers that wolves were not a threat to humans, but fascinating and intelligent animals playing an important role in the environment. This viewpoint is now predominant.

When considering environmental issues, it is important to look at all sides of an issue in as much detail as possible, because bias can interfere with your understanding of the issue. Try to get accurate information from more than one source in order to achieve a balanced perspective.

Many people were moved by the news stories about the seal hunt. Photographs showing helpless seal pups aroused sympathy for them. Is this sufficient cause to help an animal? Does it mean that less appealing animals might not be helped?

Activity 3-2:   Environmental Issue Study

In this activity, you will identify and study an environmental issue that interests you, and assess the relative merits of arguments related to the issue.

Procedure

1. Survey local newspapers and radio and TV programs in order to list some recent topics related to the environment.

2. Select one topic that interests you, and collect more information about it, using sources such as the library, government departments, environmental groups, politicians, corporations, and public surveys.

3. Identify the major interest groups involved in the issue, and set up a table presenting the arguments used by the various groups.

4. Evaluate each group's arguments, and list, *in order of importance*, what you believe are the major areas of concern, using the following headings.

environment	economics
community traditions	religious beliefs
political philosophy	other concerns

Discussion

1. a) How do you think an issue like the one you selected should be resolved? Explain.
   b) How do you think this issue will actually be resolved? Explain.

2. Explain how the demand for jobs often conflicts with protection of the environment.

3. Time is an important factor for all parties involved in environmental issues. Explain.

4. List three major Canadian environmental issues that have not yet been resolved.

Sharing Resources for the Common Good

Most environmental issues stem from the improper use of a natural resource. In some cases, a resource such as a mineral ore, a forest, or a lake is owned by a company or an individual. Owners can use the resource however they like, as long as they conform to the relevant laws. In other cases, the resource is owned by the government on behalf of the entire population. Some natural resources, such as sunshine, air, rain, and the open sea, are not owned by anyone.

A shared or common resource is one that can be used equally by an entire community. The word "common" was used in England to mean an area of pastureland that anyone in the community could use for grazing cattle or sheep. The problem with this concept was that people could use a resource without being responsible for it.

Naturally, each individual tried to put as many animals as possible onto the common grazing land, so that the land was overgrazed and its value to everyone was reduced. There was a conflict between maximizing individual gain and enjoying the common good of shared land. This dilemma has been called "the tragedy of the commons". In ecology this expression is used to describe any situation in which a common resource is shared between two or more competing users, and is ultimately damaged by a lack of responsible ownership.

Air and water are examples of common resources. Because they can be used by anyone in the community, industries have taken advantage of them as a "free" way to dump their waste products. Industries enjoy the benefit of using the common resource, while the clean-up costs must be borne by the community.

The problem of common resources is especially difficult to resolve when an international boundary is involved. Canada and the United States, for example, are involved in disputes concerning air pollution and acid rain blowing from one country to the other. Both nations also share the common resource of the Great Lakes, and must coordinate their management of its waters.

Since no one owns the open sea, fishing boats from many nations remove as many fish as they can from this common resource. No one country is responsible for limiting catches or for otherwise preserving future populations of fish. An International Whaling Commission has set quotas on whale catches, but these quotas are usually recommended by the whaling nations themselves!

In these examples, the short-term gains of particular industries or nations have taken priority over the long-term preservation of the environment. In the long run, however, industry also suffers when the resources on which industry is based are depleted.

A blob of polluted water fans out into Lake Ontario from an Etobicoke creek in Toronto. Using our waterways as dumping areas for industrial effluents will soon lead to a situation like the tragedy of the commons.

The Importance of Environmental Education

Many environmental problems arise because people are unaware of, or do not understand, basic ecological principles. Education is essential because we cannot make wise decisions about the effects of our activities on the environment if we do not understand how ecosystems work. A knowledge of ecology, in fact, can help communities to obtain more long-term benefits from their environments.

Many scientific concepts are used in the study of ecosystems, but all of them can be summarized in the following four basic principles.

1. *Everything is connected to everything else.* You have already learned that living things are connected to the abiotic environment through the cycling of essential elements, and that organisms are connected to one another through food chains and food webs. Many people make the mistake of considering parts of the environment in isolation, without realizing that a change in any one part of this interrelated system sets off changes elsewhere. Consider the simple example of a cow in a field. To a nonscientist, if you take away the cow, you are left with the field. But to an ecologist, the removal of the cow signals a shift in a balanced system. The cow has affected the plants in the field by grazing on some, leaving others, and adding manure. Removing the cow will change plant growth and distribution. Plants now left to grow will produce seeds that will attract birds or blow to neighbouring fields. The change in vegetation may attract new herbivores, such as rabbits. These in turn will bring their predators, such as foxes and hawks. Insects that laid eggs on the cow dung will disappear, along with their predators. Holes dug by the rabbits will affect soil drainage and soil organisms. In short, a seemingly simple change involving only one thing sets off changes in many other things.

The use of insecticides to kill pests, such as this spruce budworm, often has the effect of killing birds and other animals connected to the pest through food chains.

2. *Everything must go somewhere.* There is no such thing as tossing garbage "away". Garbage may be disposed of, but it remains in the environment. A common mistake is to think that air and water will make pollutants disappear. But even waste emptied into the ocean eventually turns up somewhere.

The illusion of disappearing waste comes partly from nature's recycling activities. If you toss an apple core on your school playing field, it will be broken down by bacteria in a few weeks or months, depending on the climate. In nature, one organism's waste is another's food. This natural recycling process is often jammed by the vast quantities of waste material that humans produce. Furthermore, some industrial wastes, such as plastics, cannot easily be broken down.

This baby tern's deformed beak is a birth defect, caused by chemical wastes in the Great Lakes.

3. *Nature knows best.* Sometimes environmental catastrophes arise when humans try to improve on nature without understanding its complexity. Villagers in Guyana, for example, once cultivated maize and cassava, kept a few livestock, and led poor but healthy lives. They were encouraged, however, to improve their lot by growing rice that could be sold for cash. They cleared their fields of crops and brought in machinery to dig and cultivate rice fields. The wet rice fields proved ideal breeding places for mosquitoes. Normally the mosquitoes would have fed on livestock, but the animals had been displaced along with the maize crops, so the villagers contracted malaria from the mosquitoes instead. They grew weak and unable to farm. Instead of getting richer, they got sicker and poorer.

4. *There is no such thing as a free lunch.* The full cost of the use of a natural resource is often not calculated. Fossil fuels such as oil and coal, for example, are considered cheap sources of energy, but only when the cost of finding, extracting, processing, and delivering these fuels is calculated. The final use and by-products of fossil fuels, however, are also part of the process, and involve "hidden" costs — for example, the effects of pollution. The ultimate cost of burning "cheap" oil, coal, and wood is the buildup of carbon dioxide in the atmosphere, and a possible change of climate caused by the greenhouse effect.

The four ecological principles discussed here were first published in 1971 by Dr. Barry Commoner in a book entitled *The Closing Circle*. Other ecologists have proposed similar lists, some of them much longer, but most agree that these four principles cover the basics. What do you think the title of Commoner's book means?

Humans in the Balance of Nature

Everything humans do affects the environment. Human efforts have begun, and must continue, to try to balance human activities with the natural world, working with, not against, natural processes. Human assistance can make the difference between an ecosystem surviving or disappearing. Human support and protection are sometimes essential for the maintenance of an ecosystem.

Stricter laws, consistently enforced, are required to control the impact of individuals, groups, and corporations on the environment. Quotas on hunting and fishing must be established, for example, to prevent declining populations of fish and animals. Governments can prevent overcutting of timber by replanting programs, which allow cut areas time to recover. Nature is generous when given the opportunity, and land and lakes can revert to productivity if properly managed.

Many environmental problems are simply a question of common sense. If you dump poison, it will kill. If you catch fish faster than they reproduce, they will become scarcer. If you chop down trees and do not plant new ones, forests will disappear. It is important that the public become involved in these issues and not leave matters to politicians and business people. Not only will an informed public encourage governmental protection of the environment, but they will also be more willing to honour strict protective measures when they realize these measures are in their own interest.

It is important that you learn now to accept responsibility for intelligent management of your environment. Understanding and knowledge can assist you in solving environmental problems, whether the problem is small, such as litter in a stream or park, or large, such as the flooding of a river valley by a hydroelectric dam.

This recycling plant produces a clear product from dirty, used oil. What products could you recycle in your daily life?

Observe your family's lifestyle
for a month, and then list three
ways in which they are:
a) contributing to pollution;
b) reducing the amount of
   pollution;
c) recycling products;
d) conserving energy.

Study Questions

1. Explain the relationship between environmental issues and environmental education.

2. Explain how the "tragedy of the commons" applies to:
   a) forest fires caused by humans,
   b) acidification of soil by acid rain.

3. List the four ecological principles that summarize environmental problems, and explain in your own words what each one means.

4. Describe three environmental rules, quotas, or restrictions that you have encountered.

SCIENCE IN ACTION

THE SAGA OF SOUTH MORESBY

Lying 100 km off the coast of British Columbia, the archipelago of South Moresby is made up of 138 islands with 42 lakes. This unique environment is home for a wide variety of plants and animals found nowhere else. Mild winters and heavy precipitation support a rain forest containing some of the largest trees on Earth. Mosses and lichens flourish here, and over 50 species of birds live on or around the islands, while the waters contain huge populations of fish, whales, seals, and sea lions.

In 1974, a logging company received permission to cut giant trees near the homes of the Skidegate Indians on the South Moresby islands. Along with local conservation groups, the native people launched a campaign of protest and public education that soon mobilized opinion around the world. More than 10 years of study and controversy followed, and many influential people publicly opposed the logging operation.

Finally, in 1987, the federal government agreed to establish a national park in South Moresby. Unexpectedly, the provincial government demanded compensation of $106 000 000, and after negotiations between the two governments, an agreement was reached. The federal government must still negotiate with the native people, who claim that the land belongs to them.

Even if the disputes are settled and South Moresby becomes a park, the safety of the ecosystem is not guaranteed. More and more people want to visit and study the islands. In 1982 there were 11 times as many visitors to South Moresby as there were in 1978. It may be necessary to limit the numbers of visitors and to restrict their activities in order to protect this valuable and sensitive environment.

Meet a Chemical Engineer — Rosalind Cairncross

Rosalind works in the Investigation and Enforcement Branch of the Ontario Ministry of Environment. She provides scientific evidence for investigations dealing with polluters and other environmental offenders. She also works in a laboratory examining water for contaminants.

Q. WHEN DID YOU FIRST THINK OF BECOMING A CHEMICAL ENGINEER?
A. As a child growing up in South Africa I planned to become a lawyer, but I got diverted and ended up in the chemical engineering program at university.

Q. WHEN DID YOU COME TO CANADA?
A. I came here in 1978 and began work in a company doing analytical and developmental plant work. A few years later I heard that the Ministry of Environment was hiring people to do analytical work on drinking water, so I applied for and got the job.

Q. WHAT DOES THIS JOB INVOLVE?
A. The ministry has a number of drinking water plants, which are sampled on a routine basis. Bottles of water are brought to the lab and processed and prepared for examination. I work in the drinking water unit, examining the samples for traces of organic compounds. The process used is called chromatography. We use very sophisticated, computerized machinery that requires a lot of training.

Q. HOW DID YOU BECOME INVOLVED IN INVESTIGATION?
A. The ministry prosecutes polluters, so our department gets involved with these cases. My interest began when I was preparing lab results that were to be used in environmental hearings or court cases.

Q. WHAT'S AN EXAMPLE OF AN ENVIRONMENTAL HEARING?
A. In the case of a new landfill site, there are sometimes reports of leeching. We drill holes and check to see if there is leeching into the surrounding water table. The results from our lab tests are used as evidence in an environmental hearing to determine what should be done about the landfill site.

Q. WHAT ROLE DO YOU PLAY?
A. I assist the investigator with the preparation of scientific evidence. I often interview people to get more background on the case. If it goes to court, I usually go to the courtroom to observe.

Q. WHAT SKILLS ARE REQUIRED TO BE A GOOD INVESTIGATOR?
A. The skills of a good investigator and a good researcher are closely related. You must have good analytical skills and pay attention to detail. At the same time, you must not lose sight of the context.

Q. WHAT DO YOU LIKE BEST ABOUT THIS PART OF YOUR JOB?
A. I like the non-routine nature of it. I like being able to act as an intermediary between the environment and people. There's a more human aspect which you don't get in the laboratory.

Q. WILL THERE BE LOTS OF JOBS IN THE ENVIRONMENTAL FIELD IN THE FUTURE?
A. There's certainly a lot of work to be done and the public is demanding answers, but the funding has to come from government. If these two things come together, there will probably be lots of jobs.

Review Questions

A: Knowledge

1. Define natural resource. Give three examples of major Canadian resources, and explain how each is used.

2. Four factors affect the environmental impact caused by human use of natural resources. List these factors and describe some effects of each.

3. a) What is permafrost and where is it found?
   b) What natural resource is affected by permafrost, and how?

4. a) What natural resource(s) does Canada have in greater abundance than most countries?
   b) List some uses for this resource(s).
   c) Explain how these uses may harm either the environment or the resource itself.

5. a) Define environmental stress and give three examples.
   b) Explain the relationship between human population density and environmental stress.
   c) Why are some ecosystems more sensitive to environmental stress than others?

6. Differentiate between a vulnerable species and an endangered species. Give an example of each type.

7. a) What is the "tragedy of the commons"?
   b) How does this term apply to the quality of air in Canada?

8. List four basic principles of ecology.

9. What is the balance of nature, and what role do humans play in it?

10. Zoos play an important role in the maintenance of vulnerable and endangered species. Explain.

B: Application

11. What are phytoplankton? Explain how phytoplankton can be considered a natural resource of worldwide importance.

12. a) What is the world's largest common resource, and how is it being managed at present?
    b) Is this example of resource management likely to be good for the resource? For the world's human population? Explain.

13. a) Explain why oxygen can be considered a natural resource.
    b) Where is most of the world's oxygen produced, and how?
    c) How do you think the world's oxygen supplies should be managed?

14. Agricultural productivity often conflicts with environmental management. Discuss this conflict.

15. Give three examples of common resources that you share with other people. Could the tragedy of the commons apply to any of these resources?

16. a) How does public awareness of environmental problems usually come about?
    b) Do you think the most ecologically important issues come to light this way? Explain why.

17. How could Earth's carrying capacity for humans be increased? Would this be desirable? Discuss.

C: Problem Solving

18. A highly productive agricultural area, near a major city, is being subdivided into lots for residential homes. The proposed housing development is an environmental issue in the community. List five arguments that the developers might use in favour of the new houses. List five arguments that its opponents might use against it. Who do you think should have the final say, and why?

19. Construction is taking place at a park. A hilly grassland area and a nearby creek are to be replaced by an asphalt parking lot. What environmental consequences might result? How could the parking lot be built without altering the state of the creek?

20. Which of the four basic principles of ecology apply in each of the following environmental situations, and why?
    a) A bounty on wolves causes soil erosion during the next year.
    b) Winter feeding of white-tailed deer is followed by a disease epidemic the next summer.
    c) Spraying of a weed killer causes the death of several red foxes.
    d) Construction of a dam results in the eventual disappearance of rainbow trout in a nearby stream.

Try This

1. **What's in Your Garbage?**
   Collect all the solid garbage produced by your family in one week in four containers labelled paper, glass, organic matter, and metals. Measure the mass for each category and add to determine the total. Determine the percentage of each category. List ten different ways in which you could reduce your weekly garbage output.

2. **Make a Compost Heap**
   Decaying plant material is called compost. To set up a compost heap in your backyard, stack layers of dead leaves and plant parts in a well-ventilated container outdoors. Water and turn the compost regularly to speed up decomposition of the organic matter. Decomposed matter can be used as a soil conditioner. Test it in a garden to see if it does improve plant growth.

Our Diminishing Natural Resources

The Issue: What priorities should be set for the use of natural resources?

Spider monkeys in a tropical rain forest.

Most human interaction with the environment involves the consumption of natural resources, such as plants, animals, water, and minerals. People use these resources for food, materials, and energy, and to create economic prosperity. Rapid human population growth during this century has greatly increased the demand for these finite resources, while the development of technology and machinery has enabled people to obtain resources on an unprecedented scale. Consequently, many natural resources have been damaged, reduced, or destroyed.

Resource use raises the serious problem, first recognized by ecologists, of long-term consequences that affect entire ecosystems.

Most people appreciate the short-term profit achieved by removing mature hardwoods from a forest, damming a river, or catching fish in great numbers. However, the long-term results of these activities can prove very costly. Forests lose their variety through selective cutting, and become vulnerable to disease; changes in drainage patterns caused by damming lead to erosion and flooding; and overfishing results in the decline of fish stocks. The ultimate danger is that short-term greed may forever destroy a resource.

Tropical rain forests provide a good example of the dilemma. They are a complex and rich ecosystem, containing the greatest variety and numbers of animal and plant species on Earth. Little more than a hundred years ago, tropical rain forests covered much of the land bordering on the equator. The demand for resources from developed countries, and for agricultural land and living space from populations near the forests, has reduced by more than half the tropical forest area worldwide. In the short-term, people have gained timber, minerals, food, and land. The long-term problems include:
- loss of soil through erosion by wind and rain, and by baking to hardness by the sun.
- change in climatic patterns, especially reduced rainfall.

- loss of animal and plant species, many of which could provide medicine, food, or knowledge.
- increase in carbon dioxide and smoke pollution in the atmosphere from burning of forest.

The problems of shrinking forests and spreading deserts can have effects worldwide, but resource use on a smaller scale can also raise important questions. Northern Ontario, for example, has many lakes. These lakes supply drinking water for nearby towns or cities, water for recreational fishing or boating, and sites for holiday cottages. Which use is most important? It is necessary to decide this question because one use of a resource often excludes other uses. For example, cottages should not be built around a lake used for drinking water because their wastes will pollute the lake. But the building of cottages provides employment and stimulates the local economy, which may be important in a poor community.

In this activity, you will set priorities in the use of a natural resource, drawing on a local, national, or global example. After researching the resource, its conflicting uses, and the issues involved, you will develop guidelines for managing the resource.

Exploring the Issue

A. Gathering the Evidence

1. Survey newspaper and magazine articles and books for environmental issues related to the management of natural resources.

2. Select one of the issues that you are most interested in.

3. Find more background information about the issue. Try to find materials that express different points of view.

4. Using your research materials, determine:
   a) the short-term and long-term impact of the issue on the environment.
   b) economic benefits and losses to private business, government, landowners, and residents of the area.
   c) government involvement with the issue.

B. Discussing the Issue

1. In small groups of five or six, review the information and clearly identify the issues related to each topic above.

2. Construct a table listing the advantages and disadvantages of each use of the natural resource. Evaluate the relative merits of each.

3. Discuss alternative methods of dealing with the issue. Evaluate the usefulness and acceptability of these alternatives.

4. Assess the role of science and technology in resolving the issue.

C. Making a Decision

1. Each student should assess the selected issue from all perspectives and then decide how to resolve it.

2. Compare your decision to that of others in the group. Try to reach a consensus on the issue, if possible.

D. Recommending a Plan of Action

Based on your group consensus, draw up a plan of action to resolve the environmental issue. Include guidelines for managing the resource, based on setting priorities for each use of it.

Burning down the forest for plowing and cultivation in Gambia.

Unit 1 Wrap-Up

Unit Summary

Ecology is the science that studies interactions in the environment. The unit of study in ecology, the *ecosystem*, is made up of a *biotic* and *abiotic* environment. The biotic environment is comprised of *producers* and *consumers*. The trophic levels of consumers may be linked to form a *food chain*. Interconnected food chains form a *food web*. The same information can be arranged in a *food pyramid* according to the number, biomass, or energy involved at each level. Nutrients, such as carbon, water, and nitrogen are cycled through both the biotic and abiotic environments.

All the individuals of the same species in an ecosystem make up a *population*. Population size is changed by births, deaths, emigration, and immigration. Population growth is affected by environmental factors such as availability of food and space, climate, and the amount of competition, predation, and disease.

All of the populations in an ecosystem make up its biotic community, and interact in associations called *symbiotic relationships*. Examples include *mutualism*, *commensalism*, and *parasitism*. Populations may also compete for food, space or shelter, or prey upon another population.

A *biome* is a large geographical area with a similar climate and vegetation. The *tundra*, *boreal coniferous forest*, *grassland*, *temperate deciduous forest*, *deserts*, and *tropical rain forest* are the major biomes in North America.

Natural succession is a sequence of predictable change in an ecosystem's biotic community. Its final stage is called *succession climax*. Both primary and secondary succession lead eventually to the same climax community.

Natural resources are the materials and energy we take from the environment. Humans use these resources in various ways. The use and abuse of these natural resources by humans may cause environmental stress which could eliminate habitats, population species, or pollute the environment. The wise use of these resources is essential to maintain the balance of nature in the environment.

Key Terms

abiotic	herbivore
autotroph	heterotroph
biomass	immigration
biomes	migration
biosphere	niche
biotic	omnivore
carnivore	population
community	primary consumer
competition	producer
consumer	scavenger
ecology	secondary consumer
ecosystem	secondary succession
food chain	succession climax
food pyramid	tertiary consumer
food web	top carnivore
habitat	trophic level

Unit Practice and Review

A: Short Answer

True or False

State whether each statement is true or false. Correct each false statement.

1. A population that is widely distributed in a given area has a high density.
2. All food pyramids are based on population size.
3. All food chains contain a producer.
4. Emigration is the number of individuals moving into an ecosystem.
5. Soil, rock, and ice are part of the lithosphere.

Multiple Choice

In each question below, select the best answer.

1. Organisms that use solar energy directly are called:
   a) herbivores
   b) producers
   c) omnivores
   d) primary consumers

2. In a lichen, the two organisms involved in the symbiotic relationship are:
   a) a termite and a protozoa
   b) a mushroom and a virus
   c) a fungus and a protozoa
   d) an alga and a fungus

3. Which of the following is *not* recycled in an ecosystem?
   a) water
   b) nitrogen
   c) energy
   d) carbon

4. An organism that supports a parasite is classified as a:
   a) host
   b) secondary parasite
   c) commensalistic organism
   d) predator

5. Population density is defined as the number of individuals per unit
   a) length
   b) weight
   c) time
   d) area

Complete the Statement

Complete each of the following statements with the correct word or phrase. Do not write in this book.

1. A ___?___ is a group of interconnected food chains.

2. Rock, air, water, and soil are all part of the ___?___ environment.

3. The ___?___ of an ecosystem is the maximum number of organisms an area can support without harming the environment.

4. The ___?___ occurs because of interactions between two major processes: cell respiration and photosynthesis.

5. A plant community that maintains the same species over a long period is called a ___?___ .

Matching Items

Match each item in Column A with the appropriate item in Column B.

1. *Column A*
   i) organisms living together
   ii) lives off a host organism
   iii) two organisms derive equal benefit from each other
   iv) a one-sided relationship between two organisms

   Column B
   a) parasitism
   b) commensalism
   c) competition
   d) symbiosis
   e) mutualism

2. *Column A*
   i) feeds at many trophic levels
   ii) plant-eater
   iii) not prey for other predators
   iv) meat-eater

   Column B
   a) herbivore
   b) carnivore
   c) insectivore
   d) top carnivore

3. *Column A*
   i) individuals leave their old habitat
   ii) new individuals join a population
   iii) individuals move to a new habitat
   iv) individuals are removed from a population

   Column B
   a) birth rate
   b) immigration
   c) death rate
   d) steady state
   e) emigration

4. *Column A*
   i) group of different populations sharing the same habitat
   ii) living zone on Earth
   iii) basic unit of study in ecology
   iv) grasslands, for example

   Column B
   a) ecosystem
   b) community
   c) biome
   d) biosphere

B: Knowledge and Application

1. All living things are either a predator or prey. Discuss this statement.

2. How are the terms population, community, and ecosystem interrelated?

3. Why do toxic materials that cannot be digested or excreted become more concentrated at the upper trophic levels of a food pyramid?

4. How do the terms degradable and biodegradable relate to ecology?

5. Explain how the acronym NIMBY (Not In My Back Yard) is associated with environmental issues across Canada.

6. In agriculture it is often beneficial to include a legume crop in the crop rotation. Explain why.

7. Would the classroom aquatic ecosystem studied in this unit be classified as an open or closed ecosystem? Explain.

8. Food costs are often reflected by the position of the food type in the food pyramid. Explain how economics relates to ecology.

9. Fire is not always destructive. In some instances fire is beneficial to an ecosystem. Explain and give examples.

10. Food chains and pyramids with five or more feeding levels are rare. Explain.

C: Problem Solving

1. a) How many different food chains exist?
   b) How many different i) herbivores, ii) carnivores, iii) omnivores, and iv) top carnivores are present?
   c) What effect would a bounty on wolves have on the entire food web?

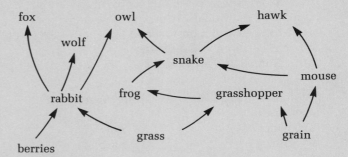

2. Which of the graphs would best represent the following ecological situation:
   a) the introduction of a new species of earthworm to an area
   b) the population number of mountain lions in Canada over the last 100 years
   c) the population number for a housefly culture which started with three male and female flies
   d) the whooping crane population number over the last 50 years

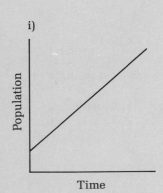

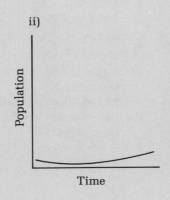

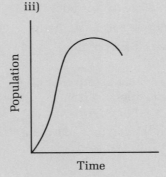

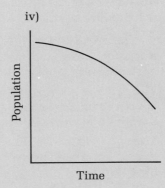

D: Challengers

1. Describe the population distribution of your family at midnight, at breakfast, during school hours, and after supper. Calculate the average population density of your home. Does this figure give a true picture of the way your family occupies its living space? Explain.

2. How long does it take an apple core, orange peel, banana peel, and an unfiltered cigarette butt to decompose in nature? Place sample items outdoors at an undisturbed observation site. Observe weekly and record the extent of decomposition. Do any of the items "disappear"? Will any? Explain.

Project Ideas

1. Insects eventually disappear in the fall. Survey the fall insect population in a selected area over a one-month period. Each day at the same time, move an insect sweep net over the designated area. Identify and record the number and types of insects observed and the air temperature. Return the insects to the area after making observations. Is there a connection between the temperature and the types of insects still active?

2. Ecological interactions go on year-round. During the winter, small mammals such as mice and voles live under the snow. Find out how such organisms:
   a) derive food from their environment
   b) breathe
   c) survive the cold winter conditions
   d) become involved in food webs above the snow.

3. Green spaces such as recreational parks and picnic areas play an important role in cities with high organism densities. In the city nearest you:
   a) what percentage of the city is set aside as green space?
   b) are the designated green spaces used by everyone or by only a few people?
   c) how much more green space do you think is needed and for what purpose(s)?
   d) should there be a Canadian law for major cities to establish a minimum green space requirement? Give reasons for your answer.

Readings

Barrett, Bruce L. and Stratton, John N. *From Nature to Man.* Toronto: Wiley Publishers of Canada Ltd., 1976. (Studies the widespread effects of human pollution of the environment.)

Hewitt, Ken. *Lifeboat — Man and a Habitable Earth.* Toronto: Wiley Publishers of Canada Ltd., 1976. (Looks at the interactions of people and their environments, particularly urban environments.)

Nebel, Bernard J. *Environmental Science — The Way the World Works.* Toronto: Prentice-Hall of Canada Ltd., 1981. (An overview of environmental interactions throughout the biosphere.)

Organisms and their External Environments

For a polar bear, the Arctic is its life-sustaining habitat. The bear's thick fur insulates it from the freezing wind and water, and its huge, broad, fur-padded feet enable quick and painless movement across the ice. A camel is as well suited to the desert's conditions as a polar bear is to the Arctic. The camel has a double row of eyelashes to protect its eyes from hot, blowing sand, and most of its body fat is stored in a hump that supplies reserve energy.

Both the polar bear and the camel are suited to their respective natural environments. Wherever they live, all organisms depend on their surroundings to supply their needs. Since organisms monitor external conditions and respond to changes, we describe them as being **adapted** to their environment. Organisms exchange matter and energy with their environment, altering it in the process.

Chapter 4
A World of Diversity

Two living organisms could hardly seem more unlike than a bacterium and a whale (see above photos). The microscopic bacterium *Escherichia coli* measures only 0.001 mm, while the massive humpback whale *Megaptera novaeangliae* is 20 000 000 times longer! Despite their differences, both organisms perform the same life functions as all other living things. They obtain food, grow, exchange gases, and dispose of their wastes in their respective environments. The humpback whale carries out these activities in the open sea, while *Escherichia coli* does so in the human intestine.

In Unit 1, you learned about the many different kinds of environments around the world. In this chapter, you will look at the different conditions found in these environments and at the enormous diversity of organisms inhabiting them. You will also learn how scientists approach the problem of classifying and naming this huge diversity of living things.

When you finish Chapter 4, you should be able to:

- describe the range of environmental conditions in which organisms manage to survive
- explain how the needs of organisms are provided by their external environments
- describe the five-kingdom method of classification
- name organisms from each kingdom and describe their usual environments
- name the levels of classification from kingdom to species
- recognize the binomial system of nomenclature

4.1   Diversity and Variation in the Environment

Environments are diverse. Table 4-1 lists the different kinds of environments that are found on Earth. Many of these environments are described in Unit I.

Not only do living organisms live and prosper in these different environments, they also cope with variations in the conditions of each environment. Even in one locale, conditions may range from dry to wet, hot to cold.

In the sea, for instance, changes in ocean currents, water temperature, water pressure, nutrients, prey, predators, and light alter the local environment. As water temperatures rise in the summer, water holds less dissolved oxygen. Fish respond by seeking cooler water which carries more dissolved oxygen.

Table 4-1:   Environments on Earth

Aquatic Environments	Terrestrial Environments
seas	tundra
estuaries and coastal waters	deserts
streams and rivers	grasslands
lakes and ponds	forests
wetlands (marshes and swamps)	

STUDY HINT

Keeping a Good Notebook
Your science notebook is the most important piece of equipment you need as a science student. It is even more important than your textbook. Many students get into difficulty because they keep poor or incomplete notebooks. It is best to keep your work arranged in chronological order, rather than putting your class notes in one section, lab reports in another, study and review questions in a third, and so on. A textbook contains many pages. If you keep most of the material you have to know in a notebook, you can save yourself a lot of reading at the end of a unit.

Do You Know?
Together with the atmosphere, the oceans control and regulate the world's climate patterns and, therefore, the distribution of the world's vegetable and animal life.

Explain why sports fishermen know that they must fish for lake trout in deeper waters in the summer time.

On land the distribution of vegetation can be explained by the combined effects of precipitation, temperature, and available sunlight. Variation in these factors determines the kind of plant life that lives in a particular environment. The warm temperatures and high rainfall of the tropics support luxuriant growths of tropical rain forest. However, the forest floor is almost barren of green plants because of the shade created by the dense canopy of leaves above.

Environmental conditions differ not only from place to place, but also from time to time. Think of the differences between a northern holiday resort in the summer and in the winter. When snow falls and the winds are cold, most of the tourists and the migrating birds of the area respond to these seasonal changes by moving to more congenial environments further south. Other animals that live in the area, such as deer, bears, and insects, cope in other ways. Deer scrape beneath the snow for food, bears go into a deep sleep, and, although many adult insects die, their eggs survive. Plants and trees of the region also respond to variations in the environment. Smaller plants usually complete their life cycle within the spring, summer, and fall seasons, while deciduous trees shed their leaves in the fall and resume growth the following spring.

Living organisms differ greatly in their ability to survive changes in their environments. Some organisms can tolerate a great deal of change, others little. The conditions within which an organism can live constitute the **range of tolerance** for that organism. While some organisms, like the polar bear and the camel, are associated with one particular set of environmental conditions, others live in a wide range of environments. Willows, for example, grow throughout North America, from Mexico to the Arctic. Willows that grow in the north are smaller and have a slower growth rate than those

Mature willow trees in Ontario reach a stately height. However, the arctic willow attains a height of only a few centimetres at the same age.

growing further south. These variations result from differences in the external environment. In the north, on average, the temperatures are colder, the winds stronger, the rainfall less abundant, and the soil less nourishing than in the south.

In the next activity you will study a particular environment, a hay infusion, and the organisms that it supports.

Activity 4-1: Preparing a Hay Infusion

A hay infusion is a simple and convenient way to grow a culture of protists and small animals. Protists are small, single-celled organisms. When kept in a jar, a hay infusion resembles a small aquarium.

Materials

hay	hot plate or gas burner
distilled water	pond water
1 L beaker	250 mL jars

Procedure

1. Cut approximately 5 g of hay into small pieces and add to 1 L of distilled water in a beaker.
2. Boil for 15 to 20 min until the water begins to turn brown.
3. Allow the hay infusion to cool, and then let it stand for three or four days.
4. Add some pond water to the hay infusion, and allow the mixture to stand in dim light for the duration of the experiment.
5. Once the culture has begun to flourish, subdivide the contents of the beaker into different jars to increase the number of cultures available.
6. In your notebook, copy the observation table below.

Day	Kind of Organisms Present	Quantity
1		
2		
3		
•		
•		
•		

A grass hay like timothy is preferred to clovers or alfalfas. If obtaining hay is a problem, a lettuce infusion would work well instead. Dry some clean lettuce leaves in an oven until they are brown and crisp. Do not use any burnt leaves for the infusion. Grind up the dried lettuce in a mortar and pestle or in a blender. Add 1-2 g of ground lettuce to 1 L of boiling water and cook for 5 min. Cool and let stand. Extra dried lettuce can be stored almost indefinitely, so that an infusion may be prepared at any time.

CAUTION: Always wash your hands thoroughly after handling any preparation that may contain microorganisms.

7. Each day, prepare a wet mount of a sample from the culture. In your table, record the kinds of organisms present and estimate the quantity of each kind in the sample. Use the illustrations in Figure 4-1 as an aid in identifying the organisms.

Discussion

1. Write a hypothesis that predicts what you expect to happen to each of the following factors as the culture ages.
   a) the amount of food available
   b) the amount of waste in the culture jar
   c) the numbers of different kinds of organisms
   d) the total number of organisms

2. List the organisms that were present at the beginning of each week.

3. a) What happens to the quantity of each kind of organism in the hay infusion as the culture ages?
   b) Suggest why the changes in a) occur.

4. The organisms in the hay infusion are mostly heterotrophs. What is their food source? What was the initial food source?

5. What will eventually happen to this culture when the food is consumed? Explain.

Life in a Hay Infusion

Boiling hay in water produces a nutrient broth, and also kills any unwanted microorganisms growing on the hay. Once the broth cools, airborne bacteria invade (infuse) the nutrient-rich liquid and begin to multiply. These bacteria feed on the broth and in turn serve as food for the protists that are introduced when pond water is added. As the newly introduced protists feed on the bacteria, they begin to reproduce. Over the next month or so, a succession of organisms appears.

Flagellated protists such as *Euglena*, *Monas*, and *Chilomonas* may be observed first, followed shortly afterwards by ciliates such as *Paramecium* and *Colpoda*. Other protists, such as *Vorticella*, *Stentor*, and *Amoeba*, take longer to become established. Rotifers (simple animals) may appear. If algae become established, the culture may sustain itself for a very long time. Algae are photosynthetic and they produce both food and oxygen needed by the consumer organisms. Without algae, the culture will eventually be depleted as the organisms die out because of lack of food.

Ciliates (ciliated protists) have their entire body surface covered by short, hairlike cilia that beat in a coordinated fashion to propel the organism through the water. Flagellated protists possess one or two whiplike flagella which serve the same purpose of locomotion.

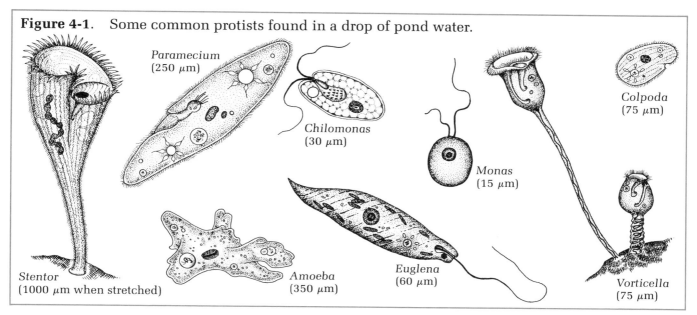

Figure 4-1. Some common protists found in a drop of pond water.

Paramecium (250 μm)

Chilomonas (30 μm)

Monas (15 μm)

Colpoda (75 μm)

Stentor (1000 μm when stretched)

Amoeba (350 μm)

Euglena (60 μm)

Vorticella (75 μm)

Obtaining Energy and Materials from the External Environment

Organisms acquire all the food, water, gases, light, and heat they need from their external environment. Food provides energy for body activities and materials for body growth and repair. Water is essential to the process of photosynthesis and to the maintenance of body fluids. Heat energy from the environment helps organisms such as insects and reptiles remain active.

Because different environments vary in their ability to provide energy and materials, living things use a variety of methods to satisfy their needs. Deserts, for example, provide very little water, but large amounts of light and warmth. The broad, flat leaves common to most plants take the form of spines in the desert cactus. These spines reduce the surface area from which water can be lost through evaporation. The stem manufactures sufficient food by photosynthesis and has a thick, waxy covering to conserve water.

Diversity in environments means diversity in food. For autotrophs, which produce their own food by photosynthesis, an essential requirement is sunlight. Plants, therefore, are limited to environments that receive sunlight. They cannot grow in permanently dark caves or deep under water where sunlight does not penetrate.

Heterotrophs, which feed on other organisms, live in environments where there is food that they can find, catch, eat, and digest.

The names used to identify the organisms illustrated are not complete scientific names. The name given is called the genus name. At times, it is virtually impossible to identify individual species. At such times, the entire genus is referred to and only the genus name is used.

In relatively clear oceans, light penetrates to depths of 100 m to 200 m. In the more turbid coastal waters, light penetration rarely exceeds 30 m. Most marine animal life living in depths below the level that light can penetrate obtains its sustenance from organic debris that falls down from above.

A polar bear in the Arctic, for example, feeds on seals and fish. The seals feed on fish, while fish feed on other fish or small photosynthetic organisms. Such food webs illustrate the pattern of predation and the flow of food energy. The availability of food is directly responsible for the migration and foraging habits of the bears. In winter, polar bears hunt seal on the pack ice. In summer, however, landbound bears subsist on berries and vegetation when seals are out of reach.

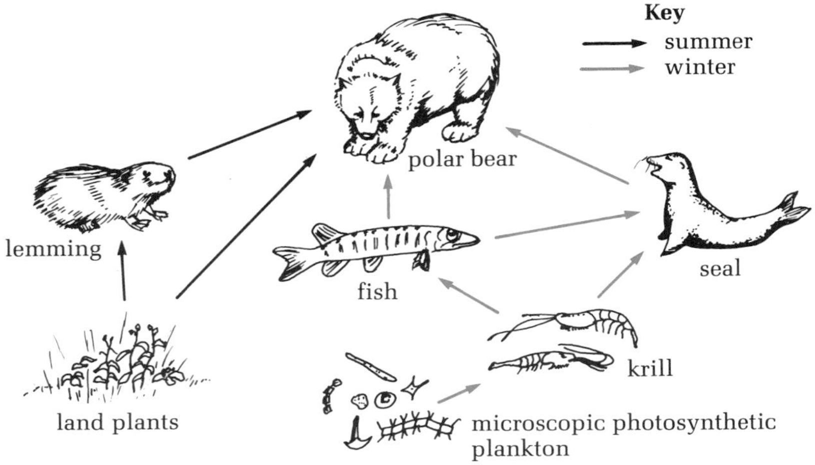

Key
summer
winter
polar bear
lemming
fish
seal
krill
land plants
microscopic photosynthetic plankton

Figure 4-2. An arctic food web.

CHALLENGER

The bacterium *Escherichia coli* normally inhabits the intestine of humans, but it can also be grown in test tubes containing a suitable nutrient broth. What temperature would provide conditions of optimal growth for this bacterium?

Study Questions

1. Define each of the following terms, using complete sentences: diversity, variation, range of tolerance, autotroph, heterotroph. Illustrate each definition with an appropriate example(s).
2. a) In a table, list five different aquatic environments and four different terrestrial environments.
   b) Distinguish between diversity of environments and variation within an environment.
   c) State two ways in which your terrestrial environment shows variation.
3. a) In a hay infusion, what type of organism is the first to grow and where does it come from?
   b) What function does the hay infusion serve for this type of organism?
   c) After pond water is added, describe the ways in which the environment of this organism changes.
4. a) Identify the materials and the types of energy that living things obtain from their environment.
   b) Explain the function of each item listed in part a).

A DEEP-SEA COMMUNITY

One of the most unusual environments on Earth was discovered in 1977 by a submarine research vessel. In the permanent darkness of the deep sea, at a depth of 2500 m, scientists discovered an amazing diversity of organisms, many of them previously unknown. These organisms were congregated around underwater hot springs called vents on the eastern Pacific sea bed. Here, very hot (350°C) water and minerals issuing from the Earth's interior mix with the frigid ocean water. At this depth, the ocean floor usually has very small populations of living organisms because of the 2-3°C cold water, high water pressure, and low food supply. The warm areas around the vents are like deep-sea "oases" in an otherwise cold, dark, and barren part of the ocean.

The lush communities of organisms living around the hot-water vents are able to flourish due to both the warmer water temperatures and a food supply based on unusual bacteria. In this community, these bacteria take the place of green plants, forming the base of a food chain able to support high densities of larger organisms. Among the animals living in this unique environment are bright red tube worms, large clams up to 26 cm long, mussels, limpets, jellyfish, marine worms, fish, and crabs.

One of the many exciting things about this discovery is that it reveals a functioning ecosystem that uses an energy source other than the Sun. The bacteria on the ocean floor cannot perform photosynthesis because sunlight does not penetrate these depths. Rather, the bacteria pro-

The hot-water vents were discovered by Alvin, a deep-sea research submarine owned by the Woods Hole Oceanographic Institute in Massachusetts, U.S.A.

duce food through a similar process called *chemosynthesis*. The bacteria use the chemical compound hydrogen sulphide issuing from the vents as a source of stored energy to make food for themselves and the entire community. Photosynthesis, therefore, is not the sole means of producing food on our planet.

4.2 Diversity of Living Things

The many different environments throughout the world result in a great diversity in the forms and behaviours of living things. Organisms are adapted to their environments. If you were to discover an animal that you had never seen before, you could, by examining it, infer something about the environment in which it lives. For example, if the animal had a very thick fur coat or a thick layer of fat, you could reasonably infer that its usual environment was a cold one. Similarly, given a certain set of environmental conditions, you should be able to infer what features would best suit an animal to those conditions. You can practise doing this in the next activity.

Activity 4-2: Matching Organisms to their Environments

As you learned in Unit I, the terrestrial environment can be divided into broad vegetation zones called biomes. Figure 4-3 shows general temperature and rainfall conditions in each biome, and the unique types of vegetation that result. Each biome sustains distinctive animals as well. Similarly, the aquatic environments listed in Table 4-1 on page 103 have their own unique plant and animal life forms.

In this activity, you will use the clues provided in the table below to identify different environments and the animals that live in them.

Procedure

1. Copy the following table into your notebook.

Biome or Environment	Conditions	Kinds of Organisms Present	Features of Each Organism that Suit it to its Environment
marsh		bullrushes, ducks	
pond	shallow, fresh water		
		caribou	
			hibernates in winter
	dry and extremely cold		
boreal coniferous forest		black bear	

2. Complete the first column by using the clues provided elsewhere in the table to identify a particular environment or biome.

3. Using Figure 4-3 as a guide, briefly summarize the climatic conditions of each environment under the heading "Conditions".

Figure 4-3. The major terrestrial biomes.

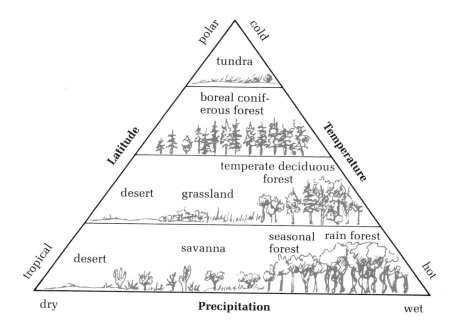

4. Under the heading "Kinds of Organisms Present", identify two plants and two animals native to each environment listed.

5. In the last column, identify some features of the organisms that enable them to flourish in their respective environments.

6. Add two more aquatic and two more terrestrial environments of your choosing to the table. Repeat steps 3 to 5 to complete the table.

Discussion

1. Suggest reasons why you would *not* expect to see:
   a) maple trees on the tundra;
   b) rainbow trout in the Atlantic;
   c) cacti in marshes;
   d) black bears in the Arctic.

2. Name the usual environment of each organism listed in question 1, and describe how each organism is suited to that environment.

3. All living organisms are capable of responding to some changes in the environment. Due to growing human populations, many

wetlands are being drained to provide space for more housing or farmland. Suggest how each of the following wetland organisms might respond to the destruction of their habitat: a) *Paramecium*, b) beaver, c) duck, d) fish, e) large willow tree.

4. Some organisms are commonly found in more than one environment. This is especially true of migratory animals such as caribou, which spend summer on the open tundra but move south into the boreal coniferous forest for the winter. State reasons for the migration of wildlife.

Diversity of Autotrophs

Every green plant needs supplies of sunlight, carbon dioxide, minerals, and water, whether it is a cactus in the desert, a kelp in the sea, or a fern on the forest floor. Yet, none of these three plants could survive in the environments where the others thrive. Each type of plant has structures and abilities that help it to grow in its own environment. The cactus is able to store water for months in its swollen stem, and its waxy covering reduces water loss. The kelp has air-filled bladders that help keep it floating near the water surface where there is more sunlight. The fern has broad, feathery leaves that absorb a maximum of sunlight in its shady environment.

Cacti like this prickly pear have features especially suited to their hot and dry environment. The bristle-covered fruit is edible.

Some types of kelp have air-filled bladders that keep the kelp floating on the surface of the water.

Ferns grow in shady habitats where soils are moist.

Even autotrophs growing in close proximity to one another may differ widely. The fern and the maple tree are both found in forests in Ontario and Quebec. However, the fern prefers the shaded forest floor, whereas the maple flourishes in open and sunny locations.

The more extreme the external environment, the more specialized are the structures developed by a plant in order to survive in that environment. In areas low in soil nutrients, for example, several types of plants have developed specialized structures designed to capture insects. Bog plants such as the sundew and the pitcher plant contain liquids that can digest captured insects. These plants can then extract essential nutrients from the insects that the soil cannot provide.

Diversity of Heterotrophs

All types of heterotrophs must actively obtain their food from the external environment. Like plants, animals show great differences in structure and design. The herbivores in Figure 4-4 all feed on plants, but they look very different from one another. Each has its own method of obtaining and eating food, and each feeds on different types and parts of plants.

The flap of the pitcher plant has nectar glands that attract insects to feed. When an insect walks further into the opening, it slips on the smooth surface to the bottom, where it is slowly digested by the plant.

Figure 4-4. Different types of herbivores.

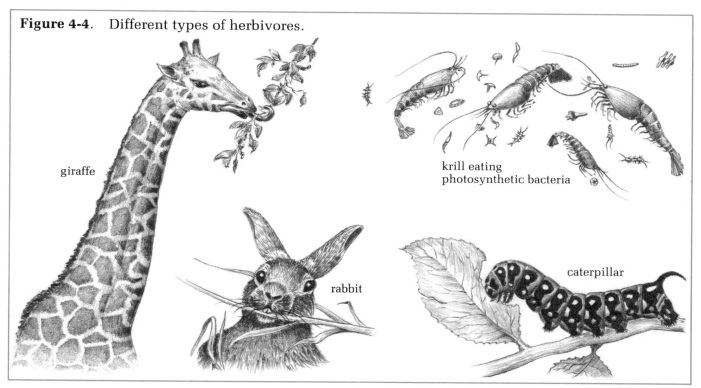

giraffe

krill eating photosynthetic bacteria

rabbit

caterpillar

Figure 4-5. All of these heterotrophs are carnivores.

owl

wolves

spider

snake

shark

Figure 4-6. Different types of decomposers and scavengers.

vultures

fungi on wood

bacteria on hair shaft

maggots

Carnivores and omnivores, too, show great diversity in appearance. All the carnivores in Figure 4-5 feed on herbivores or other carnivores, but they differ greatly in structure, in methods of hunting and feeding, and in the environments where they live.

The decomposers and scavengers in Figure 4-6 belong to a special category of heterotrophs. These organisms obtain their nourishment exclusively from dead and decaying matter.

Study Questions

1. a) List four ways in which a polar bear is suited to its environment and its way of life.
   b) Using the whale as an example, explain why it is possible to infer something about an organism's environment by examining the organism's features.
2. Explain what is meant by the phrase "organisms are suited to the environment in which they live".
3. State a reason why there are different kinds of autotrophs such as the cactus, the kelp, the fern, and the maple tree.
4. a) Name four types of heterotrophs, and list two examples of each.
   b) State how each type of heterotroph obtains its nourishment.

CHALLENGER

Although the plant kingdom makes up only 15% of all living species, plants constitute 99% of the mass of all living things on Earth. Why do heterotrophs then make up such a small proportion of the mass of living things?

4.3   Classification of Living Things

Everyone uses classification to make life simpler. You are classifying when you decide whether to put your socks in the same drawer as your pyjamas or in a drawer by themselves. A classification system groups similar things together and keeps different things apart. A good classification system must also be clear and practical for the people using it.

What evidence of a classification do you see in this photo?

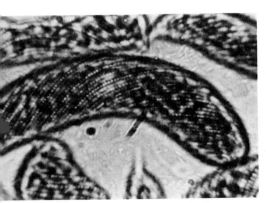

Euglena used to be classified as part of the animal kingdom and was placed in a group called Protozoa (simple animals). Today we place *Euglena* in a separate kingdom, Protista.

Scientists depend on classification to help them keep track of large amounts of data. With almost two million known kinds of organisms on Earth, biologists especially need classification systems. Given this tremendous diversity of organisms, biologists have faced the problem of which characteristics to select as a basis for sorting. Should all flying animals be grouped together, for example? Such a group would include most but not all birds, bats, and some insects. However, what about animals that can glide, such as flying squirrels, but that more often use another form of locomotion? Clearly, deciding on a useful classification system for living things takes a great deal of observation and thought. As new facts are discovered, scientists sometimes change their classification of a particular organism or devise new classification systems.

A Basis for Classification

The Greek philosopher Aristotle (384-322 B.C.) classified all living things into two major groups: plants and animals. He called these two groups "kingdoms" and listed over 500 organisms as either plant or animal. By 1550, over 6000 kinds of plants had been identified, but Aristotle's two-kingdom system of classification still proved useful.

When the microscope was developed in the seventeenth century, investigators discovered tiny forms of life previously unknown. Some of these newly-discovered organisms could not be assigned to either kingdom because they exhibited characteristics of both plants and animals. *Euglena*, for example, photosynthesizes like a plant but moves about seeking prey like an animal. The classification system was revised to maintain its usefulness. A new kingdom called "protists" was added to include these newly observed single-celled organisms.

As microscopes improved and more details of cell structures were discovered, scientists encountered more difficulties. Tiny life forms such as bacteria did not seem to belong to any of the three kingdoms. There was also disagreement about whether fungi were appropriately classified as part of the plant kingdom because they do not have chlorophyll, as all green plants do. Nor can they be considered animals or protists. In 1959 a scientist proposed a five-kingdom system of classification. This system of classification sorts all living forms into one of five kingdoms: Animalia, Plantae, Fungi, Protista, and Monera. We will also use the five-kingdom system, even though there is still not complete agreement over certain details.

Kingdom Animalia

The animal kingdom includes nearly 1 500 000 different kinds of organisms, ranging from sessile (nonmobile) corals, sponges, and anemones, to the more active worms, snails, insects, spiders, fish, amphibians, reptiles, birds, and mammals. Animals inhabit all types of environments, including fresh and salt water, forests, deserts, grasslands, and tundra. Many animals live in and around towns and cities. Some animals, called parasites, even live inside the bodies of other animals or plants.

Wherever they live and whatever they look like, all animals are made up of many cells. Each cell contains a nucleus and organelles enclosed by a cell membrane. All animals are heterotrophs that depend on finding and ingesting organic matter as their food. The majority of animals are able to move freely during at least part of their lives, and they reproduce sexually.

Kingdom Plantae

About 300 000 different kinds of plants are known. Plants grow in most land environments, as well as in both fresh and salt water. Most plants bear flowers; those that do not include cone-bearing evergreens, mosses, ferns, horsetails, and green algae. Green algae are the smallest and simplest of all plants, having no roots, stems, or leaves.

Regardless of size or complexity, all plants contain the green pigment chlorophyll and use the Sun's energy to produce their own food by photosynthesis. Hence, they are autotrophs. Plants are multicellular and reproduce sexually. Each cell has a nucleus and organelles enclosed within a cell membrane.

Many sessile animals were once mobile at an earlier stage of their lives. While the adult oyster, for example, remains stuck to a rock, the oyster larva is a free-swimming organism that travels to a new location before "settling down".

Do You Know?
The largest sequoia tree still standing measures 83 m tall and contains enough wood to make 40 five-room bungalows. These trees are far less important to life on Earth, however, than microscopic marine algae. Sometimes called "grass of the sea", these algae are estimated to perform about 90% of all photosynthetic activity on Earth.

Some biologists do not feel that algae belong in the plant kingdom. They argue that the algae more closely resemble the protists. Since the name "protist" has already come to be associated with single-celled organisms like *Paramecium*, some biologists propose a kingdom called "Protoctista" to include both the protists and the algae. According to this classification most plants are terrestrial.

The hood of this tropical plant protects the fruit underneath from the force of a torrential downpour.

Figure 4-7. The five-kingdom system of classification.

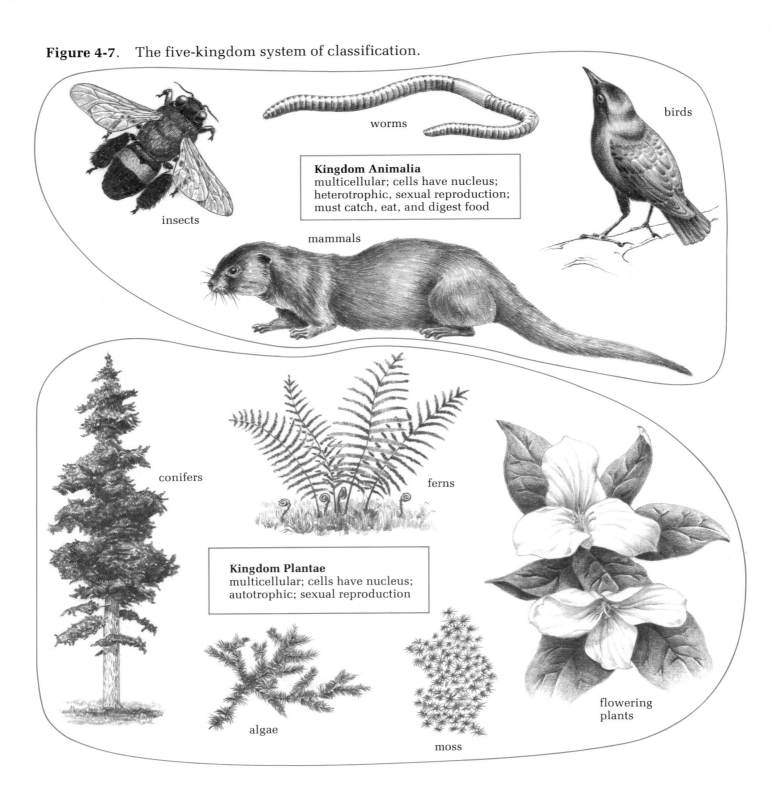

worms

birds

insects

Kingdom Animalia
multicellular; cells have nucleus;
heterotrophic, sexual reproduction;
must catch, eat, and digest food

mammals

conifers

ferns

Kingdom Plantae
multicellular; cells have nucleus;
autotrophic; sexual reproduction

flowering
plants

algae

moss

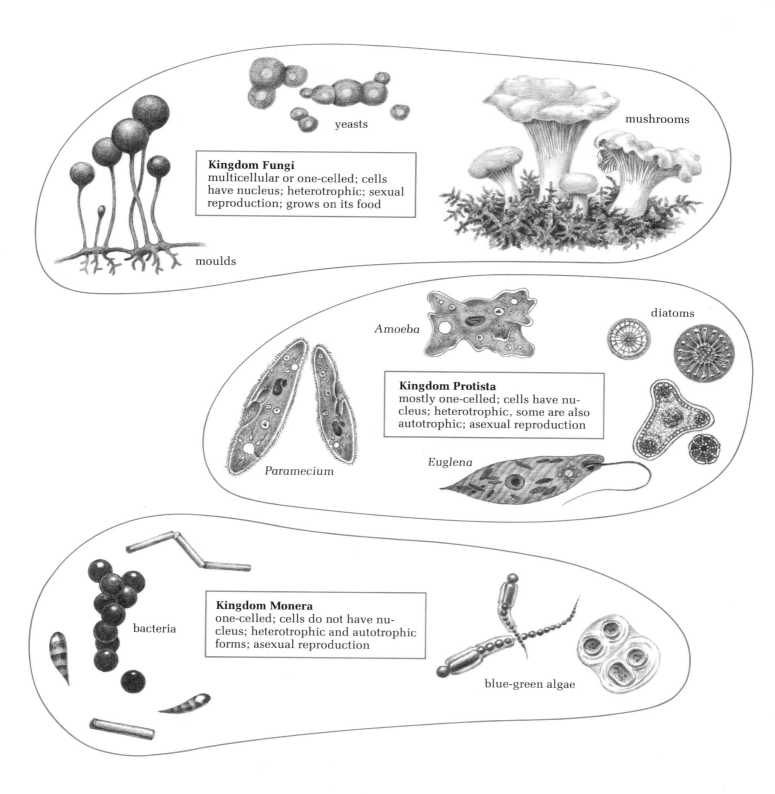

Kingdom Fungi
multicellular or one-celled; cells have nucleus; heterotrophic; sexual reproduction; grows on its food

yeasts

mushrooms

moulds

Kingdom Protista
mostly one-celled; cells have nucleus; heterotrophic, some are also autotrophic; asexual reproduction

Amoeba

diatoms

Paramecium

Euglena

Kingdom Monera
one-celled; cells do not have nucleus; heterotrophic and autotrophic forms; asexual reproduction

bacteria

blue-green algae

Do You Know?
While some mushrooms are edible, others are very poisonous and can cause death if eaten. You should never eat wild mushrooms without first identifying them using expert help.

Kingdom Fungi

Of the 100 000 known fungi, the most familiar to us are the mushrooms. The other members of this kingdom are the moulds, which grow on stale bread and other foods, and the mildew, which grows in damp places. Fungi are found in soil and air, in salt and fresh water, on and in plants and animals, and on food and clothing. Although they appear to grow like plants, fungi do not have chlorophyll, and therefore cannot carry out photosynthesis. They are heterotrophs that take in nourishment by digesting dead organic matter upon which they grow. Since they absorb food in this way, fungi are able to grow in the dark. All fungi reproduce by producing spores.

Some fungi are nuisances that produce diseases, such as Dutch elm disease, leaf blight, and rust in plants, and athlete's foot and ringworm in humans. Other fungi are useful, such as the yeasts used in baking bread and in fermenting barley and grapes to produce beer and wine. Still other helpful fungi produce important antibiotics, such as penicillin, used to treat diseases caused by bacteria.

These red cup fungi grow on decaying hardwood or on damp ground.

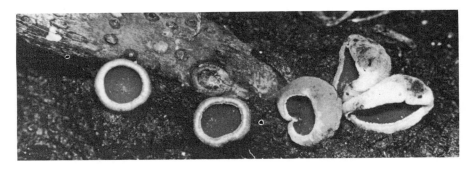

Kingdom Protista

Protists are extremely small, mostly single-celled organisms that have cell nuclei. By one estimate, there are 65 000 different kinds, many of which are still unidentified. Some protists obtain food by ingesting other organisms, as animals do, while other protists carry out photosynthesis, as plants do. Most protists live in water, both fresh and salt, or in the tissues of other organisms. One common protist is the *Amoeba*, which moves by changing its body shape. Another is the *Paramecium*, which swims through water by moving its hairlike cilia. Other protists have long, whiplike flagellae which they use to propel themselves. Protists reproduce by cell division.

Despite their minute size, some protists are found in such vast numbers in certain environments that the population can be seen with the unaided eye. For example, the "red tide" that colours sea water red at certain times of the year is caused by protists called dinoflagellates. Another type of dinoflagellate causes sea water to become luminous at night.

Kingdom Monera

The monerans consist of bacteria and blue-green algae. About 5000 different kinds have been named, but many more have not yet been identified. All of these organisms are microscopic, usually single-celled, and do not have cell nuclei. The genetic material is dispersed throughout the cytoplasm instead of being concentrated in a nucleus. Some monerans are capable of photosynthesis, others are heterotrophic. Many monerans can live only in the absence of oxygen. Some are parasitic and live inside the bodies of other organisms where they cause disease. All are capable of rapid reproduction by cell division.

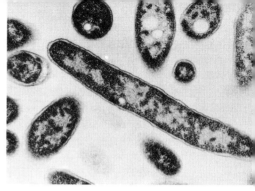

This bacterium is the moneran that causes Legionnaire's Disease.

Do You Know?
A spoonful of garden soil contains 10 000 000 000 bacteria. More bacteria reside on and in our bodies than people on this globe.

Classification Levels: Describing Degrees of Similarity

The sorting of diverse living things into kingdoms is only the first step in the process of classification. Each of the five kingdoms contains numerous kinds of organisms, many of which appear quite unlike. For example, both the elephant and the sponge have the characteristics that identify them as animals, but have very little else in common. To be useful, a classification system must be able to indicate degrees of similarity. Scientists therefore divide kingdoms into smaller groups of more similar organisms. Altogether, there are seven main levels of classification, as shown in Figure 4-8 on the next page.

The science of classification is called *taxonomy*.

Each kingdom is divided into groups called **phyla** (singular, **phylum**). The phylum Chordata, for example, includes all animals with backbones, such as humans and birds. (Such animals are called **vertebrates**.) The phylum Mollusca includes soft-bodied animals that have shells, such as snails and clams. Ninety-two phyla altogether make up the five kingdoms.

Each phylum is further subdivided into **classes**. Organisms that belong to the same class resemble one another more closely than do members of the same phylum. For example, both frogs and birds belong to the same phylum of backboned animals, the Chordata. All birds belong to the class Aves. Any two birds, even as different as the ostrich and the hummingbird, share more features in common than do birds and frogs. Frogs are members of a different class, Amphibia.

In a similar fashion, each class consists of several **orders**. The class Mammalia consists of about 20 orders. Dogs and cats belong to the order Carnivora, while humans and apes belong to the order Primates. Members of the same order resemble one another more closely than members of the same class.

Do You Know?
The largest group in the animal kingdom is the phylum Arthropoda. Arthropoda means "joint-legged animals", and includes the classes Crustacea (e.g., crayfish and lobsters), Chilopodia (e.g., centipedes), Arachnida (e.g., spiders, scorpions, and ticks), as well as Insecta (e.g., beetles and flies). Over three-quarters of all known animal species are arthropods.

There is not yet full agreement on some of the details of classification. For some animals, even the phylum is difficult to decide with certainty. A new phylum of animals called Loricifera was discovered in the early 1980s growing in the gravels off the coast of France. This phylum is the third to be discovered this century. The possibility also exists of discovering a completely new phylum in a remote or unusual location such as the deep sea vents explored by underwater submarines.

Figure 4-8. The seven levels of classification of living things.

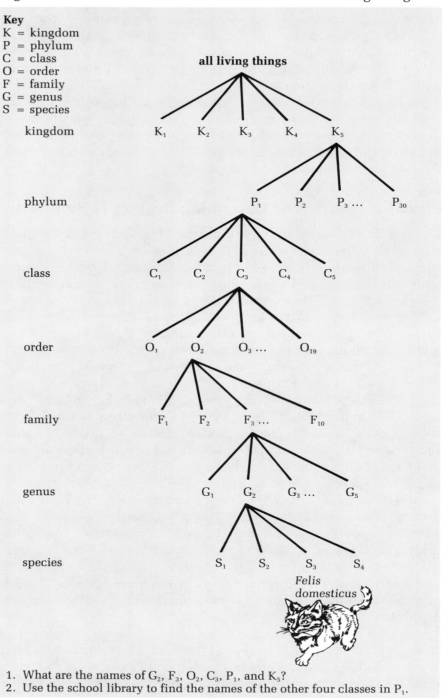

1. What are the names of G_2, F_3, O_2, C_3, P_1, and K_5?
2. Use the school library to find the names of the other four classes in P_1.

Each order, in turn, is made up of several **families**. Two well-known families belonging to the order Carnivora are the cat family (Felidae) and the dog family (Canidae). Leopards, tigers, lions, manx cats, and house cats all belong to the family Felidae, while foxes, wolves, jackals, dingos, and domestic dogs are all members of the family Canidae.

Each family includes several **genera** (singular, **genus**). The big cats, such as leopards, lions, tigers, and jaguars, belong to the genus *Panthera*. Smaller cats, such as ocelots, lynx, and the domestic house cat, belong to the genus *Felis*. Each genus is made up of similar **species**. Each known species has been given its own scientific name. For example, both the coyote and the domestic dog belong to the genus *Canis*, but they are different species. The coyote's scientific name is *Canis latrans*, while the domestic dog is called *Canis familiaris*.

Each level of classification contains fewer different kinds of organisms than the level encompassing it. Also, the organisms in each successive level are more similar to one another. In Table 4-2, you can see how humans and some familiar animals are classified at each level.

Table 4-2:   Classification of Some Familiar Animals

Classification Level	Common Name					
	Human	Dog	Red Fox	Cat	Bullfrog	Fruit Fly
Kingdom	Animalia	Animalia	Animalia	Animalia	Animalia	Animalia
Phylum	Chordata	Chordata	Chordata	Chordata	Chordata	Arthropoda
Class	Mammalia	Mammalia	Mammalia	Mammalia	Amphibia	Insecta
Order	Primates	Carnivora	Carnivora	Carnivora	Anura	Diptera
Family	Hominidae	Canidae	Canidae	Felidae	Ranidae	Drosophilidae
Genus	*Homo*	*Canis*	*Vulpes*	*Felis*	*Rana*	*Drosophila*
Species	*sapiens*	*familiaris*	*vulpes*	*domesticus*	*catesbeina*	*melanogaster*

Species: The Fundamental Group

Kingdom, phylum, class, order, family, and genus are all groups devised by biologists to simplify the study of living things. The species, however, represents an actual category found in nature. Each species is a different kind of organism. Although it is difficult to state a precise and complete definition of ''species'', the follow-

Biologists estimate that there are three to eight million undiscovered species. Around 20 new species of reptiles are discovered every year.

This animal is a cross between two species—a leopard and a lion—and is infertile.

ing guidelines can help you decide if two organisms belong to the same species:

1. All members of the same species are very similar but not necessarily identical. For example, all the dogs in the photographs below belong to the same species, *Canis familiaris*.

2. Members of the same species can breed only with one another to produce fertile offspring; they do not breed with individuals of another species in natural conditions. If two closely related species such as a horse and a donkey manage to produce offspring (a mule), the offspring is usually infertile and cannot reproduce its own kind.

The second point is not very useful in defining species of organisms that do not reproduce sexually. Many protists, for example, usually reproduce by fission. In general, where such organisms are very much alike in overall appearance, they are considered a single species.

Naming Species

The bird that we in North America call a robin is not the same bird that the British call a robin. And the animal that some people call a woodchuck, others may call a groundhog. From these examples, it is clear that while it may be all right to use common names for animals in everyday life, it would be very confusing for scientists working in different places and speaking different languages. To overcome this problem, scientists use a standard, international system of **nomenclature** (naming), based on Latin.

The scientific name given to each species has two parts. For this reason, the naming system is called the **binomial nomenclature**. The first word in the name refers to the genus to which the organism belongs. The second word usually describes some characteristic of the organism, or is based on the name of the person who discovered it. The first letter of the genus name is capitalized, and both parts of the name are italicized. Table 4-3 shows some examples of binomial nomenclature. Sometimes, if the genus name has already been identified, it can be abbreviated to the first capitalized letter followed by a period, as also shown in Table 4-3.

Binomial nomenclature allows scientists to identify any organism precisely when discussing their findings with other scientists. Such methods of classifying and organizing information are just as important to the study of biology as are microscopes and other scientific instruments.

The woodchuck, also known as the groundhog, sometimes has wrongly been called a gopher. However, the animal has only one scientific name, *Marmota monax*.

When you write or type the scientific name of an organism, underline it to identify it as italic.

Table 4-3: Examples of Binomial Nomenclature

Common Name	Scientific Name	Meaning
coyote	*Canis latrans*	barking dog
dog	*C. familiaris*	family dog
jackal	*C. aureus*	golden dog
plum	*Prunus domestica*	domestic plum
peach	*P. persica*	Persian plum
cherry	*P. avium*	bird plum
apricot	*P. armeniaca*	Armenium plum
robin (Britain)	*Erithacus rubecula*	red breast
robin (N.A.)	*Turdus migratorius*	migrating thrush

Study Questions

1. a) State two reasons for using classification.
    b) What are the characteristics of a good classification system?
    c) Why is classification especially important for the study of living things?

2. a) Describe how Aristotle classified living organisms.
    b) How did the discoveries made with the aid of the microscope affect the two-kingdom system of classification?
    c) What problems did fungi pose to a two-kingdom system of classification?

3. Summarize the characteristics of each of the five kingdoms in one short paragraph each.

4. To which of the five kingdoms do each of the following organisms belong: tulip, mussel, *Paramecium*, *Amoeba*, *Canis familiaris*, bread mould, *Escherichia coli* bacteria, yeast?

5. a) List in order from most specific to most general the seven classification levels.
    b) For the following pairs of organisms, identify the most specific classification level to which both belong: i) tigers, house cats, ii) snails, birds, iii) apes, dogs, iv) coyotes, red foxes, v) gorillas, humans.

6. Why is the use of binomial nomenclature preferable to the use of common names?

CAROLUS LINNAEUS

Carolus Linnaeus (1707-1778) was one of the world's great naturalists. His love of plants and flowers developed at an early age. When he was only eight years old, he was nicknamed "the little botanist". As an adult, Linnaeus travelled widely through his native Sweden, collecting and observing plants and animals. Linnaeus is most famous for establishing the principles for defining genera and species. He also developed a two-name system for classifying species. Until this time, each botanist devised his own name for a new species, and often many plants had several different scientific names, leading to confusion.

Linnaeus published his ideas about naming plants in his famous book *Systema Naturae* in 1735. The new system was welcomed at once by scientists, as it helped them to quickly name a new organism and place it into a specific category of classification. At that time, explorers were discovering new plants around the world at a greater rate than scientists could study and identify them, using the older methods. Linnaeus' system was so efficient that it is still used today.

We also continue to use the name this great botanist conferred upon himself. Born Karl von Linné, he Latinized his name to Carolus Linnaeus because he wrote his books in Latin. All scientists corresponded in Latin at the time, and we still use Latinized names for the binomial classification system devised by Linnaeus.

Meet a Veterinarian— Cynthia Trann

Cynthia is the veterinarian at a small neighbourhood clinic. She specializes in small animals.

Q. WHEN DID YOU FIRST THINK ABOUT THIS CAREER?
A. I first thought about it in grade one when I was asked what I wanted to be when I grew up. I said a veterinarian. It never occurred to me to be anything else.

Q. WHERE DID YOU STUDY?
A. I graduated from the University of Guelph with a degree in veterinary medicine. At that time, Guelph was the only Anglophone university east of Winnipeg offering the course. Now there's a college in Prince Edward Island as well.

Q. WHAT IS YOUR NORMAL DAILY SCHEDULE?
A. I do all the surgery in the morning because the animals have fasted the evening before. Also, I want them to be up from the anaesthetic before I go home at night. At noon I spend a few hours doing domestic chores like picking up my daughter and shopping, then return here at 3:30. All afternoon I have appointments and usually finish work at about 7 p.m. I work most Saturdays, too.

Q. DO A LOT OF WOMEN GO INTO VETERINARY MEDICINE?
A. My year was about 45% female. I think there have always been a lot of women veterinarians, and many of them go into small animal practice. Sometimes there's discrimination in large animal practice, especially when you're dealing with older farmers or the horse-racing business. But if you do a good job people will listen to you.

Q. DO YOU USE SCIENTIFIC KNOWLEDGE ON A DAILY BASIS?
A. Yes, particularly in surgery. All structures of the eye and skeletal system are related to physics. When I'm putting pins into a bone, I need to know where the stress factors are.

Q. HOW HAS THE FIELD CHANGED SINCE YOU STARTED?
A. It's becoming more and more technical. There are more specialists, such as ophthalmologists and orthopedic surgeons. People will pay a lot of money to have an electric pacemaker put into a dog's weak heart. Today animals' lives are being prolonged in similar ways to human lives.

Q. WHAT'S THE BEST THING ABOUT BEING A VETERINARIAN?
A. It's so versatile. You can choose from many specialty areas: small animal, equine, large animal, poultry, animal health, mixed practice. And there are all kinds of jobs. One of my vet friends spent six months in the Bahamas on an exchange.

Q. IS THERE ANYTHING ABOUT BEING A VET THAT YOU DIDN'T EXPECT?
A. One thing, which is that all animals are attached to people. Vets don't just look after animals, they have to think about the owners as well. It can be very hard sometimes when people's pets become sick. Once, a lady committed suicide when her cat died of leukemia.

Q. WHAT ADVICE DO YOU HAVE FOR STUDENTS INTERESTED IN BECOMING VETERINARIANS?
A. Although, obviously, you should like animals to be a good vet, you have to like people too. Dealing with people is a major part of any vet's job. You might find that people will try to discourage you, saying the profession is too tough. It *is* tough and you don't make a lot of money. But you'll have the satisfaction of helping to make different kinds of animals better, and their owners will thank you for it.

Review Questions

A: Knowledge

1. List the life functions that are common to all living things.

2. Name the two factors the environment provides for all living things.

3. Explain the difference in the meaning of the words "diversity" and "variation" when they are used to describe organisms.

4. Name the three environmental factors which determine the type of vegetation that will grow in a particular region.

5. a) Describe the types of environment that each of the following organisms inhabits: cactus, kelp, fern.
   b) Identify some of the features of these organisms that suit them to their respective environments.

6. What is meant by the range of tolerance of an organism?

7. a) Summarize the characteristics of each of the five kingdoms.
   b) Identify the particular quality that distinguishes each kingdom from the others.

8. Arrange the following levels of classification so that the first level contains the least number of species and the last level contains the greatest number of species: genus, order, kingdom, family, class, species, phylum.

9. Explain how one species can be distinguished from another similar looking species.

10. What improvement did Linnaeus introduce to the naming of organisms?

11. a) Why do most scientific names resemble Latin words?
    b) State two advantages of using scientific names rather than common names.

B: Application

12. Describe how your local environment shows variation from place to place and from time to time.

13. Generally as one travels from the poles towards the tropics, the numbers of species that live at a given latitude increase. What climatic factors in the environment may explain this observation?

14. The diagram below illustrates the general appearance of a certain type of plant in different locations on a mountain slope.

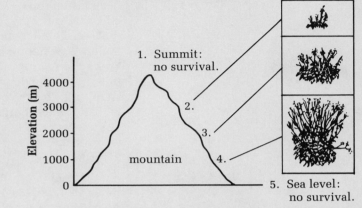

a) Describe the range of tolerance of the plant with respect to elevation.
b) What criteria do you use to determine whether the plant is doing well or whether it is doing poorly?
c) Identify where this plant seems to grow best, poorest, not at all.
d) What climatic factor parallels the change in elevation?

15. For each pair of organisms in the table below, name the level of classification shared in common that indicates their greatest similarity. The first one is done as an example.

Organisms	Classification Level Shared in Common
dog and cat	Order Carnivora
human and fruitfly	
domestic dog and red fox	
human and whale	
tiger and housecat	

16. Explain the importance of the microscope in the recognition of the protist kingdom as a separate kingdom of life.

17. Briefly summarize in a table how each of the following organisms is suited to its particular environment and way of life. Identify the environment of each organism: musk ox, whale, *Paramecium*, camel, maple tree, cactus.

18. Name three features that make it possible to group cattle and horses in the same category. Name three features that require them to be classified in separate categories.

19. a) Horses and zebras never come in contact with one another in natural conditions. However, humans have been able to cross these two animals and produce offspring. Explain whether or not these organisms should be considered a separate species or a single species.

    b) The scientific name for one of the organisms is *Equus caballus*. What is the genus name of the other organism?

20. a) Why is it not useful for a biologist to classify organisms alphabetically?

    b) Describe a situation where it might be useful to classify or group organisms alphabetically.

21. All living things require a source of nitrogen to make proteins. However, only one group of organisms is capable of using nitrogen gas and converting it into a form useable by other organisms. Identify this group of organisms. To which kingdom does this group belong?

C: Problem Solving

22. a) Using data in the graph below, name the order of appearance of the organisms in a hay infusion.

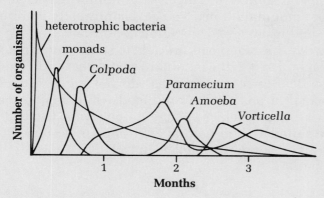

    b) Identify and explain the trend in the maximum number of organisms of each kind that occurs as the hay infusion ages.

23. a) Find how the terms "breed", "variety", and "race" fit into the scheme of levels of classification.

    b) Sometimes a species is given a three-part name. The first two names are the genus and species name, and the third provides an added description. Why is this third name sometimes used?

24. a) Based on the estimate of the number of species in each kingdom given in the text, calculate the total number of known species.

    b) Estimates of the actual number of species alive today range up to ten million. Calculate the percentage of all organisms that the known species comprise.

    c) From the examination of fossils, scientists estimate that 400 times as many organisms have lived on the Earth over its entire history as are alive today. What fraction of all the organisms that have ever lived are living today?

Try This

1. **Make a Permanent Culture**
   Try to establish a near-permanent protist culture by introducing algae into the *Paramecium* cultures.

2. **Digestion in *Paramecium***
   As an extension of the carmine powder experiment in Activity 5-1C, you can study the digestion that occurs within the food vacuoles that form at the end of the oral groove of the *Paramecium*. Stain several drops of milk with a few grains of the indicator Congo red. Add an equal amount of this mixture to a quantity of *Paramecium* culture. Prepare wet mounts of the mixture and observe the ingestion of red butterfat globules. The fat globules become enveloped in food vacuoles. As digestion of the fat takes place inside the vacuole, they will first turn a blue colour and then turn red again.

Chapter 5
Sensing and Responding to the External Environment

The external environment of the mountain goat can provide for its needs, such as food, warmth, oxygen, and water. But the same environment is also a source of danger from falling rocks, fierce winter storms, and mountain lions. The goat continually monitors its environment, and responds to changing conditions.

Wherever they live, all organisms are able to sense environmental change and respond to it. If the mountain goat detects a predator, it can attempt to flee. Even animals that do not move, such as oysters, have special means of obtaining food while coping with environmental conditions such as changing tide levels. Generally, all organisms are suited to their natural environment because they are able to sense and respond to changes in it.

When you finish Chapter 5, you should be able to:

- describe some stimulus-response mechanisms in protists and animals
- describe the sensory organs and nervous systems of some representative animals, including humans
- explain how sensing and movement are related
- compare the locomotory structures of a vertebrate and an invertebrate
- explain the role of sensory, locomotory, and nervous systems in animals

5.1 Stimulus and Response

When you are outside and the wind suddenly blows some dust into your eyes, what happens? Without thinking, you blink your eyes and they water. The swirling dust is a **stimulus** from the external environment. The blinking motion and watering of your eyes are **responses** that protect your eyes from possible damage.

More precisely, a stimulus is *a change in the environment that necessitates a response, or adjustment, by an organism.* All living organisms need to monitor their surroundings and respond to constantly changing conditions. Through their sense organs, living things detect stimuli such as light, sound, touch, smell, and taste. However, a stimulus for one organism may not be a stimulus for another, and responses differ as well. A herd of gazelles might stampede at a sudden sound, but a lion might move closer to investigate what caused it.

How might these animals respond if they smelled a lion?

Activity 5-1:   The Response of Protists to Environmental Change

In this activity you will study the protist *Paramecium* and how it responds to environmental changes. Use live *Paramecium* from the hay infusion you prepared in Activity 4-1.

Materials

microscope

protist culture (hay infusion)

medicine droppers

cavity slides

cover slips

glycerol or methyl cellulose

250 mL beaker

drinking straw

dissecting needle

0.7% salt solution

carmine powder

toothpicks

Part A: Observing the Motion of *Paramecium*

Procedure

1. Using a medicine dropper, obtain a sample of the culture and add a drop to the cavity in a slide. Cover with a cover slip.

2. Examine the sample under low, medium, and high power, using proper microscope technique. The majority of the organisms present will be the ciliated protist *Paramecium*. Note the shape of the organism and how it moves.

3. The speed of the protist through the water makes observation under high power difficult. *Paramecium* can be slowed down by adding a thickener. Clean the original wet mount and prepare a second one, adding a drop of glycerol or methyl cellulose to the new sample. Cover with a cover slip.

4. Observe the culture under high-power magnification. Reduce the light intensity to avoid overheating the specimen(s). Note the shape of the organism. Try to distinguish its front end from its rear end. Describe its motion through the fluid, and its response when it encounters an obstacle. Look for any motions the organism makes other than moving from one place to another.

5. As the culture dries, the organism slows down and eventually stops. When this occurs, look for signs of activity in the cytoplasm.

Discussion

1. Is *Paramecium* flat or three-dimensional? Describe what the organism does that allows you to answer this question.
2. a) Compare the shapes of the two ends of *Paramecium*.
   b) Explain how you can tell which is the front end.
3. Describe how *Paramecium* responds when it encounters an obstacle.
4. a) List all the types of motion you observed in *Paramecium*.
   b) Suggest a reason for its continual movement.
5. Draw a sequence of four sketches to show how *Paramecium* moves through its environment.

Part B: Examining the Responses of *Paramecium* to Soda Water and Salt Water

Procedure

1. Prepare a fresh wet mount of *Paramecium* culture on a cavity slide. Do *not* add a cover slip or a thickener.
2. Prepare weak soda water by exhaling through a straw into 200 mL of tap water for 2 min. Do not use commercially available soda water.
3. Place a small drop of soda water near the culture drop but not in the cavity.
4. Under low power, focus on the edges of both drops. Observe the direction of travel of *Paramecium* in the culture drop.
5. With a dissecting needle, draw a small amount of the soda water towards the edge of the culture drop, as shown in Figure 5-1. Note the response of *Paramecium*.
6. Repeat the above procedure except for step 2, using a clean medicine dropper and salt solution instead of soda water.

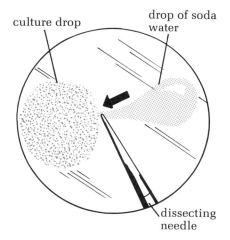

Figure 5-1. Step 5.

culture drop

drop of soda water

dissecting needle

Discussion

1. Identify the stimuli in Part B. What do they have in common?
2. Describe how *Paramecium* responds to the presence of each stimulus.

Part C: Observing the Path of Food in *Paramecium*

Biologists often use dyes called *stains* to highlight features of an organism that would otherwise be difficult to see through a microscope. In this procedure, you will use carmine powder as a stain to trace the path of food into *Paramecium*.

Figure 5-2. How *Paramecium* responds to some stimuli.

a) Response to obstacles.

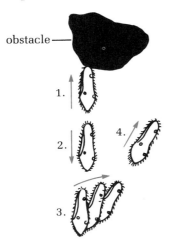

When *Paramecium* touches an obstacle (1), it reverses its motion (2), turns (3), and moves in another direction (4).

b) Response to an edible object.

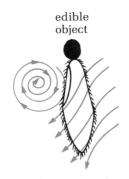

Paramecium remains at rest when it touches an edible object. The arrows indicate the direction of water currents that direct food particles towards the oral groove.

Procedure

1. Add a drop of *Paramecium* culture to a cavity slide.
2. Dip a dry toothpick first into carmine powder and then into the culture on the slide. Stir gently for a few seconds until the dye has been transferred to the culture drop.
3. After 1 min, add a drop of thickener to the stained culture. Stir again and add a cover slip.
4. Under high power, observe the movement of carmine particles around and into *Paramecium*.

Discussion

1. Describe the motion of carmine particles around the exterior of *Paramecium*. What appears to cause this motion?
2. a) Describe the passage of carmine particles into *Paramecium*. What causes the particles to move like this?
   b) *Paramecium* has a funnel-shaped canal called the "oral groove" along its side. From your observations, suggest what this canal is used for.
3. a) What does *Paramecium* eat?
   b) Is *Paramecium* an autotroph or a heterotroph? Explain.
4. a) What needs does the hay infusion provide for *Paramecium*?
   b) What threat(s) may the hay infusion pose?

Stimulus-Response in Protists

Although most protists consist of only a single cell, they can respond to a remarkably wide range of environmental stimuli, including changes in temperature, light, and gravity. Most protists are sensitive to the stimulus of touch, and respond by moving either towards or away from the object encountered. *Paramecium* responds to contact with nonedible objects by reversing the beat of its cilia, backing up, and moving forward again in a different direction. It also reverses its motion when it comes into contact with irritating chemicals, or with excessive heat or cold. Avoidance, therefore, is its principal response to negative stimuli.

Another protist, *Euglena*, shows a sensitivity to light. *Euglena* is capable both of making its own food by photosynthesis and of hunting as a predator. When there is an absence of prey, *Euglena* will migrate to regions where there is adequate light, and there carry out photosynthesis.

Stimulus-Response in Other Organisms

Like the protists, monerans are sensitive to changes in temperature, light, gravity, chemicals, and touch. Plants, too, are able to detect and respond to environmental stimuli. All plants are sensitive to light, and generally respond by growing towards this stimulus. Sunflowers move their large flower heads during the day to keep them facing the sun. Plant roots grow towards sources of water and downwards in response to gravity. Climbing plants are sensitive to touch. When part of a climbing plant touches a solid object, the plant responds by growing on or around the object to support its stems and leaves.

One of the most dramatic plant responses is found in the Venus flytrap. When its leaves are spread open, the plant is ready to catch an insect. The insides of the leaves are lined with touch-sensitive hairs that detect the presence of an insect. When two or more hairs are touched, the leaves respond by quickly shutting like a trap.

Members of the animal kingdom show the most pronounced and varied responses to stimuli. This is because animals have the most highly developed sensory systems of all organisms. You will learn more about the sensory systems of animals in Section 5.2.

Factors Affecting Stimulus-Response

The response of an organism to a stimulus depends on the nature of the stimulus, the type of sense organs the organism possesses, and the internal state of the organism. When you are hungry, for

Response to stimuli does not always involve movement. Many animals, such as rabbits, "freeze" and remain still when they detect danger. Other body responses in animals include the release of hormones and enzymes from glands. Adrenalin, the "fight or flight" hormone, is released when an animal receives a scare, and is responsible for imparting extraordinary strength to the muscles.

CHALLENGER

Animals like seals and whales have what is called a mammalian diving reflex. As soon as cold water touches the face, blood flow to the limbs is reduced and is diverted to the brain and heart. What function does this reflex serve when these animals dive in cold water?

The unusual sensory capacities of some animals sometimes make it difficult for us to study them. The ability of bats and whales to navigate by listening to reflected sounds, for example, was not understood until humans developed instruments that could measure sounds of low and high frequencies.

example, you respond to the smell of food in a different way than you would right after a large meal. Stimuli can be positive, negative, or neutral. For a rabbit, the sight and smell of grass are positive stimuli; the smell of a fox is a negative stimulus; and the sound of a croaking frog is a neutral stimulus.

Generally, an organism moves towards a positive stimulus and away from a negative one. On smelling the fox, the rabbit would probably move away from the area as quickly as possible. Such a response to the negative stimulus increases the rabbit's chance of survival. Many responses are automatic, such as the watering of your mouth when you smell appetizing food. Others are voluntary responses, such as eating a bowl of hot chicken soup.

Study Questions

1. Using complete sentences, define a) stimulus, and b) response.
2. Why is it necessary for living things to be able to respond to stimuli?
3. From your own experience, list three examples each of automatic and voluntary responses to stimuli.
4. a) Which comes first, the stimulus or the response? Explain.
   b) Explain whether it is possible to have a stimulus with no response, or a response with no stimulus.
5. a) In each of the following, describe how the organism may respond to the situation.
   i) an earthworm to a summer rain shower
   ii) a rooster to the dawn
   iii) a guard dog to a break-in
   iv) a hungry lion to a herd of gazelles
   b) In each situation above, clearly identify the stimulus causing the response.

5.2   Sensing the External Environment

Of all organisms, animals are equipped with the most highly developed sensory systems. Most animals have specialized **sense organs** to detect stimuli in the environment. The type, number, and complexity of an animal's sense organs are related to the animal's way of life. The sea anemone's stinging tentacles are sensitive to the touch of potential prey. The sharp ears of a bat can detect the reflection of its own high-pitched squeaks as they bounce off objects in its path. Many insects communicate with one another by

secreting chemicals called pheromones that can be detected by the insects' antennae.

Like other animals, humans have several senses. In the next activity, you will investigate the sensitivity and speed of human sensory responses to certain stimuli.

Activity 5-2: Testing Human Senses

For this activity, your teacher will set up work stations equipped with the required materials. Procedures for each station are outlined below. You will work in pairs, one partner acting as the "tester", the other as the "subject". Visit the work stations in the order your teacher suggests, and be sure to follow all safety precautions and any special instructions you find there. Answer the discussion questions for each station after finishing all the activities specified by your teacher.

Note: Both partners should read each procedure entirely to make sure it is thoroughly understood.

STATION A: Testing Visual Sensitivity at Low Light Levels

Materials

white cardboard tube (from paper towel roll) with cotton batting on one rim

textbook

watch or clock with second hand

mirror

Figure 5-3.

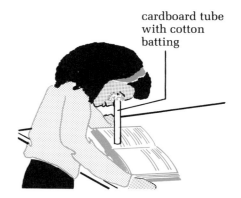

cardboard tube with cotton batting

Procedure

1. *Subject*: Keep one eye closed throughout this procedure. With the other eye, look at the print on a page of the book through the cardboard tube, as shown in Figure 5-3. The walls of the cardboard tube should be of such a thickness that they transmit very little light. If the print is visible when you first peer down

the tube, too much light is being transmitted. Thicken the walls of the tube by wrapping notepaper around the tube until it becomes just impossible to read the print. Press your head against the cushioned pad rim just firmly enough so that light cannot enter the tube from either end. As soon as it becomes impossible to read the print, give a hand signal to the tester to begin recording the time. Continue looking down the tube until the print becomes legible once again. Then, quickly raise your head and look in a mirror at your eye to observe the size of the pupil. Continue observing, and signal the tester when there is no further change in the size of the pupil.

Tester: You will be measuring two time intervals. First, measure how long the subject spends looking down through the tube at the book's print. Record the time from the subject's hand signal until the subject's head is raised to look in the mirror. At that moment, start measuring how long it takes for the pupil in the subject's eye to stop changing in size. The subject will signal when there is no further change. Record this second measurement.

2. Repeat step 1 three times and enter the average time in a chart.

Discussion

1. Identify the two stimuli that acted on the subject's eye.
2. Describe the eye's response to each stimulus.
3. Which takes longer, adjustment to dim light or to bright light? What advantage or disadvantage might this difference in response time present for humans?
4. Imagine an organism in which the response times are reversed. What advantage or disadvantage might this present?
5. What is the purpose of repeating the test three times?

STATION B: Testing Auditory Sensitivity at Low Sound Levels

Materials

metre stick

ticking watch or other low,
    constant source of sound

stool or chair in a quiet location

Procedure

1. *Tester:* Test one ear of the subject at a time. For both tests, slowly approach the subject from a distance of at least 5 m directly behind the subject's back, holding the sound source at waist

level and the metre stick in your other hand. As soon as the subject signals that he or she hears the sound, stop. Measure the distance between the sound source and the subject's ear. Repeat the procedure for the other ear.

Subject: Keep your eyes closed and remain seated throughout this test. Test one ear at a time by covering the other ear with your hand. As soon as you hear the sound source, raise your hand to signal the tester. Repeat the procedure for the other ear.

2. Average the two distances between the subject's ears and the sound source.

3. Repeat steps 1 and 2 three times. Calculate a final average distance at which the subject can detect the sound. Enter this value in a class chart on the chalkboard.

Discussion

1. Use the distances recorded in the class chart to calculate an average for all the subjects tested in the class. By what percentage does the greatest distance recorded exceed the average (e.g., by 10%, 50%, etc.)? By what percentage is the shortest distance less than the average?

2. **Make a Hypothesis:** Predict how results might be affected if some subjects had just come from a noisy cafeteria, others from a quiet library, and the rest from a normal classroom environment. Design an experiment to test your hypothesis.

STATION C: Mapping Temperature Sensitivity
Materials

8 glass rods	HB pencil
beaker of ice water	paper towels
beaker of hot tap water	chair or stool

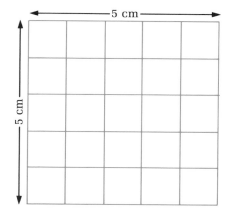

Figure 5-4.

Procedure

1. *Tester:* Place four rods in each beaker. In your notebook, draw two grids like the one shown in Figure 5-4. Label one grid "Map of Cold Sensitivity" and the other grid "Map of Heat Sensitivity". With a pencil, gently draw a similar grid on the back of the subject's hand.

Subject: Sit down and rest your hand with the grid side upward comfortably on a desk. Keep your eyes closed. As the tester touches your skin, identify the test rod as either warm or cold.

2. *Tester*: Randomly select a warm or a cold glass rod. Dry it quickly, and then use it to touch one of the squares in the grid on the subject's skin. Return the used rod to its beaker. Each time the subject correctly identifies whether the rod was warm or cold, check off the corresponding square in the appropriate grid in your notebook. For each incorrect identification, mark a cross in the corresponding square. In random order, test every square on the subject's hand with both warm and cold rods.

Discussion

1. a) What evidence did you find to indicate that the skin has different receptors (sensory detectors) for hot and cold?
   b) Which type of receptor is more common? Suggest what advantage this might have for humans.

2. Extreme hot or cold temperatures cause pain. What is the value of being able to sense pain when it causes so much discomfort?

STATION D: Testing Touch Sensors

Materials

dividers from a geometry set   chair or stool

ruler

Procedure

1. Copy the chart below in your notebook.

	Palm of Hand	Back of Hand	Inside Forearm	Back of Neck	Forehead
Minimum Separation of Dividers (mm)					

2. *Subject*: Sit down and rest your arm and hand on a desk, palm upward. Keep your eyes closed. When the tester touches you with the dividers, state whether you feel one point or two.

   Tester: Start with the dividers 1 cm apart. *Gently* touch the subject's palm. If the subject reports feeling two points, reduce the separation between the dividers by about 2 mm and try again.

Keep reducing the distance between the dividers, little by little, until the subject reports feeling only one point, even though you are touching the palm with two points. The *second last* test represents the minimum separation needed for two points to be distinguished as separate by the subject. Measure and record this minimum separation in your chart.

Note: To keep the subject "honest", the tester will, without warning, occasionally carry out a false test by touching with only one point of the dividers. The subject should never know whether to expect one point or two.

3. Repeat the touch test for the other parts of the body included in the chart. For each body part, record the minimum separation needed for two points to be distinguished as separate.

Discussion

1. Write your own definition of touch receptor. Where are touch receptors located?

2. What evidence did you find of differences in the distribution of touch receptors?

3. a) Which of the body parts tested is most sensitive to touch? What advantage(s) might this have for humans?
   b) Which of the body parts tested is least sensitive? What disadvantage(s) might result if this part had more touch receptors?

4. **Make a Hypothesis:** Predict the minimum separation needed to distinguish two points on the heel and on the sole of the foot. Design an experiment to test your hypothesis.

STATION E: Testing the Efficiency of the Sense of Smell

Materials

3 food flavouring extracts: almond, lemon, orange

cotton balls

clock or watch with second hand

stool or chair

CAUTION: Never smell any substance in the laboratory unless your teacher assures you that it is completely safe. The substances at Station E are food products that are safe for most humans to smell. However, students with known food allergies should not act as subjects at this station.

Procedure

1. *Tester*: Dampen one cotton ball with lemon extract and another with orange extract. Set the balls aside so that the subject cannot smell them. When the subject is ready, hold the opened bottle of almond extract 3 cm from his or her nose and start timing.

Figure 5-5.

Note: Although it is safe to smell foods in this way, *never* use this technique for smelling laboratory chemicals.

Subject: Remain seated and close your eyes. First, smell the almond extract by inhaling normally, but exhale through your mouth. Continue smelling, and when the odour seems sharply reduced, tell your tester. Keep your eyes closed.

2. *Tester*: Note the time when the subject reports a sharp reduction in almond extract odour, and remove the extract. Immediately hold one of the cotton balls under the subject's nose for a few seconds. Then remove the cotton ball and replace it with the other ball for a few seconds.

Subject: Try to identify the order in which the orange extract and lemon extract were presented to you.

3. Repeat the procedure several times.

Discussion

1. Describe what you observed about human ability to a) smell newly introduced odours, b) smell persisting odours, c) distinguish between different odours.

2. a) What do these results suggest about the efficiency of the human sense of smell?
   b) What advantage(s) might this have for humans?
   c) What disadvantage(s) might it present?

Sensory Systems in Humans

Humans have several senses that enable them to detect a wide variety of stimuli from the external environment. Each of these senses is associated with a specialized organ that contains **sensory receptors** for one particular type of stimulus. Together, these organs make up the sensory system. The five human senses will be discussed here: vision, hearing, touch, smell, and taste.

1. **Vision** The human eye is a complex structure that detects energy in the form of light. It can detect not only the intensity of light, but also colour, movement, and patterns. Detection of light by sensory cells is called **photoreception**. The eye's photoreceptors are two types of light-sensitive cells located in the retina on the back wall of the eye. **Cone cells** are specialized for bright light and colour reception. **Rod cells** are specialized for vision at low light levels. Human eyes have large numbers of cone cells. Animals active at night and those that live in dark places have large numbers of rod cells.

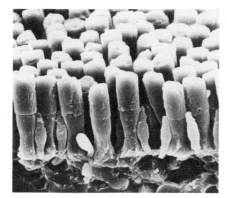

A scanning electron microscope reveals that the eye of the salamander has more rod cells than cone cells. Explain why this is so, given the fact that salamanders live under logs and fallen leaves.

Figure 5-6. The structure of the human eye.

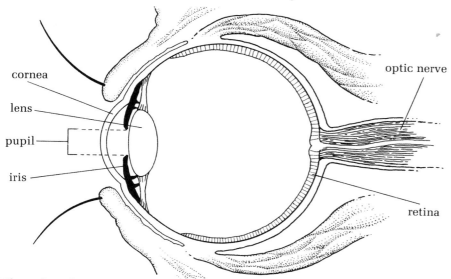

cornea

lens

pupil

iris

optic nerve

retina

The rods and cones are located on the retina.

2. **Hearing** The human ear is a complex organ that detects energy in the form of sound. When objects such as guitar strings are plucked, they vibrate nearby air molecules. These molecules, in turn, vibrate other nearby molecules forming a pattern of sound waves that travel through the air. Sound waves that reach the human eardrum cause it to vibrate, too. The vibrations then travel

Figure 5-7. The structure of the human ear.

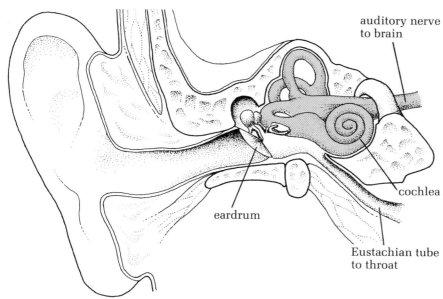

auditory nerve
to brain

cochlea

eardrum

Eustachian tube
to throat

Humans have poor colour vision at low light levels. You probably have noticed that in very dim light, it is difficult to distinguish the colours of objects, although you can tell if they appear light or dark.

Do You Know?
A honeybee's eyes are sensitive to ultraviolet light from the Sun. Since ultraviolet light passes through clouds more easily than visible light does, the bee can see the Sun on even a cloudy day. This is important because bees use the position of the Sun to help them navigate and locate food. Consequently, the appearance of flowers to a bee differs from what we see.

through a series of small bones into a coiled, fluid-filled cone called the **cochlea**. Located in the lining of the cochlea are tiny motion-sensitive hair cells. The ability to detect motion is called **mechanoreception**, and the hair cells are mechanoreceptors. When the vibrating fluid of the cochlea moves the hair cells, nerve impulses are sent to the brain where they are interpreted as sound. Because the reception of sound by the human ear requires the passage of energy through many parts, damage to any one of these parts may result in hearing loss.

3. **Touch**   In humans, touch receptors are located in the skin. Different parts of the skin have different numbers of touch receptors, so some areas of the body are more sensitive to touch than others. Touch receptors are very abundant in the lips and fingertips, allowing us to exercise very delicate control and movement of these parts. Each body hair, too, is touch-sensitive and can detect the movement of objects over the surface of the body. Touch receptors inside the joints of limbs allow us to be aware of the position of a limb without having to look at it. This is partly why we can touch the tip of the nose with a fingertip when our eyes are closed. The detection of touch, pressure, and pain are examples of mechanoreception, because the sensory cells must detect motion.

Sensory adaptation (see next page) occurs with touch as well as with smell. For example, when you put on your clothes, you notice them at first but very soon grow used to their touch. Your touch receptors remain sensitive to new stimuli, however, such as a friend's hand on your shoulder.

Figure 5-8.   Sensory receptors in the skin.

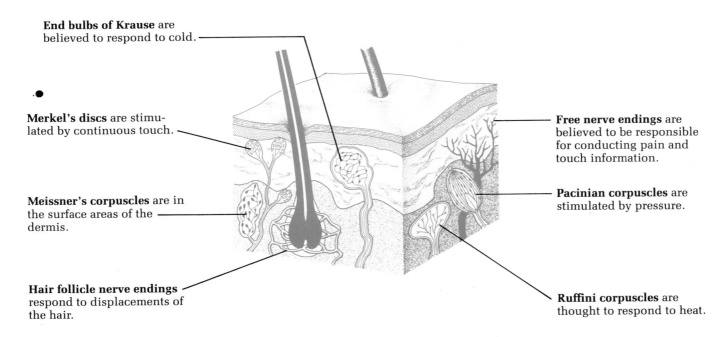

End bulbs of Krause are believed to respond to cold.

Merkel's discs are stimulated by continuous touch.

Meissner's corpuscles are in the surface areas of the dermis.

Hair follicle nerve endings respond to displacements of the hair.

Free nerve endings are believed to be responsible for conducting pain and touch information.

Pacinian corpuscles are stimulated by pressure.

Ruffini corpuscles are thought to respond to heat.

4. **Smell**   The sense of smell, or **olfaction**, detects chemical stimuli. This ability, called **chemoreception**, is one of the most widespread in nature, and is found in even the simplest organisms. Olfaction requires direct contact with the odour-causing molecules. In humans, the olfactory receptors are located high in the nasal cavity. Odour molecules inhaled with air are dissolved in the mucous lining of the nasal cavity and then brought into contact with the receptors. Humans sense new odours quickly, but soon become accustomed to them. For example, people who live near oil refineries seldom notice the unpleasant fumes. This effect is called **sensory adaptation**.

Although many animals have much keener noses than we do, our sense of smell can still save lives. The smell of smoke may wake you in time to escape from a burning house. The unpleasant smell of rotten food warns you not to eat it. Odourless fuel gases often have small amounts of foul-smelling chemicals added to them to warn people of their presence if a leak occurs.

Figure 5-9.   The human sense of smell.

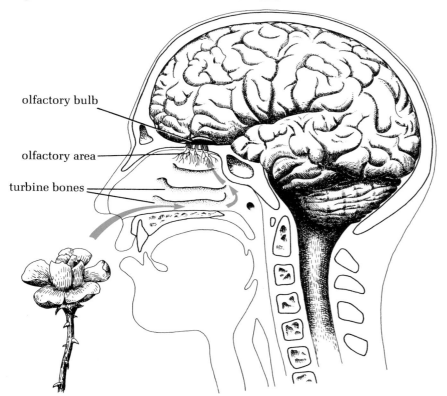

Figure 5-10.   Different parts of the tongue are able to taste one of the four basic tastes.

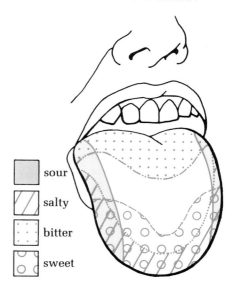

sour

salty

bitter

sweet

Taste bud

taste receptor

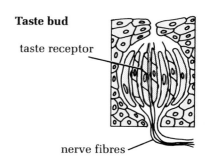

nerve fibres

5. **Taste**   The ability to detect taste is another example of chemoreception. In humans, the taste receptors are located in taste buds situated in crevices in the tongue. As in smell, the taste-causing molecules must be dissolved before they can be detected, and require direct contact with the receptors. As Figure 5-10 illustrates, human taste receptors are limited to just four categories:

Controlled experiments in which subjects wear blindfolds and noseplugs show that the individuals cannot taste any difference between orange juice and onion juice.

Some Sensory Feats in Animals

- Bats can hear frequencies as high as 150 kHz, compared with 15 kHz for the average adult human.
- A barn owl's ability to detect objects in low light levels is 50 to 100 times better than a human's.
- In good light, a golden eagle can detect a hare at a distance of almost 2 km.
- The male silkworm moth can detect the scent of a female moth when she is approximately 11 km upwind of him.

CHALLENGER

Rapid movement of body parts is generally associated with animals rather than with plants. However, the Venus flytrap readily captures insects in its leaf trap which is sprung by touch-sensitive hairs. How does the Venus flytrap accomplish such movement?

sweet, salty, sour, and bitter. All the various food flavours you can detect result from the interaction of your sense of smell with these four basic tastes.

Sensory Systems in Other Organisms

Protists possess chemoreceptors in their cell membranes. These receptors detect the presence of chemical substances or other organisms. Depending upon the nature of the molecule sensed, the organism may respond by attempting to eat or avoid it. Some protists like *Euglena* have a pigment spot that is sensitive to the presence of light. Although the *Euglena* cannot see, it will travel towards the light. When there is enough light the organism will perform photosynthesis.

Many members of the animal kingdom possess elaborate sense organs similar to those of humans. In fact, different kinds of animals possess sense organs of much greater sensitivity than those of humans. Dogs, bats, and dolphins, for example, can hear much higher sound frequencies than humans can. The sense of vision is most acute in birds of prey. The most acute sense of smell is found in some insects.

Study Questions

1. a) List the five human senses.
   b) Classify the five human senses according to whether each is sensitive to mechanical stimuli, chemical stimuli, or light stimuli.
2. How does the sensory system of humans differ from that of protists?
3. a) When city dwellers visit a farm, they often complain of the unpleasant odours when they first arrive, but then do not notice the same smells when they depart. What is this effect called?
   b) Explain the advantages and disadvantages of this effect.
4. a) Identify the two types of vision cells that humans have.
   b) During which part of the day does each type of vision cell operate?
   c) Dogs are said to see shades of black and white only. What does this indicate about their photoreceptors?
5. Which would you expect to have the greater number of touch receptors, the skin on your eyelid or on your heel? Why?

EXTENDING OUR SENSES

Our knowledge of the world is by no means restricted to what we can discover through our senses alone. Throughout human history, we have extended our ability to observe well beyond the limits of our sense organs with the invention of instruments for sensing. These high-powered, sense-extending devices have expanded our view of the world to include things that could hardly be guessed at before.

For example, the discovery of very small single-celled organisms was made possible by the invention of the microscope. Later, the electron microscope enabled us to see parts of cells in great detail, and even much smaller objects such as atoms. Some inventions gather information that no human sensory receptors can detect. An X-ray camera photographs images through opaque barriers. A Geiger counter or an ionization chamber measures levels of radiation. Radio telescopes enable us to detect radio signals from space, and they also open up the possibility of communicating with alien life forms, if such things exist.

Sense-extending inventions need not be complex to be useful. Braille, a system of raised dots representing letters, allows blind people to read with their fingers. A thermometer enables you to sense the temperature of a substance with your eyes instead of your skin. Litmus paper or a pH kit allows you to discover the acidity of a substance.

A large amount of money and research have gone into developing instruments to monitor the environment. These instruments help to forecast changes that could affect human health or the economy. Satellites help to fore-

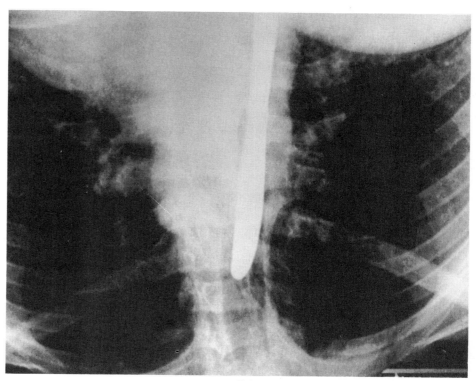

Prior to surgery, surgeons used X-rays to pinpoint the location of a table knife accidentally swallowed by a man trying to dislodge a pill stuck in his throat.

cast weather, track hurricanes, monitor the spread of pollution, and measure crop growth. Seismometers measure earthquakes. By means of such devices, we not only learn more about the world but also help make the environment healthier and safer.

Figure 5-11. The nervous systems of a) a *Hydra*, and b) a human.

a) *Hydra.*

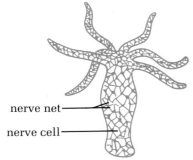

nerve net —

nerve cell —

b) A human.

cerebrum —
cerebellum —
spinal cord —

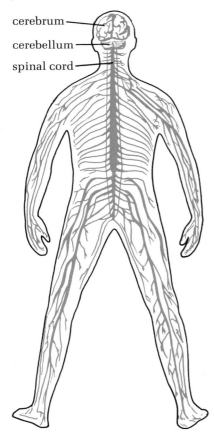

5.3 Coordinating Responses: Movement and Locomotion

Before an organism can sense and respond to environmental change, three requirements must be met. First, the organism must possess sensory receptors to detect stimuli and thus gather information about conditions in the external environment. Second, the organism must have a means of responding to changed conditions, such as the ability to move away. Finally, the organism must have a coordinating system that links sensing and responding. This system is called the **nervous system**.

How a Nervous System Works

The simplest type of nervous system in animals is that found in *Hydra*, a small freshwater jellyfish. This type of nervous system contains a network of neurons that links sensory cells with musclelike cells. The system limits *Hydra* to simple responses, such as contracting when it is touched.

In more complex animals, groups of neurons form **nerves**, while sensory cells are coordinated into specialized and highly developed sense organs. Nerve signals are coordinated through a central nervous system that consists of a nerve cord and a brain. Smaller clumps of nerve cells called **ganglia** (singular, **ganglion**) coordinate nerve signals in different parts of the body. Figure 5-11 shows a comparison between the nervous system of *Hydra* and that of a human.

Although senses and responses differ from species to species, most nervous systems share a common design. A nervous system consists of nerve cells, or **neurons**, which carry information from one part of the body to another. Neurons are classified into three types, according to their function. **Sensory neurons** carry signals from the sense receptors. **Motor neurons** carry signals to the parts of the body, such as muscles and glands, that carry out the body's responses. **Interneurons** act as connectors that carry signals from the sensory neurons to the motor neurons.

What happens in your body when your hand accidentally touches a hot kettle (see Figure 5-12)? Signals from heat receptors in your fingertips travel along sensory neurons in your arm to the spinal cord. Interneurons in the spinal cord receive the signals and relay them to motor neurons. The signals are conducted along the motor neurons to the muscles in your arm. These muscles respond by drawing your hand away from the kettle.

Figure 5-12.

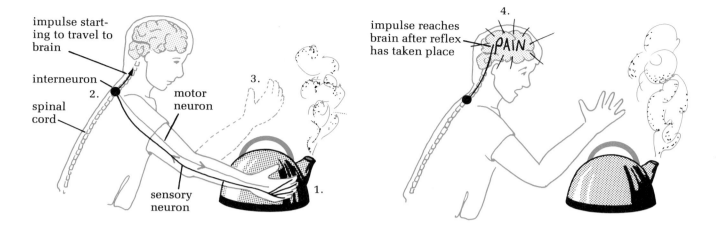

Signals from heat sensors in the fingertips (1) travel along sensory neurons to interneurons in the spinal cord. The interneurons (2) send signals to motor neurons in the arm muscles, which respond by drawing the fingers away from the kettle (3). When the impulse reaches the brain (4), pain is felt.

In a simple reflex such as this, the response is coordinated through the nerve cord in the spine. This allows the fastest possible response because the nerve signals travel a shorter path than if they first had to travel to your brain and back. You do not begin to feel the burn or think about it until the nerve signals reach your brain, a split second after they have reached the spinal cord. By that time, you have already removed your hand from the heat. However, feeling and thinking about the burn may lead to a further response, such as seeking first aid treatment.

Movement and Locomotion

For protists and animals, responses to stimuli usually involve some kind of movement. All animals are capable of moving in some way. Even a sessile animal such as a barnacle clinging to a rock can move slightly. An animal's movement is controlled by its nervous system.

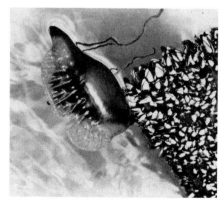

Goose barnacles grow on any solid surface, including driftwood, rocks, ship hulls, and whales. Entangled in the barnacles is a Portuguese man-of-war.

Movement from one location to another is called **locomotion**. Most animals have some means of locomotion, whether it be the slow, creeping progress of a snail or the swift flight of a falcon. Locomotion can be difficult to study because many animals move very quickly. An earthworm, however, is ideal for a study of locomotion. It is large enough to observe without a microscope, and slow enough to allow detailed observations.

Activity 5-3: Observing an Earthworm's Responses to Environmental Change

In this activity, you will be working with live earthworms. They should be handled carefully and gently, and treated with respect. When you have finished the activity, return the worms to your teacher and wash your hands thoroughly with soap and water.

Materials

box lined with moist soil and a
  lid to exclude light

live earthworms (*Lumbricus terrestris*)

flashlight with narrow beam
  (e.g., penlight)

probe

pill bottle or baby food jar

moist paper towelling

Part A: The Earthworm's Response to Light

Procedure

1. Place an earthworm in the soil-lined box. Distinguish the front end of the worm from the back end. Close the lid of the box and leave undisturbed for 2-3 min.

2. Lift the lid and shine a narrow beam of light on the front end of the worm. Record its response to the light. Close the lid of the box and leave undisturbed for 2-3 min.

3. Lift the lid and shine the light on the back end of the earthworm. Record any response.

4. Examine the earthworm carefully for the presence of eyes or other light receptors.

Discussion

1. Explain whether the earthworm's response to light is one of avoidance or tolerance.

2. Which region(s) of the earthworm was (were) sensitive to light?

3. Did you see any evidence of light-sensing body parts? If so, describe their appearances and locations. If not, attempt to explain the earthworm's ability to respond to light.

4. From your observations suggest whether you would expect earthworms to be more active in daylight or at night.

Part B: The Earthworm's Response to Touch
Procedure

1. Place an earthworm in the soil-lined box. Leave the lid open.

2. When the worm seems accustomed to its new environment, *gently* stroke its side with a probe. Record its response.

3. When the worm seems to have stopped its response, gently touch its front end with the probe. Record its response.

4. When the worm has stopped its response, touch its back end. Record its response.

5. Moisten the interior of a plastic vial and allow the earthworm to crawl into it. If necessary, *gently* encourage the worm with the probe. Once the worm is inside, record its response to its new environment.

Discussion

1. From your observations, explain whether you would expect an earthworm to crawl into its burrow front or back end first.

2. The earthworm's responses to the inside of the vial may indicate how it behaves in its burrow. Would the worm prefer the vial or the soil-lined box as a home? Explain.

Part C: Describing the Earthworm's Locomotion
Procedure

1. Place an earthworm on moist paper towelling.

2. Draw a series of 5 to 6 diagrams illustrating how the worm's body changes during locomotion. Use the discussion questions as guidelines.

Discussion

1. As the earthworm crawls, describe:
   a) any changes in the length of the worm's body;
   b) any changes in the thickness of the worm's body.

2. How are changes in length and thickness coordinated to produce locomotion?

The Nervous and Locomotory Systems of the Earthworm

Earthworms have several types of sense receptors that allow them to respond to stimuli such as light, touch, moisture, and various chemicals. The receptors are located in the earthworm's skin where they trigger sensory neurons. A central nervous system, consisting of a double nerve cord that runs the length of the worm's body, connects the sensory neurons to the motor neurons in the muscles. The nerve cord is also connected to two large ganglia in the worm's head that form a simple type of brain. Smaller ganglia are located along the nerve cord in each segment of the worm's body. These ganglia control the sensory and motor neurons in that segment, so that each segment can react and move independently.

Figure 5-13. Parts of an earthworm.

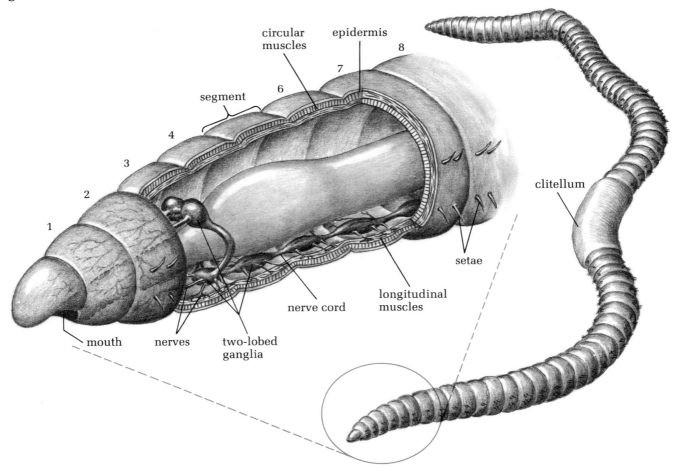

The earthworm has two sets of muscles, one perpendicular to the other. Just beneath the skin a layer of circular muscles runs around the worm's body. When these muscles contract, the worm becomes thinner and longer. Beneath these muscles is a layer of longitudinal muscles extending the length of the worm's body. When the longitudinal muscles contract, the worm becomes shorter and fatter.

Because each segment of the worm's body can act as an independent unit, the worm can elongate one part of its body while contracting another part. When the worm is moving directly forward, you can see a wave of motions passing along its body. Small bristles, called setae, that protrude from the worm's sides and bottom allow the worm to anchor part of its body to the ground and pull itself along.

The earthworm's locomotory system is internal and cannot be observed in a living specimen. Most organisms have some locomotory structures located on the outside of their bodies where they can be readily examined.

Figure 5-14. Parts of a grasshopper.

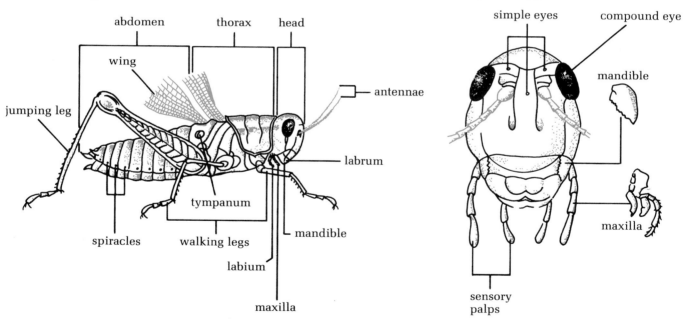

Locomotory Apparatus
1. The wings are for short-distance flight.
2. There are 3 pairs of legs. The large jumping legs enable the grasshopper to jump up to 20 times its body length horizontally and 10 times its length vertically.

Sensory Apparatus
1. The antennae are the organs of smell.
2. The compound eyes form multiple images.
3. The simple eyes form crude images at close range.
4. The sensory palps are extensions of the mouth parts and bear the organs of taste.

Figure 5-15. Parts of a perch.

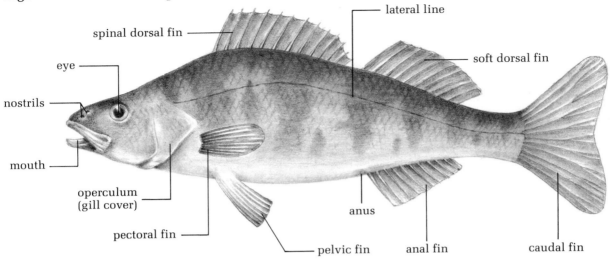

Sensory Apparatus
1. The nostrils lead to internal olfactory sacs.
2. There are taste buds in the mouth.
3. The tongue cannot move but acts as a touch organ.
4. The lateral line detects vibrations in the water, caused by predators, prey, etc.

Locomotory Apparatus
1. The dorsal fins act like a keel and maintain an upright position.
2. The anal fin also helps to maintain an upright position.
3. The caudal fin propels the body forward.
4. The pectoral and pelvic fins control steering and maneuvering.

Activity 5-4: Comparing Sensory and Locomotory Structures in an Insect and a Fish

An animal does not move until its nervous system receives signals from the environment. Thus, the primary sense organs are located on the animal's exterior. In this activity you will compare the sensory structures and locomotory systems of the grasshopper (an invertebrate) to those of the yellow perch (a vertebrate).

Specimens preserved for use in biology courses are obtained from species with abundant populations. Often the specimens are raised especially for study. To minimize the number used, treat preserved specimens with respect. When the procedure is finished, dispose of the specimens as directed by your teacher.

Materials
preserved grasshopper

magnifying glass

outline diagram of a grasshopper

live grasshoppers for display and reference, if possible

preserved perch

outline diagram of a perch

microscope slide

microscope

dissecting tray

2 dissecting probes

Part A

Procedure

1. Copy the following chart in your notebook to record your observations.

Sense	Sense Organ or Body Part	Number of Sense Organs	Location of Sense Organ
sight			
hearing			
touch			
smell			
taste			

2. Examine the preserved grasshopper for structures that it might use to see, hear, touch, taste, or smell with. Label the sense organs on the outline diagram of the grasshopper.

3. Identify the locomotory structures of the grasshopper, and determine how many of each kind the grasshopper possesses. Label these structures on your diagram, using Figure 5-14 as a reference.

4. If live grasshoppers are available, study their sensory organs and mode of locomotion (modes of locomotion include flying, walking, swimming, and so on).

CAUTION: After handling preserved specimens, wash your hands thoroughly. Chemicals in the preservatives could harm your skin through prolonged exposure, or could cause food contamination.

Discussion

1. At which end of the grasshopper are most of the sense organs located? Suggest a reason why this is so.

2. How do the grasshopper's sensory structures for smell and taste differ from those of humans?

3. a) The grasshopper has three pairs of legs. One pair differs markedly from the other two. Describe two modes of locomotion that the grasshopper can accomplish with its legs.
   b) Identify a third mode of locomotion and the body structures the grasshopper uses to achieve it.

Part B

Procedure

1. Identify and label the locomotory and sensory structures of the perch on the outline diagram provided, using Figure 5-15 as a reference.

2. Remove one scale from the flank of the fish and another scale from the lateral line. Prepare a wet mount with the two scales side by side, and observe the slide with a microscope at low power. Sketch and label the scales.

3. Push the two probes gently into the nostrils of the perch to determine whether the nostrils are connected with one another and/or with the mouth cavity. Record your observations.

Discussion

1. a) How do the two scales you took from the perch differ from one another?
   b) Beneath the lateral line are motion-sensitive cells that respond to vibrations in the water. Given this fact, explain why the scales covering the lateral line are different from scales anywhere else on the fish's body.

2. a) How many nostrils does the perch have?
   b) Are all of the nostrils connected to one another? Suggest reasons for the arrangement you observed.
   c) Describe how you were able to determine whether or not the nostrils were connected to the mouth cavity. What was the result of your investigation?

3. Suggest functions for each of the perch's fins. Check your suggestions by examining fish in the classroom aquarium.

Locomotion in Other Organisms

Depending on where and how they live, different organisms get from place to place by running, swimming, flying, jumping, wriggling, hopping, crawling, gliding, or walking. This diversity in modes of locomotion matches diversity in the environment. Most protists live in aquatic environments and move around by swimming. Some species use the wavelike beating of cilia, some propel themselves with a single whiplike flagellum, while others glide along by extending pseudopodia ("false feet"). Aquatic animals also have different structures and methods for swimming.

Land animals, too, exhibit a diversity of structures for locomotion in their environments. The cheetah is designed to run with powerful legs and a flexible back that can coil and lengthen like a spring. The powerful hind legs of a kangaroo allow it to make great leaps, while its long, heavy tail keeps its body balanced. A different sort of tail is used by the spider monkey as an extra "hand" to help it swing from tree branch to tree branch.

The large thighs of the grass frog permit it to leap large distances on land.

The jellyfish uses a form of jet propulsion, similar to that of the octopus and the squid, to move through water.

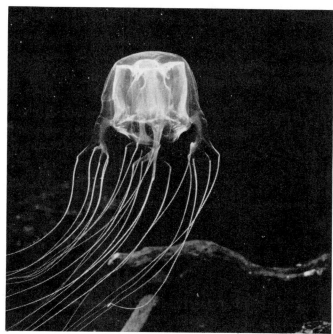

Like many other birds of prey, the bald eagle has a very wide wingspan that enables it to glide for long periods of time.

Gymnasts are capable of a wide range of movement, including somersaults, flips, and twists.

Three major groups of animals have wings for moving though the air. Insects have wing blades that twist as they fly, producing the same effect as a helicopter's rotating propeller. Birds have lightweight bones and wings shaped like a plane's, covered with feathers. Bats, the only mammals that fly, have wings that each consist of a layer of skin attached to the side of the body and supported by the forelimbs and elongated finger bones.

Human Locomotion

Consider all the ways in which you can move, such as walking, running, jumping, hopping, swimming, crawling, and rolling. The combination of an internal skeleton and a complex nervous system allows humans a great range of movement. Athletes and dancers are trained for even greater ranges of movement than the ordinary person.

Humans have also artificially expanded their capacity for locomotion through simple devices—such as snowshoes, skis, diver's flippers, skateboards, and hot air balloons — and through more complex inventions—such as bicycles, cars, airplanes, boats, and submarines. Whether a machine is simple or complex, however, its operation still relies on human responses to environmental stimuli. Driving a car, for example, involves the sensory system, the nervous system, and the locomotory system of muscles and skeleton. Drivers must use their eyes and ears to detect environmental changes, and move their eyes, heads, arms, hands, and legs in response to what they see and hear. Machines that extend our capacities for locomotion have enabled us to venture into many environments that we could not otherwise.

Study Questions

1. Describe the three requirements that must be met for an organism to sense and respond to stimuli.
2. a) What are the three types of neurons?
   b) Describe the function of each type.
3. Distinguish between movement and locomotion.
4. Describe the relationship between the complexity of the nervous system of an organism and its range of movement.
5. Explain in detail:
   a) the structure of the earthworm's muscles;
   b) the role of the setae in the earthworm's locomotion.

CHALLENGER

In terms of the arrangement and operation of the two layers of muscles, the earthworm and the human intestine are very similar. Using your knowledge of how the earthworm moves, describe how the contents of the intestine are moved along its length.

Meet a Meteorologist— Michael Leduc

Michael works for Environment Canada and is in charge of the summer severe weather forecasting program for Ontario.

Q. WHAT FIRST ATTRACTED YOU TO METEOROLOGY?
A. I've always been interested in weather. When I went to see the movie "The Wizard of Oz" I thought the tornado at the beginning was the best part. I like the fact that meteorology is a "hands-on" science, relating to real phenomena.

Q. HOW DID YOU GET YOUR FIRST JOB?
A. Every year the Department of Environment recruits about 30 meteorology students in their final year. I was studying at McGill. I went to an interview, got accepted, and took a nine-month course from Environment Canada before being sent to Gander, Newfoundland. It turned out to be a very interesting experience. Gander has spectacular weather—lots of wild storms. We did public forecasts, forecasts for aviation, and marine forecasts from that office.

Q. WHERE DID YOU GO NEXT?
A. To a military base in Ottawa. I came to Toronto in 1975, and in 1979 I got a new position of looking for potential severe thunderstorms in the summer and issuing warnings for them. This is now an established program that runs from April to September.

Q. WHAT'S A TYPICAL SHIFT LIKE IN THE SUMMER?
A. When I arrive in the morning, I study maps that are computer outputs of atmospheric models. These come from our surface and aerological observing stations across North America. The maps have coded estimates of temperature, humidity, wind pressure, cloud amounts, precipitation, etc., and the fronts separating two different air masses are marked. Weather usually forms along these frontal zones. We get reports from the surface stations every hour and upper atmosphere reports from the aerial balloons twice a day.

Q. WHAT IS THE PROCEDURE FOR ISSUING A SEVERE WEATHER WARNING?
A. Well, as an example, I was on duty on May 31, 1985, the day when tornados hit Barrie and other parts of Ontario. I could see right away that it was going to be a bad day. One of the difficulties of forecasting severe weather is that storms develop on a small scale so that only a few areas get them. We can't narrow it down. We issued a severe weather watch which means potential storms.

Q. WHAT HAPPENED THEN?
A. We watched the weather intensify rapidly, and issued a severe thunderstorm warning for various areas. Later a big tornado touched down in the Bruce Peninsula area and another in Barrie. We were unaware that the two strongest tornados on record in Ontario had occurred, though we did know that damaging storms were taking place. It was a day I'll never forget—I think I was here until midnight.

Q. WHAT DO YOU DO AFTER THE SUMMER STORM SEASON?
A. We review our performance and try to develop new techniques. After the day of the Barrie tornado, for instance, we knew we needed to improve our warning system. I looked through the files at all the major tornados over the last 20 years, searching for patterns. By the 1986 summer season, we had new rules in place.

Q. WHAT QUALITIES MAKE A GOOD METEOROLOGIST?
A. You can't be too much of a perfectionist because nature doesn't always cooperate. I like working in teams to come up with a solution to a scientific problem. And every day is an entirely new situation.

Review Questions

A: Knowledge

1. Describe how *Paramecium* responds to each of the following stimuli: solid object, soda water, and salt solution.

2. How does *Paramecium* respond when it encounters a negative stimulus?

3. Distinguish between sensing a stimulus and moving in response. Illustrate with an appropriate example.

4. Copy and complete the following table by identifying the appropriate sensory structures of humans, grasshoppers, perches, and *Paramecium*. If a particular sensor is absent in an organism, enter "nil" in your table.

Receptor	Human	Grass-hopper	Perch	Paramecium
sight				
taste				
smell				
touch				
hearing				

5. Describe the role that each of the following plays when an organism coordinates its response to a stimulus: stimulus, receptor, nervous system, locomotion.

6. a) List the three factors that affect the response of an organism to a stimulus.
   b) What are the body parts an organism must have in order to be able to sense and respond to an environmental stimulus?

7. a) Distinguish between negative, neutral, and positive stimuli.
   b) State an example of each kind of stimulus for one organism of your choice.

8. List the sensory receptors for each of the five human senses.

9. What is the difference between motor and sensory neurons?

10. Explain how the earthworm moves from place to place without appendages such as legs.

11. Summarize in a table the types of locomotion and the locomotory structures employed by each of the following organisms: *Paramecium*, earthworm, grasshopper, perch, and human.

B: Application

12. *Euglena* and *Paramecium* are both members of the protist kingdom, yet the former is capable of responding to light while the latter is not. What does this imply about the sensory repertoire of *Euglena* compared to that of *Paramecium*?

13. Neither the earthworm nor *Euglena* can see, yet both are capable of responding to light. How is this possible?

14. List the human senses that are used when a person drives a car or rides a bicycle. Briefly describe the role that each of these senses plays.

15. a) With reference to the kinds of visual receptors in our eyes, explain why colours are not distinguishable at night.
    b) Many people believe that bulls respond to the waving of a red cape. Others argue that bulls cannot see colour and respond to the movement of the flag. How might this controversy be resolved by examining the types of cells in the retina?

16. In the word "stimulus-response", which is the cause and which is the effect?

17. Name the functions of the nervous system.

18. State plausible human responses to the following stimuli:
    a) moving from a dark room to a brightly lit one
    b) hearing a sudden loud noise
    c) moving to a higher altitude

19. Rearrange the following events in the proper order of occurrence:
    a) nerve signal travels along motor neuron
    b) stimulus occurs
    c) muscle contracts
    d) nerve signal travels along sensory neuron
    e) receptor is stimulated

20. Is a nervous system necessary for an organism to respond to environmental stimuli? Describe two examples that support your statement.

21. a) Draw a map of the tongue, showing the location of the different taste receptors.
    b) The *Impatiens* plant produces small white spheres that look like sugar on the margins of its leaf stalk. Where on your tongue would you place one of these spheres to verify that it is indeed made of sugar?

22. The density of pain receptors over the surface of the human body is similar to the density of touch receptors. Using this information, explain why it hurts much less when you get a needle in the arm than when you pin-prick your fingertip.

C: Problem Solving

23. Find out why military personnel on night manoeuvers use red lights for illumination rather than regular white lights.

24. Moths are nocturnal animals. Find out why a) they hover around outside light sources at night, and b) the surfaces of their eyes do not reflect light.

Try This

1. **Make a Wormery**
   Earthworms can be kept and maintained in the classroom. Make a wormery by fitting an old styrofoam picnic cooler, 30 cm × 45 cm × 30 cm, with a glass front. Fill the container three-quarters full with rich soil or peat moss and some old fallen leaves from a woodland. Water until moist, but not too wet.

   The best time and place to collect earthworms is on warm rainy evenings in parks, golf courses, or lawns. The maximum population density in the wormery should be 50 worms per 20 L of soil. Cover the wormery and keep it in a cool place (15°C) away from strong light and heat. Check it weekly for moisture; the soil should be moist and crumbly, never soaked. Add new bedding on a monthly basis. Feed the worms twice a week with lettuce and milk-soaked bread, cornmeal, or oatmeal. Bury the food, unless the wormery has been prepared with plenty of old leaves. If mould develops, remove it. If mites appear, the entire worm farm must be discarded because mites can spread to plants, animals, and people.

2. **Tennis Ball Toss**
   Standing 2 m to 3 m away from a partner, toss a tennis ball back and forth. Do this ten times. Without changing the rhythm of the toss, close your right eye. Continue tossing the ball another ten times. Then open the right eye and close the left, again without altering the rhythm of the toss. Compare your ability to catch the ball with one eye closed. Describe any adjustments you had to make to assure a successful catch after you altered your vision.

Chapter 6
Altering and Adapting to the External Environment

On the open tundra of the Canadian Arctic, musk oxen form a protective circle to defend themselves from predators such as wolves. Strong grinding teeth and a long digestive tube enable the musk oxen to feed on the tough, dry arctic vegetation. Thick fur insulates them from the cold. Both the behaviour and the physical structures of the musk oxen suit their particular environment. If the animals were not well-suited, they would not survive.

Features and behaviours that enable an organism to suit or fit its environment are called **adaptations**. The musk oxen's thick, hairy coat and defensive behaviour are adaptations to arctic conditions.

Throughout their lives, organisms interact with their environment in complex ways. In some of these interactions, the environment alters the organisms. In others, the organisms alter the environment. For example, the musk ox removes food, water, and gases from its environment. After processing these raw materials, the animal produces waste products which it returns to the environment. These wastes in turn become raw materials for other organisms to use. In this chapter, you will investigate some of the ways in which organisms are adapted to and alter the external environment.

When you finish Chapter 6, you should be able to:

- compare the composition of air before and after the process of gas exchange by animals
- describe the cycles in which organisms exchange materials with their environment
- describe how humans and animals alter, and are altered by, the environment
- identify and explain some adaptations that enable animals to survive environmental conditions and environmental change
- distinguish between behavioural and structural adaptations

6.1 Exchanging Materials with the Environment

The external environment is the only source of energy and materials that all living organisms need to survive. In addition to obtaining food, organisms also exchange gases. Oxygen is absorbed while carbon dioxide is eliminated. Land-dwellers exchange gases with the air around them, while aquatic organisms exchange gases with the water.

Land vertebrates use organs called lungs to exchange gases. Lungs are open sacs inside the body, connected to the outside by a tube. As air is inhaled, oxygen diffuses from the lungs into the bloodstream. Carbon dioxide diffuses in the opposite direction.

Figure 6-1. Respiratory system of a human (land vertebrate).

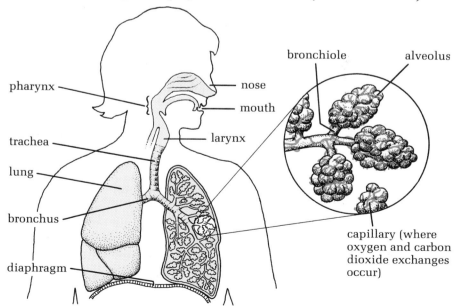

pharynx

trachea

lung

bronchus

diaphragm

nose

mouth

larynx

bronchiole

alveolus

capillary (where oxygen and carbon dioxide exchanges occur)

Some animals, such as frogs, salamanders, and earthworms, can obtain limited amounts of oxygen from the air through their thin moist skins. Eels can absorb oxygen dissolved in water through their skins.

Aquatic vertebrates exchange gases through their gills (see Figure 6-2). As water flows over the gills, dissolved oxygen diffuses into the fish's bloodstream, and carbon dioxide diffuses out. Insects have a system of air tubes called tracheae extending throughout their abdomens (see Figure 6-3). These tracheae are connected to the outside through spiracles, holes which the insect can open or close.

Figure 6-2. Respiratory system of a fish.

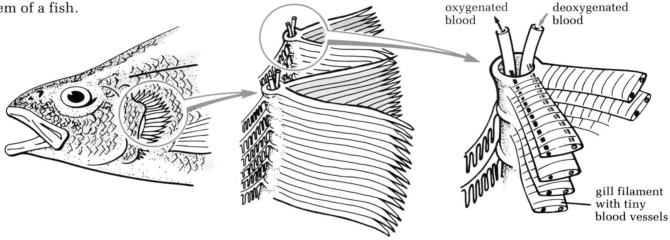

Figure 6-3. Respiratory system of a grasshopper.

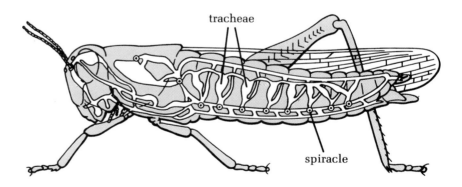

The quantities involved in gas exchange differ greatly from species to species. Warm-blooded species consume more oxygen for the same body mass than do cold-blooded species. The consumption of oxygen also varies with the size of the organism. Human infants breathe about 33 times per minute, adults only 14 times. An active animal breathes more frequently than a resting one.

When you are asleep, your breathing rate slows down. Animals that hibernate breathe only a few times a minute, appearing almost not to breathe at all.

Regardless of these differences, all animals alter the air by breathing it. In the next activity, you will compare the composition of air before and after it has been used for breathing by a human.

Of all vertebrates, the humming-bird shows the greatest range in its consumption of oxygen. At night these birds go into a state of torpor, or very deep sleep, reducing their oxygen consumption from a daytime resting level of 14 mL/g/h to a level of 0.8 mL/g/h.

Activity 6-1:   Exchanging Gases with the Atmosphere

In this activity, you will detect the presence of carbon dioxide using the indicator solution bromthymol blue.

Materials

2 250 mL Erlenmeyer flasks

2 two-hole rubber stoppers

2 lengths of long glass tubing

2 lengths of short glass tubing

1 length of short rubber tubing

glass or plastic Y-tube

disposable or sterilizable mouthpiece

bromthymol blue solution

unlined white notepaper

2 L graduated bottle

pail large enough to submerge the 2 L bottle with room to spare

rubber or tygon tubing

disposable or sterilizable mouthpiece

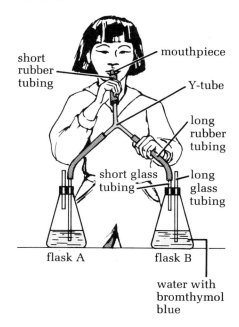

bromthymol blue solution

Figure 6-4.   Apparatus for Part A.

Part A: Comparing Exhaled and Inhaled Air
Procedure

1. To each Erlenmeyer flask, add 100 mL of water. Then add equal quantities of bromthymol blue solution (about 5 drops) to each flask until the water is coloured light blue. Set both flasks on a sheet of white paper.

2. Assemble the apparatus as illustrated in Figure 6-4. Be sure that one rubber tube is connected to the *long* glass tube in flask A. The second rubber tube should be connected to the *short* glass tube in flask B.

3. Insert a mouthpiece into the short rubber tubing at the top of the Y-tube.

4. Exhale and inhale steadily through the glass tube without removing your mouth, until you observe a colour change.

Discussion

1. a) Describe the change, if any, that occurred in flask A.
   b) Where did the bubbles in flask A come from?
2. a) Describe the change, if any, that occurred in flask B.
   b) Where did the bubbles in flask B come from?
3. What change in the bromthymol blue solution indicates the presence of carbon dioxide?
4. Explain why the change in flask A occurred there, rather than in flask B.
5. State a conclusion that describes how air is altered during the breathing process.

Part B: Determining Your Lung Volume

In Part B, you will determine the volume of air that is altered by one inhalation.

Procedure

1. To the pail, add water deep enough to immerse the 2 L bottle completely. The pail itself should not be full.

Figure 6-5.   Apparatus for Part B.

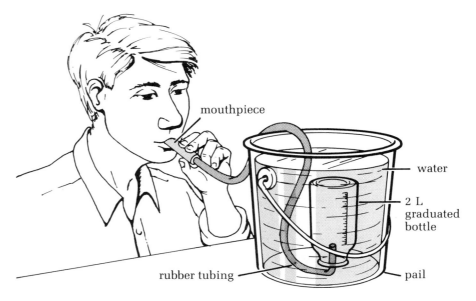

2. Submerge the bottle so that it fills with water. Invert the bottle under water so that no air enters it.
3. Insert the rubber tubing into the inverted bottle. Attach a clean mouthpiece to the other end of the rubber tubing.

4. After inhaling normally, exhale into the mouthpiece. Do not exhale any more breath than you normally would.

5. Measure the volume of exhaled breath using the graduations on the bottle.

6. Repeat steps 4 and 5 to obtain a total of five readings. From these, calculate the average volume of one exhaled breath.

7. Count the number of exhalations during relaxed breathing over an interval of 3 min. Calculate the number of exhalations per minute.

Discussion

1. a) How do you think the quantity of air inhaled compares to the quantity of air exhaled? Explain.
   b) On the basis of this activity and your answer to part a), how much air is inhaled with each breath on average?

2. a) Calculate the average number of inhalations (breaths) per day.
   b) Calculate the average volume of air inhaled each day.

3. The atmosphere contains only 20% oxygen. Calculate the average volume of oxygen inhaled during one 24-h period.

4. Exhaled breath contains 4% carbon dioxide. What is the percentage of oxygen in the exhaled breath? Explain your answer.

5. Based on your findings in this activity, explain the meaning of the term "gas exchange".

How Gas Exchange Alters the Environment

Gas exchange occurs because of a chemical process that takes place inside body cells. You will recall that this process is called cell respiration. The following equation shows what happens during respiration.

$$\text{oxygen} + \text{sugar} \longrightarrow \text{carbon dioxide} + \text{water} + \text{energy}$$

Oxygen must be present for cell respiration to take place. During respiration, oxygen and sugar are converted into carbon dioxide, water, and useful energy. Gas exchange occurs when oxygen molecules are removed from the external environment, and carbon dioxide molecules are added. By using oxygen from the environment for respiration, organisms alter the composition of the atmosphere around them. If gas exchange occurred without some way of replacing the oxygen in the atmosphere, all the oxygen would eventually be used up and the level of carbon dioxide would increase. Fortunately, the composition of the atmosphere remains fairly constant because of a second chemical reaction that occurs in green plants. You will recall that this process is called photosynthesis. The following equation shows what happens during photosynthesis.

$$\text{carbon dioxide} + \text{water} + \text{light} \longrightarrow \text{sugar} + \text{oxygen}$$

Carbon dioxide, the waste product of respiration, thus becomes a raw material for photosynthesis. The carbon dioxide gas is used to make sugar, and oxygen is released into the atmosphere where it is once again available for respiration. This recycling process maintains the atmospheric conditions needed to support living things.

Exchanging Other Materials: Elimination and Excretion

Gases are not the only materials that living things exchange with the environment. After using water and food for life processes, animals also produce liquid and solid waste materials in the form of urine, feces, and sweat. These products are released into the external environment by the processes of elimination and excretion. Decomposer organisms such as bacteria recycle these waste products by using the materials for their own life processes.

Does your household sometimes accumulate large numbers of empty bottles before you get around to returning them to the store? The recycling process in nature also builds up backlogs of certain materials from time to time. This happens when materials are added to a system faster than they can be removed. If too many animals congregate regularly in one spot, their waste production may exceed the recycling capacity of the decomposers. This situation is found in some caves, where bat droppings accumulate, and on certain islands, where the wastes of sea birds build up.

Our capacity to produce large quantities of garbage becomes apparent on occasions when garbage accumulates.

Study Questions

1. What is gas exchange?
2. a) Name three types of respiratory organs, and the type of animal to which each belongs.
   b) Name the usual environment of each animal identified in a).

3. List three factors that determine the amount of oxygen gas required by an organism.

4. a) Describe how animal respiration alters the composition of air.
   b) Identify the process which balances animal respiration.
   c) Explain why the combined action of these two processes is referred to as the carbon cycle.

5. Identify other exchanges that take place between living organisms and their external environment.

SCIENCE IN ACTION

USING WASTE AS A RESOURCE

Every day the 250 000 cormorants in this colony catch nearly 100 t of sardines and contribute to the production of guano.

On several islands around the coasts of Peru and California, the local people harvest excrement produced by large populations of cormorants, pelicans, and gannets. The waste, called *guano*, is sold as a rich fertilizer. This kind of guano contains about 11 to 16% nitrogen, 8 to 12% phosphoric acid, and 2 to 3% potash. Altogether, about 200 000 t of guano are collected annually off the coast of South America.

This unusual natural resource has been harvested for hundreds of years. By the nineteenth century, the old accumulations of guano were used up, and since then, only the new guano produced each year is collected on most islands. This still represents a substantial resource since the bird populations—and their annual waste production—are generally so large.

In southwest Africa, artificial platforms have been built in coastal lagoons to help develop valuable guano deposits. Sea birds rest on the platforms and eliminate wastes. When enough waste has accumulated, the platforms are towed to shore and the guano is collected.

The anchovy fishing industry off the western coast of south America may have an effect on the guano industry in some areas.

In the early 1960s there were an estimated 18 million guano-producing birds off the coast of Peru. Many of these sea birds feed on anchovies. Since commercial fishing has greatly reduced the anchovy population, there is now direct competition between the birds and people for these fish. The eventual result may be a decline in the bird population and, consequently, in the production of guano.

6.2 Altering the Environment

Every organism alters its environment simply by living in it. No species, however, does this so deliberately or on such a large scale as human beings. The impact of human activities on the environment is sometimes beneficial, but often has unforeseen consequences that threaten all living things.

One result of industrial activity, for example, has been an increase in atmospheric pollution which disturbs the balance of gases in the atmosphere. The large-scale burning of fossil fuels (coal, natural gas, and oil) began in the early 1700s, and has increased greatly in this century. Fossil fuel exhausts add many poisonous gases to the atmosphere, such as sulphur dioxide, nitrogen dioxide, carbon dioxide, and carbon monoxide. Measurements show that levels of carbon dioxide in the atmosphere have risen over 30% in the past 100 years. Carbon dioxide contributes to the warming of the atmosphere, a phenomenon known as the greenhouse effect. The oxides of nitrogen and sulphur mix with water vapour in the atmosphere to produce acid rain.

Burning fossil fuels is only one of many human activities that alter the external environment. It is difficult to predict the consequences of these activities, but the next activity may help you to understand the complex nature of environmental interactions.

Thermal power generating stations use coal as their energy source. The smoke produced is high in sulphur and nitrogen oxides, which combine with water in the atmosphere to produce acid rain.

Figure 6-6. The greenhouse effect.

The "greenhouse effect" refers to the warming of the atmosphere due to the rise in the amount of carbon dioxide gas in the atmosphere. Carbon from fossil fuels and tropical rainforest combines with oxygen during burning to produce CO_2. During the last hundred years, large-scale combustion of these fuels has increased the concentration of CO_2 in the atmosphere by 30%. If current rates of fossil fuel consumption continue to rise, the CO_2 concentration in 2060 is expected to be nearly double that in 1850.

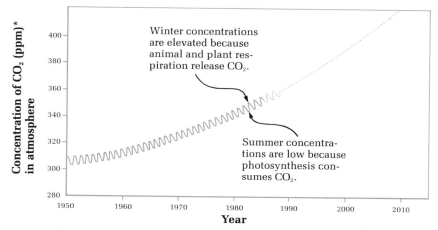

*The CO_2 concentration in the atmosphere is usually expressed in units of ppm (parts per million). For a concentration of 340 ppm CO_2, there are 340 parts of CO_2 for every million parts of air.

How Elevated Levels of Atmospheric CO_2 Result in Global Warming

Since sunlight warms the Earth's surface more than the atmosphere, the surface transfers heat to the atmosphere. Some of this heat is absorbed by gases in the atmosphere, including CO_2. The rest of the heat is radiated into space. As the concentration of atmospheric CO_2 rises, the amount of heat increases, thereby warming the atmosphere.

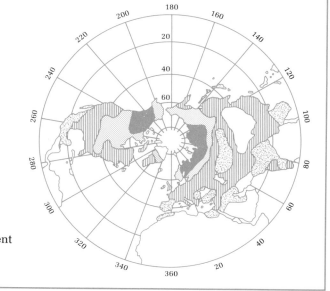

Temperature Change (°C) since 1850

over 2   −1 to 0
1 to 2   insufficient data
0 to 1

Activity 6-2: Packing for a Space Flight

Photographs of the Earth from space have given us an entirely new perspective on our home planet. Now we can see that "Spaceship Earth" is limited both in size and resources. In this regard, it is similar to any vehicle that ventures into the inhospitable realm of space. In order to maintain healthy crews, both Earth and a spaceship must have self-contained life-support systems.

In this activity you will generate a list of requirements that a self-contained spacecraft must meet in order to sustain a crew in space.

Procedure

1. Your teacher will divide the class into groups of four. One member of each group will be appointed recording secretary. The secretary will draw a large table with two columns, one labelled "Problems", the other labelled "Solutions". The secretary will record all problems and solutions suggested by the other group members.

2. The rest of the group will brainstorm. Brainstorming is a "thinking-out-loud" activity in which *every* suggestion related to the topic is recorded. Do *not* evaluate any of the suggestions at this time. The point is to generate as many ideas as possible. They can be evaluated later. While brainstorming, consider the factors listed in step 3, as well as any other factors that occur to you.

3. Factors to consider:
   a) *The nature of space*
      In what ways does space pose dangers to the lives of the crew members? How can the crew be isolated from space? What kinds of protection will the crew require?
   b) *The needs of the crew*
      Assume the crew is to remain in orbit for two months. What does the crew need to live and work productively, in terms of the amount of living space, food, air, waste disposal, privacy, leisure time, entertainment, exercise, etc.? Be realistic. Your spacecraft cannot exceed the size (mass) of any vehicle available today.

4. Generate a list of potential problems that might be encountered in space. Each suggestion will be recorded by the secretary.

5. Generate and record a second list of solutions for these potential problems.

6. Examine both lists. Eliminate any entries that do not seem appropriate. Has anything been missed? If so, add it to the lists. Be sure that each problem identified has a corresponding solution, and vice versa.

7. Rewrite both lists, ranking the entries from most important to least important.

8. List the items and the processes required to provide an adequate life-support system on a spacecraft.

Discussion

1. For each problem listed in step 7, state whether "Spaceship Earth" has a similar problem and how it has been solved.

2. For each item or process listed in step 8, identify the corresponding item or process on Earth.

3. What do your discussions reveal about the effects of human activities on "Spaceship Earth"?

How Humans Alter the External Environment

Like all animals, humans can survive only in an environment that provides them with sufficient food, shelter, warmth, and other materials. However, unlike other animals, people can modify a hostile environment to create a suitable living space for themselves. Humans can now live almost anywhere in the world, thanks to specially designed dwellings, clothes, and artificial heating and cooling methods.

Humans can survive in a diverse range of environments due to their ability to alter the environment to suit their needs. The igloo (left) acts as an insulator to provide a warmer interior, while the white walls of an Egyptian home (right) reflect heat energy to create a cool interior.

In many parts of Canada, the natural environment has been changed dramatically by humans to create a habitable environment for large numbers of people. Where there were once forests, swamps, rivers, and many wild animals, there are now fields, highways, and cities. The prairies where bison herds ate wild grasses are now covered by vast fields of grain and herds of beef cattle. Although these changes to the environment have made life easier for us, they have created unforeseen problems for other animals and plants, and even for ourselves.

One basic problem is the accumulation of waste. When humans congregate in large numbers, the volume of waste they produce is difficult to get rid of. The disposal of garbage and sewage is one of the largest problems facing most cities. In addition, many discarded materials are not biodegradable and are sometimes even toxic, thus causing harm to all living things. The topic of waste management is discussed in Unit 7.

How the External Environment Alters Humans

Just as people alter the environment, so the environment can alter humans. Unlike the musk oxen discussed at the beginning of the chapter, people do not seem to be designed for one particular environment. Peoples who have lived in the Arctic for generations are essentially the same as those who have always lived in the tropics. There are, however, small differences that make certain body features better suited to certain environments. Dark skin, which has a large amount of pigment that protects it from burning, is an advantage in tropical areas. An insulating layer of fat beneath the skin is an advantage in cold climates. A higher density of oxygen-carrying red blood cells is an advantage at high altitudes, where the oxygen level is lower.

Some physical differences are inherited, others are acquired. Most light-skinned people respond to increased sunlight by developing a darker skin, or tan. People who move to a higher altitude develop more red blood cells. Adjustments to environmental change are called **physiological adaptations**, because they involve a change in the body's chemistry.

There are limits to how much and how quickly the human body can alter in response to changes in the external environment. Developing a tan takes days, and some people cannot develop a deep tan at all. Adapting to high altitudes may take weeks, but people could never adapt to the low oxygen levels above 6000 m. They would die instead.

The Peruvian Indians and their pack animals have become adapted to the low oxygen levels in the mountains where they live.

At high altitudes, air pressure is lower and the environment holds less oxygen. Above 6000 m, a person becomes faint or unconscious, and could die from lack of oxygen. People and animals living on mountains usually have a greater tolerance for low oxygen levels. The llama, for example, is able to hold more oxygen in its blood than most other mammals.

Study Questions

1. a) From your experience, list five ways in which humans are altering the global environment.
   b) Identify a consequence of each alteration listed above.
2. a) Explain what is meant by the statement "Spaceship Earth is limited both in size and resources".
   b) Describe the implications of the above statement.
3. Identify some ways in which humans have changed the physical environment to make it more habitable for themselves.
4. Identify some ways in which the environment affects humans.
5. Explain fully what is meant by the term "physiological adaptation".

CHALLENGER

State the law of science that sums up the problem associated with the accumulation of residential and industrial wastes.

6.3 Adapting to Environmental Change

Unlike humans, most organisms cannot do much to create a friendlier environment for themselves. However, some species are able to tolerate a wide range of conditions, whereas others can respond only to very slight changes. For example, the panda can eat only one kind of food, bamboo. The more specialized the organism, the less likely it is to be able to live in a different environment. Consequently, the conversion of bamboo forests into fields for agricultural production threatens the survival of the panda.

When changes in the environment are so great that an organism cannot adjust, the organism must either move to a more favourable area or perish. For example, no dinosaurs exist today, but dinosaur fossils have been found in all parts of the world, including the Arctic. Study of the surrounding rocks shows that the dinosaurs lived in environmental conditions which differed from present conditions. The climate was much warmer and probably wetter. However, about 63 million years ago conditions changed suddenly all over the Earth. Unable to adapt to this change or move elsewhere, the dinosaurs died out. Their disappearance is a large-scale example of **extinction**, a process that occurs when a species cannot adapt to environmental change.

Insects are the most adaptable animals on Earth. Some insect species, such as the cockroach, have survived almost unaltered for 300 million years, despite environmental changes that killed off many thousands of other animal species. There are several reasons why insects can survive massive and sudden changes in their external environments. During the course of their lives, most insects undergo dramatic alterations in appearance and behaviour. The

The current theory accounting for the mass extinction of the dinosaurs is a collision between the Earth and an extraterrestrial object.

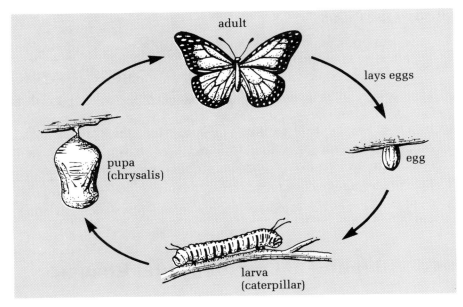

Figure 6-7. The life cycle of a butterfly.

Honeybees, which seek the nectar and pollen of flowering plants, play an important role in the pollination and reproduction of these plants. Since the bees and the plants depend on one another, they are said to be *co-adapted*.

butterfly, for example, starts as an egg, hatches out as a caterpillar, encases itself in a chrysalis, and emerges in its adult life as a flying organism. Immature insects often eat food different from that eaten by the adults, and therefore can survive in different environments. A dragonfly nymph, for example, lives underwater and feeds on aquatic organisms, while the adult flies above the pond and catches its prey in the air. The fact that one species can live in two environments enables insects to survive in larger numbers. For example, while many adult insects cannot survive cold weather, the egg or pupa is better adapted to survive cold conditions.

Another reason for the success of insects is that they reproduce in very large numbers. It has been estimated that a single pair of houseflies could produce 1.9×10^{20} descendants in a single summer, if all the offspring of each generation were to survive and breed. This number of flies would cover the Earth to a depth of 14 m! In reality, of course, the majority of offspring do not survive to breed, but only two are needed to replace the parents and maintain the population.

Yet another factor in the success of insects is that they have a short lifespan. This means that they can produce many generations within a short time. Because of this, any inherited advantages can be passed on relatively quickly, from generation to generation. Over a long period of time, this rapid reproduction has produced great variety in insect species. Nearly three-quarters of all animal species are insects.

Adaptation by Inherited Variability

Unless you have an identical twin, you do not look exactly like your brothers or sisters. Nor do you look exactly like your parents. You have some characteristics inherited from each parent, but they are combined in a way that is unique. Every human family is living evidence of the variability that results with the inheritance of characteristics. It is through small variations in inherited characteristics found among individual offspring that organisms have the potential to adapt to the environment. If an individual possesses a characteristic that gives it an advantage in the environment, any offspring that inherit this characteristic may have a better chance of surviving than those that do not. Consider a baby bird that inherits a slightly longer beak than its siblings. If it can use this beak to obtain more food, it may have a better chance of survival than the others. After a few generations, the inherited characteristic of a longer beak could be more widespread in the population. The long beak is then described as an adaptation because it is a feature that improves the likelihood of survival.

Members of families, though sharing obvious resemblances, also exhibit genetic variability.

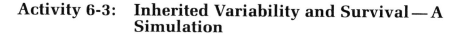

Activity 6-3: Inherited Variability and Survival—A Simulation

In many species, inherited colour has an effect on survival. This is particularly true of insects since it affects how they appear to predators. To examine how colour may influence ability to survive, you will perform a simulation. Rather than using real organisms, which do not always cooperate, you will use coloured discs to represent an imaginary species called *Discus chroma*.

Materials

The Organism: All members of *Discus chroma* are identical in shape and size but differ in colour.

The Population: An assortment of paper-punch discs cut from coloured construction paper, wrapping paper, clear acetate sheets, etc. Initially, the population consists of equal numbers of each colour.

The Habitat: Discus chroma lives on any flat surface, such as desks and floors in classrooms, hallways, gymnasiums, and cafeterias, where it feeds on dust and leftover lunches.

Procedure

1. In this simulation, your teacher or student helpers will distribute the *D. chroma* population in different areas of its habitat,

placing the tiny "organisms" wherever they might be likely to hide. You and your classmates will play the role of predators that feed on *D. chroma*. The predator that finds the largest number of prey wins. You will be allowed to hunt for 5 min at a time.

2. Repeat the hunt in different habitats.
3. Record the number of prey of different colours collected on each hunt in a chart like the one below.

Habitat	Colour of *Discus chroma*					
	red	blue	green	black	clear	etc.
hallway						
gymnasium						
classroom						
etc.						

Discussion

1. a) For each habitat, identify the colour most favourable to the survival of *Discus chroma*.
   b) Identify the least favourable colour for each habitat.
2. Explain how colour affects the survival of *D. chroma*, and why.
3. Consider the results of the simulation in any one of the habitats. Which colour(s) of *D. chroma* were most successful at survival? Which colour(s) were least successful? Predict the dominant colours in the next generation.
4. a) Are all predators equally adept at capturing *D. chroma*? What ability must the predator have to catch *D. chroma*?
   b) Could this ability be inherited? Explain.
5. In nature, environments may change suddenly. Suppose a new blue floor is installed in your school. Predict which colour(s) of *D. chroma* would be best adapted for success in this changed environment. Which colour(s) would be least adapted for success? Explain.

The Process of Adaptation

The process of adaptation through inheritance of suitable variations takes several generations before the small improvements become widespread. Since the lifespan of many insect species lasts only a few weeks or months, adaptive changes in insects can be observed within a human lifetime. An example of this type of adaptation is that of the peppered moth, a common British species. Until 1845, most peppered moths had light-coloured wings with dark markings, but small numbers of dark-coloured moths were seen occasionally. Within 50 years, however, the dark variety made up 99% of the population found near industrial cities. The reason for this dramatic change in the moth's appearance was a change in the environment caused by air pollution. Smoke and soot from cities had darkened the bark of trees in the area. Light-coloured moths, which showed up clearly when they settled on the bark, were more readily picked off by insect-eating birds, while darker moths were harder to see. The darker moths, therefore, had a higher survival rate and reproduced more of their kind. They survived because they were better adapted to the changed environment than were the light-coloured moths.

These photos clearly show how the colour of the background can influence the detection of light- and dark-coloured pepper moths by predators.

No matter how well suited a species is to its environment, however, it continues to produce variations in its offspring. With each generation comes an opportunity for change and improvement. If the variation occurs at a time of environmental change, the individuals with the variation may have a better chance of survival, causing the genetic make-up of the population to change gradually. Many variations are neutral and neither harm nor help an individual. Variations in human eye colour, for example, continue to be found because these characteristics do not affect an individual's chances of survival.

A keen sense of vision, sharp talons, and a curved beak make the hawk a formidable predator.

Types of Adaptation: Structural and Behavioural Adaptation

Any inherited physical feature that increases an organism's chance of survival is called a **structural adaptation**. The curved talons and curved beak of a hawk are examples of structural adaptation. The hawk, spotting moving prey from the air, can swoop down to catch it easily with its claws and then rip the prey open with its beak.

Organisms can also inherit types of behaviour that might increase their chances of survival. Like structural adaptations, these **behavioural adaptations** develop over long periods of time. Two well-known examples are migration and hibernation. These two adaptations allow animal species to cope with seasonal changes in the environment. Other behavioural adaptations reduce an animal's chances of being eaten by a predator. The "freezing" (motionless) behaviour of the young killdeer when it sees a larger animal enables it to blend in with its environment and so escape detection.

Adaptation to Seasonal Change

Organisms living in environments that undergo a regular change of seasons must become adapted to survive. For example, both weasels and rabbits show a structural adaptation to seasonal change. They grow a thick coat of white fur in the late fall to adapt to the cold and snowy conditions of winter.

The weasel is a predator that hunts year-round. The colour change of its coat is a seasonal adaptation that provides camouflage. Camouflage increases the weasel's chances of success as a hunter.

Hibernation is a state, similar to deep sleep, in which an animal can remain without food for weeks or months. Hibernating animals, such as groundhogs, find a suitable shelter where they will be protected from the most severe weather and other animals. Before they hibernate, these animals eat a great deal and accumulate extra reserves of body fat to supply them with energy throughout the winter. During hibernation, their breathing and heart rates are much lower than when the animals are active, and their body metabolism operates very slowly. Hibernating animals are not easily awakened and remain in this state until spring.

The seasonal movement of animals along a predictable route is called **migration**. In Canada, herds of caribou migrate from the open tundra to the shelter of the boreal forest for the winter. In east Africa, antelopes and zebras migrate along the path of the rains. The best-known migrators are birds. Many Canadian species fly south in late fall to spend the winter in places where temperatures are moderate and food can be found. Often, migrating birds are species that feed on insects that are unavailable in northern areas in the winter. Birds that do not migrate are generally those that feed on plants or animals that are available in the region year-round.

Figure 6-8. Hibernation of a groundhog.

Some animals, such as squirrels and bears, may spend days or weeks of cold weather in a deep sleep, but still are not true hibernators. They may awaken on warm days in winter, and even go out to look for food.

Some desert animals become dormant in summer when water is scarce. This is called *estivation*. Various desert frogs, snakes, and lizards can estivate.

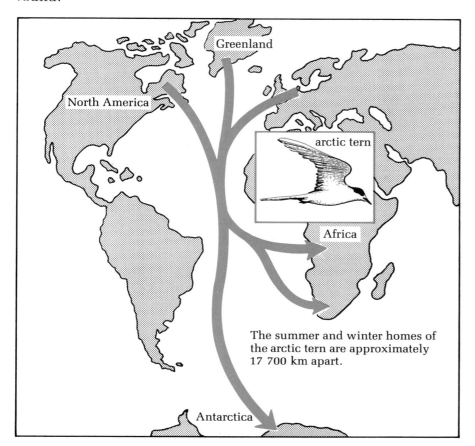

Greenland

North America

arctic tern

Africa

The summer and winter homes of the arctic tern are approximately 17 700 km apart.

Antarctica

Figure 6-9. The migratory path of the arctic tern.

When wolves are organized in packs, they increase their success of killing large prey.

Adaptation through Social Structure

Many animals improve their chances of survival by living in groups or societies rather than alone or in pairs. Social living arrangements make it easier for an animal to mate, find food, and avoid danger. Wolves, for example, are able to hunt and capture prey larger than themselves, such as caribou and moose, only when organized in packs. A lone wolf would have great difficulty capturing animals this large.

Some of the best understood social behaviour outside that of humans is found among social insects such as ants, termites, and bees. All the offspring in a bee colony are produced from the eggs of a single female, the queen bee. The work of the colony is done by infertile female worker bees that spend their lives acquiring food, feeding the young, and protecting the colony. A few male bees, called drones, are produced solely to act as breeders, and do no work at all. Because its structural and behavioural adaptations are so specialized, no individual bee could survive on its own. Such organisms have become adapted to living only in colonies where the survival of the individuals depends on the survival of the colony as a whole.

Figure 6-10. The three types of honeybee.

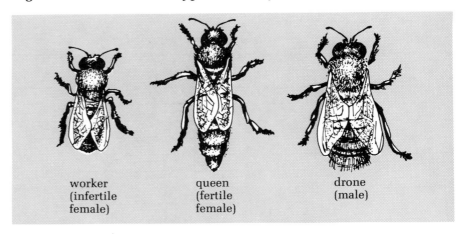

worker
(infertile
female)

queen
(fertile
female)

drone
(male)

Activity 6-4: A Research Report on Adaptation

Any structure or activity that makes an organism better suited to live and reproduce in its usual environment is an adaptation. In this activity, you will prepare a research report on structural or behavioural adaptations.

Procedure

1. For this activity you will write a 500-word report on an adaptation of your choice. This activity will require using the library to search for information, making notes from a variety of sources, compiling a reference list (bibliography) of books and magazines consulted, and preparing rough and final drafts of your report. The following steps list some guidelines to follow.

2. Choose a topic that you find interesting and that is approved by your teacher. If you cannot find sufficient information on your topic, choose another topic.

3. Learn to use the library indexes to find pertinent information. Ask the teacher-librarian for assistance.

4. Write down the bibliographic information for each reference on a separate index card.

5. In your report, demonstrate how the adaptation you have selected makes the organism better suited to its way of life. Using index cards, make notes that summarize the main points, writing down one point on each card.

6. When you feel you have consulted enough sources and have made sufficient notes, arrange the cards in a logical order. Dispose of cards with information that does not fit in.

7. From the ordered cards, prepare a rough draft.

8. Edit the draft, making changes and improvements. Correct all spelling and grammatical errors. Compile the bibliography by arranging your reference cards in alphabetical order according to the authors' last names. Rewrite or type the entire report neatly. If you include illustrations, make sure they are clearly labelled.

Learning as an Adaptation

Human behaviour is more flexible than that of other animals. We are constantly learning and adapting our behaviour to changing conditions throughout our lives. Some social behaviour can spread rapidly through a human population. For example, in North America the behaviour of smoking in public is much less common now than it was even a decade ago. Most people now realize that smoking damages health, and so have changed their behaviour from smoking to nonsmoking.

One group in North American society is smoking in ever greater numbers. Medical authorities are alarmed at the sharp increase in smoking among teenaged girls. Reasons for this behaviour are unclear, but the health consequences can be predicted from records for male smokers. The most likely outcome is an increased incidence of lung cancer, heart disease, and emphysema among this group in the decades ahead. Research also shows that women who smoke generally have smaller babies.

Behaviour may be of two types: innate or learned. Sometimes we call innate behaviour *instinct*. A particular action or behaviour is considered instinctive when it occurs perfectly the first time it is performed. Learning, however, involves trial and error. Learned behaviour is the product of experience.

This "igloo garage" houses a snow-mobile used by its Inuit owner for hunting.

Learned behaviour can spread in animal populations as well. In Japan, for example, one monkey learned to separate seeds from sand on the beach where it lived, by throwing handfuls of the mixed seeds and sand into the water. The seeds floated on the water's surface, where they could be picked off. Soon all members of the group had learned the same behaviour.

Human activities have altered the environment more rapidly during this century than ever before. Many people living today were born at a time when there were no television sets, radios, airplanes, computers, widespread vaccinations, video recorders, or many other things that affect our lives today. Because of our great learning capacity, we have generally been able to adapt to these rapid changes in society, technology, and the environment. In this century, some groups of people have even made a transition from a hunting and gathering way of life to the technological age. Modern technology is sometimes combined with a traditional way of life. For example, many Inuit hunters now pursue prey with snowmobiles and rifles.

If humans can change their behaviour so dramatically, can they also learn to preserve a life-sustaining external environment? The danger of rapid change in the environment, as you have discovered, is that it kills organisms that cannot adapt to rapid change. Many human activities may now be life-threatening to the human species itself, as well as to other life forms. We must learn to change our behaviour more, and our environment less, in order to preserve the conditions necessary for our survival.

Study Questions

1. List three reasons for the success of insects as a group.
2. What is meant by inherited variability?
3. a) Identify two types of adaptation that organisms can inherit.
   b) Provide three examples of adaptation in each of the following organisms, and identify the type of each adaptation: duck, polar bear, camel, maple tree, cactus.
4. Explain why a single termite could not survive on its own.
5. Explain how each of the following organisms is adapted to seasonal change: caribou in winter, geese in winter, maple trees in autumn.
6. How can learning be considered an adaptation?

Meet a Wildlife Biologist — Darrell Dennis

Darrell works for the Canadian Wildlife Service, a branch of Environment Canada. His job involves monitoring migratory bird populations.

Q. WERE YOU ALWAYS INTERESTED IN WILDLIFE?
A. Yes. I grew up on a farm with few other children around. I spent a lot of time in the woods and was always fascinated by the wildlife. But I didn't think of it as a career initially — I did my university degree in chemistry.

Q. WHY DID YOU DECIDE NOT TO PURSUE A CAREER IN CHEMISTRY?
A. I didn't like the idea of working in an urban environment, so I went to the University of Guelph and did a Master's degree in zoology.

Q. IS IT EASY TO FIND WORK IN THE WILDLIFE PROTECTION FIELD?
A. No. Employment opportunities are very limited. I was lucky to be offered a job with this agency in Sackville, New Brunswick after graduation.

Q. WHAT DOES YOUR PRESENT JOB INVOLVE?
A. Our office is in London because the best waterfall habitats are nearby, on the shores of Lake Erie and Lake St. Clair. To manage game-bird populations effectively, we need to study population trends, productivity, habitat use, mortality factors, and the impact of human activities. We take appropriate action based on this information.

Q. ARE THERE SEASONAL PATTERNS TO YOUR WORK?
A. Yes. For instance, in early January I prepare for the analysis of 10 000 waterfowl parts — duck wings and goose tails — that are sent to us by hunters. From these we can tell the species, sex, and age of the birds. This gives us an idea of what's out there.

Q. IS SPRING A BUSY TIME?
A. This year we're preparing for a Giant Canada Goose survey. The populations of these geese are increasing dramatically, from about 2000 birds in 1967 to 80 000 in 1987. The survey will be done on a cooperative basis with all the American states covered by the Atlantic flyway (one of four migratory paths in North America). In early June we'll begin a program to reduce the bird numbers on the Lake Ontario waterfront. We will ship 1000 birds from the Toronto Islands to the states that want to start a breeding program.

Q. WHAT ARE YOU MOST PROUD OF IN YOUR CAREER?
A. My work on black ducks and mallards. For years people were saying there was something wrong with black ducks because their numbers were decreasing. Everyone thought it was over-hunting. Fifteen years ago I proposed that the problem was hybridization, or cross-breeding with mallards. Today there seems to be support for my theory, and that is satisfying.

Q. WHAT ADVICE DO YOU HAVE FOR A STUDENT INTERESTED IN THIS FIELD?
A. There aren't many jobs in wildlife management, and most of them are government jobs where the pay is low. During periods of government expansion there will be more jobs. You have to be prepared to be away from home a lot. I have been away as many as 25 weeks in a year, doing field work. But the most important thing is to be really passionate about wildlife — most of us in this field eat, breathe, and sleep wildlife.

Review Questions

A: Knowledge

1. Name the two processes carried out by living organisms that are central to the carbon cycle.

2. Name the process whereby oxygen enters and carbon dioxide leaves the bloodstream during gas exchange.

3. a) Write the photosynthesis and respiration equations.
   b) Explain how these two processes are related to each other as gas exchange processes.

4. Describe how the composition of air is changed by breathing.

5. Name the type of gas exchange structure found in each of the following organisms: mammals, fish, insects.

6. In a table, list ways humans have altered the environment. Group these alterations according to whether they have harmed the environment, harmed humans, and/or benefited humans.

7. In addition to gas exchange, identify other exchanges between living organisms and their external environment. Classify these as exchanges of energy, exchanges of matter, or both.

8. Describe the difference between structural and behavioural adaptations.

9. Explain the differences between the following four usages of the term "adaptation":
   a) adaptation as a process
   b) adaptation as a feature
   c) physiological adaptation
   d) sensory adaptation

10. Describe how your body responds when you:
    a) move to higher altitudes where oxygen levels are lower.
    b) spend long hours in the summer sun without protective clothing.
    To what general class of adaptations do these responses belong?

11. a) Explain why insects are considered to be the most adaptable of animals.
    b) What reasons can be given for their success?
    c) What do we mean when we say one kind of organism is more successful than another kind?

B: Application

12. Aquatic organisms have exposed gas exchange structures on the exterior of their body. Land animals, however, have their gas exchange structures enclosed within the body, connected to the air supply by small narrow passages. What is the reason for the difference between aquatic organisms and land animals?

13. a) What is meant by the greenhouse effect?
    b) What are some possible consequences of the greenhouse effect? Group these consequences under the headings "Beneficial" and "Detrimental".
    c) Examine the photosynthesis equation. Suggest a possible benefit of the greenhouse effect to plants.

14. Photographs of the Earth from space have introduced us to the idea of "Spaceship Earth". Explain whether this is a good description of our planet.

15. Explain how inherited variability makes adaptation possible.

16. a) Name two adaptations that help animals deal with the problem of food scarcity during severe winters.

b) For each adaptation, list five animals that exhibit it.

17. Organisms die when they are deprived of oxygen. Suggest why this occurs, by considering the respiration equation.

18. Whales, dolphins, seals, penguins, and fish are considered to be adapted to swimming. What is similar about the locomotory features of all these animals that permits us to say they are so adapted?

19. The arrowleaf plant *Sagittaria sagittifolia* is common in bogs of North America. The three illustrations below show that this species can grow on land, in water, or partially submerged in water.

a) Compare the appearances of the plants in the three habitats.

b) What is the name given to the difference in appearance of members of the same species?

c) Which form of *S. sagittifolia* would likely survive during a flood? During a drought?

C: Problem Solving

20. For every carbon dioxide molecule consumed by photosynthesis, one molecule of oxygen is released as a waste product. Similarly, for every oxygen molecule consumed by respiration, one molecule of carbon dioxide is released. Given these one-to-one exchanges, suggest a reason why there is more than 600 times as much oxygen in the atmosphere as carbon dioxide. (*Hint*: Consider where coal and oil fit into the carbon cycle.)

21. State definitions of the terms "camouflage" and "mimicry" as they apply to living organisms. Describe how camouflage and mimicry can be considered adaptations. Provide one specific example of each.

Try This

1. **A *Daphnia* Culture**
Daphnia is a small freshwater crustacean that is easy to culture in the lab. The behaviour and adaptation of *Daphnia* to such factors as the acidity of the water, temperature, oxygen, and food supply can be examined.

2. **Watching Dandelions Grow**
Dandelions can be quite variable in their growth habit. Some plants grow so that the leaves are flat to the ground, while others have their leaves in a more upright position. Examine a lawn that is cut frequently (once a week) and one that is cut rarely (once a month). Compare the proportions of the two types of dandelion in each lawn.

Managing the Planet

The Issue: Should we manage the Earth's resources?

What is required to sustain life on "Spaceship Earth" in the future?

Before the twentieth century, human demands on the Earth's resources sometimes created problems, such as deforestation, pollution, and the extermination of species on a local scale. The Earth as a whole, however, still had abundant resources. Today, the situation is different. Human beings are now the most common large species on the planet. Our increasing demand for resources and our destructive activities in finding and using them have created urgent, worldwide problems that may threaten our future survival.

Is the damage to Earth beyond recovery, or can responsible human management of resources limit the danger and ensure the needs of future generations? The urgency is made greater because the human population will double in only 35 years, from five thousand million to ten thousand million. We must find enough food, energy, clothing, and housing materials for this increasing population without further upsetting and overtaxing the Earth's resources.

Many of the Earth's important resources are renewable. Given proper management, they can be sustained and can provide indefinitely for human needs. If we plant trees at the same, or at a greater, rate than we chop them down, forests will survive. If we breed fish or allow them to breed at a rate that replaces those we catch and consume, fish will survive. In other words, we could harvest natural resources as a farmer manages crops, ensuring plentiful yields yearly.

Even metals and minerals, which are considered nonrenewable resources because they are finite in quantity, can be recycled. Currently, we mine metals to make products, and then throw away these products when they are no longer useful, instead of salvaging the materials for recycling. We could also design and manufacture products to last longer. This would reduce the need to mine a diminishing resource, as well as lessen the damage to the environment caused by dumping wastes.

Despite our knowledge about the need for sensible resource management, we continue our wasteful and eventually self-destructive activities. We are driven by short-sighted economic considerations and greed. The whaling industry, for example, hunted whales to the brink of extinction, although the whalers knew that they could not sustain their use of this resource. Will we repeat this pattern with other resources, needlessly destroying them instead of preserving and maintaining them for the future?

In this activity, you will look at the implications of the awareness that the Earth is not a boundless and infinite resource. At present, the Earth is our only home, and it is limited. If we do not learn how to manage its resources for the future, we may not have a second chance.

Exploring the Issue

A. Statement of the Issue

A growing human population continues to deplete the Earth's resources and to destroy the environment. The realization that the Earth cannot easily sustain a large human population will require that we manage the Earth's resources wisely.

B. Selecting Cases for Study

The object of this exercise is i) to identify specific cases where solutions to the above-mentioned problems have been put into effect, and ii) to examine the potential for the management of planetary resources on a worldwide scale.

Each member of the class should pick a resource management problem from the list below and cooperate with other students working on the same problem. To examine a wide range of issues, the entire class should deal with all the problems listed.

Worldwide problems of resource management:

- soil erosion and loss of soil fertility
- deforestation of tropical rain forests
- overcutting of Canadian forests
- spread of deserts
- overgrazing of marginal pasturelands
- drainage of wetlands
- overharvesting of coastal fisheries
- pollution of coastal waters
- acid rain
- atmospheric pollution
- species extinction
- garbage disposal

C. Gathering the Evidence

1. Relevant information can be obtained from magazine and newspaper articles, popular scientific journals, reference books, films, and television programs. Each member of a group should find a minimum of five references on the topic.

2. Make a bibliographic notation of each reference on an index card. On this card, summarize the type of problem, its causes, and solutions.

D. Studying the Problems and their Causes

1. Identify the underlying causes for each problem.

2. Make an oral presentation to the class, summarizing the causes of the problem you have selected.

3. Reconvene as an entire class and draw up a list of causes. Classify the causes as major or minor.

4. Identify those causes common to several problems.

E. Suggesting a Course of Action

1. Summarize the programs introduced to solve the problems you have studied. Evaluate these programs as long-term solutions.

2. Compare the efforts expended in these programs to the effort needed for a comprehensive solution to the general problem of global resource management.

3. Identify and list the factors that might hinder the solving of the problem. Consider economic, cost, political, and cultural factors and results.

4. State the costs and sacrifices that these programs entail, and identify who is to bear these expenses.

5. Evaluate the relative merit of these programs and the time frame (e.g., one year, ten years, one hundred years) over which they will be effective.

6. Reconvene as a class, and try to come to a group consensus on the adequacy of current solutions to problems of global resource management.

Unit 2 Wrap-Up

Unit Summary

Differences in rainfall, sunlight, temperature, and other conditions create a diversity of aquatic and terrestrial environments. Associated with these environments is a great *diversity* in the forms and behaviours of living things. Living organisms exchange materials and energy with their surroundings and are adapted to the particular environments in which they live.

To keep track of almost 2 000 000 known kinds of organisms on Earth, scientists classify all living things into one of five *kingdoms*: *Animalia*, *Plantae*, *Fungi*, *Protista*, or *Monera*. To indicate degrees of similarity within each kingdom, scientists divide the kingdoms into smaller groups of more similar organisms. These levels of classification are called *phylum*, *class*, *order*, *family*, *genus*, and *species*. Two similar organisms belong to the same species if they can breed to produce fertile offspring under natural conditions. Scientists assign a two-part Latinized name to each species, according to a standard, international system called the *binomial nomenclature*.

Organisms are suited to their particular environments and can sense and respond to a wide range of environmental *stimuli*. Most animals have specialized sense organs to detect stimuli in the external environment. Each sense organ contains *sensory receptors* for one particular type of stimulus. The nervous system coordinates the reception of the stimulus and an appropriate movement in response. The more refined the nervous system, the more complex the response of the organism to environmental stimuli, and therefore the more complex its behaviour. Response to a stimulus usually involves movement of a part of the organism or movement of the entire organism from one place to another. Organisms have *locomotory structures* that suit specific environments.

Through the process of *gas exchange*, *eating*, *excretion*, and *elimination*, all organisms exchange materials and energy with the external environment, and thereby alter the environment. Humans have altered their environments on a massive scale, sometimes with disastrous and negative consequences. As we alter the Earth, so too will it alter us.

The process of *adaptation* is a fundamental way by which organisms become suited to their environments, a process possible only because of *inherited variation*. Since the offspring resulting from sexual reproduction are not identical, it is possible that some may be better suited to the environment than others. Those that are better suited can also be expected to leave more offspring that have inherited the favourable variation than those that have not. After many generations the entire population will exhibit the favourable feature. By this process organisms become better adapted to their environment. Such features and behaviours which suit an organism to its way of life and its environment are also referred to as adaptations.

Key Terms

adaptation	nervous system
behavioural adaptation	order
binomial nomenclature	phylum
class	range of tolerance
classification	response
diversity	sensory receptors
environmental interactions	species
family	stimulus
gas exchange	structural adaptation
genus	suited to the
inherited variability	environment
kingdom	variation

Unit Practice and Review

A: Short Answer

True or False

State whether each statement is true or false. Correct each false statement.

1. In the classification of living things, organisms belonging to the same order resemble one another more closely than organisms belonging to the same genus.

2. Since all plants are autotrophs, then all autotrophs are members of the Kingdom Plantae.

3. Responses to an environmental change generally result in some kind of movement.

4. Organisms can respond to stimuli only within the range of tolerance of the organism.

5. Gills, a streamlined body shape, and overlapping scales are some structural adaptations of fish.

Multiple Choice

In each question below, select the best answer.

1. Which of the following organisms would most closely resemble the one named *Felis domesticus*?
   a) *Felis lynx*
   b) *Neofelis nebulosa*
   c) *Panthera leo*
   d) *Prunus domesticus*

2. The general environmental conditions found in the boreal coniferous forest (taiga) are:
   a) hot year-round, with wet and dry seasons
   b) cold winters, warm summers, almost no precipitation
   c) cold winters, warm summers, average precipitation
   d) moderate winters, hot summers, average precipitation

3. Different animals are members of the same species if they:
   a) live in the same habitat and eat the same food
   b) share similar physical characteristics
   c) mate and produce fertile offspring
   d) reproduce asexually and produce identical offspring

4. Which one of the following kingdoms includes organisms with cells in which the genetic material is organized differently from that in the other kingdoms?
   a) Monera   c) Fungi
   b) Protista   d) Plantae

5. Sensory receptors are:
   a) cells in the brain that interpret stimuli
   b) special cells sensitive to environmental stimuli
   c) nerve cells that send stimuli to the muscles
   d) nerve cells that send stimuli to the spine

Complete the Statement

Complete each of the following statements with the correct word or phrase. Do not write in this book.

1. Changes in temperature, light, and length of day are all examples of environmental __?__ .

2. The phenomenon whereby we sense new odours immediately, but soon become accustomed to them is called __?__ .

3. In the human eye, __?__ cells are specialized for colour vision while __?__ cells are specialized for vision in dim light.

4. The two-part naming system devised by Linnaeus is called __?__ .

5. The greenhouse effect is a result of an __?__ in the amount of carbon dioxide gas in the atmosphere.

Matching Items

Match each item in Column A with the appropriate item in Column B.

1. *Column A*
   i) the single-celled *Paramecium*
   ii) the brewer's yeast *Saccharomyces cerevisiae*
   iii) *Homo sapiens*
   iv) the plum *Prunus domesticus*
   v) the bowel bacterium *Escherichia coli*
   vi) the house cat *Felis domesticus*

   Column B
   a) Protista
   b) Monera
   c) Fungi
   d) Plantae
   e) Animalia

2. Column A
   i) vision
   ii) hearing
   iii) touch
   iv) smell
   v) taste

Column B
   a) chemoreception
   b) photoreception
   c) mechanoreception

3. Column A
   i) structural adaptation
   ii) social structure
   iii) behavioural adaptation
   iv) learning

Column B
   a) hibernation
   b) behaviour based on imitation
   c) predator's canine teeth
   d) hunting in packs
   e) migration
   f) camel's hump

B: Knowledge and Application

1. a) List five different ways in which your local environment shows variation.
    b) For each variation listed in a) above, choose a particular organism and describe how it adapts to environmental changes.

2. List the needs of the organism that are provided by the external environment.

3. a) Why do scientists use classification?
    b) Explain how the classification levels kingdom, phylum, class, order, family, genus, and species are used to compare degrees of similarity among organisms.
    c) Briefly summarize in a table the characteristics of each of the five kingdoms of organisms.

4. a) Which kingdom of organisms shows the most varied responses to environmental stimuli, and why?
    b) What three factors affect an organism's response to a stimulus?

5. a) What are the functions of the nervous system?
    b) Although sensory structures and responses differ from species to species, most nervous systems share a common design. Explain.

6. Name and state the function of the locomotory structures used by the following organisms:
   a) *Paramecium*
   b) *Euglena*
   c) the perch *Perca flavescens*
   d) the earthworm *Lumbricus terrestris*
   e) the grasshopper *Dissosteira carolina*

7. List some devices, tools, or instruments that broaden and extend our senses. For each instrument, identify the sense it augments and the information it provides.

8. Each morning a person hears an alarm clock, wakes up, and gets out of bed. Describe the path of the nerve signals, starting with the original stimulus (the alarm) to the response (getting out of bed).

9. a) Write the equations for photosynthesis and respiration. Describe two ways in which these processes are related to each other.
    b) Respiration and photosynthesis are examples of gas exchange. Name some other exchanges that take place between organisms and their external environments.

C: Problem Solving

1. Explain how it is possible to assign each of the two million living organisms a unique, two-part, Latinized name when languages usually have only several hundred thousand words. (A large dictionary of the English language has 500 000 entries, for example.)

2. At a distance of 4 m, the human eye can resolve points about 1 mm apart. At this distance, the field of vision is approximately 12 m. Since the rod and cone cells are the units of resolution in the eye, then each square millimetre in the field of vision corresponds to one rod or cone cell. Estimate the number of cone and rod cells in an eye by calculating the area of the 12 m diameter circle, in square millimetres, using the equation area $= \pi r^2$.

3. When exercising vigorously and breathing deeply, we may inhale and then exhale about 4 L of air with each breath. If the amount of air breathed in 1 min is 200 L, calculate the number of breaths per minute.

4. The amount of CO_2 in the atmosphere is expressed in parts per million (ppm). In 1980, the concentration of CO_2 in the atmosphere was 340 ppm; that is, there were 340 particles of CO_2 for every million particles of air. In 1850, the concentration of CO_2 was 265 ppm.

   a) Calculate the percentage increase of CO_2 over the past 130 years.

   b) An equal percentage increase in CO_2 is expected between 1980 and 2020. Calculate the projected amount of CO_2 in the atmosphere in 2020.

D: Challengers

1. About 80% of all our sensory information is received by the eyes, yet we can perform many tasks with our eyes closed. Suggest how it is possible to touch the end of your nose with the tip of your finger when your eyes are closed.

2. The lamprey eel is a parasite of trout in the Great Lakes. Human interference with the reproductive cycle of the lampreys in the streams emptying into these lakes seemed to keep lamprey numbers in check. However, recent studies show that lamprey numbers are rising because the eels are completing their life cycles in the lakes rather than swimming upstream. How may this be interpreted as an adaptation by the lamprey?

3. Protists used to be called Protozoans. Find out why this name is now inappropriate, given the five-kingdom system of classification. (*Hint:* Discover the literal translation of "Protozoan".)

4. Since scientists in 1850 did not measure the concentration of CO_2 in the atmosphere, how do present-day atmospheric scientists determine the amount of CO_2 in the atmosphere at that time?

Project Ideas

1. Can the earthworm learn? Construct a T-maze approximately 30 cm long and 20 cm across the top of the T. Place sand paper in one of the forks of the T, and moist soil in the other fork. Release a worm at the base of the T many times, and record the number of times this worm avoids the sandpaper in favour of the moist soil.

2. The response of *Paramecium* to the force of gravity can easily be studied. Transfer some of the *Paramecium* culture to a test tube 30 cm long and stopper the tube securely. Allow it to stand until the movement of the organisms appears stable. Then invert the test tube and observe what happens.

3. Devise an experiment to observe the response of *Paramecium* to electric current. Design the experimental setup so that the organism's response can be monitored when the polarity of the electrodes is reversed.

4. Write a brief research report on the most common causes of hearing loss.

Readings

Horton, Casey, ed. *Atlas of Anatomy.* London: Marshall Cavendish Books Ltd., 1985. (A colourful depiction of the structure and functions of the human body.)

Jollands, D., ed. *Patterns of Life on Earth: Science Universe Series.* New York: Arco Publishing Inc., 1984. (A brief description, with colourful photographs of life cycles, behaviours, and habitats.)

Mitchell, James, ed. *The Illustrated Reference Book of Animals.* Leicester: Windward, 1982. (A well-illustrated and clearly written book containing a wealth of information.)

Myers, Norman, ed. *GAIA: An Atlas of Planet Management.* Garden City, New York: Doubleday and Company, 1984. (Not just an ordinary atlas.)

III

Organisms and Their Internal Environments

Both the *Paramecium* and the elephant are adapted to live in their usual external environments. However, the African elephant's habitat in the tropical woodland differs greatly from the *Paramecium*'s habitat in freshwater ponds.

The internal environments of these organisms also present a great contrast. The *Paramecium*'s internal environment is contained entirely inside a saclike membrane. Within this single cell, tiny cell parts work together to maintain suitable conditions for the *Paramecium*'s life functions. The elephant's internal environment consists of millions of cells, all working together to carry out the elephant's life functions. But despite obvious differences in size, body plan, and way of life, these two organisms have a great deal in common.

Chapter 7
Systems for Exchanging Gases

Gases moving in and out of the body are vitally important to this horse, and to all other living things. Normally, these gases cannot be seen. Only the cloud of exhaled breath that you see on a wintry day provides visible evidence of the molecules being expelled from the horse's internal environment. In Unit 2, you learned that animals do more than simply use the air around them. Inside the animal's body, oxygen from the external environment is exchanged for the waste gas, carbon dioxide. This process is called **gas exchange**.

This chapter will focus on gas exchange in protists and animals. First, you will review why gas exchange is vital. Then, you will contrast the methods that protists use to get gases into their internal environment with those used by animals. Finally, you will explore the diversity of body systems by which animals exchange gases with their external environments.

When you finish Chapter 7, you should be able to:

- discuss the surface characteristics of structures used for gas exchange
- differentiate breathing, gas exchange, and respiration
- describe the organization of multicellular organisms
- explain the structure and function of the gills in an aquatic organism
- compare gas exchange systems in aquatic and terrestrial organisms

7.1 Energy and Materials for the Internal Environment

An organism's **internal environment** includes everything inside it. To maintain conditions suitable for life functions, the internal environment requires energy.

In earlier studies, you learned that plants obtain the energy they need from food molecules such as glucose. Plants make their own glucose in the process of photosynthesis, using solar energy from the external environment. Heterotrophs, however, cannot make their own glucose molecules. They depend on the energy stored in food made by autotrophs.

While food is the basic source of energy for all life functions, it cannot deliver energy to living organisms directly. The problem is twofold. First, food cannot enter all parts of an animal's body directly, even though every part requires energy. Second, most food energy is stored in a form that body cells cannot use.

You may recall that plants obtain energy from their food by means of the chemical reaction described in this word equation:

$$\text{glucose (from photosynthesis)} + \text{oxygen (from air)} \xrightarrow{\text{enzymes}} \text{carbon dioxide (to air)} + \text{water vapour (to air)} + \text{useable energy}$$

This process is called **cell respiration**, because it only takes place in living cells. Protists and animals obtain energy from food in exactly the same way. Cell respiration solves both of the problems mentioned above. Since it occurs inside every cell, respiration provides energy for all parts of the body, no matter how distant the parts are from the external environment. In addition, cell respiration releases energy in a form that cells can use.

The basic life functions include:
- breaking down food for nutrients
- respiration to release food energy
- removing wastes
- growth, repair, and reproduction
- response to stimuli (e.g., motion)

Cell respiration can only take place in the presence of enzymes, which are biological catalysts that assist in chemical reactions. The cell itself manufactures these enzymes, which it can use again and again.

Most organic food molecules, such as carbohydrates, fats, and proteins, can be used as a source of energy once they have been broken down.

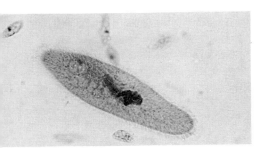

Protists like this *Paramecium* can exchange gases with the external environment by diffusion through the cell membrane.

Diffusion occurs because all cell membranes are semipermeable. This means they act like microscopic sieves. Small molecules such as water, oxygen, and carbon dioxide readily pass through cell membranes. Larger molecules that cannot diffuse across the cell membrane must be broken down into smaller molecules that may pass through cell membranes.

Before respiration can occur, the cell needs glucose and oxygen. Both of these materials must be obtained from the external environment. The details of obtaining glucose from food will be discussed in Chapter 8. The rest of this chapter will focus on the problems of supplying oxygen gas molecules to the internal environment, and sending waste carbon dioxide gas back to the external environment.

Gas Exchange in Protists

For protists, the entire internal environment is contained inside one cell. Most protists are aquatic, and the water they live in contains dissolved oxygen molecules. These oxygen molecules can reach the protist's internal environment by simply diffusing through the cell membrane to the cytoplasm inside.

Once there, the oxygen is taken up by the mitochondria. These cell organelles carry out respiration, using up some of the oxygen inside the cell. When the oxygen level inside the cell drops below that of the water outside, more oxygen diffuses inward. Waste molecules of carbon dioxide and water are removed from the cell by diffusing outward through the cell membrane. Both the oxygen and the carbon dioxide stay dissolved at all times.

Because gas exchange can only take place at the surface of a cell, the amount of surface area is important. In Activity 7-1, you will investigate the reasons for this.

Activity 7-1:   Surface Area and Gas Exchange

In Part A of this activity, you will consider how surface area and body volume would affect gas exchange in three imaginary, giant "protists". In Part B, you will observe a living amoeba and make measurements to compare its surface area to its volume.

Materials

compound light microscope

microscope slide (depression type)

cover slip

metric ruler

culture of amoeba

clean dropper

Given: Surface area of a rectangular solid = length × width × number of sides

Volume of a rectangular solid = length × width × height

Procedure

Part A: Surface Area-to-Volume Ratio in Giant "Protists"

1. Copy the chart below in your notebook.

Protist	Surface Area (S)	Body Volume (V)	Surface Area-To-Volume Ratio (S/V)
A			
B			
C			

2. Figure 7-1 shows three possible shapes for giant protists. For each, calculate the surface area, the volume, and the surface area-to-volume ratio. Enter these values in your chart. (Hint: Be sure to include all six surfaces when calculating the surface area of each protist.)

Discussion

1. a) Which of the three giant protists has the greatest volume?
   b) Which of the three has the greatest surface area?
   c) Explain why your answer to a) differs from your answer to b).

2. Which of the three giant protists would have the greatest need for oxygen? (Hint: The need for oxygen is linked to the need for energy, and thus to the size of the organism, that is, to its mass and volume.)

3. a) Which giant protist has the greatest surface area-to-volume ratio?
   b) Suppose all three protists are immersed in identical samples of water. Which do you think would collect the most dissolved oxygen? Explain why.
   c) Explain the link between your answers to a) and b).

4. a) Suppose protist A splits into 2 equal cells along the coloured line. Explain how this would affect i) its volume, ii) its surface area, and iii) its surface area-to-volume ratio.
   b) Explain how splitting in two would affect protist A's ability to collect oxygen.
   c) Would splitting in two affect protists B and C in the same way? Explain.

Figure 7-1.

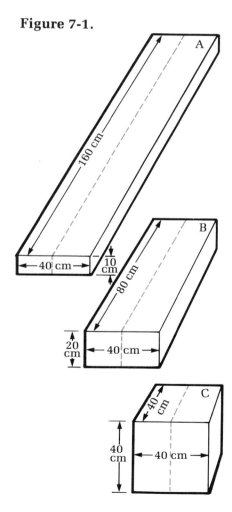

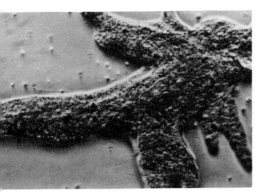

The surface area-to-volume ratio will change as the *Amoeba* changes its shape.

Part B: Surface Area-to-Volume Ratio in *Amoeba*

Procedure

1. Determine the diameter size of the field of view for the intermediate magnification level.
2. Prepare a wet mount of an *Amoeba*. Observe the *Amoeba* under the microscope at intermediate magnification. Note its movement and any other behaviour.
3. Estimate the length and width of the *Amoeba* you are viewing.
4. Assume that the *Amoeba* is 0.5 mm thick. Calculate its surface area, volume, and surface area-to-volume ratio.

Discussion

1. Could you see the *Amoeba* exchanging gas with its external environment? Explain your answer.
2. Could you see it exchange any other material with its external environment? Explain your answer.
3. How might the *Amoeba*'s movement assist gas exchange with the external environment?
4. Compare the surface area-to-volume ratio of an actual *Amoeba* with the ratios of the imaginary giant protists. Which do you think can exchange gases more efficiently, the actual *Amoeba*, or one of the imaginary protists?
5. All *Amoebae* are microscopic in size. Explain how the *Amoeba*'s body plan prevents it from growing as large as a human.

Living on a Cellular Level

All organisms carry out respiration at the cellular level. In large organisms, however, obtaining oxygen for respiration presents a problem that microscopic protists do not encounter. Because a protist is so small, oxygen molecules can diffuse from its surface to its centre very quickly. But a single-cell body plan is impractical for large organisms, because diffusion from the surface alone could not deliver oxygen quickly enough to all parts of the body. Larger animals need a great deal of oxygen, and must exchange gases rapidly. They solve this problem by having a multicellular body plan, and body systems which help distribute gases to all the cells in the body.

Some multicellular organisms, such as sponges and jellyfish, do rely on diffusion for gas exchange. Because they are made up of many cells, however, and not just one large cell, these organisms have a much greater surface area of cell membrane through which to collect oxygen and give off waste gases. Most of their body cells are in direct contact with the water in which they live, making this process practical.

In the majority of large animals, however, most body cells have no direct contact with the external environment. The body must therefore have specialized systems to provide 1) a large, moist surface where oxygen can be dissolved and exchanged, 2) a method for delivering oxygen molecules to the gas exchange surface, and 3) a way to carry dissolved oxygen to distant body parts where it can be used in cell respiration.

In humans, for example, the large, moist surface is located inside the lungs. Oxygenated air is moved into the lungs by **breathing**, a muscular action that also moves waste carbon dioxide gas out. Dissolved gases are carried around the body by circulating blood. In the next section, we will examine some of the body systems found in humans and other multicellular animals.

Oxygen from the external environment is not directly available to the internal cells of this copper rockfish.

Study Questions

1. Explain the difference between an organism's internal and external environments by giving an example of each.

2. a) Write the word equation for cell respiration.
   b) Explain where the materials needed for cell respiration come from, and where the materials produced go to.

3. a) Define the term gas exchange.
   b) Why is gas exchange important to an organism's internal environment?
   c) Describe how gas exchange occurs in a protist.

4. a) Define the term breathing, as it applies to humans. Does it apply to protists? Explain.
   b) How do breathing, gas exchange, and cell respiration differ? What do they have in common?

5. a) Explain the relationship between a cell's volume, its surface area, and its surface area-to-volume ratio.
   b) Explain how the factors listed in a) affect gas exchange.

6. a) Explain why all organisms larger than a protist are multicellular.
   b) Name two multicellular organisms that exchange gases by diffusion.
   c) Explain why all larger animals require a specialized system to exchange gases.

Figure 7-2.

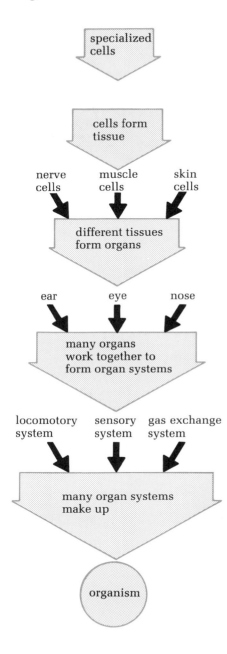

specialized
cells

cells form
tissue

nerve cells   muscle cells   skin cells

different tissues
form organs

ear   eye   nose

many organs
work together to
form organ systems

locomotory system   sensory system   gas exchange system

many organ systems
make up

organism

The eye is part of the body's sensory system. It is made up of several different types of tissue.

7.2 Biological Systems in Larger Animals

In protists, all life functions are carried out by a collection of organelles inside a single cell. These very small structures are capable of performing and coordinating all the physical and chemical activities that the protist needs to stay alive.

Larger organisms, however, are organized in a different way. They are not simply a collection of cells like individual protists, all working in the same way to carry out their life functions. Instead, multicellular bodies are structured into biological systems, each of which is responsible for particular functions and activities.

The basis of this body plan is **cell specialization**, which means that different cells perform different life functions. Muscle cells, for example, can contract and produce movement, while skin cells are specialized to protect the body surface.

Groups of specialized cells are organized into **tissues**. A tissue consists of a group of similar cells that work together to perform a similar job. For example, your ability to breathe depends on the contraction and movement of muscle tissue composed of many similar muscle cells.

Tissues, in turn, are grouped into **organs**. An organ consists of several different tissue and cell types working together at a particular task. For example, the human eye is an organ made up of muscle tissue, nerve tissue, skin cells, sensory cells, and blood cells. Their common task is to convert light into nerve impulses.

Finally, **organ systems** are made up of groups of different tissues and organs that work together to perform a specific life function. The sensory system, for example, includes many sensory organs such as eyes, ears, and skin, together with the coordinating nerves.

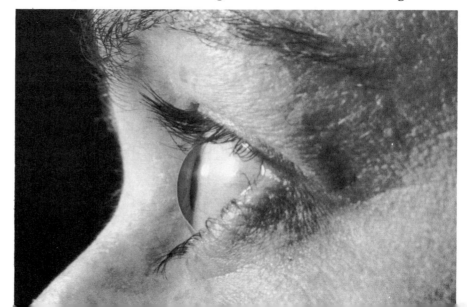

The locomotory system, which brings about body movement, is made up of skeletal muscles and bones.

Most body systems are internal, and therefore difficult to study in living animals. For centuries, scientists depended on external evidence to learn about what was going on inside the human body.

Activity 7-2:   External Evidence of Internal Systems

In this activity, you will use your fingers or a stethoscope to "listen" to your internal environment. With your teacher's help as needed, listen at several of the sites indicated in Figure 7-3. If convenient, listen to your partner's internal environment as well as your own. Devise a method to record your observations.

The first stethoscope was made from a wooden tube in 1816 by René Laënnec, a French physician.

Discussion

1. a) What external evidence did you find of internal activity within your body?
   b) What external evidence did you find of a coordinated internal system (one made of several components working together)?
2. a) If you already know something about this system, give its name, and describe its function(s).
   b) Suppose you had never learned anything about this system. What could you *reasonably* conclude about its function(s), using only the evidence you could gather in this activity?
3. If you had two stethoscopes, each at a different site, what similarities and differences might you observe? Explain.
4. a) Describe some further experiments that might help you learn more about this system.
   b) What difficulties might you encounter in carrying out these experiments?

Figure 7-3.

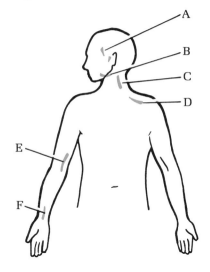

Systems for Gas Exchange

By observing a horse after it has had a long gallop, you can see some evidence of the system it uses for gas exchange. Its sides heave, and breath steams from widened nostrils. If you touch its side, you can feel its heart beating strongly. But this evidence is limited, and to learn more, you need to look inside the animal.

What sort of structures might it use to allow it to bring in air and to get oxygen to all its cells?

Most animals have a specialized **gas exchange system** to deliver oxygen to the internal environment and carry carbon dioxide back to the external environment. The structure and operation of such systems depend on two important facts about gas molecules. Firstly, they must be dissolved in fluid before they can pass through a membrane. Secondly, they can only pass through very thin membranes, such as those surrounding cells.

The variety of external environments on our planet has resulted in a diversity of gas exchange systems among animals. The systems used by water dwellers, for example, differ in many ways from those of land dwellers. But all gas exchange systems include the following features: 1) a moist, thin membrane, 2) a structure that maximizes the surface area of the membrane, and 3) a method of delivering oxygen to the membrane. In the next two sections, you will look at the design of various gas exchange systems used by animals living in different environments.

Study Questions

1. a) What is cell specialization?
   b) Define and give examples of the terms tissue, organ, and organ system.
2. Compare the terms organ and organelle by describing their similarities and differences.
3. Order the following terms in a sequence that makes sense and explain the basis for your sequencing: cell, organ, organ system, organelle, organism, tissue.
4. a) Gas exchange depends on two important facts about gas molecules. What are these facts?
   b) i) List the features required by all gas exchange systems.
      ii) Explain the function of each feature.
5. a) Explain why large animals require a specialized body system for gas exchange, while protists do not.
   b) Explain why gas exchange systems vary so much from one species to another.

BREATHING AT HIGH ALTITUDES

Pilots and mountain climbers encounter a problem with thin air at high altitudes. "Thin air" refers to the reduced air pressure and decreased gaseous oxygen in the air at locations high above sea level. If you breathe thin air at a height of 3000 m above sea level, you can expect to experience slow reaction times, and a dulling of your senses and mental skills. The problem can be overcome by breathing a supplementary source of oxygen under pressure—either from a tank through a mask or in a pressurized cabin.

For most people, breathing at altitudes over 5000 m would cause temporary blindness, fainting spells, convulsions, and death. But people who have lived in high altitudes for a long time function quite comfortably. Peruvian Indians, for example, are adapted to the thin air on the Andes mountains. Inhabitants of high-altitude areas have deeper chests, more surface area for the air sacs of their lungs, more red blood cells for carrying oxygen, more iron in their red blood cells,

A jet pilot with the Snowbird aerobatic team breathes through an oxygen mask.

and more capillaries in their body tissues. These adaptations provide physical advantages for high-altitude living.

7.3 Gas Exchange Systems for Water Dwellers

Many water dwellers, such as fishes, salamanders, and lobsters, use **gills** for gas exchange. In most fishes, each gill includes numerous fingerlike projections called **gill filaments**, a **gill arch** to support the filaments, and a **gill cover** or **operculum** to protect them.

Figure 7-4.

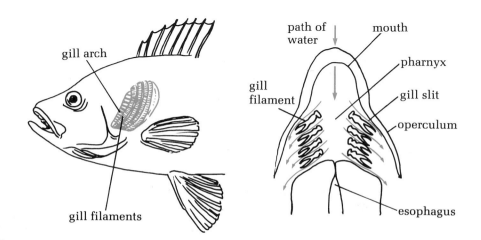

Note the external gills in the mud puppy.

The operculum also makes pumping motions that force water across the gill filaments. Oxygen dissolved in the water diffuses through the thin membrane of the gill filaments into the blood. Waste carbon dioxide from cellular respiration diffuses the other way, from the blood into the water. The constant movement of water over the gills brings in more oxygen and carries away the carbon dioxide. The large surface area of the many gill filaments maximizes the quantity of gases they can exchange. They also have a rich blood supply to transport dissolved oxygen to other parts of the fish's body.

The mud puppy shown in the photograph is a type of salamander with dark red, bushy, external gills on each side of its neck. The branching structure of these organs provides a large surface area for gas exchange. Their external location provides ready access to oxygenated water. A disadvantage of external gills, however, is that the delicate gas exchange membrane is sometimes unprotected. Any injury to the gills can result in a great loss of blood. Most aquatic animals, including fishes, have internal gills with some kind of protective cover over them.

In Activity 7-3, you will investigate how a fish gets oxygen for its internal environment. Before you begin this activity, however, it is important to review the following guidelines for animal care.

▶ How To Care for Lab Animals

Animals are an important study aid for the life sciences. Living and preserved specimens permit firsthand observation of animal structures. Studying structural parts directly promotes a more complete understanding of the operation of an organ, organ system, or the entire organism.

Live animals, such as goldfish, mice, rats, fruit flies, and chameleons, can serve as classroom pets and as valuable exhibits for observing life processes. If properly maintained and cared for before, during, and after experimentation, live animals can be an integral part of the "living" science classroom or laboratory in your school.

Activity 7-3:   Breathing Rate and Temperature in Fish

You cannot observe the process of gas exchange in a living fish directly, but you can measure gas exchange indirectly by looking at the external evidence of breathing. In a fish, **breathing** is the action that moves oxygenated water in and out. You can determine the breathing rate of a fish by counting the number of beats made by its operculum in a given period. In this activity, you will investigate how the breathing rate of a fish is affected by the temperature of its external environment.

Materials

small clean beaker (e.g., 500 mL)	clean thermometer
large clean beaker (e.g., 1000 mL)	clean stirring rod
goldfish	clock with second hand
dip net	ice cubes

Procedure

1. **Make a Hypothesis:** Predict how the breathing rate of a goldfish will change when its water is cooled.

2. Place a goldfish in a small beaker, with enough aquarium water to cover the fish completely and allow it to swim.

3. Place a thermometer in the beaker and record the temperature of the water. Count the number of times the fish's operculum opens during a 15 s interval. Perform two more trials, and average your results. Multiply by four to get the average breathing rate per minute. Record the temperature and the average breathing rate in a chart with the following headings.

Temperature (°C)	Average Breathing Rate per Minute

4. Add about 250 mL of cold tap water to the large beaker. Lower the small beaker with the goldfish and thermometer into the large beaker. With a stirring rod, carefully stir the water in the small beaker.

5. After 3 min, measure and record the temperature of the water in the small beaker. Perform three separate trials to determine the fish's breathing rate at this new temperature. Record the average breathing rate per minute beside the new temperature in your chart.

Figure 7-5. Be careful when you place the goldfish in the beaker with the dip net.

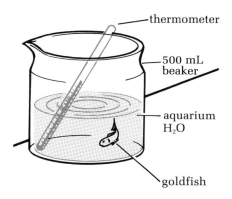

Figure 7-6.

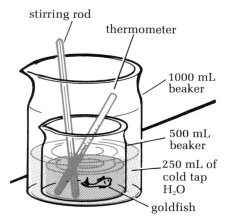

6. Add ice cubes to the large beaker while gently stirring the contents of the small beaker. When the fish's water is cooler by 5°C, determine the average breathing rate per minute as before. Record the results in your chart.

7. Repeat step 6 until you reach a final temperature near 0°C.

8. Follow your teacher's directions for warming the fish to room temperature before returning it to the aquarium.

9. Graph the data recorded in your chart.

Discussion

1. Why are three 15 s trials performed for each breathing rate observation?

2. What is the importance of stirring the fish's water before reading its temperature?

3. a) Does the breathing rate of a fish increase or decrease with reduced water temperatures?
   b) Comment on the validity of your hypothesis.

4. a) Based on your observations so far, what effects should increasing the water temperature have on the breathing rate of the fish? Explain why you think so.
   b) Oxygen is more soluble in cold water than in warm water. How does this fact affect your answer to a)?

5. Warm-blooded animals maintain a constant body temperature regardless of their surroundings. The body temperature of cold-blooded animals varies according to environmental conditions. Would your goldfish be classified as a cold-blooded or warm-blooded animal? Explain why you think so.

Do You Know?

Because cold waters contain more oxygen than warm waters, the seas of the Arctic and Antarctic are among the most biologically productive in the world. The amount of minute floating organisms, called zooplankton, is about ten times greater in the Antarctic waters than in the tropical waters of the Atlantic.

Gas Exchange in Fish

You may have heard people say "I feel like a fish out of water" when they are in a helpless condition. A fish out of water cannot breathe, even though air has a higher oxygen content than water (20% oxygen in air, 0.5% in water). The gills of a fish are designed to extract dissolved oxygen from water. In air, the gill filaments collapse, stick together, and dry out.

The oxygen-carrying capacity of water depends partly on its temperature. Cold water holds much more oxygen than warm water, and for this reason cold water usually supports many more organisms. People who go fishing know, for example, that on a warm summer day, most fish are in the deeper parts of the lake where the water is cooler and where there is more dissolved oxygen.

A few fishes, like the common carp and the catfish, can survive in sluggish, warm water with a low oxygen content. The carp can supplement its oxygen supply by taking in a bubble of air from the surface, then holding the bubble in its mouth near the moist gills, where the oxygen can dissolve.

Most fishes use a combination of swimming movement and a pumping action of their mouths or gill covers to ensure the movement of oxygen-containing water around their gills. Most sharks cannot pump water. Instead, they must keep their mouths open while swimming to force water over the gills and out the gill slits. Tuna and mackerel have no active pumping mechanism and must keep swimming to keep water moving around their gills. If they stopped swimming, they would suffocate.

The lungfish has a specialized gas exchange system that includes both gills and a "lung". It survives out of water by taking air into the "lung", which is actually a pouch growing from the gut. Some lungfish have poorly developed gills and must take in air through their mouths to survive, while others can exchange gases equally well in water (through their gills) or on land (through their "lungs").

The above examples show that the details of gas exchange systems vary from one fish species to another. Most such systems, however, depend on gills for gas exchange.

Gas Exchange in Other Aquatic Organisms

Fishes are not the only aquatic animals that use gills. Lobsters are large active arthropods, each with twenty pairs of gills to supply its gas exchange needs. The gills of a lobster are feathery expansions of its body wall, and are richly supplied with blood.

Clams are molluscs that have sievelike gills, perforated with numerous tiny pores, and covered with cilia. The beating of the cilia moves water across the gills and forces it through the tiny pores. The water enters tubes running through the gills, and leaves the clam through a posterior opening.

A starfish is an echinoderm with an elaborate gas exchange system covering its body surface. The starfish's "skin gills" are fingerlike structures projecting from the body cavity. The thin,

Most sharks swim constantly to deliver oxygenated water to their gills. Those that can pump water do so only when they settle on the bottom.

The lungfish survives prolonged dry spells by building a cocoon of mud around itself and using air stored in its "lung", or air bladder.

Do You Know?
Clams use their gills for feeding as well as for gas exchange. Particles of food brought in with the water are trapped on the surface of the gills as the water filters through the gill pores. The food particles are entangled in mucus secreted by the gills, and are then carried to the clam's mouth by the beating of the cilia.

An average-sized clam passes 2.5 L of water over its gills every hour. The surface area of your lungs is approximately equal to that of a tennis court. This large surface area allows for the three hundred thousand million tiny blood vessels (capillaries) in the lungs to be spread out around the air sacs.

exposed surface of the gills is protected by the starfish's heavy spines. Small pincers located in spaces between the spines pick off small animals and any other material that might damage the skin gills. Cilia also help to keep the starfish's skin clean and to circulate water over the skin gills.

In summary, aquatic organisms have a variety of body systems designed to exchange gases. But all of these gas exchange systems include the three essentials: 1) a thin, moist membrane, 2) a structure to maximize its surface area, 3) a method of delivering fresh water to the membrane. As oxygen diffuses from the water into the animal's internal environment, carbon dioxide diffuses back out.

Study Questions

1. a) What structural feature of gills enables them to provide a large surface area?
   b) How do external and internal gills differ? Name one organism having each type.
   c) What is the advantage of internal gills?

2. Delivering fresh supplies of oxygen-rich water or air to a gas-exchange surface is also known as breathing.
   a) Describe breathing in a water dweller with internal gills, such as a fish. Name any structures involved.
   b) Explain why water dwellers with external gills need no special structures for breathing.

3. Newborn tadpoles have external gills, but these gills disappear as the young animal matures. What problems faced by adult frogs would make gills of any kind useless?

4. In general, larger organisms require larger, more complex gas exchange systems. Explain why.

5. Sharks are cold-blooded fish, while dolphins are warm-blooded mammals. Both animals are very active. If both have approximately the same mass, which will use more oxygen in a day, a dolphin or a shark? Explain.

6. An efficient gas exchange system requires a large surface area with a rich blood supply.
   a) In most water dwellers, this surface is located in gills on or near the outside of the animal's body. Explain.
   b) In most large land dwellers, this surface is located in lungs, deep inside the animal's body. Explain.

7.4 Gas Exchange Systems for Land Dwellers

It might seem at first that gas exchange in the air should be easier than in water. Water contains only 0.5% oxygen at most, while air contains 20% oxygen. The problem for land dwellers, however, is that oxygen cannot diffuse through a cell membrane until the gas molecules have been dissolved in fluid. Thus, the first requirement for a gas exchange system in land animals is a thin, moist membrane that can be kept from drying out.

Very few land dwellers get oxygen through their outer body covering, because this method of exchanging gases has two limitations. It restricts the animal to a damp habitat, since the skin must remain moist. It also restricts the animal's size, because a larger surface area has a greater risk of drying out. Earthworms get all of their oxygen through their skin. Frogs can exchange gases through the lining of the mouth as well as the skin. They can get enough oxygen this way only when they are quiet, however. During active periods, the frog must also exchange gases through its lungs.

Lungs are saclike projections inside the body. They serve as a container to hold the air while gas exchange takes place all over the thin, moist membrane lining the lungs. Humans and many other animals depend on lungs for gas exchange. In Activity 7-4, you will investigate the structure of a mammalian lung.

Activity 7-4:   Mammalian Lung Dissection

Dissection is a valuable tool for learning about the internal environment. It is important to learn as much as possible from each dissection in order to minimize the number of organisms involved. One benefit of dissecting a single organ, such as a lung, is that the animal specimen is used for some other purpose besides the dissection. This first dissection will be demonstrated. Watch your teacher's method carefully. Note the importance of following a precise and systematic dissection procedure.

Materials

Part A

mammalian lung

dissecting instruments

Part B

unlined notepaper

ruler

scissors

A frog takes in oxygen through its outer body covering.

Part A: Lung Dissection

Procedure

1. Observe the external features of the mammalian lung. Identify all visible parts. Note the mass of the organ.
2. Identify any tubes as either air passageways or blood vessels.
3. With a scalpel, cut near an air passageway into the lung tissue. Follow the passageway. Note the variation in the size of the tubes and tubules.
4. Locate the largest blood vessels in the lung. Trace their pathway as they branch into smaller and smaller tubes.
5. Cut through the lung tissue and observe the individual air sacs. Estimate the size of an air sac.

Discussion

1. The mass of a human heart is greater than that of a lung, even though the lung has more volume. Discuss the reason for the relatively low mass of a lung.
2. The lungs contain numerous blood vessels. Why is abundant blood important in the operation of the lungs?
3. a) In a living mammal, the membrane lining the lung must remain moist. Explain why.
   b) How does the structure of the lung help to keep the lining moist?
4. How does the structure of the lung ensure even distribution of incoming air throughout the organ?

Part B: Designing a Model for Gas Exchange

Procedure

1. Determine the perimeter of a piece of white paper. Record this value.
2. Rule the paper into 3 cm squares.
3. Cut up the squares, and arrange them in a pattern that gives the greatest possible perimeter. Determine this maximum perimeter, and record its value.

Discussion

1. By how many times did rearranging the squares increase the perimeter of the paper?
2. Compare the final arrangement of squares with the structure of the mammalian lung.

3. a) What structural feature(s) ensure(s) that the mammalian lung has the maximum possible surface area?
   b) Why is it important for a lung to have the maximum possible surface area?

Gas Exchange for Terrestrial Vertebrates

Amphibians, such as frogs and salamanders, are terrestrial for only part of their life cycle. For example, when a frog is in the totally aquatic tadpole stage, it exchanges gases through external gills. As amphibians mature, most lose their gills and develop lungs.

Frogs breathe by contracting muscles in their throat and mouth to fill their lungs with air. The floor of the mouth is lowered, and air is drawn in through the nostrils by the lowered air pressure inside the mouth cavity. The floor of the mouth is then raised to force the air down into the lungs. Air is forced out of the lungs by contraction of the frog's body muscles and the elastic recoil of the lungs themselves.

Many amphibians also exchange gases through skin and mouth surfaces. All other land vertebrates rely entirely on lungs to provide a surface for gas exchange.

Birds must have high rates of gas exchange to allow for the activity of flight. A bird's lungs are connected to numerous air sacs in its body, giving a bird about twice the amount of surface for gas exchange as a mammal of the same size. Birds breathe by contracting both chest and abdominal muscles to force air out. As the muscles relax, air rushes in.

Figure 7-7. How a frog breathes.

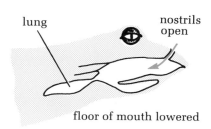

lung — nostrils open

floor of mouth lowered

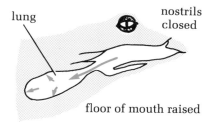

lung — nostrils closed

floor of mouth raised

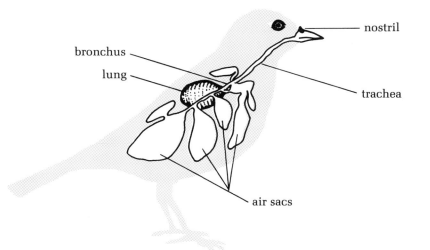

bronchus

lung

nostril

trachea

air sacs

Figure 7-8. The lung system of a bird, showing the lung's connection to several air sacs.

Do You Know?

People did not understand the gas exchanges that occur during breathing until late in the eighteenth century. In 1777, the scientist Lavoisier showed that a bird breathing in a closed jar used up oxygen and produced carbon dioxide. This was the first recorded observation of the exchange of these gases in the process of breathing.

Figure 7-9. Movements of the diaphragm and rib cage change the volume of the chest to draw air into the lungs or force it out.

Figure 7-10. A close-up of an earthworm's outer layer of skin, showing how its moist skin acts as a gas-exchange surface.

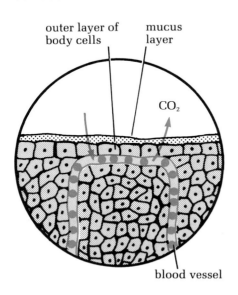

Most reptiles and all mammals breathe by expanding and contracting the chest cavity through muscle action. This changes the air pressure inside the chest cavity, and either forces air out or lets it rush in. Because turtles have a rigid outer shell, they cannot expand and contract their bodies in this way. They use the muscles that draw their head back into their shell to compress their abdomen, which in turn squeezes the lungs.

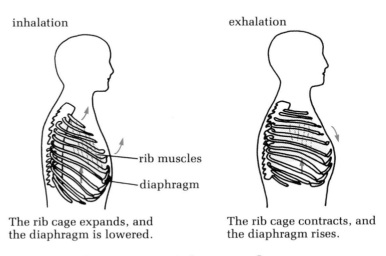

inhalation — exhalation

rib muscles
diaphragm

The rib cage expands, and the diaphragm is lowered.

The rib cage contracts, and the diaphragm rises.

Gas Exchange for Terrestrial Invertebrates

Much more variation in methods of gas exchange exists among terrestrial invertebrates.

The components of the earthworm's gas exchange system, for example, include a thin outer skin and a network of blood vessels near this skin surface. As long as the skin is kept moist by secretions from the mucous glands, gas exchange can take place. Drying prevents gas exchange, and the earthworm quickly dies.

By contrast, the grasshopper's gas exchange system enables it to obtain oxygen without living in a moist external environment. The main components of this system are spiracles, tracheae, and air sacs. **Spiracles** are tiny, valved openings along the abdomen which allow air in and out. The tubular **tracheae** run from the spiracles throughout the insect's body to carry outside air into the internal environment. Air sacs attached to the tracheae are inflated or deflated by pumping motions of the insect's body. Oxygen diffuses through the moist lining of the sacs into the body fluids surrounding the sacs. The waste gas, carbon dioxide, diffuses from the fluids into the air sacs, and is exhaled into the external environment through the spiracles.

Figure 7-11. An external view of a grasshopper's spiracles.

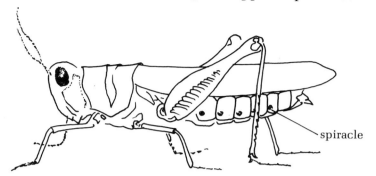

spiracle

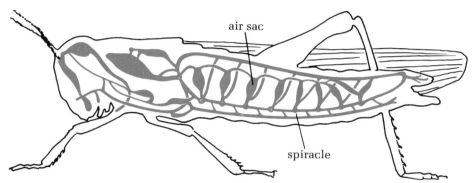

air sac

spiracle

Figure 7-12. The internal anatomy of a grasshopper's respiratory system.

Spiders have gas exchange organs called **book lungs**. These are air-filled sacs that connect to the outside through a slitlike opening. To maximize surface area, the walls of each sac contain many page-like folds. Air circulates freely in the spaces between the "pages", which are filled with blood.

Figure 7-13. Air is drawn into the spider's lung and then expelled by muscular action. Gas exchange takes place across the membranes of the book lung.

Study Questions

1. a) Which has the greater dissolved oxygen content: water or air?
   b) In which environment is gas exchange easier: water or air?
   c) Explain why the answers to a) and b) differ.
2. a) Which of the following animals breathe air before exchanging gases: earthworm, grasshopper, human?
   b) Explain the difference between breathing and gas exchange.
3. a) Describe gas exchange in the earthworm and the frog.
   b) What structures for gas exchange are present in the frog but not in the earthworm?
   c) Of what advantage are these additional structures?

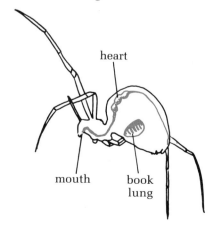

heart

mouth

book lung

4. a) Define the term gas exchange system, with two examples from this section.
   b) List all components of the grasshopper's gas exchange system, and state the function of each.
5. How does the frog obtain most of its oxygen
   a) during the spring, when it is actively swimming and catching insects?
   b) during the dry season, when it is buried in cool, moist mud?

DR. NORMAN BETHUNE (1890-1939)

Dr. Norman Bethune was an adventurous and inventive Canadian surgeon who developed a successful way of treating what used to be a common fatal disease of the lungs. The disease, tuberculosis, killed hundreds of thousands of people worldwide. Tuberculosis is caused by a bacteria that produces cavities and bleeding in the lungs. Infected people are unable to breathe properly, and rapidly grow weak. Until the 1920s, the only treatment was prolonged rest and fresh air, and many people died from this disease.

Norman Bethune was particularly interested in tuberculosis because he contracted it himself while practising surgery in Detroit, in 1926. At first he was very depressed, but then he decided to study all he could about the disease. He read about a new surgical treatment that involved inserting a hollow needle between the ribs into the chest cavity. Air was pumped through the needle, and the air pressure caused the infected lung to collapse. Once the lung was collapsed, it could rest and have a good chance of recovery, while the remaining lung carried out the work of gas exchange.

Bethune asked his doctors to try this procedure on him. They were reluctant at first because there was very little chest surgery performed at that time. Bethune was insistent. The operation was performed, and within a few weeks Bethune's condition had improved so much that he was released from the hospital.

Bethune went on to work in a Montreal hospital, where he soon became one of the greatest chest surgeons on the continent. He designed several new surgical instruments for chest surgery, some of which are still used today. He also improved the artificial pneumothorax apparatus for treating tuberculosis by collapsing the lung. Bethune's other contributions to human health included the development of a

Bethune during the Spanish Civil War, when he introduced the mobile blood transfusion service.

mobile blood transfusion service, and his support of a social medical system, or medicare.

Nowadays, Bethune is far more famous for his medical assistance to the Chinese government during the final stages of World War II. After his death from infection in 1939, the Chinese came to regard him as a hero. Monuments have been erected throughout China in Bethune's honour, and students there learn about his life and work in school.

Meet a CAT-Scan Technician— Janine Morrison

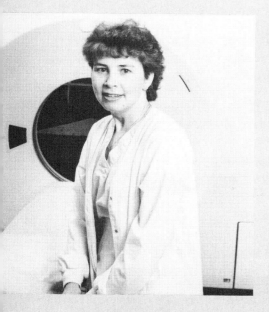

Janine is a registered technician in the X-ray department of Toronto General Hospital. She is qualified to operate a CAT- or CT-scanner.

Q. WHAT DOES "CAT" STAND FOR?
A. It stands for Computerized Axial Tomography. It's a diagnostic test that shows axial, or cross-sectional, slices of anatomy.

Q. WHAT IS THE DIFFERENCE BETWEEN A REGULAR X-RAY AND A CAT-SCAN?
A. In conventional radiography, X-rays pass through the patient to a film that records anatomical shadows to produce a flat image. In CT, X-rays are generated by a rapidly rotating tube and measured by electronic detectors. The rays are converted into computer language and the computer uses the data to reconstruct images.

Q. WHERE DID YOU STUDY TO BECOME A MEDICAL TECHNICIAN?
A. I took the two-year radiography course at the Toronto Institute of Medical Technology. You can also take similar courses at community colleges.

Q. WERE YOU ALWAYS INTERESTED IN THIS FIELD?
A. I didn't want to be a doctor or a nurse, but I wanted to do something in the field of medical science. In high school during a career week, someone from the Institute came to talk to us. I thought radiography sounded very interesting.

Q. HOW DID YOU GET INTERESTED IN CAT-SCAN?
A. I became interested in it during the two years I worked here as a radiographer, and applied for a position in the CAT-scan department last year. I'm lucky to be in a hospital that has these machines. They're very expensive, so many smaller hospitals don't have them.

Q. WHAT DO YOU DO WITH A PATIENT HAVING A CAT-SCAN?
A. I position the patient on the table, make him or her comfortable, and explain the procedure. I also help the doctor if the patient needs an injection. Most cases require a dye to be injected into a vein so that clearer images are produced. I feed information on the patient into the computer, then start the machine. The table moves the patient slowly into a large tube (the scanner). Pictures come up on the screen and I make a hard copy. The entire process usually takes 30 to 45 min, depending on what images are required.

Q. HOW OFTEN DO YOU DO CAT-SCANS?
A. On a normal shift, we might have 16 to 18 cases booked. We not only see patients in this hospital but also referrals from other hospitals that don't have CAT-scanners. The demand is so high that there's a three- to six-month wait for outpatients needing a CAT-scan. This hospital is a trauma centre, so we also get a lot of emergencies and life-threatening situations.

Q. WHAT'S THE BEST PART OF YOUR JOB?
A. I like working on a one-to-one basis with the doctors. You feel involved and can see firsthand what is going on. This is also a field where there are constant advancements and new things that can be done with a scanner. I like working with it because you can see results right away.

Q. WHAT'S THE MOST IMPORTANT CHARACTERISTIC FOR SOMEONE IN YOUR JOB?
A. You have to be good with people. You're dealing with frightened patients and impatient doctors who want everything yesterday. And you have to stay calm. You have to be able to reassure the patients who often don't know what is going on.

Review Questions

A: Knowledge

1. a) Define breathing, gas exchange, and cell respiration. Be sure to state the function of each.
   b) Describe how breathing, gas exchange, and cell respiration are related.
   c) Explain how these three processes differ.

2. a) What is a gas exchange surface? Give two examples.
   b) Why must all gas exchange surfaces remain moist?

3. a) Why do living things need to exchange gases?
   b) How does the surface area-to-volume ratio of a living cell affect its ability to exchange gases?

4. a) Define the term body system.
   b) Name three body systems that you have studied so far, and state the function of each.

5. a) Protists do not have body systems for gas exchange. Choose a protist and explain how it exchanges gases.
   b) Explain why most animals do require specialized body systems for gas exchange.
   c) Some animals can exchange gases without using a specialized body system. Citing an example, explain how this is possible.

6. List the three features required by all gas exchange systems.

7. With the help of two labelled sketches, compare the gas exchange system of a fish with that of a mud puppy.

8. Compare the gas exchange system of a grasshopper with that of a mammal, with regard to:
   a) the organ(s) containing the gas exchange surface,
   b) where each organ is located,
   c) how the gas exchange surface is kept moist,
   d) how oxygen-containing air reaches the gas exchange surface.

B: Application

9. Under what circumstances might a protist need to increase its surface area? How would the protist probably do this? Explain.

10. *Volvox* is a colonial organism comprising numerous identical single cells, each of which carries out all normal life functions. Explain how a multicellular organism such as a dog differs from a collection of cells in a *Volvox* colony.

11. Hooking a fish by its gill causes far more bleeding than hooking it elsewhere. Explain why.

12. On extremely hot days, a frog may dive to the bottom of a pond and burrow into the cool mud. How would it then exchange gases?

13. In an average human, the surface area of the lungs is about 40 times that of the skin.
    a) Why is such a large lung area needed?
    b) What structural feature(s) make(s) it possible for that much lung surface to be contained inside the chest cavity?

14. The so-called "hairy frog" (*Astylosternus robustus*) has numerous hair-like filaments growing out of its skin. What function do you think these filaments perform? Give reasons for your answer.

15. Many insecticides used to kill grasshoppers attack the gas exchange system. Why might such insecticides be more effective than those that attack the digestive system?

16. Humans can tolerate a wide range of climatic extremes. Air in the external environment may be hotter than body temperature, or much cooler, depending on the weather. How do you think the human body adjusts incoming air to body temperature before the air reaches delicate lung tissue?

C: Problem Solving

17. a) Cell respiration is a chemical process. Which of nature's cycles depends on cell respiration to circulate materials?
    b) What other important chemical process is

involved in this cycle? Draw a labelled sketch to show how these processes are related.

18. A hummingbird at rest consumes 35 000 mm³ of oxygen gas per gram of body mass, while a human consumes only 200 mm³.
    a) What do you think accounts for the difference in the rate of oxygen consumption?
    b) How do you think carbon dioxide production in a hummingbird and a human compares? How does the amount of energy produced in these organisms compare?

19. In 1772, the British scientist Joseph Priestley conducted a series of experiments that suggested a connection between breathing and burning. First, a bell jar was inverted over a burning candle. After a few minutes, the flame went out. In a second experiment, the bell jar was inverted over a live mouse. After a few minutes, the mouse died. But when the same experiments were repeated with a green plant inside the bell jar, the mouse survived and the candle flame persisted.
    a) Why did the candle flame go out in the first experiment? Why did the mouse die in the second experiment?
    b) What exchange of gases took place between the green plant and the candle flame?
    c) Why did this experiment suggest to Priestley a connection between breathing and burning? Would a modern scientist agree that burning and breathing are alike? Explain.

20. In humans, breathing rate is controlled by a group of brain cells called the respiratory centre. These cells are very sensitive to the amount of carbon dioxide in the blood. At the slightest increase of carbon dioxide, your respiratory centre sends signals to increase the number of times you inhale each minute. Very high levels of carbon dioxide cause panting. What circumstances might increase the concentration of carbon dioxide in your blood? How might panting alter the concentration of carbon dioxide in the blood?

Try This

Maximizing Surface Area
a) Place 16 sugar cubes in a 4 × 4 arrangement on a piece of paper to form a block 4 cubes wide, 4 cubes long, and 1 cube high. Wrap the block and trim the paper where necessary to make it fit the block's surface exactly. Unwrap the block, and flatten the paper. The surface area of the block is now represented by the piece of paper.
b) Repeat the wrap-fit-flatten sequence with a single sugar cube on another piece of paper. The paper now represents the surface area of one cube. Trace and cut 15 more pieces of paper so you have a total of 16.
c) To compare areas, place the paper surfaces from b) on top of the surface produced in a). How many paper surfaces are left over? Is the surface of the block 16 times greater than the surface of one cube? Explain.
d) How does this exercise demonstrate the benefits of multicellularity?

Chapter 8
Systems for Digesting Food

The complex internal environment of the cow uses grass as a source of energy. The cow converts some of the matter in grass into the glucose it needs for cell respiration. It also uses the nutrients in grass to make quite different materials, such as horns, hair, and milk for a nursing calf. Clearly, the cow is a living chemical factory, and the grass is its raw material.

For the cow, grass is also an excellent source of **nutrients** — all the elements and compounds it needs for life functions. One animal's food, however, may be quite useless to another. Newly born cattle, for example, cannot use grass right away for food energy. People get sick if they try to eat grass. But calves and most humans can process cow's milk.

Processing nutrients for the internal environment is usually called **digestion**. Digestion is a major life function for all animals. In this chapter, you will learn how some protists and animals prepare food for use by their internal environments through digestion.

When you finish Chapter 8, you should be able to:

- describe digestion in a one-celled organism
- describe the four major steps of digestion
- discuss the role of chemical and physical breakdown in digestive systems
- explain the role of enzymes in chemical breakdown
- compare the digestive systems of various invertebrate and vertebrate animals

8.1 Nutrients for the Internal Environment

All living things need nutrients to carry on their life functions. Both protists and animals get nutrients from food. However, most food is a complex mixture of materials that must be broken down to extract the nutrients from it. For example, corn stores energy in molecules of fats (oils), carbohydrates, and proteins. If you eat corn, your internal environment must be able to convert these materials into useable nutrient molecules such as glucose. Foods like corn also contain materials such as cellulose. Cows can convert the large molecules of cellulose to glucose or other simple sugars, but your body cannot use them at all. Your internal environment must be able to return this waste to the external environment.

All heterotrophs share the same food processing challenge. In protists, the entire internal environment is contained inside one cell. That single cell must carry out many steps before the energy in its food can be released by the mitochondria.

The first step in the digestive process is called **ingestion**. In a protist such as *Paramecium*, ingestion involves getting food inside the cell.

Activity 8-1: Investigating Ingestion in Protists

Ingestion in *Paramecium* can be easily observed by adding a coloured indicator to its food. For this purpose, your teacher will have prepared a suspension of yeast and Congo red indicator.

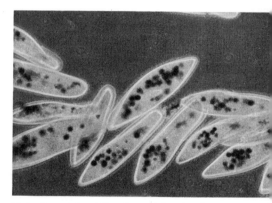

Note the stained food particles in the *Paramecium*.

Figure 8-1. If a depression slide is not available, make your own by forming a ring of petroleum jelly on a microscope slide.

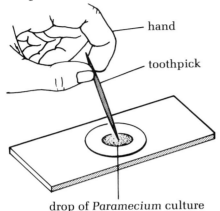

hand

toothpick

drop of *Paramecium* culture

Yeast is used by the *Paramecium* as food. The Congo red indicator clings to the yeast and allows you to follow its pathway inside the *Paramecium*.

The methyl cellulose slows *Paramecia* down so you can observe them more easily.

Materials

culture of *Paramecium*

compound microscope

microscope slides (depression type)

clean droppers

Congo red indicator

yeast suspension

methyl cellulose

toothpicks

cover slips

Procedure

1. Place a drop of the culture on a microscope slide. Add a drop of the coloured yeast suspension.

2. After a few minutes, add a drop of methyl cellulose and then stir the mixture gently with a toothpick.

3. Prepare a wet mount by placing a cover slip over the culture. Observe under low, intermediate, and high power magnifications.

4. Draw a diagram to show ingestion in *Paramecium*. The bubbles enclosing the ingested yeast are called food vacuoles. Use arrows to show the direction in which they move.

Discussion

1. Why is it important
   a) to wait a few minutes before adding methyl cellulose to the culture?
   b) to stir after adding the methyl cellulose?

2. Describe the process of ingestion in *Paramecium*.

3. Congo red is an acid indicator that changes from red to blue in the presence of an acid.
   a) How soon after ingestion does this colour change occur in *Paramecium*?
   b) What do you think is causing this colour change? Explain.

4. a) What evidence suggests the existence of currents in cell cytoplasm?
   b) Did the food vacuole in your *Paramecium* move clockwise or counterclockwise?
   c) Do all *Paramecia* show the same current flow direction for their vacuoles? (Compare results with your classmates.)

5. a) Does the *Paramecium* use all of the food it ingests? Support your answer with evidence from this activity.
   b) Explain why the *Paramecium* might need to eliminate some of the food it ingests.

6. a) How does gas exchange occur in *Paramecium*?
   b) What observed behaviour of your *Paramecium* may assist gas exchange? Explain.

How Protists Process Nutrients

Ingestion brings food inside the cell of a protist, and traps it in a temporary structure called a **food vacuole**. Further processing is needed before useable nutrient molecules can enter the cell cytoplasm.

In the next step, digestive juices from the cytoplasm diffuse through the membrane lining the vacuole. Chemicals in these juices attack the food inside the vacuole, causing chemical breakdown. This converts large food particles to smaller nutrient molecules. Absorption occurs as these small molecules diffuse outward through the vacuole membrane into the cytoplasm. There, currents in the cytoplasm carry nutrient molecules throughout the cell.

During chemical breakdown, food proteins form amino acid molecules, which the cell uses for growth. Fats break into small molecules such as fatty acids. Once these pass through the vacuole membrane, most recombine to form large fat molecules, which are then stored to meet future emergency energy needs. Carbohydrates (sugars and starches) break down to form glucose for immediate use by the mitochondria, which then release energy for the cell's activities.

Amino acids, fatty acids, and glucose are all examples of nutrients. However, some parts of the food cannot be chemically broken down into small nutrient molecules. Materials that cannot pass through the membrane remain in the vacuole, until they are ejected in a final step called **egestion**.

Protists like the *Paramecium* also have another type of vacuole, called a contractile vacuole, that collects and pumps out water.

Figure 8-2. The four steps of digestion.

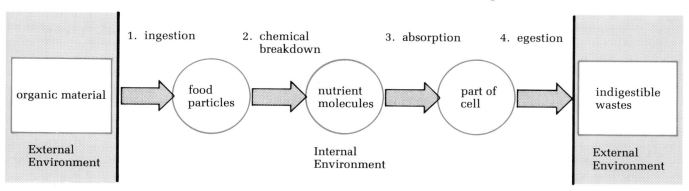

The steps of digestion can be listed in an orderly sequence: ingestion, chemical breakdown, absorption, and egestion. In protists, these steps all take place inside a single cell. Larger animals process nutrients in a similar sequence, but need specialized body systems to do so. These systems will be discussed in Section 8.3. First, however, we need a closer look at the most important step in the sequence: the process of chemical breakdown.

Study Questions

1. Clearly explain the difference between
   a) food and nutrients.
   b) ingestion and egestion.
2. a) Why does most food have to be digested before it can enter a cell?
   b) Name three nutrients that can be obtained from food.
   c) Which nutrient does the cell use as a source of energy?
   d) What cell organelle uses this nutrient to produce energy?
3. List the steps used by a protist for processing nutrients, and describe the function of each step.
4. Describe the digestive function of a food vacuole in a unicellular organism.
5. Discuss the importance of diffusion in digestion for a *Paramecium*.
6. *Paramecia* have hairlike projections on their outer body covering that enable movement. How might these cilia assist in the digestive process?

8.2   The Process of Chemical Breakdown

Chemical breakdown of food is required because only small molecules can enter the internal environment. Often, food consists of such large pieces that physical breakdown is needed before chemical breakdown can begin.

Physical Breakdown of Food

Physical breakdown reduces large pieces of food to small chunks or particles. Animals use a variety of methods for this step. In humans, physical breakdown takes place in the mouth, and is accomplished by biting and chewing. Herbivores, such as cattle,

use grinding teeth to reduce tough grass stalks to a pulp before swallowing. Carnivores, such as cheetahs, use teeth adapted for tearing off chunks of meat, which are then swallowed whole. Birds also ingest their food whole, but grind it after swallowing in an internal organ called a **gizzard**.

However, no amount of chewing or grinding will ever break chunks of food into particles small enough to enter cells. That job requires actual rearrangement of the molecules in the food. All animals carry out this step with chemicals called **digestive juices**.

In humans, chemical breakdown begins in the mouth, where a digestive juice called **saliva** is added to the food. Saliva, which is mostly water, acts as a lubricant while food is ground or chewed. But saliva also contains a digestive chemical called amylase. In Activity 8-2, you will investigate how amylase affects food.

Activity 8-2:   The Action of Digestive Juices

For health reasons, you will use purchased purified amylase in this activity, rather than human saliva. The reaction in the test tube will be the same as the one that takes place in your mouth.

Materials

starch solution	1 L beaker (for boiling water bath)
amylase solution	4 test tubes
Lugol's iodine	test tube rack
Benedict's solution	test tube holder
dropper	graduated cylinder (10 mL or 25 mL)
Bunsen burner	100 mL beaker

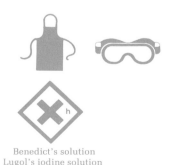

Benedict's solution
Lugol's iodine solution

Procedure

1. Draw a chart like the one below for your observations.

Test Tube	Starch Test	Test Tube	Glucose Test
A		B	
C		D	

2. Label the four test tubes A, B, C, and D. Place them in a rack and add 4 mL of starch solution to each.

3. Add 3 mL of amylase solution to test tubes C and D. Let them sit for 10 min. Meanwhile, carry out steps 4 and 5. (See Figure 8-3.)

Figure 8-3. How to prepare the test tube for Activity 8-2.

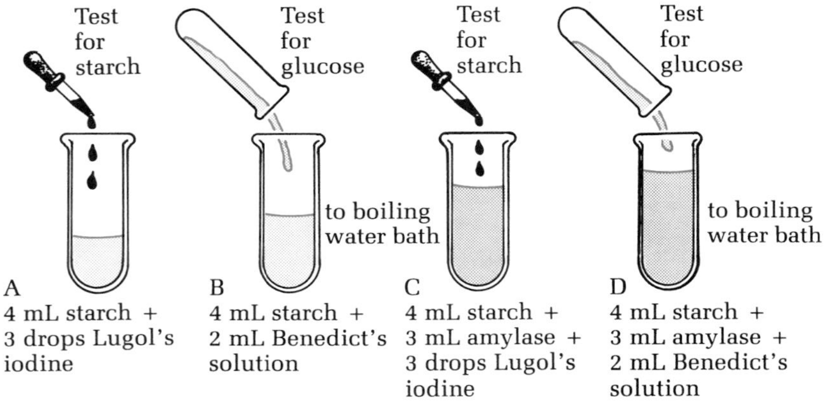

Test for starch

Test for glucose

Test for starch

Test for glucose

to boiling water bath

to boiling water bath

A
4 mL starch + 3 drops Lugol's iodine

B
4 mL starch + 2 mL Benedict's solution

C
4 mL starch + 3 mL amylase + 3 drops Lugol's iodine

D
4 mL starch + 3 mL amylase + 2 mL Benedict's solution

Figure 8-4. The procedure for testing for glucose, performed on test tubes B and D.

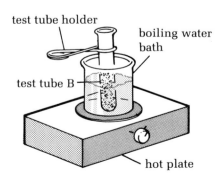

test tube holder

boiling water bath

test tube B

hot plate

4. Perform the standard test for starch on the contents of test tube A as follows. Add 3 drops of Lugol's iodine and observe any colour change.
NOTE: Test tube A is known to contain starch. This trial shows you how the test works when starch is present. In your chart, enter a positive (+) sign beside A and describe the colour you see in the tube. (If this colour is not produced, the result would be negative for starch.)

5. Perform the standard test for glucose on the contents of test tube B as follows. Add 2 mL of Benedict's solution, and swirl to mix. Place the test tube in a boiling water bath for 3 min, and observe any colour change. (See Figure 8-4.)
NOTE: Test tube B contains only starch, not glucose. This trial shows you how the test works when there is no glucose present.

In your chart, enter a negative (−) sign beside B, and describe the colour you see in the tube. (If glucose is present, the colour will change from blue to red. This result would be positive for glucose.)

6. Perform the standard test for starch on the contents of test tube C. In your chart, show whether the result is positive or negative for starch.

7. Perform the standard test for glucose on the contents of test tube D. In your chart, show whether the result is positive or negative for glucose.

Discussion

1. Describe the standard test for starch
   a) when the result is positive. In which test tube(s) did this occur?
   b) when the result is negative. In which test tube(s) did this occur?

2. Describe the standard test for glucose
   a) when the result is positive. In which test tube(s) did this occur?
   b) when the result is negative. In which test tube(s) did this occur?

3. Explain the purpose of each test tube in this activity.

4. What was happening to the starch in test tubes C and D during the 10 min waiting period? Explain how you know.

5. Suppose test tubes C and D had been tested for starch and glucose after waiting only 2 min. What results do you think would have been obtained? Explain.

6. a) If you chew a mouthful of potato long enough, it will start to taste sweet. Explain why.
   b) Write a simple word equation to describe the action of amylase on starch.

Enzymes and Digestive Juices

Most multicellular organisms have a variety of digestive juices. Different fluids are produced in different parts of the digestive system, and have different functions. The stomach, for example, produces gastric juices, and the mouth produces saliva.

Saliva has three constituents. Water moistens the food to help break it down physically by dissolving or suspending food particles. **Mucin**, a slippery substance, lubricates the food and helps it pass down the digestive tract. **Amylase** chemically converts starch in the food into the sugar maltose.

Amylase is an example of an **enzyme**. Enzymes are molecules that speed up chemical reactions in living things. Without this help, digestive reactions would not produce nutrients from food fast enough. Reactions in beakers and test tubes can often be speeded up by adding heat, but living things die if they get too hot. In the presence of enzymes, however, breakdown reactions take place rapidly at normal body temperatures. Thus, enzymes play a vital role in digestion for all heterotrophs.

In humans, food passes from the mouth to the stomach, where gastric juices are added. Gastric juices contain hydrochloric acid, which dissolves minerals found in food and kills bacteria. But the acid also inhibits the action of salivary amylase, preventing the further breakdown of starch in the stomach. The chemical breakdown of starch continues in the small intestine.

All of the chemical reactions that break down large food molecules involve digestive enzymes. Each enzyme is specific to a particular reaction. For example, gastric juice also contains the enzyme **pepsin**. Pepsin has no effect on the breakdown of fats or starches. Its only job is to speed up the first of many reactions that eventually break protein down into amino acids.

When the partly digested food passes into the small intestine, it is attacked by other digestive juices. **Bile** from the liver contains no enzymes, but subdivides blobs of fat into very fine droplets ready for faster chemical breakdown. Enzyme-containing juices are secreted by the pancreas and the intestine itself. Some digest fats, some digest proteins, and others complete the breakdown of starch into simple glucose molecules. The glucose and all other nutrient molecules are then absorbed through the lining of the intestine into the bloodstream.

The term "digestion" is sometimes used to refer only to the chemical breakdown of food. In protists, all such digestion takes place inside the food vacuole, and is a fairly simple process. "Digestion", however, can also be used to describe the entire sequence of steps, from ingestion to egestion. More complex animals have many specialized structures inside their bodies for processing food at different stages. The system of organs that animals use for processing foods to obtain nutrients is called a **digestive system**. Section 8.3 will explore this in more detail.

The hydrochloric acid in gastric juices makes amylase inactive, but helps to activate pepsin. The acid also controls the pyloric valve that releases food from the stomach into the small intestine.

Do You Know?
All digestive enzymes assist in chemical breakdown reactions. However, many other enzymes in other parts of the body are involved in synthesis reactions: those that combine small molecules to build more complex ones. The processes of cell growth and cell division, for example, both require the formation of large protein molecules, which the cell builds from smaller, simpler amino acid molecules.

The enzymes present in a cell vary depending on the cell type. An average mammalian cell contains about 3000 different kinds of enzymes.

The average adult human eats 1.5 kg of food daily, and produces 0.4 kg of waste each day.

Study Questions

1. a) Explain the difference between physical breakdown of food and chemical breakdown.
   b) Explain why most heterotrophs require both types of breakdown to digest their food.

2. a) What structures carry out physical breakdown in humans? in birds?
   b) What heterotrophs do not require physical breakdown? Explain.

3. a) How is chemical breakdown carried out in protists?
   b) How is it carried out in humans?

4. a) With an example, explain the meaning of enzyme.
   b) For most chemical reactions, adding heat produces the same effect as enzymes. Explain why living organisms use enzymes instead.

5. a) Enzymes are said to be specific. With an example, explain what this means.
   b) Do enzymes always cause chemical breakdown? Explain.

6. a) Where does digestion take place in protists? in humans?
   b) Define the term digestive system.

THE PROBLEM OF BEING "OVERWEIGHT"

In North America, most human digestive systems are overworked. One of the symptoms of overeating is increased body mass, or obesity. This widespread condition has resulted in a continent-wide search for an easy cure for obesity. An assortment of strategies and plans such as hypnosis, body-wrapping, pills, mind control, and fad diets have surfaced as possible solutions to overeating and the problem of excess body mass.

A few surgical techniques have also been introduced as a means of overcoming obesity. For many years, doctors have been performing intestinal by-pass surgeries for patients who cannot control their mass through dieting. By-pass surgery involves shortening the small intestine. The result is that less food is absorbed into the bloodstream. Another technique, which is less drastic, involves the stapling of the stomach to reduce volume. Stainless steel staples reduce the stomach volume, and therefore the food intake, of the obese person. Stomach volume can also be reduced by a newer method that involves placing a hollow rubber ball into the stomach.

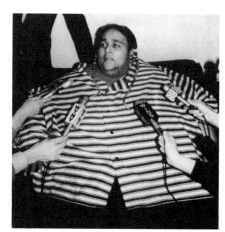

Walter Hudson reduced his mass from 545 kg to 364 kg.

Once inflated, the balloonlike structure occupies space in the stomach, and thus prevents large intakes of food.

8.3 Investigating Digestive Systems

Regardless of their size or complexity, the function of all digestive systems is the same. They bring in food from the external environment, and then break the food down into molecules of a kind and size that the internal environment can absorb.

Every digestive system includes organs or structures to carry out four major steps: ingestion, digestion (i.e., physical and chemical breakdown), absorption, and egestion. In the next activity, you will identify the structures of the earthworm's digestive system.

▶ How to Get the Most from a Dissection Activity

To learn as much as possible from a dissection, it is necessary to practise careful, precise dissection techniques. If you follow correct procedures, observe carefully, keep complete records, and make detailed diagrams, you can help to minimize the number of organisms used for dissection.

The digestive system of a multicellular organism contains many parts. As you expose these parts, section by section, each should be related to the digestive system as a whole. Be sure you can follow the pathway of food from the site of entry to the site of exit. ◀

Activity 8-3: Exploring the Earthworm's Digestive System

The earthworm is a member of phylum annelida, the segmented worms. In this dissection, you will examine the structures it uses for the internal systems discussed in this unit.

Figure 8-5.

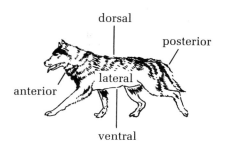

Materials

preserved earthworms	hand lens
straight pins	scissors
scalpel	dissecting probe
dissecting pan	forceps

Procedure

1. Using Figure 8-5 as a guide, identify the anterior, dorsal, ventral, posterior, and lateral regions of your specimen. Find the mouth and anus as well.

2. Locate the clitellum, a bandlike structure about $\frac{1}{3}$ of the way from the earthworm's anterior end. The clitellum is the boundary between the earthworm's anterior and posterior regions.

3. Numbering the worm's many rings permits easier identification of its body parts. Use the ring number system to describe the position of the clitellum.

4. Place the worm in the dissecting pan with its dorsal side up and its posterior end facing you. Secure the worm to the wax by placing a few straight pins through its skin.

5. Make an initial scalpel cut at the centre of the posterior end. With scissors, cut carefully along the worm's midline towards its anterior end. (See Figure 8-6.)

Feel along the segments of the earthworm for bristles called setae, which help the earthworm to move.

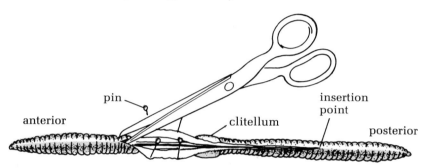

Figure 8-6.

CAUTION: Always cut away from your body and keep blade(s) parallel to the surface of the animal.

6. Carefully pull back the skin and connective tissue, revealing the internal organs. Note how thin the skin is.

7. Stretch out the skin and pin it back. Note the rich supply of blood vessels near the skin.

8. Locate the digestive tube that connects the mouth to the anus. Find the pharynx, esophagus, crop, gizzard, and intestine. Draw and label a diagram of the earthworm's digestive system.

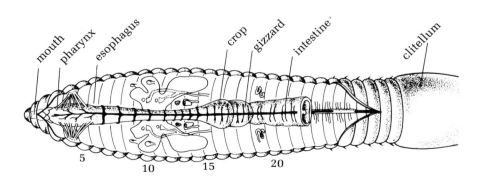

Figure 8-7. The digestive system of an earthworm.

9. Locate the five-part tubular heart at the worm's anterior end. Two major blood vessels lead from the heart. You will find one in the dorsal region, and one in the ventral region.

10. Look for the thin white ventral nerve cord, which is part of the earthworm's nervous system. Just above the pharynx, locate the brain. Examine it closely with a hand lens.

Figure 8-8. The circulatory, nervous, and excretory systems of an earthworm.

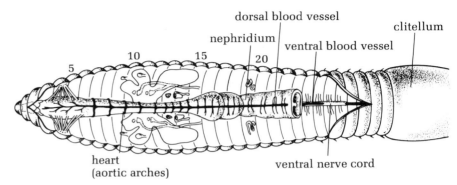

11. With a hand lens, locate and examine the small excretory organs called nephridia, attached to the lateral walls of the worm.

Discussion

1. Organisms are often dissected ventral side up. Why is the earthworm dissected with the dorsal side up instead of down?

2. What body parts would you see if you were looking at a cross-section of segment:
   a) 7?　　　　b) 11?　　　　c) 19?

3. a) Where do physical and chemical digestion of food occur in the earthworm's digestive system?
   b) What does the earthworm's digestive system suggest about the type of food it eats? Explain.

4. In Chapter 7 you learned about the earthworm's gas exchange system.
   a) What body part or organ does the earthworm use for this purpose?
   b) Did you see any evidence that the part named in a) is used for gas exchange?
   c) Did you see any evidence of other body parts attached to the part named in a)? If so, what do you think these other parts are used for?

Structures for Digestion in Earthworms

The earthworm feeds on decaying organisms found in the soil. As the earthworm burrows and moves through the earth, it ingests large quantities of soil, sand, and tiny pebbles, together with its food. This material is pulled into the mouth by the sucking action of the muscular pharynx. From here, it is pushed further down the digestive tract by rhythmic contractions of the esophagus, which passes the food into a thin-walled storage chamber called the crop.

The earthworm ingests soil as it burrows through the ground.

Active digestion begins in the next part of the digestive system —the gizzard. This area has thick, muscular walls that grind the food. Particles of sand or grit taken in with the food help this process of physical breakdown. Once the mixture has reached a pastelike consistency, it is passed on to the intestine, where chemical digestion takes place. Enzymes produced by the walls of the intestine help convert the large molecules of food into simpler molecules.

The small nutrient molecules are then absorbed through the lining of the intestine into the earthworm's bloodstream. As materials that cannot be digested continue down the intestine, some of the water mixed with them is absorbed.

The final stage in the process is egestion, in which the undigested wastes are eliminated through the anus. These wastes are sometimes deposited on the surface of the earth, forming small cylindrical plugs of fine soil known as worm castings.

Castings are excellent as a soil conditioner for gardens.

Structures for Other Systems in Earthworms

Although the digestive system takes up much of the space in an earthworm's body, structures connected with other major systems can also be easily observed. The nervous system consists of a small "brain", or ganglion, lying above the pharynx, and a double nerve cord running down the ventral side of the body. The circulatory system is made up of two large tubes: a dorsal blood vessel and a ventral blood vessel. Smaller distributing vessels run through the rest of the body to the intestine and the skin. Blood is pumped through the system by five simple hearts called aortic arches.

Figure 8-9. The reproductive system of an earthworm.

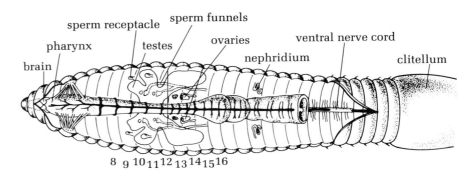

The excretory system of the earthworm is based on organs called nephridia. Every segment of the worm except the first three and the last has two nephridia. These organs excrete their waste to the outside, through a small pore opening on the ventral surface. The earthworm's reproductive system is very specialized. Each individual has both male and female reproductive organs, which include testes, sperm and egg sacs, and ovaries. Sperm receptacles in segments 9 and 10 open to the surface and receive sperm from the other partner during mating.

Study Questions

1. What is the function of each of the following digestive structures in the earthworm?
   a) crop
   b) pharynx
   c) gizzard
   d) mouth
   e) intestine
   f) anus

2. Why is sand or grit essential in an earthworm's diet?

3. What earthworm structure(s) carries (carry) out:
   a) ingestion?
   b) physical breakdown?
   c) chemical breakdown?
   d) absorption of small nutrient molecules?
   e) egestion?

4. a) What role do enzymes play in earthworm digestion?
   b) How does this compare with the role of enzymes in protist digestion?

5. In most multicellular organisms, the digestive system is closely linked to blood vessels. Why is this association so important?

6. Earthworms play an important role in recycling materials for the biosphere. Explain how.

SCIENCE IN ACTION

EATING UP POLLUTION

Heterotrophic organisms survive on an amazing variety of different foods, but perhaps the strangest sources of nutrients are such unlikely-seeming materials as plastics, oils, and even pesticides. The discovery of pollution-eating microbes began in the late 1970s, and since then many forms have been described. How did their strange eating habits arise?

The chemical structure of the unusual new foods consists of very large and stable molecules that most organisms cannot break down with their digestive enzymes. It has been known for some time, however, that the digestive tracts of many animals, both vertebrate and invertebrate, carry microorganisms that can break down the large, complex molecules of cellulose and lignin found in plant materials. The ability of some microbes to feed on the large molecules of this

Scientists in Britain use microbes to convert plastic wastes into protein that can be used as cattle food.

natural plant material can be said to have prepared them to be able to digest the molecules of synthetic pollutants. After all, why should it be any harder to digest plastic or oil than to digest wood?

Once the biochemical basis for the digestion of large molecules was understood, some scientists began to use genetic engineering to redesign microbes, producing new forms to break down particular chemicals. Some of these new microorganisms can digest pollutants such as PCBs. A bacterium that feeds on iron pyrite is being used to remove pollution-causing sulphur from coal.

But not all pollution-eating organisms are genetically engineered, and not all are bacteria. For example, scientists have learned that the common white-rot fungus can break down a number of harmful pollutants, such as DDT. There have also been experiments with a mould that might help to clean up slimy waste from phosphate and potash processing.

8.4 Comparing Digestive Systems

Every digestive system must be able to perform the same set of tasks: ingestion, absorption, digestion, egestion. Details of the structures animals use for these tasks vary considerably. However, when digestive systems are compared, it becomes clear that there are only a few basic designs.

The Bag System

Animals such as the hydra, sea anemone, and jellyfish have a digestive system consisting of a baglike structure with only one opening that serves as both mouth and anus. Their food, usually small animals, is captured by stinging tentacles, which then draw the prey towards the bag opening. Once inside the digestive cavity, the food is partially broken down by enzyme action and absorbed into special cells lining the bag. Digestion is completed inside food vacuoles in these cells.

The sea anemone has a single body opening through which both ingestion and egestion must take place.

Figure 8-10. Sea anemones and jellyfish belong to the same phylum (Cnidaria) and have the same basic body plan.

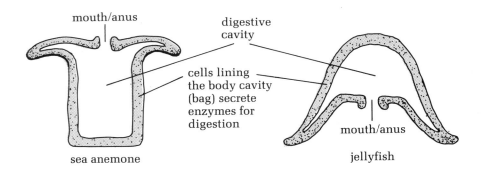

Insects have two basic types of mouth parts: one is for chewing and the other is for sucking.

The Tube System

Most animals have a digestive system that consists essentially of a tube with two openings — the mouth and the anus. Within this basic design, there are variations in the complexity and importance of the different parts, and in the way food is conducted along the tube.

The earthworm has a fairly simple tube system, with limited specialization of its parts. The mouth is little more than an opening at one end. The grasshopper, by comparison, has highly developed mouth parts for physically breaking up its food. The earthworm's simple mouth limits it to taking in food particles already small enough to enter. The grasshopper can tear and chew larger food until the food particles are small enough to ingest.

Mouth openings show an enormous variety of form and structure from species to species, related to feeding habits. Animals such as snakes and some fishes are able to ingest food almost as large as themselves. At the other extreme, some of the largest whales can feed only on the most minute ocean organisms. Special filtering structures inside the whale's mouth enable it to strain out millions of one-celled organisms from the sea water, but prevent it from eating anything larger. Many animals have specialized teeth. Some, such as snakes, use teeth only to capture and hold their prey, which is then swallowed whole. Other animals use teeth for biting, tearing, grinding, and chewing, so that their food is already partly digested before it passes further down the digestive tube.

In birds, which lack teeth, the physical breakdown of food occurs in a specialized part of the digestive tract called the gizzard. Its muscular walls squeeze and grind the food with the help of small stones and pebbles ingested by the bird.

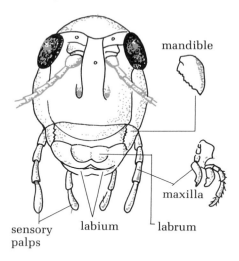

Figure 8-11. The grasshopper has highly specialized mouth parts for biting and tearing its food.

Figure 8-12. The digestive system of a bird.

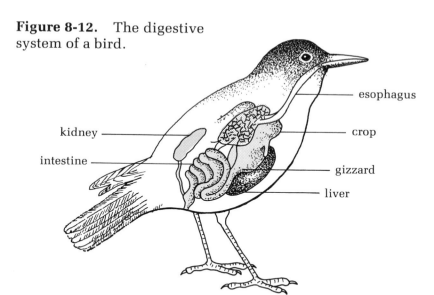

Do You Know?
Some birds, such as owls, eliminate much of their indigestible waste through their mouth (regurgitation) rather than their anus (defecation). Indigestible parts of their prey, such as the bones, teeth, and hair, are separated from the flesh by the grinding action of the bird's gizzard. Digestible material passes on through the digestive tract, while indigestible parts are tightly squeezed together to form a pellet, which is regurgitated back into the mouth and spewed out.

Some animals have developed a storage organ near the beginning of their digestive tract, such as the crop in birds and earthworms. This allows them to take in large amounts of food during a short time, and then digest the food more slowly later. The earthworm's crop is part of its main tube, but some storage organs are blind sacs opening off the main tube. In a female mosquito, for example, most of the abdominal cavity is filled with a large blind-ended sac that opens near the beginning of the main digestive tract. The mosquito feeds on blood, and fills the sac at one meal. The stored blood can last the insect several days.

The part of the digestive tube concerned with absorption is modified in many animals to increase its surface area. The advantage of a large surface is that digested food can enter the circulatory system more rapidly. In mammals, the digestive tube is elongated and coiled, and the lining of the tube has many tiny projections called villi which increase the surface area available to absorb nutrients. In some fishes, such as sharks, the intestine is relatively short, but contains a spiral valve—like a screw tightly enclosed in the tube. The food cannot move in a straight path, but follows the curves of the spiral, and therefore travels past a greater area of absorptive surface.

Herbivore System vs Carnivore System

Many adaptations of the basic digestive tube are related to the diet of the animal. Plant eaters, or herbivores, need ways of breaking down and absorbing sufficient nutrients from plant material, which is more difficult to digest than meat. This is because plant cells are surrounded by cellulose, which is difficult to digest.

For this reason, plant eaters usually have longer, more coiled intestines than meat eaters, to provide more time to break down cellulose and extract the maximum amount of nutrients. Most mammalian herbivores, such as cows, sheep, and antelopes, also have grinding teeth, and spend a lot of time chewing their food to break down physically the plant cells.

Ruminant animals, such as the cow, are often said to have four "stomachs". In fact, these are simply chambers which help to hold the food during processing. The rumen, which is the first part of the stomach, contains vast numbers of bacteria and protists which help to digest and ferment the cow's food. The cow, like other mammals, has no cellulose-digesting enzymes of its own, and relies on the microorganisms in its stomach to break down the plant cellulose. The rumen can also regurgitate the partly digested food back up the esophagus to the cow's mouth, to be chewed again. This is called "chewing the cud", and occupies a great deal of the cow's time.

Figure 8-13. Partly digested food passes from the cow's rumen back to the mouth, where it is chewed as cud before passing to the other stomach chambers for complete digestion.

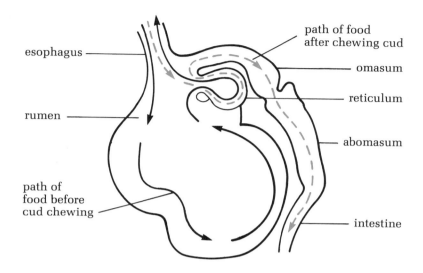

The rabbit has a different method of processing hard-to-digest plant food. First, the food passes through the rabbit's digestive tube as usual. Then, the rabbit ingests its own feces so that the partly digested food in them gets another trip through the intestine. Like all herbivores, the rabbit spends most of its waking hours feeding.

By contrast, carnivores such as lions and wolves are able to gorge on a large meal and then go without eating for several days. Because carnivores are meat eaters, they do not face the problem of digesting cellulose. Their feeding habits are reflected by their digestive tracts, which are much shorter than those of herbivores.

Like most carnivores, the coyote has just one stomach chamber and a short intestine.

Activity 8-4: Comparative Anatomy of Digestive Systems

Like all other biological systems, digestive systems vary greatly from one kind of animal to another. Much can be learned by comparing the digestive structures of different phyla and species. In this activity you will collect and compare data for five types of digestive systems on a copy of the following chart. In the blanks, name the structures used for each step of digestion in the animals listed. All of the information needed can be found in this chapter.

	Invertebrates		Vertebrates		
	Earthworm	Grasshopper	Fish	Bird	Mammal
Ingestion					
Physical breakdown					
Swallowing					
First stage of chemical breakdown					
Subsequent stages of chemical breakdown					
Absorption of nutrients					
Egestion					

Discussion

1. All digestive systems have the same overall function. Name this function and explain its importance.
2. a) In your chart, which two digestive systems are most similar? Are these animals similar in any other way? Explain.
   b) Which two digestive systems are least similar? Are these animals equally different in other ways? Explain.
3. a) The chart arranges the steps of digestion in a particular sequence. Is the sequence the same for all animals? Explain.
   b) Can all of the steps take place simultaneously in a living animal? Explain.
4. Many people think digestion takes place in the stomach. According to your completed chart, is this true for humans? for any other animal? Explain.

5. a) According to your chart, which are more common: animals with a gizzard or animals without?
   b) Explain the function of a gizzard. How is this function carried out by animals without a gizzard?
6. a) Which of the animals in your chart has the most complex digestive system?
   b) Does the degree of complexity depend more on diet or on the size of the animal? Explain.
7. Animals are classified as vertebrates or invertebrates on the basis of their skeletal and nervous systems. Are the digestive systems of the two groups also clearly different? Explain.
8. a) How could this chart be used to make a hypothesis about the digestive system of a honeybee? a kangaroo? a snake?
   b) Based on your answer to a), what is the value of comparative anatomy?

Interaction of Biological Systems

Although each biological system plays a specific role, no system can operate by itself. For example, the sensory and locomotory systems interact with the nervous system and with each other, so that animals can respond to changes in the external environment.

To maintain a suitable internal environment, the systems for gas exchange and digestion must also interact. Even though they seem to function separately, both systems provide molecules for cell respiration by moving materials from the external environment into the animal's body. Both systems also use a similar process to deliver those molecules to the internal environment.

In humans, for example, oxygen molecules diffuse through the lining of the lungs. Glucose molecules diffuse through the lining of the intestine. But simply getting inside is not enough. Before cell respiration can occur, the glucose and oxygen must be carried to every cell in the body. The process that links the two systems by doing this is called circulation. How it occurs will be discussed in Chapter 9.

Study Questions

1. Compare the bag type of digestive system with the tube type by describing:
   a) what they have in common,
   b) how they differ.

2. Compare the digestive system of a typical herbivore (e.g., a cow) with that of a typical carnivore (e.g., a cat) by describing:
   a) what the two systems have in common,
   b) how they differ.

3. Would your answers to question 2 also apply to a herbivore such as the grasshopper and a carnivore such as the spider? Explain.

4. Which type of animal normally requires a longer digestion time — a herbivore or a carnivore? Explain why.

5. All digestive systems include parts or organs that never hold food. Name two such organs, and describe their role in digestion.

6. Would you expect a very active organism to have a bag type of digestive system or a tube type? Explain why.

7. In mammals, food is moved along the digestive tube in "pulses". What type of tissue must be present in the walls of these tubes? Explain.

A WINDOW TO DIGESTION

In 1822, an unfortunate accident occurred at a Canadian trading post when a trapper named Alexis St. Martin was accidentally shot in the stomach. The shotgun blast blew a large hole in the victim's left side, exposing part of the ribs, muscles, and the wall of the stomach.

Dr. William Beaumont, an army physician from a nearby American post in Michigan, was called to treat Alexis St. Martin. For the next two years, Dr. Beaumont treated the infections invading the wound. The healing of the wound left a hole leading to the inside of the stomach. A flap of stomach wall covering the hole prevented food from falling out. This flap could be easily depressed, allowing direct observation of the stomach's interior.

Recognizing an unusual opportunity to study human digestion in action, Dr. Beaumont convinced Alexis St. Martin to become an experimental subject. Over a period of eleven years, Beaumont conducted experiments on human digestion. One type of experiment involved tying bits of food to string, and slipping them through the opening. This research revealed information such as: the temperature of digestion, the stages of digestion for cooked and uncooked meat, and the digestive capabilities of gastric

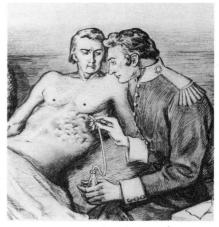

William Beaumont and Alexis St. Martin.

juices that Beaumont removed from the stomach.

After years of serving as a "human guinea pig", Alexis St. Martin returned to a normal life, and lived to the ripe old age of eighty-two.

Science-Related Career

Meet a Kinesiologist — Carol McLeod

Carol works at Feet First, a foot-care centre where people are treated for problems of the feet and lower limbs and are fitted with corrective devices.

Q. WHAT IS KINESIOLOGY?
A. It is the scientific study of human movement.

Q. WERE YOU ALWAYS INTERESTED IN THIS FIELD?
A. No, I first thought of going into a Fine Arts program, but then in Grade 13 I decided I wanted something more people-oriented. Luckily I had kept up my maths and sciences, so I still had options.

Q. HOW DID YOU LEARN ABOUT KINESIOLOGY, AND WHERE IS IT TAUGHT?
A. I knew someone in the field, and went to an open house at the University of Waterloo to see the kinesiology department. That convinced me. I enrolled at Waterloo and did an Honours Bachelor of Science, specializing in kinesiology. It is also taught at Simon Fraser University. At Guelph and Windsor they teach Human Kinetics, but that is slightly different.

Q. WHAT DID YOU STUDY AT UNIVERSITY?
A. In the first two years there was a lot of pure science, such as physics and biology. Every course had a lab, so there were a lot of experiments and research. I also took psychology and sociology courses that dealt with topics like behaviour modification and the social psychology of sport.

Q. DID YOU DO YOUR DEGREE ON A CO-OP PROGRAM?
A. No, I didn't, because the co-op program takes five years and I wanted to be finished in four. But co-op allows you to get business experience because you work part-time, and this also helps financially.

Q. WHERE ARE THE JOB OPPORTUNITIES IN KINESIOLOGY?
A. There are jobs in fitness clubs —to be a fitness director you must have a degree in kinesiology. Kinesiologists work in rehabilitative settings where they are part of a health care team. There are also some jobs in the occupational health and safety division of different government ministries. In the United States, corporate fitness testing in large companies is a big growth area. I think this will become popular here, too.

Q. WHAT DOES YOUR JOB AT FEET FIRST INVOLVE?
A. I'm a biomechanical specialist, trained in biomechanics and gait analysis of the lower limbs and feet. When someone comes in with a problem, we do an analysis. First I take down the person's history—where the pain is, what type of shoes the person wears, what activities he or she does, etc. Then I observe how the person walks. I put him or her on the treadmill and tape the gait on a video camera. I use the videotape as an analytical tool, showing the person exactly what is happening and where the problem is. We then recommend suitable footwear or corrective action if necessary.

Q. WHAT SORT OF CORRECTIVE ACTION MIGHT YOU RECOMMEND?
A. I might recommend treatment in a physiotherapy clinic, or a custom-made corrective device called an orthotic that fits inside the shoe.

Q. WHAT DO YOU LIKE BEST ABOUT YOUR JOB?
A. I like the fact that it's people-oriented. It's very satisfying to be able to relieve someone's pain or make him or her more mobile.

Review Questions

A: Knowledge

1. Heterotrophs use food from the external environment as a source of energy and materials.
   a) What must happen to the food before it can be used by the internal environment? Explain why.
   b) Explain how the energy is released. What is it used for?
   c) What are the materials used for? Are all the materials used? Explain.

2. a) Give three examples of food. Are maple leaves a food? Explain.
   b) Define the term nutrient, and give three examples.
   c) How are foods and nutrients related? How do they differ?

3. List the four major steps of digestion, and describe the function of each.

4. a) Choose a representative one-celled organism. Describe how it carries out each step of digestion.
   b) Repeat a) for a representative vertebrate.
   c) Repeat a) for a representative invertebrate.

5. Make a copy of the following chart and then complete it.

	Grasshopper	Earthworm
Structures for ingestion		
Methods of ingestion		
Structures for physical breakdown		
Methods of physical breakdown		

6. a) Define the term enzyme.
   b) Name two enzymes and explain precisely what each one does.
   c) Which step of digestion depends on enzymes? Explain why.

7. In humans, saliva contains water, mucin, and amylase. Explain the digestive function of each component and identify its role as physical or chemical.

8. Consider the following substances: pepsin, hydrochloric acid, and bile.
   a) Describe the usual action of each.
   b) What do the three substances have in common?
   c) Explain how they differ.

9. Animal digestive systems can be classified into two types, according to the kind of digestive cavity.
   a) State the two types of digestive systems and name one animal for each type.
   b) Do both types of system carry out the same steps of digestion? Explain.

10. a) Which has a digestive system most like that of a grasshopper: a fish, a bird, or a mammal? Support your answer.
    b) Which has a digestive system most like that of an earthworm: a fish, a bird, or a mammal? Support your answer.

11. The digestive system of an animal must be linked to its gas exchange system. Explain why, and name the structure(s) or system(s) that provide(s) this link.

B: Application

12. Biologists identify two types of digestion: extracellular, which takes place outside the cell, and intracellular, which takes place inside a cell. Use these terms to classify digestion in each organism below.
    a) *Amoeba*   d) earthworm
    b) *Paramecium*   e) frog
    c) grasshopper   f) human

13. Name two digestive juices that are not enzymes. Describe the function of each.

14. The mass of a grasshopper is about the same as the mass of a common earthworm. Which animal probably has the longer digestive tube? Give reasons for your answer.

15. a) What is the digestive function of a crop? Name two animals that use a crop for this function.
    b) Repeat a), substituting a gizzard.
    c) Humans do not have crops and gizzards. Do humans have organs that perform the same functions? Explain.

16. Name a vertebrate carnivore and an invertebrate carnivore. What similarities and differences would you expect to find in their digestive systems?

17. While gulping down lunch, a student eats an order of french fries too fast for the salivary amylase to act on the food before it is swallowed.
    a) How and where will the starch in the food be broken down? How and where will the fat be broken down?
    b) How does the answer to a) differ from what would occur if the food were adequately chewed?
    c) What is the benefit of chewing food? Explain why dogs remain healthy even though they gulp down their food without chewing.

18. The grasshopper's digestive system includes six pairs of pouches attached to the stomach. What is the most likely function of these pouches? Give reasons for your answer.

19. Certain birds of prey swallow their food whole. The gizzard compresses some parts of the prey into a hard pellet, which the bird regurgitates.
    a) What body parts do you think these pellets contain? Explain.
    b) Do you think pellet regurgitation removes the need for egestion? Explain your reasoning.

20. A microscopic look at the lining of an animal intestine shows that it is thickly "carpeted" with villi: tiny, finger-like projections richly supplied with blood vessels. What function do the villi play in digestion? Explain.

C: Problem Solving

21. Many gardeners say that earthworms are a sign of productive soil. How might earthworms make soil more suitable for plant growth?

22. Racoons normally dip their food in water before eating it. Many people think this behaviour shows that racoons are "clean". But racoons lack salivary glands. What is the most likely reason for the racoon's behaviour? Explain.

23. Intestinal bypass surgery involves shortening the small intestine of an obese patient to less than 20% of its original length. Explain how this could lead to permanent weight loss.

24. A patient with a serious digestive disorder can eat only liquid meals that contain fatty acids, amino acids, and glucose. Which digestive steps are not required to digest this type of meal? What parts of the patient's digestive system are probably malfunctioning? Explain.

25. In horses and rats, the appendix is a large, functional digestive organ. It is thought that early humans also had a highly developed appendix. In modern humans, however, the appendix is a vestigial organ (i.e., a tiny, non-functional structure). Could this change in humans be the result of changes in diet? Explain.

Try This

Eat a Potato

Place a piece of ordinary white potato in your mouth. While chewing steadily, answer the following questions, based on your observations.
a) Which teeth are used for biting and which for chewing? Is the tongue essential for chewing? What role does it play?
b) How soon does extra saliva start flowing into your mouth? How long does it continue to flow?
c) How does the texture of the potato change as you chew? Which changes do you think are probably caused by the water in the saliva? by the mucin?
d) At what point does the food in your mouth form a ball? What path is followed by the ball of food as you swallow?

Chapter 9
Systems for Circulating Materials

The public transportation system of a large city is an intricate but organized collection of widely varied components. These include vehicles, networks of wire and track, fuel, and the city's streets. The function of such a system is to move citizens between their homes and the places where they work and play. A system as complex as this one could easily become unbalanced, such as in a blizzard when large huddles of people are waiting for fleets of stalled vehicles. Maintaining a balance requires the smooth functioning of each component, and constant coordination to ensure that the vehicles circulate on schedule.

A living thing is also an intricate but organized collection of components. Each living cell requires a share of the oxygen and nutrients consumed by an organism, and each cell produces waste. For living things, it is vitally important that materials arrive where they should and when they should. Unicellular protists have organelles to create a suitable internal environment, while multicellular animals have organs and organ systems.

In Chapter 7 you learned how the gas exchange system brings oxygen to the internal environment, and removes carbon dioxide. In Chapter 8, you learned how the digestive system delivers nutrient molecules and eliminates wastes. This chapter will introduce the circulatory system, which distributes materials so that every cell gets its share, and which also removes cell wastes. You will first consider the components needed for circulation, and compare the two basic types of circulatory systems. You will then study the circulation of some representative animals in greater detail. Finally, you will learn how circulation works with digestion and gas exchange to maintain an internal balance.

When you finish Chapter 9, you should be able to:

- describe the circulating fluid and other components of circulatory systems
- compare open and closed circulatory systems
- compare the circulation in protists, invertebrates, and vertebrates
- discuss the contribution of gas exchange, digestion, and circulation in maintaining internal balance
- describe the function of the lymphatic system

9.1 Components for Circulation

Protists have no special organelles for circulation. In the amoeba, for example, the cytoplasmic streaming that makes locomotion possible also circulates all cell fluids. Thus, as oxygen and nutrient molecules diffuse inward, they are carried throughout the cell. Any wastes produced in the cytoplasm also circulate, and eventually diffuse into the external environment. Circulation in other protists is similar.

Figure 9-1. Cytoplasmic streaming in the *Amoeba* and the *Paramecium* carries materials throughout the body of these single-celled organisms.

Indigestible solid wastes never enter the cytoplasm of a protist cell. Instead, they stay trapped in the food vacuole, which eventually migrates to the cell's surface, bursts open, and ejects the solids into the external environment.

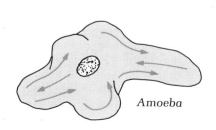

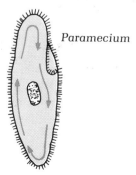

Paramecium

Amoeba

Circulatory Fluids

Circulation in multicellular animals requires **plasma**, a fluid that can carry molecules of nutrients, oxygen, and carbon dioxide. To do this, plasma needs a high concentration of water to keep the molecules dissolved. Usually, plasma also contains special cells that can carry large numbers of gas molecules. In mammals, for example, red blood cells carry molecules of oxygen. The circulating fluid and the cells together are called **blood**.

The blood of multicellular organisms is usually red, but there are exceptions. For example, the white meat of the lobster in the photograph shows no evidence of red blood. Organisms such as lobsters and grasshoppers circulate a clear, colourless fluid that performs the same function as the red blood found in earthworms, humans, fish, frogs, and alligators.

Regardless of colour, blood always circulates internally. Circulating fluids are never exchanged with the external environment. Thus, circulation differs from gas exchange and digestion, both of which have organs connected to the animal's external surroundings.

Tubes and Vessels

Just as subway trains travel through underground tunnels, so blood travels through the body in a network of tubelike vessels. In mammals, thick-walled vessels called **arteries** carry blood containing oxygen and nutrients to various parts of the body. The arteries branch into smaller and finer vessels called **capillaries**. These thin-walled vessels carry blood right into the tissues. Blood plasma, containing molecules of oxygen and nutrients such as glucose, diffuses out from the capillaries into spaces between the body cells where it becomes **tissue fluid**.

Figure 9-2. Arteries are connected to veins by a network of thin-walled capillaries.

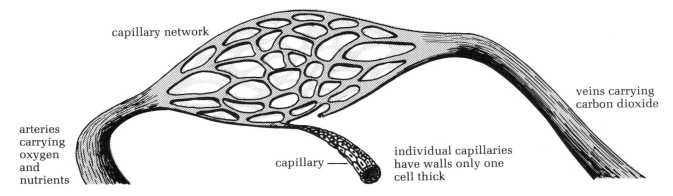

capillary network

veins carrying carbon dioxide

arteries carrying oxygen and nutrients

capillary —

individual capillaries have walls only one cell thick

Oxygen and nutrients enter individual cells by diffusion from the fluid that surrounds the cells. Inside the cell, enzyme-assisted reactions such as respiration form waste products such as carbon dioxide. All of these waste molecules diffuse out through the cell membrane into the tissue fluid. Tissue fluid containing the dissolved waste matter diffuses into the capillaries where it becomes blood plasma. The capillaries that conduct deoxygenated blood empty into larger vessels called **veins**.

All blood vessels are connected in a network that conducts fluid to every cell in the organism's body. The gases, nutrients, and waste materials can move between the cells and the capillaries by diffusion. But diffusion is not enough to carry the blood along the larger vessels. Another method, using some kind of pump, is needed to push the blood around the body.

Circulatory Pumps

While investigating the earthworm's digestive system, you may have noticed a network of red blood vessels surrounding the digestive tract (see Figure 9-3). As food is digested, the nutrients are absorbed by blood in capillaries near the intestine. These capillaries are connected to the dorsal blood vessel, which carries the blood forward to muscular tubes called aortic arches, or hearts. The hearts contract rhythmically to pump the nutrient-rich blood backward through the ventral blood vessel. Capillaries deliver it to the earthworm's cells. Valves in the hearts and in the dorsal vessel prevent the blood from backing up.

In larger animals, the circulatory pump is a separate organ known as the heart. In the following activity, you will study the structure of a mammalian heart.

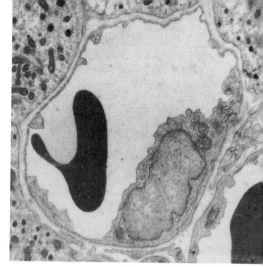

Note the diameter of the capillary in comparison to the red blood cells.

Do You Know?
Oxygen is carried in the blood of most vertebrates by attaching to a protein called **hemoglobin**. This protein contains iron atoms, and gives the blood its red colour. There is, however, a species of fish found in Antarctic waters that has no hemoglobin. The cold water contains so much dissolved oxygen that the fish has no need for a special oxygen-carrier in its blood.

Figure 9-3. Note the direction of the blood flow through the aortic arches of the earthworm.

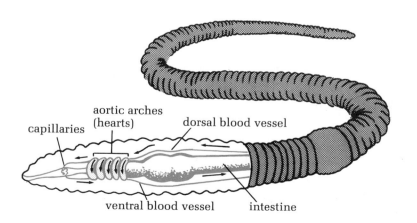

aortic arches
(hearts)

dorsal blood vessel

capillaries

ventral blood vessel   intestine

Figure 9-4. A mammal's heart acts like a double pump. The "right heart" pumps blood through the lungs. The "left heart" receives the oxygenated blood from the lungs and pumps it to the rest of the body.

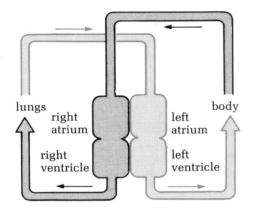

Do You Know?
The heart sound, "lubb-dubb", is the sound of the valves closing. Rheumatic fever often leaves scar tissue on the valves, which interferes with the blood flow through the heart.

Vessels called arteries always carry blood *away* from the heart, while veins always carry blood *toward* the heart.

Activity 9-1: The Dissection of a Mammalian Heart

To maximize the learning value of this activity, it is important to preview the structure of the four-chambered mammalian heart (see Figure 9-4). Two upper chambers, or **atria** (singular: **atrium)** receive blood. Two lower chambers, or **ventricles**, pump blood out. A thick wall called the **septum** divides the right and left sides of the heart.

The right chambers circulate deoxygenated blood through the lungs, while the left chambers circulate oxygen-rich blood through the rest of the body. One-way valves keep blood from flowing backwards between muscular contractions.

Deoxygenated blood enters the right atrium through the **superior vena cava** (from the head and upper part of the body), and the **inferior vena cava** (from the legs and lower part of the body). From the right atrium, deoxygenated blood enters the right ventricle which pumps it through the **pulmonary artery** to the lungs. There, the waste carbon dioxide diffuses out, while fresh supplies of oxygen diffuse in.

Oxygenated blood from the lungs returns through the **pulmonary vein** to the left atrium. From there, the blood passes into the left ventricle, which pumps it out to the rest of the body through the body's largest artery, the **aorta**. Arteries branching from the aorta carry oxygenated blood throughout the body.

In the following activity, you will perform a dissection to locate some of the major heart structures.

Materials

fresh or preserved mammalian
   heart (pig, cow, or sheep)

dissecting pan

scalpel

scissors

probe

Procedure

1. Identify the four heart chambers and all major vessels.

2. Make a horizontal cut in each atrium (see Figure 9-5). Examine the chambers, any attached vessels, and all valves. Push a probe through each valve, in both directions if possible.

3. Make a vertical cut in both ventricles (see Figure 9-5). Examine the chambers, any attached vessels, and all valves. Again test the valves with a probe.

4. Using a dissecting probe, trace the circulation through the side of the heart that connects to the lungs.

Figure 9-5. A mammalian heart, showing the major parts and the incisions made in steps 2 and 3.

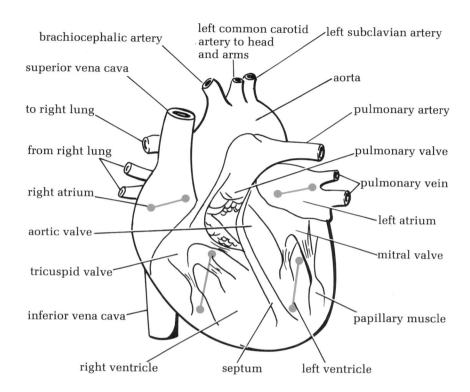

5. Repeat step 4 on the side of the heart that connects to the rest of the body.

6. Locate the aorta. With scissors, cut vertically away from the vessels branching off the aorta. Examine these vessels as your teacher directs.

7. Keep the dissected heart nearby as you answer the discussion questions.

Discussion

1. a) The heart is not symmetrical. Which side is larger, the pulmonary side (leading to the lungs), or the systemic side (leading to the rest of the body)?
   b) Why should one side of the heart need more muscle tissue than the other?

2. What clues can be used to identify the front and back of the heart?

3. a) The heart has only one-way valves. What happened when you tried to push through a valve the opposite way?
   b) Why are one-way valves needed?

4. The heart has two types of one-way valves. (See Figure 9-5.) Some separate the atria from the ventricles. Others separate the ventricles from major blood vessels. Name the two types. How do they differ in size, structure, and complexity?

5. a) The heart has two types of vessels. Some carry blood towards the heart; others carry blood away. Which vessels have a greater diameter? Which vessels are more elastic?
   b) Explain why two types of blood vessels are needed.

6. A small hole in the septum can create a serious circulation problem. Identify the problem and explain why it is so serious.

Circulation: The Endless Flow

Blood circulates continuously in multicellular organisms, transporting dissolved gases, nutrients, and wastes, like passengers on an endless, circular commuter train. The network of fine capillaries ensures that every cell of the body is on the route of this efficient transportation system.

Although the circulatory system itself is enclosed, its "passengers" can come and go between the internal and external environments. For example, an oxygen molecule from the air might "hop onto" a blood cell in the earthworm's circulatory system by diffusing first through a skin cell at the worm's front end and then diffusing into a capillary. From there it could flow via the ventral blood vessel towards the internal environment near the worm's tail. There the oxygen molecule could leave the circulatory system by diffusing out of another capillary, and into a muscle cell. After respiration, a waste carbon dioxide molecule from the muscle cell would enter the circulatory system by diffusing through a capillary wall into the blood. The carbon dioxide is carried along until it reaches a capillary near the skin surface, where it diffuses into the external environment. Smooth functioning of the internal environment depends on this type of interaction between the systems for gas exchange and circulation.

The digestive system also uses the circulatory system for transportation. For example, digested food in the form of nutrient molecules enters the earthworm's bloodstream by diffusing into capillaries that surround the small intestine. From there, the nutrient molecules may be carried to any cell in the body—one in the worm's brain, for instance. After the cell uses the nutrients, waste molecules enter the capillaries by diffusing from the tissue fluid surrounding the cell. The cellular wastes are carried by the circulating blood to particular sites in the body where they are collected for excretion. In the earthworm, for example, such wastes enter the coiled excretory tubules called **nephridia**. In a human, waste products are collected by the kidney cells.

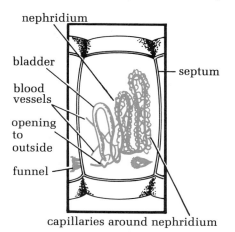

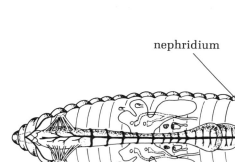

Figure 9-6. The earthworm's cellular wastes are collected from the blood by the nephridia, and excreted to the outside by a pore on the ventral surface.

Study Questions

1. Protists have no circulating tubes or vessels. Despite this, nutrients and oxygen molecules circulate freely. Explain.

2. List all of the components needed by a circulatory system, and describe the function of each.

3. Explain the difference between:
   a) plasma, blood, and tissue fluid
   b) arteries and capillaries
   c) arteries and veins

4. a) What materials are needed for cell respiration to occur?
   b) Explain the role of capillaries in cell respiration.

5. The earthworm's skin has an abundance of capillaries. Why are they located there, rather than anywhere else in the worm's body?

6. The circulatory system is often referred to as the body's link between the internal and external environments. Explain.

7. In what way is a city's transportation system similar to the circulatory system of a multicellular animal?

ARTIFICIAL HEARTS

Dr. Barney Clark, a retired dentist, made medical history in 1982 when his own heart was cut away and replaced by a plastic heart. The Jarvik artificial heart, which pumped Clark's blood around his body for nearly four months, consisted of two plastic spheres, each containing a diaphragm that was driven up and down by compressed air. Plastic tubes leading from the artificial heart were attached to the patient's own blood vessels.

Although the heart is one of the simplest organs in the body — it is basically a muscular pump — it is nevertheless remarkably difficult to duplicate. The heart performs its double pumping action — pumping blood first through the lungs and then through the rest of the body —

40 million times a year; it is equipped with an automatic control mechanism that tells it when to speed up or slow down, and when to pump more or less strongly; and it has its own built-in power supply.

One problem with the artificial heart given to Barney Clark was the size of the power supply. The Jarvik artificial heart was driven by compressed air, delivered by a 170 kg apparatus mounted on a trolley beside Clark's bed. This "power pack" has now been reduced to the size of a briefcase, but operates only three to four hours before it needs recharging.

A second problem with the artificial heart is that its mechanical action could damage the blood and lead to clotting. Clark was given large doses of anticoagulant drug to avoid this problem, but these drugs may have damaged his other organs. The new heart may also have pushed the blood too hard for Clark's other organs, which were

Dr. Robert Jarvik holds the artificial heart he invented.

wasted after his long heart disease.

There have been a few more implants of artificial hearts, but given the present stage of technology, doctors believe such implants are much less useful than a heart transplant from a human donor.

9.2 Investigating Circulatory Systems

Most animals have a circulatory system with a system of tubes and a muscular heart to pump a circulating fluid around the body. All circulatory systems can be classified into two major types: open and closed.

Open Circulation

In open circulatory systems, the circuit of tubes and vessels is incomplete, and the circulating fluid can pour out of the tubes into the body cavity. This forms slow-moving pools of blood that bathe

the animal's tissues and deliver nutrients and oxygen to the cells. Continued pumping pressure eventually brings the pooled blood back into tubes that return it to the "pumping station", the heart.

Open circulatory systems are found in 90% of Earth's animal species. These include all members of the phylum arthropoda: lobsters, spiders, crabs, scorpions, and every type of insect. Figure 9-7 shows the open circulation in a grasshopper. Its blood is pumped through a muscular, seven-chambered heart into large cavities located among the body tissues.

The slow rate of open circulation is not a great disadvantage in insects because oxygen molecules are carried by a separate system of air tubes and not by the circulatory system. An insect's blood serves mainly to deliver nutrients and to collect cell wastes. The **Malpighian tubules** that lie in the body cavity gather these wastes from the blood, and pour them into the digestive tract for elimination through the anus.

Clams, snails, scallops, and most other members of phylum mollusca also use open circulation. The remaining mollusks and all other animal species use closed circulation.

Closed Circulation

In closed circulatory systems, the circulating fluid remains inside blood vessels throughout its circuit around the body. The earthworm's closed system shown in Figure 9-3 is much less complex than the squid's. The squid pumps blood through a branching network of small capillaries by two separate mechanisms—one for deoxygenated blood going through the gills, and one for re-oxygenated blood going to other tissues.

This arrangement is similar to the closed mammalian system, in which one side of the heart pumps deoxygenated blood through the lungs while the other pumps re-oxygenated blood through the rest of the body. In Activity 9-2, you will investigate the closed circulatory system in another vertebrate—a fish.

Figure 9-7. In a grasshopper, blood is pumped by a muscular, seven-chambered heart into a dorsal vessel. From there it flows out into spaces among the body tissues.

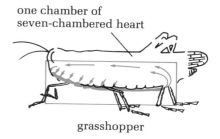

one chamber of
seven-chambered heart

grasshopper

Review the stages of gas exchange in Chapter 7 on pages 203-204 if necessary.

The cuttlefish, like the squid, has a closed circulatory system.

Activity 9-2:   The Anatomy of a Perch

Vertebrates are classified by the protective backbone encasing their spinal cord. They also share many other structural features. By studying one vertebrate, you can learn many facts that apply to most of the others. The perch is often chosen as a representative vertebrate because it is common, and easily raised in a hatchery.

In this activity, you will dissect a perch in order to examine vertebrate systems for gas exchange, digestion, and circulation.

Materials

preserved perch	scalpel
dissecting pan	scissors
forceps	hand lens
dissecting probe	straight pins

Procedure

Part A: External Anatomy

1. Place the fish in a dissecting pan. Carefully examine its nostrils and eyes.

2. Draw an outline diagram of the fish (see Figure 9-8) and label each type of fin described below.

   - pectoral fin — on the lateral surface, behind the operculum
   - pelvic fin   — front fin on ventral surface
   - anal fin   — back fin on ventral surface
   - dorsal fin   — on dorsal surface
   - caudal fin   — at posterior end

Figure 9-8.   The major external features of a perch.

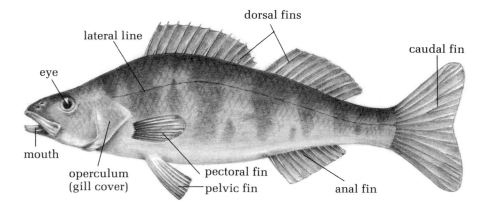

3. Open the mouth of the fish, and note its teeth and tongue. With a probe examine the pharynx. Lift the operculum, and examine the gill slits and filaments with the hand lens.

4. Remove a scale from the side of the fish. With a hand lens or compound microscope, observe its shape and size and note the concentric rings. (Each dark ring represents a year of growth. How old is your fish?)

5. Locate the lateral line that extends from front to back. This lateral line is believed to be a pressure-sensitive organ for the fish.

Discussion

1. What do you think is the function of:
   a) pectoral fins?
   b) anal fins?
   c) caudal find?
   d) dorsal fins?

2. How does the colouring of the dorsal, ventral, and lateral sides differ? What advantage might this give the perch?

3. How does the perch keep its gills supplied with fresh water? Why is this important?

Part B: Internal Anatomy

1. To examine the internal anatomy of the perch, hold the fish with its ventral side upward. Follow the cutting pattern shown in Figure 9-9 as described below.

   a) Insert the pointed end of the scissors through the body wall just in front of the anal opening. Cut forward in a straight line towards the operculum.
   b) Cut upward behind the gills to a point just below the lateral line.
   c) Cut upward at the anal end to a point just below the lateral line.
   d) From the top of line B, cut towards the top of line C. Cut straight, and stay just below the lateral line.

   You have now cut a rectangular flap. Remove it carefully to expose the internal organs.

Figure 9-9. Make your cuts in the order and direction shown.

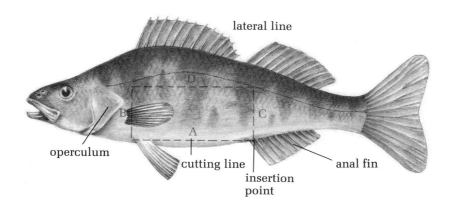

lateral line

operculum

cutting line

insertion point

anal fin

2. Remove the operculum to expose the gills of the fish. Locate the gill opening and filaments. Trace the steps in fish gas exchange.

3. Locate the following parts of the digestive system: esophagus, stomach, pyloric caeca, intestine, and liver. Draw and label a diagram showing these parts.

Figure 9-10. The internal anatomy of the perch.

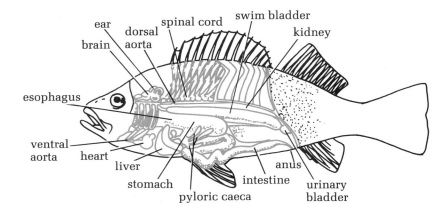

4. Locate the large swim bladder, dorsal to the digestive tract. The bladder acts as a float that adjusts to let the fish swim at any desired depth.

5. Locate the heart with its two chambers. Note the dorsal and ventral aortas attached to the heart.

6. Locate the brain, kidneys, and urinary bladder in your specimen.

Discussion

1. a) What evidence is there of a rich blood supply in the gills?
   b) Why is this rich blood supply important?

2. What evidence is there that the perch's circulatory system is closed?

3. What evidence is there that the perch's circulatory system is linked to the systems for digestion and gas exchange?

4. What other systems seem to be involved in maintaining the perch's internal environment? Explain.

5. If a perch had a damaged swim bladder that could hold no air, what would the fish do — sink to the bottom or float on the water's surface? Explain.

The Circulatory System in Fishes

Dissecting a fish shows the major parts of its closed circulatory system — heart, arteries, and veins. The capillaries, however, are too fine to be seen without a microscope. Capillaries must have very thin walls to allow the diffusion of dissolved gases and wastes. Arteries, on the other hand, need very thick walls to withstand the force exerted as the blood is pumped from the heart. In this respect, fish and mammal systems are similar. However, a fish's circulation does not return oxygenated blood to the heart before sending it to other parts of the body.

The oxygen requirements of fish vary from species to species. Trout, for example, require water with a high oxygen content, while catfish can survive in water with a much lower oxygen content.

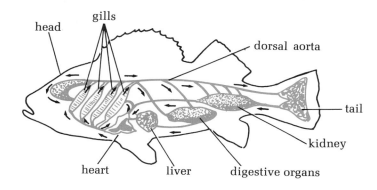

Figure 9-11. The blood from a fish's heart goes directly to the gills for oxygenation, and then continues around the body.

Study Questions

1. a) Clearly explain the difference between an open and a closed circulatory system.
   b) Which type is most common in the animal kingdom?
2. a) Describe open circulation in the grasshopper.
   b) What other animals probably have a similar system? Explain.
3. a) Describe closed circulation in the fish.
   b) What other animals probably have a similar system? Explain.
4. Compare the efficiency of open and closed circulatory systems.
5. a) The fish has a two-chambered heart. What is the function of each chamber?
   b) What are the limitations of the fish heart as compared to the four-chambered mammalian heart?
6. Do animals such as humans really have a completely closed circulatory system in which the fluid never leaves the vessels? Discuss.

WILLIAM HARVEY
(1578-1657)

From the time of Aristotle, in the fourth century B.C., it was believed that blood vessels carried both blood and air, and that blood moved in the body by ebbing and flowing, like the tides in the sea. Scholars supported these ideas for nearly 2000 years, until an English physician, William Harvey, upset the old beliefs with experimental evidence of blood circulation.

After medical studies at Cambridge University, William Harvey became physician to King James I. Although he was taught the ideas of Aristotle, and those of the second century physician Galen, Harvey was curious about the function of the heart and decided to conduct his own research. He dissected all kinds of living things, and learned about human anatomy from post-mortem examinations. From his observations and experiments, he concluded that the heart acted as a pump, and that blood circulated through the lungs and around the body. He rejected the idea that blood vessels contained air. Harvey correctly described the function of heart valves in preventing the backward flow of blood, and he was the first scientist to measure the capacity of the heart and to estimate the total amount of blood in the body.

In 1628, Harvey published his important discoveries in a small book entitled *On the Motion of the Heart and Blood in Animals*. The book made him famous throughout Europe, but he was also strongly opposed by many other physicians, who did not like the destruction of so many long-held beliefs.

9.3 Comparing Circulatory Systems

In Unit II, you learned that animals are classified on the basis of body plan, or structure. Thus, a biologist studying a crayfish would expect to find its circulatory system similar to that of a grasshopper, which is in the same phylum—Arthropoda.

Even within the same phylum, however, important differences can be observed. For example, fishes and frogs belong to the same phylum as penguins and people. Figures 9-12 to 9-15 show that while these vertebrate classes have the same basic circulatory plan, the heart structures differ. The size and design of a vertebrate's heart is related to the animal's way of life.

Circulation in Fishes and Amphibians

Blood passes through the small, two-chambered heart of a fish only once on each round trip. During a single circuit, oxygen-poor blood is pumped from the heart to the gills for reoxygenation, and then flows directly to other parts of the body before it comes back to the heart.

This "single pump" action delivers blood at low pressure. **Blood pressure** measures how intensely blood pushes on the vessel walls. Blood at high pressure delivers oxygen to the capillaries more efficiently, so low blood pressure could be a disadvantage. However, the cold-blooded fish needs less oxygen than a warm-blooded animal of the same mass. Furthermore, gills extract oxygen from water more efficiently than lungs extract it from air. For these two reasons, a single pump system easily meets the needs of a fish.

Air-breathers, however, need systems that can produce more pressure. Amphibians such as frogs solve this problem with a three-chambered heart that acts as a "double pump". In the first circuit, oxygen-poor blood is pumped to the lungs to collect oxygen, and returned to the heart. Then the oxygen-rich blood is pumped through a second circuit around the rest of the body. Pumping the blood twice produces the extra pressure required.

However, the single ventricle allows blood from body systems to mix with blood from the lungs. As a result, the cells never receive

Figure 9-12. A fish's heart.

Figure 9-13. A frog's heart has three chambers.

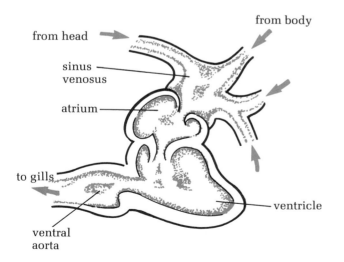

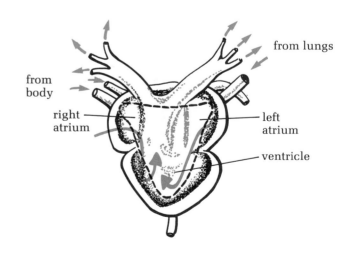

fully oxygenated blood. Although adequate for cold-blooded amphibians, this arrangement cannot meet the needs of warm-blooded animals.

Circulation in Birds and Mammals

Both birds and mammals have four-chambered hearts that are well-suited for their warm-blooded, air-breathing way of life. The double pump action provides the required blood pressure. Two distinct ventricles separate the circuits so cells receive fully oxygenated blood.

But as blood brushes past the vessel walls, it loses pressure, especially if it travels a long way. Thus, large mammals need powerful hearts to move oxygen-rich blood all around the body. They also need arteries with thick, strong walls because the pressure of blood emerging from the heart is so great. In humans, for example, a severed aorta can spurt blood 2 m.

To maintain this much pressure, a separate blood supply is needed to allow rapid cell respiration in the heart muscle. In humans, this is provided by a **coronary artery**, which branches from the aorta soon after it leaves the heart.

Although its circulatory system is similar, a bird needs more energy than a mammal of the same mass, both for flight and to keep its body about 3 °C warmer. To make faster cell respiration possible,

Any blockage of the coronary artery starves the heart muscle of nutrients and oxygen. Over time, the muscle cells die, and may cause a heart attack.

Figure 9-14. A mammal's heart.

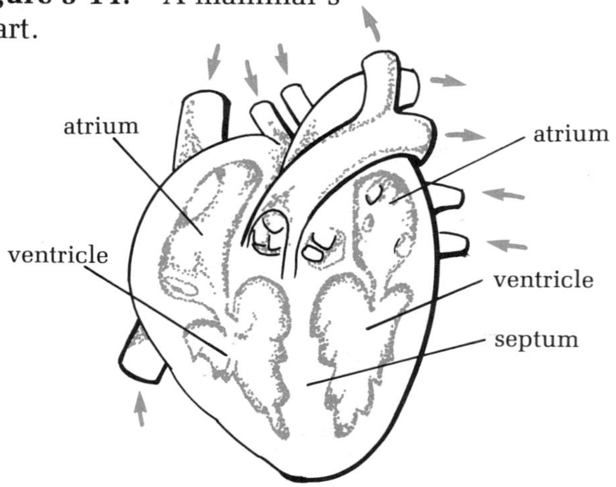

atrium

atrium

ventricle

ventricle

septum

Figure 9-15. A bird's heart.

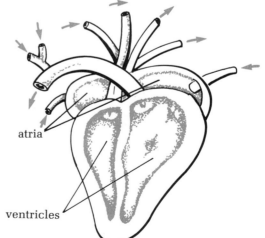

atria

ventricles

a bird's heart is extra large—up to 2.4% of body mass, compared to less than 0.8% in most mammals. A bird's heart also beats very fast—up to 1000 beats per minute for a hummingbird. By contrast, the maximum rate for most humans is only 180 beats per minute, and then only for short periods.

Activity 9-3: Animal System Survey

In Unit III, you have studied the systems for three major life functions: gas exchange, digestion, and circulation. Whether you do one or both parts, this activity will give you an opportunity to consolidate what you have learned.

(NOTE: In Part B you are asked to make a hypothesis. The objective is not to get the "right" answer, but to apply what you have learned to make a reasonable hypothesis.)

Part A: Comparative Anatomy

Prepare a presentation to compare gas exchange, digestion, and circulation in protists, invertebrates, and vertebrates. Choose one species to represent each category. Possible methods of presentation include:

- a chart
- a poster that shows similarities or differences
- an essay of about 200 words
- a short talk for your class

Do You Know?
Some birds, such as the herring gull and the penguin, have a circulatory adaptation to prevent heat loss through their feet. Special conducting vessels in their legs collect heat from the warm arterial blood flowing to the feet, and transfer it to the cooler venous blood going back to the heart. This conserves heat in the bird's body core, leaving its feet at a cooler temperature.

Discussion

1. Which method of presentation was most effective? Why?
2. In simpler life forms, the internal environment is more closely connected to the external environment than in higher life forms. Discuss this statement.
3. Less than 3% of all animal species are vertebrates. What are some reasons for this?

Part B: Applied Anatomy

So far in this unit, only mammals, birds, amphibians, and fishes have been used as examples of vertebrates. But alligators, lizards, turtles, and snakes are also vertebrates. On the scale of animal development, these reptiles are thought to be more advanced than fishes and amphibians, but less advanced than birds and mammals. Reptiles are cold-blooded. Some spend their lives in swampy environments, while others live in the desert.

Figure 9-16.

Procedure

1. Figure 9-16 shows the outline of a typical reptile. Title three full-page copies of this outline as follows: 1) "Gas Exchange Systems of a Reptile", 2)"Digestive System of a Reptile", 3) "Circulatory System of a Reptile".

2. **Make a Hypothesis.** Based on your present knowledge of gas exchange, draw a labelled sketch to predict the gas exchange system of a reptile. (HINT: Ask yourself questions such as: Are reptiles more likely to have gills or lungs?)

3. Repeat step 2 for digestion, using arrows to trace the path of food and nutrients.

4. Repeat step 2 for circulation, using arrows to trace the path of blood.

5. After completing steps 1 to 4, consult a reference book to check your predictions and to obtain information for the discussion questions below.

Discussion

1. How is body temperature related to gas exchange and blood circulation in the reptile?

2. The complexity of the reptile heart varies. Describe and discuss this variation.

3. The history of the egg is the key to the rise of the reptiles. Explain what this means.

Study Questions

1. a) Explain clearly how double pump circulation differs from single pump circulation.
   b) Which system is better? Explain.

2. What relationship exists between an animal's normal body temperature and its circulatory system?

3. Why do birds require a greater oxygen supply and a larger, more powerful heart than reptiles?

4. A four-chambered heart is really two separate hearts attached together. Discuss this statement.

5. Which class of animals has the most complex circulatory system: fishes, amphibians, reptiles, birds, or mammals? Explain why.

9.4　Maintaining Internal Balance

So far, biological systems have been discussed as if they were independent. In fact, they are interconnected. Consider a racehorse bursting out of the starting gate. As it accelerates, its heartbeat increases to supply more oxygen and nutrients to the locomotory system. Its digestion slows to a minimum, so that more blood can circulate between the gas exchange system and the muscle cells.

A racehorse in full gallop. What biological systems are in play? How are they connected?

The breathing rate increases as its internal environment demands more and more oxygen to replace that being used by the mitochondria. Nongaseous cellular wastes are excreted all over the horse's body in droplets of sweat, which cool the horse as they evaporate. Even though its heartbeat and breathing rate may triple or double, the horse's temperature remains almost constant.

Humans also must balance internal needs with external conditions, for living things can carry out their life functions only by maintaining a constant internal environment. In animals, each body system interacts with the others to achieve this balance, some slowing down as others speed up, and some working together. The role of the nervous system in coordinating interactions was discussed in Unit II. But many other coordinating systems play a role in maintaining a stable internal environment.

Figure 9-17. Lymph nodes in humans are concentrated in the armpits, groin, elbows, and knees.

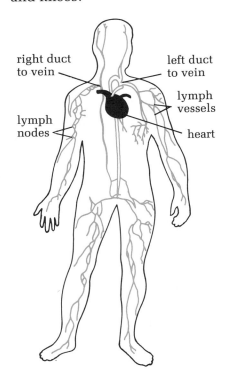

right duct to vein

left duct to vein

lymph vessels

lymph nodes

heart

The Role of the Lymphatic System

The **lymphatic system** consists of a network of tubes that collect the tissue fluid bathing the spaces between body cells. When the colourless liquid passes into these tubes it is called **lymph**. Highly permeable vessel walls allow the lymph to collect large particles such as bacteria and transport them to the **lymph nodes**. The nodes are enlarged clusters of knotted tubes that filter the lymph. Special cells in the nodes destroy foreign organisms. The remaining liquid re-enters the blood circulation through a duct leading to a vein near the heart. Although the two circulations are interconnected, the lymphatic system has no pump. The lymph is moved along as the vessels are squeezed by nearby muscle tissue.

The Role of Excretion

In protists and animals alike, all cell activities release waste products into the internal environment. Although most cellular wastes are harmless in small quantities, they can be poisonous if they accumulate. The **excretory system** eliminates cellular wastes into the external environment through special structures such as sweat glands and kidneys (in humans), nephridia (in earthworms), or contractile vacuoles (in *Amoebae*).

Gaseous wastes such as carbon dioxide and some water vapour are excreted through the skin or the gas exchange surface. Disposing of nitrogen-containing wastes produced when proteins break down inside cells is more difficult. In animals, the circulatory system collects these nitrogenous wastes from the cells and carries them to an excretory organ, such as a kidney. There, they are concentrated and excreted in the form of urine or similar waste products.

Note how excretion differs from egestion, which expels undigested food from the digestive tube. These materials never enter the internal environment. By contrast, excreted materials are produced by chemical reactions within the cells of the internal environment.

All protists and animals require a constant outflow of cellular wastes as well as a constant inflow of nutrients and oxygen to carry out their life functions. An organism can only continue to live as long as this exchange maintains an internal environment that differs from the external environment. Maintaining this balance requires coordinated interaction of many biological systems. As you go on to further studies, you will learn more about the other internal systems that enable digestion, circulation, and gas exchange to function in a coordinated way.

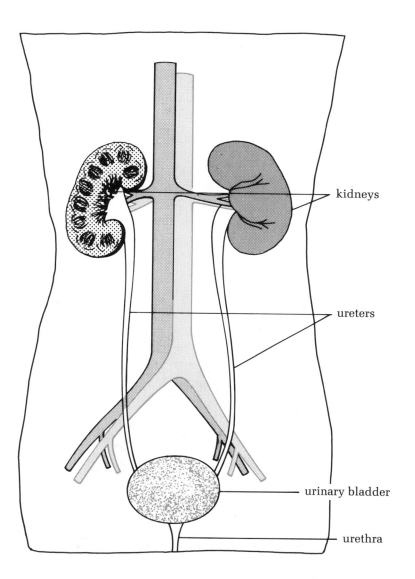

kidneys

ureters

urinary bladder

urethra

Figure 9-18. The human excretory system must interact with the digestive system in order to maintain internal balance.

Do You Know?
An infection can inhibit the kidney's ability to process waste materials in the body. If it is not properly treated, the build-up of waste materials interferes with internal balance. In fact, the accumulation of waste may cause death.

Study Questions

1. Explain why maintaining an internal balance is important.
2. What is the role of circulation in maintaining internal balance? of digestion? of gas exchange?
3. What are some of the other body systems that assist in maintaining a constant internal environment?

4. Construct a table and compare the lymphatic and circulatory systems under the following headings:
   - type of fluid
   - difference in composition of fluid
   - major function
5. An excretory organ such as the kidney is specialized for eliminating certain waste products. What are the waste products and where do they come from?
6. How are the digestive, gas exchange, and circulatory systems involved in excretion?

THE ARTIFICIAL KIDNEY

The primary function of the kidneys is to eliminate cellular wastes from the blood. If the kidneys fail to perform this basic function, individuals will die of poisoning from their own wastes. A person with partially or totally nonfunctioning kidneys has only two choices: a kidney transplant, or treatment on a kidney dialysis machine. Since matching kidneys are not readily available, most patients must rely on the kidney dialysis machine to purify blood until an organ becomes available for transplant.

A plastic shunt is implanted between the artery and the vein in an arm or leg, and the patient is hooked up to the dialysis unit by means of an arterial shunt. Blood is carried from the arterial

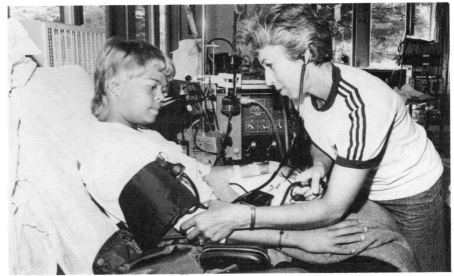

A young patient with a kidney defect has her blood circulated through a kidney dialysis machine.

shunt through the dialysis machine, where it is purified and then returned, by means of a venous shunt, to the kidney patient.

Inside the kidney machine, a series of semipermeable dialysis tubing is bathed in a dialysis solution. Wastes from the patient's blood diffuse into the solution. Purified blood is then returned to the patient. The entire dialysis process takes three to six hours. The number of visits per week to a hospital's kidney dialysis unit varies according to the condition of the patient.

Meet a Cardiologist— Dr. Brian Gilbert

Brian is the Chief of Cardiology at Mount Sinai Hospital in Toronto. He spends part of his time teaching medical students at University of Toronto Medical School where he is an associate professor.

Q. WHEN DID YOU DECIDE TO BECOME A DOCTOR?

A. Not until the end of high school. I was accepted into pre-med at the University of Toronto and also did my medical degree there. Later I went to Duke University in North Carolina to specialize in cardiology.

Q. WHAT DOES A CARDIOLO-GIST DO?

A. I diagnose and treat patients who are sent to me by a family doctor or an internist because of a heart problem.

Q. WHAT'S INVOLVED IN A TYPICAL PATIENT EXAMINA-TION?

A. I first take the patient's history and list their complaints, such as chest pains, shortness of breath, or dizziness. Then I examine the patient in the examining room. I take the blood pressure and look at the blood vessels in the eyes—these are the only blood vessels you can see without going into the body. I palpate (touch medically) all the major vessels and use a stethoscope to listen to them. I also listen to the heart sounds to see if there are any abnormal murmurs or gallops. In each case, I look for anything abnormal that would indicate a disturbance in the blood flowing through the vessels.

Q. DO MOST PATIENTS REQUIRE MORE TESTS?

A. Yes, and the next step is to decide which of many diagnostic tests to use. If the tests show that the patient has a cardiac problem, I then have to decide on the treatment. Three choices exist. One is to treat the patient with drugs. The second is to use an invasive procedure, such as inserting a catheter into a blood vessel and treating the problem under fluoroscope. The third option is surgery which is the only choice for certain problems.

Q. WHAT ARE YOU MOST PROUD OF IN YOUR CAREER?

A. I was involved in the introduction of two-dimensional echo cardiography to Canada. This is a diagnostic method using ultrasound that bounces sound waves off various parts of the heart in order to build up a whole picture of cardiac anatomy and function. I had trained in this when I was in North Carolina. When I came to this hospital in 1976, it didn't have any of these machines. Now they're an integral part of any cardiac patient's examination.

Q. IS IT DIFFICULT TO KEEP UP WITH SUCH A RAPIDLY CHANGING FIELD?

A. The changes in cardiology are greater than in any other medical field. There have been great advances in drug therapy, invasive procedures, and surgery. For instance, when the first heart transplant was performed in 1967, the patient lived only eighteen days. Now the survival rate is up to 75% for the first year.

Q. WHAT ADVICE DO YOU HAVE FOR A STUDENT INTER-ESTED IN BECOMING A CARDI-OLOGIST?

A. Be prepared to work hard. Math and sciences are important, but don't neglect languages and English. A major lesson for me was finding out how important communication is. After all, you are dealing with people's lives, not just their medical problems.

Review Questions

A: Knowledge

1. a) List the two primary functions of a circulatory system.
    b) What materials must all circulatory systems be able to carry?
    c) Explain where these materials must be circulated and why.

2. a) Describe circulation in protists, and explain why they do not require special circulatory systems.
    b) Explain why most animals do need specialized body systems for circulation.

3. Each circulatory system has three major components. List these components and explain the function of each.

4. Discuss the following pairs of terms. Explain what they have in common, how they differ, and how they are related to circulation.
    a) artery vs capillary   d) blood vs lymph
    b) artery vs vein   e) lymph vs plasma
    c) blood vs plasma   f) lymph vs tissue fluid

5. The circulatory systems in multicellular animals are of two basic types.
    a) Name both types and list two animals for each.
    b) Explain how the two types of circulation differ.
    c) Which type is more common? What advantage(s) does it have over the other type?

6. Describe the circulatory system of:
    a) a representative vertebrate
    b) a representative invertebrate

7. All materials used by living things come from the external environment and eventually return there. But circulatory fluids have no direct contact with the external environment. How do these fluids obtain fresh materials and discard wastes?

8. a) Why is the mammalian heart sometimes called a "double pump"?
    b) Name an animal having a "single pump"

type of heart. Explain how this type of heart differs from a double pump.

9. a) Describe in detail the route followed by blood as it flows through a mammalian heart. Begin where deoxygenated blood enters the heart.
    b) Describe in general terms the route followed by blood as it flows through a mammalian body. Begin where reoxygenated blood leaves the heart.

10. How does the pressure of blood as it leaves the heart of a fish change as it travels towards the tail? Explain what causes this change.

11. Humans and many other animals have two circulatory systems. Name the second system and explain its function.

12. a) List the body systems involved in maintaining a constant internal environment.
    b) Name two organs or body parts associated with each system.
    c) Describe the role each system plays in maintaining internal balance.

B: Application

13. Consider the following organisms: snake, shark, owl, honeybee, clam, *Euglena*, weasel, polar bear, mosquito, toad, brook trout, jellyfish. Giving reasons for your answer in each case, name those which probably have:
    a) open circulation
    b) closed circulation
    c) a two-chambered heart
    d) a three-chambered heart
    e) a four-chambered heart
    f) a lymphatic system

14. Both veins and lymph vessels have one-way valves.
    a) State the function of these valves and explain how they assist in circulation.
    b) Would you expect to find one-way valves in arteries too? Explain.

15. a) Is an animal's size related to type of circulation? Defend your answer.

b) Is an animal's activity level related to type of circulation? Defend your answer.

16. In multicellular organisms, each living cell is bathed in a liquid called tissue fluid. The cell exchanges nutrients, gases, and wastes with the tissue fluid. How does this arrangement compare with the exchange of materials in a single-celled organism such as *Paramecium*?

17. Animals such as humans have two circulatory systems. Construct a chart that compares the functions and components of these two systems.

18. Compare the circulatory system of a fish with the subway system of a city:
   a) What components of the fish's system have a function similar to the subway tunnels? the subway trains? the passengers? the stations? In each case, explain your reasoning.
   b) What device is used to move objects in a subway system? in a circulatory system? Discuss similarities and differences.

19. Choose a representative protist, invertebrate, and vertebrate. Construct a chart that compares circulation in these organisms.

20. a) Name an animal with a heart that pumps reoxygenated and deoxygenated blood separately.
   b) Name an animal with a heart that mixes the two types of blood together as they are pumped.
   c) What is the relationship between heart structure and an animal's activity level?

21. Plasma, the circulating fluid component of blood, may also appear as tissue fluid or lymph. Explain the meaning of this statement.

22. A circulatory system is a collection of components. Construct a simple labelled diagram that names the components and shows how they are related to each other.

C: Problem Solving

23. The word "artery" comes from the Greek word for "windpipe". This term was used because ancient autopsies showed blood pooled in veins, while arteries were empty. It was therefore believed that veins carried blood, while arteries carried air. Explain why the arteries of a dead animal might be found empty.

24. Reptiles such as snakes and lizards have an incomplete septum that partly separates the two sides of the single ventricle. Suppose the septum was completed through surgery. What change in the reptile's circulation would result? What other changes might follow?

25. Sickle cell anaemia is a disabling, inherited disorder with symptoms that include aching muscles, severe abdominal pain, swollen and painful joints, dizziness, and shortness of breath. Few patients survive beyond the age of forty. The disorder is caused by a defective gene that distorts the blood cells. Instead of smoothly rounded discs, the patient's cells are distorted into a thin, elongated shape resembling a crescent moon. How might this distortion affect blood circulation and thus account for some of the symptoms? Explain.

26. How would you expect circulation in a warm-blooded animal to differ from that in a cold-blooded animal when the surrounding environment is at a temperature near: a) 0°C b) 40°C?

Try This

Take a Pulse
After resting for 3 min, measure your pulse in beats per minute. Next, hold your breath for as long as you can. Immediately after your first exhalation, measure your pulse again. After resting for 3 min, measure your pulse a third time. Compare the three readings and try to explain why they differ.

An Aging Canadian Population

The Issue: What responsibility should we have towards the elderly?

These women are part of the Older Women's Network, formed by two Toronto widows to deal with the problems of women over age 55.

Aging can create many problems for elderly individuals and for society in general. Some older people can manage their lives better than others, but old age usually involves some loss of independence. Illness and disability increase with age, decreasing the ability of people to look after themselves. The problems of older people are aggravated by poverty and unemployment.

In the past, most elderly people depended on their families to look after them. Today, there are more elderly people than ever before. Many of them no longer live with, or even near, their relatives. A typical example is that of a 72-year-old widow, Mrs. Millie Earle. After their marriage, Millie and her husband John bought a house and had children.

Eventually, the children grew up, married, and moved away. John died shortly after his retirement. Since then Millie has lived alone in the house, looking after herself. Recently, however, Millie has suffered from arthritis in her hands and recurring dizzy spells, which make it difficult for her to do household tasks. Because of the rising costs of utilities, food, and taxes, she cannot afford to pay someone to help her. What are the options in our society for people like Millie, and should we do anything to change conditions for the elderly?

The number of Canadians over 65 is now growing twice as fast as the general population. Statistics Canada estimates that the over-65 group will grow from 2.3 million (10% of the population) today to about 7 million (27% of the population) by 2013. In other words, about one in four Canadians will be a senior citizen. If many of these people will require nursing home care or hospitalization for long periods, who will pay the costs? When the proportion of elderly in the population is relatively small, the government can use public money to help fund care. Will that be possible when the elderly make up a large part of the total population?

These questions must be answered soon, to plan for the increase of elderly people in society. Should older people be allowed to work, so they may help support themselves? Should we encourage healthy lifestyles, to reduce the risk of illness and the care it requires? How can older people be regarded as an asset rather than a liability to the rest of society?

In this activity, you will consider some questions related to the shift in age structure in the Canadian population. You will have the opportunity to develop guidelines about the responsibilities for the citizens of tomorrow —both the elderly, and those who may have to care for them.

Exploring the Issue

A. Gathering the Evidence

1. Read about the issue in magazine and newspaper articles, books, and materials from government agencies. Try to find materials that express different points of view.

2. Using research materials and information from local officials, determine:
   a) the number of post-65-year-olds in your town or city;
   b) the type of research being done in the science of aging, gerontology;
   c) the reasons for Canada's predicted shift in age structure over the next 25 years;
   d) the availability of retirement or nursing homes for the elderly in different parts of the country.
   (Note that Victoria, B.C., has a higher proportion of retired people than any other major centre.)

3. a) Find out what special provisions or services are available for the elderly in your village, town, or city.
   b) What provisions are made by the government of Ontario, and by the federal government?

4. What is the financial status of the elderly in Canada? How many individuals live on a fixed income? How are the elderly protected against inflation? What percentage of the elderly lives below the poverty line?

5. Visit a senior citizen home. Interview administration, nurses, and residents of the institution. What does it cost to live in a nursing home? What is the price range? What is the quality of life in nursing homes?

6. Find out how the treatment of the elderly in Canada compares with that in other countries.

B. Discussing the Issue

1. In small groups of five or six, review the information and clearly identify the problems raised by the material you have gathered.

2. Assemble a list of the special needs of an elderly population. Consider how these needs could be met in a future society.

3. Discuss how else cities and towns might prepare for an increasing proportion of elderly people.

4. Discuss what steps could be taken to encourage individual families to look after their elderly members.

5. Discuss the importance of maintaining a high standard of living for the elderly.

6. Discuss whether there is a generation gap between the elderly and other age groups, and how this might affect the question of responsibility for care of the elderly.

C. Making a Decision

1. Each student should personally assess the issue of an aging population and come to a decision about how this issue should be dealt with by society.

2. Compare your decision and reasons with those of the other members of your group. Try to come to a consensus about the issue.

D. Recommending a Plan of Action

Based on your group consensus, draw up a plan of action for the federal, provincial, and city or town governments, outlining what steps they should take to deal with this issue.

Unit 3 Wrap-Up

Unit Summary

All living things interact in various ways with their external environment. In single-celled *protists*, food and gas molecules from the external environment diffuse through the cell membrane into the internal environment and are then distributed by the circulating *cytoplasm*. Multicellular animals require specialized *body systems* for these functions.

All *gas exchange systems* require a thin, moist *membrane*, a structure such as gills or lungs to maximize the membrane's surface area, and a method of delivering oxygen to the membrane. This oxygen is transported by the circulatory system to the body cells, where it reacts with *glucose* to release energy through *cell respiration*. Waste carbon dioxide is transported to the external environment.

Every organism's internal environment requires a continuous supply of nutrients. In multicellular animals, large food molecules from the external environment are broken down into small nutrient molecules by a *digestive system*. *Digestion* involves four distinct steps: *ingestion*, *digestion* (i.e., physical and chemical breakdown), *absorption*, and *egestion*. *Enzymes* play a vital role in digestion by speeding up the rate of chemical breakdown.

Both the gas exchange and digestive systems depend on the *circulatory system* to transport oxygen and nutrient molecules to the individual body cells. *Plasma* in the circulating blood carries the nutrients, while red blood cells carry the oxygen. Both oxygen and nutrients diffuse from the *capillaries* into the *tissue fluid*. From there, they diffuse into the cell, while waste products and carbon dioxide diffuse from the cell to the tissue fluid for collection by the blood. Gas exchange, digestion, and circulation work together with numerous other body systems to maintain internal balance.

Key Terms

amylase	lymph
arteries	nutrient
bag system	open circulation
breathing	organ
capillaries	organ system
cell respiration	pepsin
closed circulation	plasma
digestion	surface area
egestion	tissue
enzyme	tissue fluid
gills	tube system
ingestion	veins

Unit Practice and Review

A: Short Answer

True or False

State whether each statement is true or false. Correct each false statement.

1. Animals such as earthworms, sea anemones, and jellyfish have a bag-like digestive system.

2. Cell specialization means that different types of cells perform different life functions.

3. Amylase is a protein-digesting enzyme that chemically breaks down starch into the sugar maltose.

4. Gastric juice contains the enzyme pepsin, which chemically breaks down proteins.

5. All gas exchange systems require a thin, moist membrane, a structure that maximizes the surface area of the membrane, and a method of delivering carbon dioxide to the membrane.

Multiple Choice

In each question below, select the best answer.

1. Cell respiration requires the absorption of:
   a) glucose and carbon dioxide.
   b) oxygen and glucose.
   c) carbon dioxide and water vapour.
   d) oxygen and water vapour.

2. The endless flow of blood circulation refers to a(n):
   a) blood flow under high pressure.
   b) open circulation system.
   c) closed circulation system.
   d) constant movement of circulating fluids.

3. Malpighian tubules are excretory structures found in:
   a) earthworms   c) grasshoppers
   b) fish   d) jellyfish

4. The slippery substance in saliva that lubricates food is called:
   a) mucin   c) pepsin
   b) amylase   d) bile

5. Which of the following is not a nutrient for humans?
   a) fatty acids   c) glucose
   b) amino acids   d) cellulose

Complete the Statement

Complete each of the following statements with the correct word or phrase. Do not write in this book.

1. The ___?___ is the wall dividing the left and right sides of a four-chambered heart.

2. The special excretory structures of the earthworm are called ___?___ .

3. ___?___ from the liver physically breaks down large fat globules into tiny fat droplets.

4. Tiny, valved openings along a grasshopper's abdomen that allow gas exchange are called ___?___ .

5. Large animals are multicellular in order to provide a large enough ___?___ for gas exchange.

Matching Items

Match each item in Column A with the appropriate item in Column B.

1. *Column A*
   i) support structure
   ii) protective gill cover
   iii) organ of gas exchange
   iv) finger-like projections

   Column B
   a) gills
   b) gill filaments
   c) gill arch
   d) operculum

2. *Column A*
   i) chemical and physical breakdown
   ii) takes place by diffusion
   iii) intake of food
   iv) removal of wastes

   Column B
   a) ingestion
   b) egestion
   c) absorption
   d) digestion

3. *Column A*
   i) supplies blood separately to the heart muscle
   ii) drains venous blood from the head and upper body
   iii) carries deoxygenated blood to the lungs
   iv) largest artery of the body

   Column B
   a) superior vena cava
   b) pulmonary artery
   c) aorta
   d) coronary artery

4. *Column A*
   i) site of physical digestion
   ii) site of chemical digestion
   iii) storage chamber
   iv) assists intake of food

   Column B
   a) crop
   b) pharynx
   c) intestine
   d) gizzard

B: Knowledge and Application

1. Red blood cells are approximately .007 mm in diameter. The capillary vessels are so tiny that these red blood cells have to line up one by one to get through the capillary. How might this slow transport of cells through very small vessels aid circulation?

2. Long distance runners from countries at high altitudes have an advantage over other runners in Olympic competitions. Explain why.

3. Explain how the respiratory, digestive, and circulatory systems are interrelated in living things.

4. Describe the difference between plasma, tissue fluid, and lymph according to:
   a) where they are found,
   b) materials they contain,
   c) major function(s) of each.

5. Suppose a circulatory system is providing an inadequate supply of oxygen to the body cells. What would the gas exchange, digestive, and circulatory systems probably do to try to correct this situation?

6. Firefighters overexposed to the hot air of flames often die. What effect do you think the hot air has on the respiratory system?

7. Green plants circulate materials in much the same way that most animals do. Construct a chart to compare plant and animal circulation according to:
   a) materials circulated,
   b) transportation vessels,
   c) movement of materials in vessels.

C: Problem Solving

1. The digestive tract is made primarily of protein. The stomach, which is part of the digestive tract, is one of the sites of protein digestion. How do you think the protein-digesting enzyme, pepsin, knows enough to break down only the food molecules and not the stomach? What happens to the stomach lining if protein-digesting enzymes start eating away the lining?

2. Shock is the most common cause of human death. Consult a reference book to find out what shock is, and its relationship to the circulatory system.

3. Coronary by-pass surgery has become a very common method of correcting poor circulation around the heart. Consult a reference book to find out what vessels are replaced and how they are replaced.

4. Nutritionists and physicians advise us to drink plenty of water. Citing examples from this unit, explain why water is important to gas exchange, digestion, and circulation in humans.

D: Challengers

1. The human egg cell is one of the largest human cells. It is a sphere approximately 140 μm or 0.14 mm in diameter. If the volume of a sphere is $4/3\ \pi r^3$ and the surface area of a sphere is $4\ \pi r^2$, what is the surface area-to-volume ratio of a human egg cell? Compare this to the ratio for another body cell 0.05 mm in diameter. How does this comparison explain why human egg cells begin to divide so rapidly after fertilization?

2. A cook walks into a large oven holding a steak. The oven temperature is 115°C. After several minutes, the cook emerges and shows no ill effects. The steak, however, is partly cooked. Explain how a human can withstand such temperatures without being cooked like the steak.

Project Ideas

1. Obtain a preserved frog and, following your teacher's instructions for dissecting it, observe:
   a) all of its gas exchange surfaces, noting how the structure of its lung compares to that of a mammalian lung.
   b) its three-chambered heart, tracing the path of blood through the frog's heart, lungs, and body systems.
   c) how the circulatory system is connected to the digestive and gas exchange systems, identifying the vessels that carry oxygenated blood to the cells and those that carry deoxygenated blood away from the cells.

2. Obtain a Venus flytrap or other insectivorous plant from a nursery, and observe its digestive system in action. How does this plant carry out ingestion, digestion, absorption, and egestion? In what ways is its system similar to an animal's? How does it differ?

Readings

Panati, Charles. *Breakthroughs*. Boston: Houghton-Mifflin, 1980. (An update on many breakthroughs in disease treatment, nutrition, behaviour, and aging.)

Purtilo, David T. *A Survey of Human Diseases*. Don Mills: Addison-Wesley, 1978. (Discussion of the causes, symptoms, and treatment of the human body's major diseases and disorders.)

Heat Energy

Canadians have good reason to be interested in heat: winter temperatures in Ontario, for example, can fall below −60°C. In an environment as cold as this, obtaining heat from sources such as wood, oil, and natural gas is vital to human survival. Even wearing the proper clothing in winter can mean the difference between life and death.

Humans also have to be able to cope with extremely high temperatures. By wearing an insulated and flameproof protective suit, the firefighter in the photograph can walk near a raging fire. The ability to produce and control heat is an essential part of modern life.

What is heat exactly? Is it a form of matter? How can it be measured? Is heat the same as temperature? If not, how do they differ? What happens when heat is transferred? Such questions puzzled scholars for hundreds of years. Not until scientists developed a clear understanding of energy could they propose a satisfactory explanation for heat.

Molten iron is poured into a steelmaking furnace at Algoma Steel in Sault Ste. Marie, Ontario

Chapter 10
The Nature of Heat

We depend in many ways on the use and control of heat. Over 80% of the world's electricity is generated using heat obtained from fossil fuels and uranium. Huge quantities of heat are required to refine iron ore and to make steel. Much of this metal goes to automobile factories, where heat is used to shape the parts and weld them together. Finally, the engine in the finished car operates using heat obtained from a burning fuel.

In this chapter, we study the development of the scientific model now used to explain both the nature of heat and the meaning of temperature. We also identify the main characteristics of heat, and investigate the most common sources of heat in our society. Finally, we examine the factors affecting the amount of heat that can be transferred to and from an object.

When you finish Chapter 10, you should be able to:

- state the main postulates of the kinetic molecular theory
- explain the nature of heat and how it differs from temperature
- describe the major sources of heat
- list the factors affecting heat capacity, and explain how each factor affects the amount of heat transferred

10.1 A Scientific Theory for Heat

Each person in your classroom is giving off about as much heat as a 100 W light bulb. This heat is produced from the chemical energy stored in the food we eat. Rubbing your hands together or lighting a fire also produces heat. Our homes contain many other sources of heat. Furnaces, for example, are designed to produce large amounts of heat, while appliances such as refrigerators give off heat as well, although this is not their main function.

Heat can be produced in so many ways that early scientists had problems developing a satisfactory theory to explain heating effects. One major obstacle was that they did not clearly understand the concept of energy. Scientists now define **energy** as the **ability to do work on some form of matter**. **Work** is done when an object is moved through a distance by a force acting on the object. When you push a book across a desk, you use energy to do work on it. While the book is moving, it possesses a kind of energy called **kinetic energy** (also called "energy of motion"). All moving objects possess kinetic energy. When a moving object, such as a hockey stick, hits another object, such as a puck, some kinetic energy is transferred.

Activity 10-1: The Properties of Heat

In this activity you will study some effects produced by heat, in order to identify some of its characteristic properties. You will also determine if heat is a form of energy.

Materials

one-hole rubber stopper with
  30 cm glass tubing inserted

250 mL Florence flask

small beaker

large beaker

thermometer

potassium permanganate
  crystals

2 petri dishes

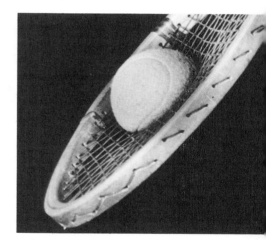

When the tennis racquet hits the ball, kinetic energy is transferred to the ball.

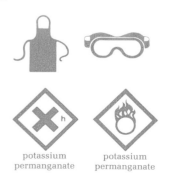

potassium
permanganate

potassium
permanganate

CAUTION: Handle the stopper-and-tubing assembly carefully.

Procedure

1. Half-fill the small beaker with water, and lower the stopper-and-tubing assembly into it. Placing a finger over the upper end of the glass tube, lift the entire assembly out of the water, and place the stopper into the top of the Florence flask. Remove your finger from the glass tube, and gently but firmly push the rubber stopper into the Florence flask.

2. Hold the flask between your hands. Record what happens.

3. Place the small beaker containing 150 mL of hot tap water inside a large beaker containing 150 mL of cold tap water. Measure the temperature of the water in each beaker a) immediately, and b) after 5 min.

4. Repeat step 3, but this time place 150 mL of hot water into the large beaker, and 150 mL of cold water into the small beaker.

5. a) Half-fill a petri dish with cold water and place a potassium permanganate crystal in the middle of the dish.
   b) Repeat step a), filling the second petri dish with hot water before adding a crystal of the same size.
   c) Record what happens in both petri dishes after each has sat for 10 min.

Discussion

1. a) Suggest an explanation for your observations in step 2.
   b) Based on the definition of energy given earlier, what evidence suggests that heat is a form of energy? Justify your answer.

2. a) In steps 3 and 4, what can you infer about the transfer of heat between the two samples of water?
   b) Based on observations from this activity and your own experience, write a general statement describing the direction of heat transfer between two objects or materials.

3. What can you infer from your observations in a) and b) of step 5 about the effects of heat on matter?

4. What evidence in this activity suggests that heat is related to kinetic energy?

5. Basing your answer on the five senses, what properties of heat can you identify by observing samples of hot and cold water?

What Is Heat?

By the end of the seventeenth century two scientific theories for heat had been proposed. One theory proposed that heat was a kind of fluid. The other theory proposed that heat was related to the motion of particles.

The Caloric Theory of Heat

The theory that heat was a fluid was stated formally by the Scottish scientist Joseph Black around 1750. At that time, most scientists believed that light and many other familiar phenomena could be explained in terms of different kinds of fluids. They concluded that heat was an invisible fluid substance, which they called "caloric", that flowed into and out of matter during heat transfers. The postulates of the caloric theory are shown in Table 10-1.

Although this theory now seems unreasonable, it was accepted until the 1850s because it seemed to explain most of the facts then known about heat. The flow of caloric could explain the heating and cooling of different forms of matter, as well as the direction of heat transfer. It could also explain changes of state and thermal expansion. Early scientists believed that when ice was heated, caloric flowed into it until the ice became liquid. They thought a solid expanded when heated because the added caloric increased its volume.

The heating effects produced by friction, however, could not be satisfactorily explained by the movement of caloric, and this

Table 10-1: Postulates of the Caloric Theory

1. All objects contain a certain amount of caloric.

2. Caloric flows from an object at higher temperature to one at lower temperature.

3. If caloric flows out of an object, the temperature of the object decreases, and if caloric flows into an object, the temperature of the object increases.

4. When matter is broken apart (for example, when substances are burned or cut) large amounts of caloric are released.

5. Caloric is more strongly attracted to some substances than to others.

6. Caloric is massless, invisible, odourless, and tasteless, but it can be felt.

7. Caloric cannot be created or destroyed.

Aristotle (384-322 B.C.) proposed that there were four "basic elements" of matter: earth, fire, water, and air. He also proposed that fire was actually heat.

Joseph Black

Although the idea that heat consisted of some kind of fluid was well established by the mid-1700s, it was not until 1787 that the Caloric Theory was formally named by a group of French scientists, including Antoine Lavoisier (1743-1794).

Early in the eighteenth century, the concept of invisible fluids was used to explain effects in four areas of science: the caloric fluid for heat, the (luminous) ether fluid for light, the effluvia fluid for electricity, and the austral and boreal fluids for magnetism. The apparent success of this group of fluid theories convinced many scientists that they had identified a common model that unified existing scientific knowledge.

caused some skepticism about the caloric theory. However, scientists could not propose a more convincing model without experimental evidence.

The Kinetic Molecular Theory of Heat

The theory that heat was related to the motion of particles had been proposed much earlier than the caloric theory. In the early 1600s, the English scientist Francis Bacon suggested a direct relationship between heat and motion. Around 1650, two other English scientists, Isaac Newton and Robert Boyle, proposed, independently of each other, that heat was related to the motion of particles of matter. Boyle suggested that nails become heated when hit by a hammer because the particles in the nail are set into violent motion. There was no convincing way, however, to demonstrate the existence of these vibrating particles.

In 1798 the American-born Count Rumford was supervising the boring of brass cannons at Munich, in Bavaria (now a part of Germany). He noticed that far more heat was produced by the boring process than he thought could be accounted for by the caloric theory. Supporters of the caloric theory insisted that the caloric was obtained from the surrounding air.

Rumford thought otherwise, and carried out a series of experiments to determine the source of the heat. To exclude the air, he

Count Rumford's drawing of his cannon boring apparatus. The shaft on the right, turned by horses, rotated the cannon barrel against the stationary drill at the left.

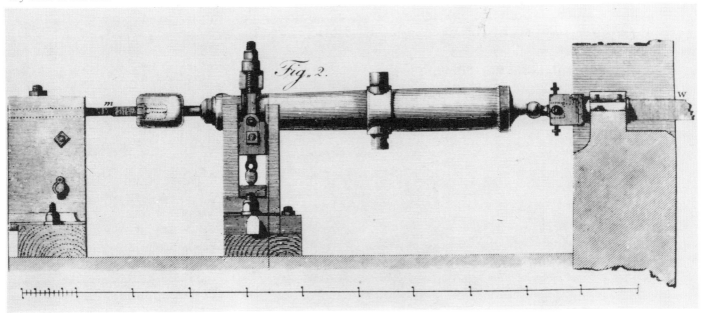

surrounded the cannon with a wooden box and filled the box with water. Horses then began to turn a blunt boring tool inside the cannon, producing large friction forces. The water gradually warmed up. After about three hours, onlookers were astonished to observe that the water began to boil without the use of a fire.

Rumford concluded that the heating effects could not be explained in terms of caloric. The caloric could not have come from the water, or the air surrounding the water, because the water had actually gained heat, instead of giving it to the cannon. He realized that the boring process could produce heat continuously for an indefinite period, a fact that could not be explained by the caloric theory.

These results convinced Rumford and many other scientists that caloric did not exist. Rumford proposed that heat had been produced by the motion supplied by the boring tool to the particles of matter in the brass cannon. However, he did no further experiments, and his ideas were not widely accepted. During the next fifty years, the development of the steam engine, combined with the major scientific discoveries listed below, finally led to the development of a satisfactory theory for heat.

- England, early 1800s: Physician and physicist Thomas Young proposed the modern concept of energy and clarified the difference between force and work.

- England, 1808: John Dalton, an English schoolmaster, produced experimental evidence for the particle theory of matter.

- Italy, 1811: Italian scientist Count Amedeo Avogadro first used the word "molecule" to describe the tiny particles which make up matter.

- England, 1827: Robert Brown, a Scottish physician and botanist, observed that pollen grains moved erratically in water, even though the water appeared perfectly still. This effect became known as "Brownian motion", although its significance was not understood by Brown at the time.

- Europe, 1830s: Scientists concluded that the spontaneous mixing of gases, the spontaneous dissolving of solids in water, and Brownian motion had the same cause. All three phenomena provided evidence that particles of matter were continually in motion and had kinetic energy.

- Southeast Asia, 1842: Julius Mayer, a German physician, proposed that heat and work were equivalent to one another by analyzing data obtained from previous experiments done with gases.

James Joule

These scientists made major contributions to the development of the kinetic molecular theory.

Julius Mayer

Thomas Young

Von Helmholtz is credited with establishing the principle of conservation of energy.

- England, 1840s: English physicist James Prescott Joule completed a series of experiments showing that mechanical, electrical, and chemical energy could all be converted into heat. In his most famous experiment, he measured the amount of heat produced by a specific amount of work, and thus established that heat was a form of energy.

- Germany, 1847: German physician Hermann von Helmholtz published a widely-read article based on all the ideas of his predecessors. He presented his findings so convincingly that the concept of energy became firmly established, and the caloric theory was finally abandoned.

By combining the concept of energy with the particle and kinetic theories of matter, scientists developed a composite theory known as the **Kinetic Molecular Theory of Matter**. This theory can explain all the effects produced by heat. The postulates of the kinetic molecular theory are shown in Table 10-2. Scientists finally concluded that heat is that form of energy which is transferred from a hot body to a cold body. The transfer of heat is related to the motion (kinetic energy) of particles of matter.

The kinetic molecular theory explains why heat is transferred from a hot substance to a cold one. Consider what happens when a hot stone is placed in cold water. The particles in the hot stone have much more kinetic energy than the water particles. When the slow-moving water particles collide with the fast-moving stone particles, the water particles speed up and their kinetic energy increases. These faster-moving water particles in turn collide with other water particles, transferring more kinetic energy.

The kinetic molecular theory can also explain how friction produces heat. When you rub your hands together, some of the molecules on the surface of one hand strike molecules on the surface of the other hand. During these collisions, the molecules on both hands speed up, increasing their kinetic energy. The kinetic energy of these molecules continues to increase as long as the rubbing action continues, and the surfaces of your hands become hotter.

Table 10-2:   Postulates of the Kinetic Molecular Theory

1. All matter is composed of many tiny particles called molecules.

2. The molecules are separated from one another by empty space. The distance between molecules is large compared to their size.

3. All molecules are constantly moving in some manner, and therefore possess kinetic energy.

4. When heat is added to matter, the molecules absorb the energy and move faster (i.e., their kinetic energy increases). When heat is removed, the molecules slow down (their kinetic energy decreases).

Study Questions

1. List four reasons why heat is essential in a modern society.
2. Define the term energy, and describe an example in which energy is used to do work.
3. a) State the main postulates of the caloric theory.
   b) List three heating effects that can be explained by the caloric theory. Explain one of these effects in terms of this theory.

4. a) Define heat.
   b) What scientific ideas and concepts were combined to develop a satisfactory explanation for heat?
5. a) State the main postulates of the kinetic molecular theory.
   b) In which direction does heat move between hot and cold objects? Explain why, in terms of the kinetic molecular theory.
   c) Explain how heat is transferred to a metal mug when hot liquid is poured into it, in terms of the kinetic molecular theory.

WANTED: NEW SCIENTIFIC MODELS

Scientific models often change as a result of new technological inventions which sometimes arise from a different field of study. The various models developed to explain the function of the human heart illustrate how this can happen. Until the 1600s, the heart was thought to be a kind of furnace that supplied the body with energy. Blood entering the heart was observed as dark in colour, while blood leaving the heart was bright red. This was considered evidence that the "furnace" had added energy to the blood. Exhaled breath (seen as condensed water vapour on cold days) was interpreted as the "fumes" or "smoke" produced by the furnace.

Then, in the seventeenth century, mechanical pumps were invented to remove water from deep mines. Gradually, the heart came to be thought of as a kind of pump rather than a furnace. The scientific model of the heart as a pump is still used today.

In the ongoing process of scientific discovery, both old and new scientific models are continually being tested, modified, and sometimes discarded. For example, one of the greatest breakthroughs in physics in recent years has been the development of superconductors, materials that conduct electricity without heating up (see page 481). Until the early 1980s, all known superconductors required operating temperatures of $-250°C$ or lower. By 1987 some newly developed materials became superconducting at temperatures as high as $-173°C$. Now the models that once explained superconductivity are no longer adequate. Scientists are trying to develop completely new models in an effort to understand how and why superconductivity occurs.

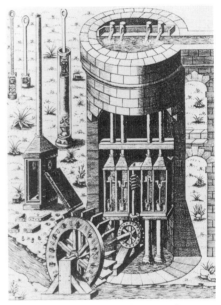

Early pumps such as this may have prompted the idea of the human heart as a kind of pump.

10.2　The Meaning of Temperature

In earlier studies, you learned that temperature is a measure of the intensity of heat. The kinetic molecular theory makes it possible to expand that simplified definition. In terms of the kinetic molecular theory, **temperature** is defined as **a measure of the average kinetic energy of the molecules in a substance**. The average kinetic energy of the molecules in a sample of hot water is greater than that of the molecules in a sample of cold water. As heat is added to a substance, the kinetic energy of all its molecules increases, and so does the temperature.

Temperature is that property of a substance which determines its ability to transmit heat to, or receive heat from, another substance. Heat is transferred from the substance at higher temperature to the substance at lower temperature. Two objects or substances are at the same temperature if neither one transfers heat to the other when they are in contact. When heat is added to a substance, the temperature of the substance increases.

This expanded definition of temperature lets us define heat more precisely. **Heat is the energy transferred from one substance to another, due to the temperature difference between them**. Thus, to extend our knowledge of heat we must measure the temperature of substances.

Do You Know?
On a hot day (30°C), the average speed of air molecules is about 440 m/s, and on a cold day (−20°C), the average speed is about 400 m/s.

Temperature Scales and Fixed Points

All methods of measuring temperature depend on observing changes in some physical property of a substance as its temperature changes. The most common property used is the expansion that occurs as heat is added to a liquid. The liquid-in-glass thermometer shown in the photograph is based on this principle. Although this type of thermometer is common now, it took centuries to develop.

Most early attempts to measure temperature were unreliable because they involved the heat sensors in human skin. Around 1592 Galileo developed the first air thermometer, which detected temperature changes by the rise and fall of liquid in a tube. However, this device did not measure temperature numerically; it simply compared liquid levels. To measure temperature accurately, it is necessary to calibrate thermometers with a numbered scale of some kind.

Today, temperature scales are based on two characteristic properties of a very common substance: the freezing point and boiling point of water (see Figure 10-1). These are referred to as "fixed

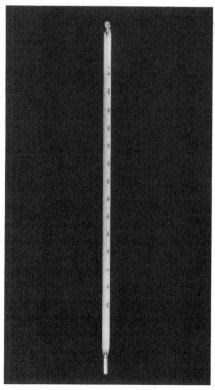

A common liquid thermometer.

Figure 10-1. The Celsius temperature scale.

On the Celsius temperature scale, the interval between the fixed points is divided into 100 equal divisions.

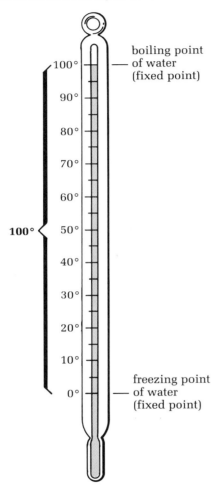

boiling point of water (fixed point)

100°

freezing point of water (fixed point)

points''. The interval between these two fixed points is then divided into equal intervals called degrees.

In science laboratories, the most common temperature scale is the one devised by Anders Celsius (1701-1744), a Swedish astronomer. In the Celsius temperature scale, the upper fixed point is 100°C, the temperature of steam from water boiling under standard atmospheric pressure. The lower fixed point is 0°C, the temperature of melting ice. Both the ice and the boiling water must be pure, as impurities will lower the melting point and raise the boiling point. If an uncalibrated thermometer is marked with these two fixed points, and 99 equally-spaced lines are scratched on the glass between them, each space will equal one degree Celsius.

Activity 10-2: Temperature Change During Heating

In this activity, ice is heated until the resulting water boils. By recording temperature values at regular time intervals, some surprising observations can be made.

Materials

Bunsen burner
retort stand
ring clamp
wire gauze
250 mL beaker

75 mL crushed ice mixed with 15 mL ice water
stirring rod
thermometer
beaker tongs

Part A: Recording Temperature Data
Procedure

1. Draw a chart in your notebook with the following headings: *Time (min), Temperature (°C)*.

2. **Make a Hypothesis:** Read the following steps and predict the temperature change(s) that will occur as the substance is heated at a steady rate.

3. Set up the apparatus as shown in the photo on the opposite page, without the beaker of ice water. Allow the burner flame to heat the wire gauze and ring clamp for 3 min before you do step 4.

4. Add the crushed ice and ice water to the beaker. Stir the mixture and record its temperature.

5. Place the beaker on the warmed wire gauze immediately. Stir the mixture continuously with the stirring rod, and record the temperature at 0.5 min intervals.

6. After the ice has disappeared, continue stirring and heating the water. Record its temperature every 0.5 min, until it has been boiling for 5 min.

Discussion

1. Why was it necessary to heat the wire gauze and ring clamp before placing the beaker on the gauze?

2. Compare your hypothesis with what occurred in the activity. Comment on the comparison.

3. What evidence is there of "fixed points"? Explain why this term is suitable for describing what you observed.

4. How could this procedure be used to calibrate a thermometer which had no scale marked on the glass stem? Describe in detail the steps required to produce a finished thermometer.

Part B: Analyzing the Data

Procedure

1. From the data in your table, plot a graph of temperature (vertical axis) versus time (horizontal axis).

2. Draw the smoothest line possible through the points you have plotted.

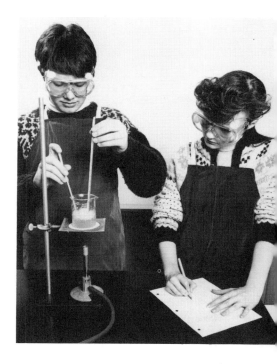

In step 1, place the 0°C mark on the vertical scale at least two large squares above the base line of the graph paper.

Discussion

1. Heat was added at a constant rate throughout the activity. Describe the temperature changes that occurred.

2. The graph can be divided into three distinct regions.
   a) What is happening to the substance being heated when the temperature is increasing steadily?
   b) Explain what is happening to the substance in terms of the kinetic molecular theory.

3. a) What is happening to the substance in the graph regions where the temperature is not increasing steadily?
   b) What is happening to the average kinetic energy of the molecules of the substance while it is being heated in these regions? Explain how you know this.
   c) What is happening to the heat being added to the substance in these regions?

4. Write a general statement about the relationship between heat and the temperature changes that occur when a pure substance is heated from the solid state to the gaseous state.

5. Why is a thermometer essential for understanding the relationship described in question 4?

Temperature, Heat, and Thermal Energy

When ice is heated until it becomes a vapour, some unexpected temperature changes occur. As Figure 10-2 shows, adding heat does not always cause an increase in temperature. The temperature stops rising twice: first when the ice melts, and once again when the water boils.

Figure 10-2. The temperature remains constant both when ice melts and when water boils.

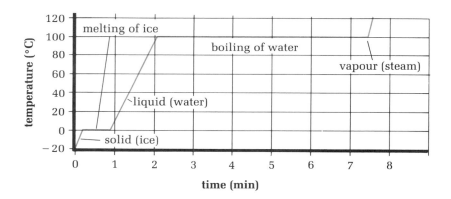

This behaviour is puzzling. When heat is added to ice, the total energy of the ice must surely increase, and yet there is no temperature change. According to the kinetic molecular theory, this constant temperature means that the average kinetic energy of the molecules does not increase during either melting or freezing.

Thermal Energy

How can energy be added to ice without also increasing the kinetic energy of its molecules? To answer this question we must consider the thermal energy of a substance. Figure 10-3 shows a model that helps to explain thermal energy. In this model, the molecules in a solid crystal jiggle about a fixed point as though they were held together by tiny springs. The molecules in the model have two kinds of energy: energy stored in the springs holding them together (potential energy), and kinetic energy due to their motion.

Each molecule in the model acts like a ball bouncing back and forth on a spring, as shown in Figure 10-4. For a brief instant when the spring is either fully stretched, as in a), or fully compressed, as in c), the ball is not moving at all and thus has no kinetic energy. However, the distorted spring does have some energy stored in it. This stored energy is called **potential energy**. As the ball moves back and forth, the kinetic energy of the ball, as well as the potential energy stored in the spring, are constantly changing.

Figure 10-3. The molecules of a solid crystal are held together by forces acting like springs.

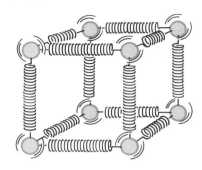

Figure 10-4. This model shows the relationship between kinetic and potential energy of molecules in a solid.

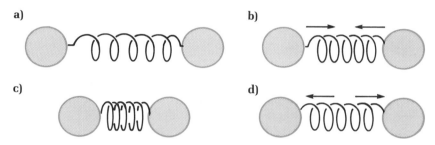

In a) and c), the balls are not moving but potential energy is stored in the spring. In b) and d), the spring is neither stretched nor compressed, but the balls have kinetic energy.

The forces acting on molecules in matter differ from those acting on the ball-and-spring model. However, the total energy of each molecule alternates constantly between potential and kinetic energy in a similar way. The total of the two kinds of energy is what scientists term the thermal energy of the molecule. **Thermal energy is defined as the total potential and kinetic energy any sample of matter has as a result of the random motion of all its molecules**.

Thermal energy is sometimes called internal energy.

Now we can explain what happened to the heat added during melting, when the temperature did not change. Only the potential energy of the molecules increased as the ice was melting. As heat was added, the molecules moved farther apart, weakening the attractive forces holding the molecules in their fixed positions. Only when all the molecules of ice had increased their potential energy enough to move freely could their kinetic energy begin to increase. When that occurred, the temperature of the water could rise once again.

The English philosopher John Locke (1632-1704) suggested the following experiment: put one hand in hot water, the other in cold water, and then put both hands in a third container of warm water. Try this, and suggest reasons for what you observe.

Study Questions

1. a) Define temperature.
   b) Distinguish between heat and temperature, in terms of the kinetic molecular theory.
2. a) Why were early types of thermometers unreliable?
   b) Explain what is meant by the term "fixed points", and how they are used to calibrate liquid-filled thermometers.
3. a) Define thermal energy.
   b) Distinguish between thermal energy and heat.
4. a) What factors affect the thermal energy of a substance?
   b) What happens to the energy of the molecules of a pure substance when i) its temperature is increasing, and ii) the substance is changing state?

10.3 Sources of Heat

Table 10-3: Forms of Energy that Produce Heat

thermal

electrical

chemical

nuclear

mechanical

sound

All the forms of energy listed in Table 10-3 can be converted to heat. Most of the heat we use in our everyday lives is obtained from from sources of thermal, electrical, and chemical energy.

Three different forms of energy are used to produce the heat given off by the camping stove, electric kettle, and hot mug of soup.

Activity 10-3:   Investigating Sources of Heat

In this activity you will produce heat using five different forms of energy.

Materials

electric lamp	100 mL graduated cylinder
dark-coloured object	copper sulphate solution
two pieces of wood	powdered zinc
thick wire (e.g., coat hanger)	test tube
bicycle pump	test tube rack
400 mL beaker	rubber stopper
matches	warm water (about 45°C)
Bunsen burner	

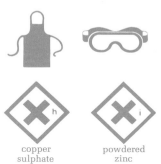

copper
sulphate

powdered
zinc

Procedure

1. Place a dark-coloured object near, but not touching, an incandescent light bulb that is not switched on. Touch both the bulb and the dark-coloured object. Switch on the light bulb, and after 10 min touch the object again. Hold your hand near (but do not touch) the light bulb. Record your observations.

2. Rub two pieces of wood against one another for 2 min. Touch the rubbed surfaces both before and immediately after rubbing. Record your observations.

3. Holding a piece of wire with both hands, bend it back and forth rapidly several times until it breaks. Touch the broken ends of the wire. Record your observations.

4. Touch the air outlet at the bottom of a bicycle pump. After operating the pump for 2 min, touch the outlet again. Record your observations.

5. Pour 300 mL of warm water into a beaker and place your hand in the beaker. Record your observations.

6. Strike a match and light the Bunsen burner with it. Record all the ways heat is produced in this step.

7. Pour 10 mL of copper sulphate solution into a test tube. Touch the test tube. Add 2 g of powdered zinc to the solution and place a stopper in the top of the test tube. Shake the test tube vigorously and touch it again.

Discussion

1. a) List all the sources of heat used in this activity.
   b) For each source, identify the form of energy that was converted into heat.
2. In terms of the kinetic molecular theory, explain how the heat was produced in a) step 2, b) step 3, and c) step 4.
3. Using Table 10-3, identify any forms of energy not used to produce heat in this activity, and suggest why each form was not suitable for use in a school laboratory.

The Primary Source of Heat

There is only one direct source of heat: the thermal energy in a substance. Remember that heat is the energy transferred due to the difference in temperature between two substances. The thermal energy of an object increases when either its mass or its temperature increases. Also, when a substance melts or vaporizes, its thermal energy increases, even though the temperature remains constant.

When you soak in a hot bath, your body gains heat from the thermal energy in the hot water. The heat released from volcanoes and hot springs is obtained from the thermal energy in the Earth's interior, called **geothermal energy**. In some countries, such as Iceland, where the Earth's crust is thin, the geothermal energy can be used to heat houses and produce electricity.

The hot springs near Banff, Alberta were discovered by rockhunting railway workers in 1883.

The Wairakei Geothermal Site in New Zealand. Geothermal energy is being used to heat homes and produce electricity.

Indirect Sources of Heat

Forms of energy other than thermal energy cannot be converted directly into heat. First, the energy must be converted to thermal energy. Then the thermal energy can be transferred as heat to other forms of matter.

1. **Electrical Energy**. All devices that use electrical energy produce heat. Some devices, such as toasters, ovens, and water heaters, are designed to convert all the electrical energy into heat energy. Others, such as loudspeakers, flashlights, and the electric motors that operate fans and food processors, convert most of the electrical energy into forms of energy other than heat. However, because these devices are not 100% efficient, they always produce some ''waste'' heat.

When you plug in an electric heater, an electric current flows through the heating coil. An electric current consists of a flow of electrons through a conductor such as tungsten wire. The moving electrons collide with the tungsten molecules, increasing the kinetic energy of the molecules. These collisions increase the thermal energy of the conductor. Its temperature rises, and heat is transferred from the hot conductor to the surrounding air.

2. **Chemical Energy**. Some of the chemical energy stored in food is converted into thermal energy during cell respiration. Warm-blooded animals use this energy to help maintain their body temperature. In another example, burning oil or natural gas in a furnace increases the thermal energy of the gases produced by the chemical reaction. These hot gases transfer heat to the cooler metal sides of the furnace. The metal then heats air in the heating ducts, which distribute the heated air throughout the house.

A molecule of oil in a fossil fuel or food consists of a complex combination of hydrogen and carbon atoms. Because of its structure, the molecule has chemical potential energy stored in it. When the molecule is combined with oxygen, water and carbon dioxide molecules are produced and energy is released. This energy increases the kinetic energy of the molecules formed by the chemical reaction, and therefore the thermal energy of the gases.

3. **Nuclear Energy**. A nuclear power station produces large amounts of thermal energy. This energy is used to boil water, producing the steam needed to spin large, wheel-like discs called steam turbines. The turbines then operate electrical generators to produce electrical energy.

These electrical home appliances produce heat.

Table 10-4: Energy Values of Various Fuels and Food

Substance	Specific heat of combustion (kJ/kg)*
Fuels	
alcohol (ethyl)	3.0×10^4
coal	3.2×10^4
gasoline	4.7×10^5
hydrogen	1.4×10^4
methane	5.5×10^4
wood (pine)	2.1×10^4
Food	
bread (whole wheat)	1.0×10^4
beef (sirloin)	9.1×10^4
egg (boiled)	6.8×10^3
egg (fried)	9.1×10^3
milk (whole)	2.9×10^3
peanuts	2.5×10^4
potato (boiled)	3.2×10^3
potato chips	2.4×10^4

*The amount of energy released when 1 kg of a fuel or food is burned is called the specific heat of combustion. (4.2 kJ is equal to one Calorie.)

Another method of releasing nuclear energy involves the combination of two hydrogen nuclei to form a helium nucleus. This process, known as nuclear fusion, produces the Sun's radiation. Scientists around the world are trying to develop a practical method of controlling nuclear fusion as a way to provide a plentiful and clean supply of energy for the future.

These workers are removing some of the special tiles attached to the space shuttle that protect it from the heating effects caused by air friction during re-entry.

Do You Know?

When sound energy is converted into heat energy, very little heat is produced. The heat energy equivalent to the total sound energy emitted over a 90-min period by 50 000 spectators at a football game is only enough to heat one cup of coffee.

The energy stored in the nucleus of all atoms is called **nuclear potential energy**. Elements such as uranium are said to be radioactive. They have unstable nuclei which sometimes break apart or decay in a process called *nuclear fission*. When this occurs, large amounts of thermal and radiant energy are produced. This energy speeds up the molecules of the surrounding matter and increases its thermal energy.

4. **Mechanical Energy.** The energy possessed by a moving object, such as a car or a hammer, is called **mechanical kinetic energy**. This energy can be converted to thermal energy in four basic ways: friction, percussion, compression, and distortion.

Friction (rubbing). In winter we often rub our hands together to warm them. The rims on bicycle wheels and the brake drums in cars become hot when the brakes are applied because of friction.

Percussion (hitting). When you hit a nail several times with a hammer, the nail head warms up.

Compression (squashing). When air is pumped into a bicycle tire, the compressed air becomes hotter.

Distortion (bending). When a paper clip is bent back and forth a few times it breaks and the broken ends feel hot.

When friction or percussion occurs, only the molecules at or near the surface of the object have their kinetic energy increased. When objects are rubbed together, the molecules on both surfaces strike one another and speed up, thus increasing their kinetic energy. The molecules continue to increase their kinetic energy for as long as the rubbing action lasts. Similarly, the molecules of the hammerhead strike the molecules on the top of the nail, forcing them to move faster.

When compression or distortion occurs, molecules throughout the object may increase their kinetic energy. When you pump air into a tire, the air molecules are forced closer together and therefore collide more often, so that their kinetic energy increases. The molecules in the region where a paper clip breaks have been forced to rub against each other, thus increasing their kinetic energy.

All forms of energy can be converted completely to thermal energy and then transferred as heat. All energy converted to heat eventually helps increase the thermal energy of the Earth itself. Scientists throughout the world are concerned about the problems that may arise due to increases in the thermal energy of the Earth's surface and atmosphere. Even small increases in the average temperatures around the Earth could cause major damage to the environment.

Study Questions

1. a) List the three forms of energy we most commonly use to produce heat.
    b) For each form of energy in a), list two common sources found in the home.
2. a) What form of energy is the only direct source of heat? Explain why.
    b) How could geothermal energy be useful in the future?
3. List three ways heat can be produced by each of the following: a) electrical energy, b) chemical energy, and c) mechanical energy.
4. Explain, in terms of the kinetic molecular theory, how the thermal energy of the following objects increases: a) the filament in an incandescent lamp, b) car tires after a long journey, c) a tennis ball during a game, d) the gases above a candle flame.

THOMAS L. WILLSON
(1860-1915)

As a young boy, Canadian Thomas Willson developed a passion for science. He became particularly interested in electricity and its effects on chemical reactions. While working for a company in the United States, he developed an electrical process for extracting aluminum. In 1891 he founded the Willson Aluminum Company, but continued to experiment with processes for extracting other metals. During a series of experiments designed to extract the metal calcium, Willson accidentally produced a compound that would make his fortune.

By passing a very large electric current through a mixture of coal tar and lime, Willson produced the compound calcium carbide, which can be used to produce acetylene gas. When acetylene gas is burned it produces useful amounts of light. Soon large amounts of calcium carbide were produced for this purpose throughout the United States.

As soon as he discovered the compound, Willson applied for a patent which he later sold to a company still well-known today —Union Carbide. Upon returning to Merriton, Ontario in 1896, Willson opened the first factory in Canada to produce calcium carbide and acetylene.

Later, it was discovered that when acetylene is combined with large amounts of oxygen, an intensely hot flame results. The

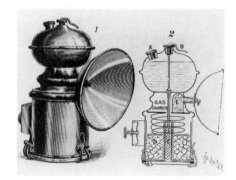

An early bicycle lamp (1900) that used acetylene gas for fuel.

development of the oxy-acetylene welding torch provided an even greater demand for calcium carbide. The oxy-acetylene welding process is still a major method of heating metals to fuse them together.

10.4   Heat Capacity

When using heat, we add it to some kind of matter. We add heat to air when warming our homes, to water when washing clothes, and to saucepans when cooking food. The amount of heat that can be added to a sample of matter depends on its heat capacity. The **heat capacity** of an object is the amount of heat required to raise its temperature by 1°C.

The SI unit of heat capacity is **joules per degree Celsius (J/°C).**

Activity 10-4:   What Factors Affect Heat Added to Matter?

In this activity you will study the factors affecting the amount of heat that can be added to an object or material.

Materials

2 styrofoam cups
   labelled A and B
Bunsen burner
retort stand
ring clamp
wire gauze
250 mL beaker
beaker tongs

test tube
test tube holder
thermometer
stirring rod
balance
100 g of metal shot (iron, lead,
   or copper)

Procedure
Part A

1. Read the procedure and design a suitable table for recording your observations in all three parts of the activity.

2. Pour 100 g of tap water into styrofoam cup A, and another 100 g of tap water into styrofoam cup B. Measure and record the temperature of the water in both cups.

3. Set up the equipment as shown in the photo. Heat 100 g of water in the beaker to a temperature of 50°C.

4. Quickly pour the hot water from the beaker into cup A. Stir the mixture and record the maximum temperature.

5. Repeat steps 3 and 4, this time heating the water in the beaker to a temperature of 80°C and pouring the hot water into cup B.

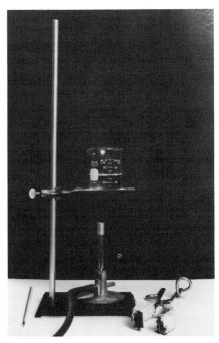

Do not stir the mixture with the thermometer.

Part B

6. Pour the water out of the styrofoam cups and repeat step 2.
7. Pour 150 g of water into the beaker, and heat the water to a temperature of 60°C.
8. Quickly, but carefully, pour 50 g of the hot water into cup A, and the remaining hot water into cup B.
9. Stir both mixtures and record the maximum temperature of the mixture in each cup.

Part C

10. Pour the water out of the styrofoam cups and repeat step 2.
11. Place 100 g of lead shot in a test tube, and stand the test tube in the beaker. Add sufficient water to the beaker to ensure that the water level in the beaker is above the level of the lead shot in the test tube. Heat the water (and thus the lead shot) until the water temperature reaches 60°C.
12. Quickly pour the heated lead shot into the water in cup A, and 100 g of the hot water from the beaker into cup B. Stir both mixtures and record the maximum temperature of the mixture in each cup.

Discussion

1. For each part of the activity, state what factor(s) was (were) a) changed, and b) controlled.
2. a) What can you infer about the amount of heat added to each sample of heated water that was poured into the styrofoam cups in Part A? Explain your answer.
   b) Explain the difference between the samples of heated water in Part A, in terms of the kinetic molecular theory.
3. a) What can you infer about the amount of heat transferred to each sample of hot water that was poured into the cups in Part B? Explain your answer.
   b) Explain the difference between the samples of heated water in Part B, in terms of the kinetic molecular theory.
4. What can you infer about the amount of heat transferred to each sample of matter that was poured into the cups in Part C? Explain your answer.
5. Write a general statement identifying the factors that can affect the amount of heat transferred to a substance. Explain how this statement is related to heat capacity.

If the mass of a substance being heated is doubled, twice as much heat is required to produce the same temperature change.

The symbol °C is used to denote a change in temperature, as well as a specific temperature. The boiling point of water is written as 100°C; a change in temperature from freezing point to boiling point is also written as 100°C.

Factors Affecting Heat Added to Matter

The amount of heat needed to warm a school on a winter's day is much greater than that needed to heat water for a bath. However, the amount of heat required in each situation depends on exactly the same factors: 1) the mass of the substance being heated, 2) how much its temperature must change, and 3) the kind of substance being heated. Some simple experiments show why each of these factors affects the transfer of heat.

1. **Mass.** Suppose a saucepan containing 1 kg of water at 20°C is placed on a heated stove element and takes 4 min to reach a temperature of 60°C. Using the same procedure on the same element, it will take 8 min to heat 2 kg of water to the same temperature. The stove element is supplying heat at the same rate in each case. Therefore, if the mass of a substance is doubled, twice as much heat is required to produce the same temperature change.

This result can be explained in terms of the kinetic molecular theory. The temperature change is the same for both samples of water, and so the average kinetic energy of all the water molecules in each sample is increased by the same amount. Because there are twice as many molecules in 2 kg of water as there are in 1 kg, twice as much heat is needed to heat the larger amount of water.

2. **Temperature Change.** Suppose a saucepan containing 1 kg of water at 20°C is placed on a hot stove element that supplies heat at a constant rate. After 1 min, the water temperature is 30°C, an increase of 10°C. After 3 min, the water temperature is 50°C, an increase of 30°C. As you would expect, it takes three times as long to increase the water temperature by 30°C as it does to increase it by 10°C. Three times as much heat is required to increase the temperature of a substance by 30°C, compared to that required for a temperature increase of 10°C.

In terms of the kinetic molecular theory, when heat is added to water molecules, their kinetic energy increases. Three times as much heat is required to increase the average kinetic energy of the water molecules to produce a temperature change of 30°C, compared to a change of 10°C.

3. **Type of Substance (Specific Heat Capacity).** Suppose two saucepans, containing 1 kg of cooking oil and 1 kg of water respectively, are heated at a constant rate using two identical stove elements. In this case, predicting the temperature increase of the oil compared to that of the water is much more difficult. However, experiments show that it takes nearly twice as long to increase the temperature of water by 10°C as it does for oil. For the same mass, about twice

as much heat is required to produce a specific temperature change in water compared to cooking oil.

Just as each substance has a specific density, so each one also has a specific ability to absorb heat. This ability is called **specific heat capacity**, and is defined as **the amount of heat that must be added to raise the temperature of 1 kg of a substance by 1°C**. The specific heat capacities of various substances are listed in Table 10-5.

Because heat is a form of energy, the unit used to measure heat is the **joule (J)**. Specific heat capacity is measured in **joules per kilogram degree Celsius (J/(kg·°C))**. The specific heat capacity of water is 4200 J/(kg·°C). This means that raising the temperature of 1 kg of water by just 1°C requires the addition of 4200 J of heat, more than for any other common substance listed.

The kinetic molecular theory partially explains differences in the specific heat capacities of different substances. The specific heat capacity of a substance depends to some extent on the relative mass of its atoms or molecules. Substances with relatively small particles generally have a higher specific heat capacity. This is partly because for the same mass, low-density substances have more particles that need to have their kinetic energy increased.

Applications of Heat Capacity

Water's large specific heat capacity enables it to absorb large amounts of heat before reaching its boiling point. Water is therefore used in the cooling systems of car engines to remove the large amounts of unuseable heat produced by the burning fuel and by friction.

Even the weather patterns occurring across a large land mass such as Canada are affected by the great heat capacity of water. The huge amounts of thermal energy that can be stored in large bodies of water affect the range of temperatures of the land nearby. Average winter temperatures are higher near oceans compared to inland. For example, although Vancouver is 500 km closer to the North Pole than Toronto, it has much milder winters. Thermal energy from the Pacific Ocean warms the winds that blow across Vancouver all winter long.

Study Questions

1. a) Define the term heat capacity.
   b) What three factors affect the amount of heat added to matter?

Table 10-5: Specific Heat Capacity of Various Substances

Substance	Specific heat capacity (J/kg°C)
aluminum	900
brick	3 000
concrete	2 900
copper	390
glass	840
gold	130
human body (average)	3 470
ice	2 116
iron	460
lead	130
protein	1 700
rock	880
sand	800
silver	230
wood	1 760
alcohol (ethyl)	2 300
alcohol (methyl)	2 500
glycerine	2 400
mercury	140
vegetable oil	2 000
water	4 200
air	995
carbon dioxide	836
helium	5 250
hydrogen	14 400
nitrogen	1 040
oxygen	916
steam	2 020

c) Explain, in terms of the kinetic molecular theory, what happens to the thermal energy of an object when i) its mass decreases, ii) its temperature increases.

2. a) Define the term specific heat capacity.
   b) Which would have the greatest effect on 10 kg of water at 20°C: i) adding 2 kg of water at 100°C, or ii) adding 5 kg of aluminum at 100°C? Explain your answer.

3. a) Which of the common substances listed in Table 10-5 is best suited for storing thermal energy in a solar home? Explain why.
   b) What are the advantages of using water as a fluid for cooling car engines? What are the disadvantages?

4. How does the heat capacity of water affect the climate in various regions of Canada?

PERMAFROST

About one-fifth of Canada is covered with a huge expanse of coniferous forest consisting mostly of black spruce. Another third of Canada lies beyond the tree line, where the lichen-covered tundra eventually gives way to polar deserts.

The kind of vegetation that can grow in these regions is determined by short growing seasons, very cold winters, cool summers, and a possibility of frost at all times of the year. These severe conditions combine to permit the survival of only the hardiest plants and animals. One factor limiting plant growth is the presence of *permafrost*. Permafrost is ground that stays permanently frozen all year round. Permafrost is found in almost 60% of Cana-

A pingo is a conical hill with an ice core. Pingos often form on top of springs where water is forced up through the permafrost.

da's land mass, and is most extensive in the far north. In the Arctic Islands, for example, permafrost 550 m thick has been measured.

In more southern permafrost regions, the surface ice melts, providing a thin layer of soil that is sometimes suitable for plant growth. However, the ground beneath the soil remains frozen, limiting the amount of growth.

Houses, buildings, and structures such as oil pipelines built in a permafrost region are usually erected on posts sunk into the frozen ground. In some houses that have rested on or in the ground, the heat from the floors has melted the permafrost underneath. In such situations, the houses have gradually sunk into the ground, often at unusual angles.

Meet a Mechanical Engineer — Judy Jung

Judy is a building services consultant for Johnson Controls. Her job involves selling and designing heating systems.

Q. VERY FEW WOMEN GO INTO MECHANICAL ENGINEERING. WHY DID YOU CHOOSE IT?

A. It's true there are few women in this field—in my graduating class of 80 mechanical engineering students at the University of Calgary, only 3 were women. But I have always liked the courses, and I think it is the most versatile area of engineering.

Q. WAS ENGINEERING YOUR GOAL AS A CHILD?

A. Not at all. I thought engineers operated trains and built bridges. I was always good at math and physics, though, and on the very last day for submitting applications to university I decided on engineering.

Q. DID YOU FIND THE UNIVERSITY COURSES DIFFICULT?

A. I had difficulty compared to my male classmates because I had never seen engines or the inside of a car. I didn't know about gears and things that a lot of men already were familiar with. I really had to work to visualize some of these mechanical concepts, and I was determined to show that women could do the course.

Q. WHEN DID YOU MOVE TO TORONTO?

A. In 1986, soon after I graduated. That was a difficult year for the economy in Calgary, and I decided to move east before a new batch of graduates hit the market. Engineering is such a volatile business that one year can make a difference between getting a job and being unemployed. I applied to companies in the HVAC (heating, ventilation, and air conditioning) industry, since I had specialized in thermodynamics. Eventually, I got this job with Johnson Controls.

Q. WHAT DOES A SALES ENGINEER IN YOUR FIELD DO?

A. I deal with customers who usually are building owners. I work with them to come up with a design for the heating, ventilation, or air conditioning system of their buildings. I research the job, do the preliminary design, price the system, and sell the concept to the customer. If it is accepted, an application engineer does the final design based on my preliminary one.

Q. WHAT IS A TYPICAL SALES JOB LIKE?

A. I meet with the customer to learn what he or she wants—maybe the building is old and the system has to be upgraded. I look at the building and/or obtain mechanical drawings of it, and then start to design a system. Afterwards, I price it and present it to the customer. If it is accepted, then I follow through by making sure that someone designs, installs, and completes the assignment.

Q. IS THERE ALWAYS SOMETHING NEW TO LEARN IN THIS FIELD?

A. The training goes on all the time. Every time a new product comes out, we attend seminars to learn about them. We're always changing and upgrading systems.

Q. WHAT DO YOU LIKE BEST ABOUT YOUR JOB?

A. I like the fact that there's variety. I've never wanted to be in the research end or stuck behind a desk from 9 to 5. Everything has to work together and it's like solving a puzzle. Even though I have supervisors and managers, the way a job goes is all up to me.

Review Questions

A: Knowledge

1. Distinguish between thermal energy and temperature, in terms of the kinetic molecular theory.

2. Explain what happens to the molecules of a substance when it is a) heated, and b) cooled.

3. a) Why did scientists support the caloric theory for so long?
   b) What eventually caused them to reject this theory?
   c) List two other examples of scientific models or theories that have been revised or discarded.

4. Describe how to calibrate a liquid-filled thermometer.

5. a) Explain temperature, in terms of the kinetic molecular theory.
   b) Describe two objects that have the same temperature but different quantities of thermal energy.

6. a) When calibrating a thermometer, why must pure water be used?
   b) Why is it necessary to use steam, rather than boiling water, to determine the higher fixed point?

7. List eight devices in the home that produce heat from electrical energy.

8. Distinguish between heat capacity and specific heat capacity.

9. Why does a house that cools to 16°C overnight take so long to heat up when the temperature of the thermostat is raised to 21°C the next morning?

B: Application

10. Why do you think the development of the steam engine had an effect on the development of the kinetic molecular theory?

11. If a scientist tries to explain the results of an experiment using a scientific theory and is unable to do so, what should she do? Explain why.

12. "A scientific theory should not be changed or abandoned unless all scientists are in agreement." Comment on this statement.

13. a) What is unusual about the temperature of a mixture of ice and water as the ice is being melted?
    b) What kind of energy possessed by the molecules of a substance is most affected when a change of state is occurring? Explain why.

14. a) What happens when you experience rope burn?
    b) Why do athletes sometimes experience something similar to rope burn when playing on artificial turf?

15. List three ways heat produced by friction a) can be useful, b) can cause problems, c) is too small to be noticed.

16. List three different ways in which metals are joined together using heat.

17. How is heat produced in a) a rotting compost heap, b) a natural hot springs, c) running, d) sawing a piece of wood?

18. Why does a squash ball become softer and warmer after being used in a game?

19. Explain what happens to meteorites as they fall towards the Earth's surface.

20. Why is heat energy transferred from one hand to another when they are rubbed together, but is not transferred when the hands are simply held together?

21. a) What form of energy is used to make a safety match burn?
    b) Why is a safety match safer than an ordinary match?

22. Why does a house stay warm for so long in the evening following a hot day, even if windows are opened to allow cool outside air to flow in?

23. Why does an architect need to know the specific heat capacities of different substances when designing a solar home?

24. a) What devices used for adding heat to substances in our homes have controls to limit the amount of heat that can be added?

b) Explain what might happen if these controls were not present.

25. Why are winter temperatures higher on the west coast compared to places at the same latitude in the prairie provinces?

26. What environmental problems could occur due to the installation of elevated oil pipelines in Canada's arctic regions? Suggest some ways of solving these problems.

C: Problem Solving

27. Suppose you were given the task of mass-producing thousands of liquid-filled mercury thermometers.
    a) What problems might occur i) while the thermometers were being manufactured, and ii) while they were being calibrated?
    b) Suggest ways to correct or minimize the problems identified in a).

28. a) Draw a simple block diagram of a car. In the diagram, identify all car parts where heat is produced or transferred as the engine converts the chemical energy of the fuel to thermal energy.
    b) List any other devices in a car that produce significant amounts of heat as the car is driven.
    c) Repeat a) for i) a complete stereo system while a record is played, ii) a hair dryer in operation, and iii) a chainsaw cutting wood.

29. Every day we use many litres of heated water, and then throw it away while it is still warm. Suggest some practical ways to a) reduce the amount of heated water used, b) reclaim some of the thermal energy in the heated water before it is discarded.

30. a) Design an experiment to simultaneously compare the specific heat capacities of several metals, such as copper, brass, aluminum, zinc, lead, and iron, using a single block of ice.
    b) Predict what would happen and draw a diagram to illustrate the result.

Try This

1. **Hot Ice**
   ''Which freezes faster, tap water or water that has been boiled?'' Design and carry out an experiment to answer this question.

2. **Making a Thermometer**
   It is possible to make and calibrate a liquid-filled thermometer, using thick-walled glass tubing with a thin bore. Discuss this project with your teacher and obtain approval before attempting any part of it.

How many different chemical changes are being caused by heat from the stove top elements?

Chapter 11
The Effects of Heat on Matter

When heat is added to the water in a kettle, the water temperature increases steadily until the boiling point is reached. At 100°C, the liquid water rapidly changes state. As heating continues, the gaseous water expands and pushes out to mix with air in the room. All these heating effects are examples of physical change because no new substances form.

Heat can also be converted into other forms of energy. By heating different substances, we can produce light and sound, and make objects move. Under special conditions, heating two pieces of metal will cause an electric current to flow. Heat can also cause chemical changes, such as those produced when food is cooked.

In this chapter, you will study the most common physical changes produced when matter is heated, and apply the kinetic molecular theory to explain what you observe. You will also learn to calculate the quantity of heat involved when heat is transferred from one object or material to another.

When you finish Chapter 11, you should be able to:

- describe some practical applications of, and problems caused by, the expansion of matter
- explain the expansion of matter and its effects in terms of the kinetic molecular theory
- calculate the amount of heat transferred from one substance or object to another
- calculate the amount of heat required to change samples of matter from one state to another

STUDY HINT

In this chapter, you will calculate quantities of heat using several different equations. "How to Solve Science Problems Involving Equations" on pages 323 to 325 outlines a methodical approach to calculating answers to numerical problems in science.

11.1   Heat and Thermal Expansion

What do the buckling of railway lines in hot weather and the upward flight of a glider have in common with using a candy thermometer to make fudge? In each case, adding heat to matter causes an increase in volume known as **thermal expansion**.

Gliders are able to soar upwards because heated air rises as it expands.

Activity 11-1:   Exploring Heating Effects

In Part A, you will make predictions about the effects of thermal expansion on solids, liquids, and gases, and then test your predictions by experiment. In Part B, your teacher will demonstrate some energy conversions that occur when heat is added to different kinds of matter.

Materials

ball and ring apparatus	thermometer
Bunsen burner	one-hole stopper with glass
bimetallic strip	tube (30 cm) attached
2 pieces of glass tubing (30 cm)	Florence flask
fireproof mat	deflagrating spoon
250 mL beaker	magnesium ribbon (6 cm)

tongs	protective glove
thermocouple	dry ice (1 cm^3)
electrical meter (ammeter)	balloon

Part A: The Thermal Expansion of Matter

Procedure

1. **Make a Hypothesis:** Before you begin the procedure, read each step carefully. Predict what volume changes (expansion effects) will occur and what you will observe as a result. Record your predictions.

2. Try passing the metal ball through the ring when both are at room temperature. Then heat the ball in the burner flame and try to pass it through the ring again. Record what happens.

3. Heat the bimetallic strip by passing it through the burner flame. Allow the bimetallic strip to cool down. Record what happens.

4. Hold two pieces of glass tubing firmly at one end and heat the other ends in the burner flame for about 2 min. Place the hot end of one tube on a fireproof mat and allow it to cool slowly. Dip the hot end of the other tube into a beaker of cold water. Record what happens. Dispose of the beaker's contents according to your teacher's instructions.

5. Gently hold the bulb of the thermometer between your fingers until no more change is observed. Record what happens.

6. Place the rubber stopper with the glass tube into a Florence flask filled with air. Invert the flask and place the end of the glass tube under water in a beaker. Hold the flask in your hands for 3 min. Record what happens.

Discussion

1. Compare your predictions with your observations. Comment on any differences.

2. Explain, in terms of the kinetic molecular theory, what you observed in steps 2 and 3.

3. Explain, in terms of the kinetic molecular theory, what happened when the glass tubing was cooled a) slowly, and b) quickly.

4. a) Compare the expansion rates of the solids, liquids, and gases observed in this activity.
   b) Explain, in terms of the kinetic molecular theory, the differences in expansion rates for the three states of matter.

Part B: Heating Effects and Energy Conversions (Teacher Demonstration)

As your teacher demonstrates each step below, record your observations and identify all physical changes, chemical changes, and energy conversions.

Procedure

1. Heat an empty deflagrating spoon in a burner flame for 2 min, then allow it to cool.
2. Hold a piece of magnesium ribbon with a pair of tongs and place one end of the magnesium in the burner flame.
3. Connect the thermocouple to the electrical meter (ammeter). Place the junction of the two wires in a burner flame.
4. Using a protective glove, place a small piece of dry ice inside a balloon. Hold the neck of the balloon closed for 3 min, then release it.

Discussion

1. State the evidence for each physical and chemical change you observed.
2. Identify each step in which adding heat resulted in an energy conversion. For each conversion list the form(s) of energy produced.
3. What was the source of the heat that was added in step 4? Explain what happened.

The Effects of Thermal Expansion

All substances expand and contract with changes in temperature. In a mercury thermometer, both the glass tube and the mercury inside it expand when heat is added. However, each substance expands at a different rate for the same change in temperature. Table 11-1 compares thermal expansion rates for several substances. Liquids expand more than solids for the same temperature change. Notice that mercury expands about 18 times as much as Pyrex glass. Gases are not listed in the table because gases expand and contract at the same rate.

Table 11-1: Coefficients of Thermal Expansion

Substance	Coefficient of linear expansion (per °C)	Coefficient of volume expansion (per °C)
Solid		
aluminum	24×10^{-6}	72×10^{-6}
brass	19×10^{-6}	56×10^{-6}
brick and concrete	$10\text{-}14 \times 10^{-6}$	36×10^{-6}
glass (pyrex)	3.3×10^{-6}	10×10^{-6}
glass (window)	9.0×10^{-6}	27×10^{-6}
invar	0.83×10^{-6}	2.5×10^{-6}
lead	27×10^{-6}	87×10^{-6}
oak (across fibre)	54×10^{-6}	160×10^{-6}
oak (along fibre)	5×10^{-6}	15×10^{-6}
quartz	0.4×10^{-6}	1.1×10^{-6}
steel or iron	12×10^{-6}	35×10^{-6}
Liquid		
ethyl alcohol		1100×10^{-6}
gasoline		950×10^{-6}
mercury		182×10^{-6}
water		210×10^{-6}

The coefficient of volume expansion for most gases and air at constant pressure is 3400×10^{-6} per °C.

According to the kinetic molecular theory, thermal expansion occurs because adding heat increases the kinetic energy of molecules. Faster-moving molecules collide more often, hit each other harder, and rebound farther. Because this requires more space, a rise in temperature causes an increase in volume. If the temperature falls, however, the molecules lose kinetic energy and the volume decreases again.

Figure 11-1. When heat is added to a solid, the molecules vibrate more rapidly, taking up more space.

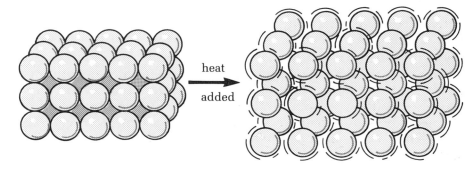

Even though the expansion rate for solids is low, the volume changes that occur can cause problems. For example, brittle substances, such as glass and concrete, break easily if cooled quickly or unevenly. The part of the object being cooled contracts more than the hot parts nearby, and cracking results. Pyrex glass, which has a very low expansion rate, was developed specifically to overcome this problem.

Problems also arise when solids with different expansion rates are sealed together. In television tubes and light bulbs, for example, metal wires passing through the glass are sealed to it. Unless the wires have the same expansion rate as the glass, the metal-to-glass seal will break. Likewise, the steel and concrete used in building construction must have similar rates of expansion.

Solids expand and contract at an equal rate in all directions. However, if a solid object is long and narrow, its length will change much more than any other dimension. This too can cause problems. Care must be taken when electrical power lines are installed to ensure that they do not sag too low in summer or snap in winter. Long steel girders in buildings often have slotted holes to allow bolts to slide as the girders lengthen and shorten with temperature changes.

Thermal expansion of liquids and gases can also cause problems. When bottles, jars, and cans are filled, a small space must be left at the top to allow for liquid expansion. Overheating sealed containers, such as cans of paint, aerosol cans, and butane lighters, can cause explosions, especially if the contents are flammable.

There are many practical applications of thermal expansion, however. For example, because most metals expand more than glass, tightly sealed metal lids on jars can be released by holding them under hot water. Another common application is the bimetallic strip, shown in the photograph at the right. It consists of two metal strips fused together. When heat is added, one metal expands more than the other, so that the strip changes its shape. Bimetallic strips are often used as switches for controlling flashing lights and electrical equipment. Perhaps the most common application of thermal expansion is the thermometer.

On January 28, 1986 millions of people around the world saw the televised launch of the Space Shuttle Challenger end in fiery disaster shortly after lift-off. Investigation revealed that the accident was caused by unusually low temperatures at the launch-time. Because of these low temperatures, some of the rubber seals used in the main rocket assemblies contracted sufficiently to allow fuel to leak out, causing a huge explosion.

Do You Know?
The length of a steel bridge 400 m long will increase by about 34 cm as the temperature changes from $-40°C$ in winter to $30°C$ in summer.

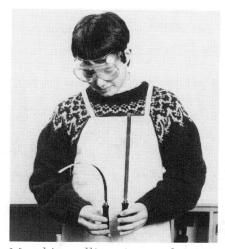

Most bimetallic strips used in science classrooms are made of iron and brass.

On long bridges, several expansion joints may be required to allow for thermal expansion.

Figure 11-2. A clinical thermometer.

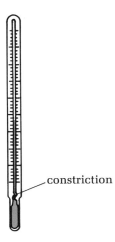

constriction

Why is a constriction necessary in the bore of a clinical thermometer?

Some common liquid-filled and bimetallic thermometers.

Thermometers For All Temperatures

The design of most familiar thermometers is based on differences in thermal expansion. Mercury and alcohol are used in liquid-filled thermometers because their expansion rates are much larger than that of glass. The range of temperatures to be measured often determines the most suitable material for making the thermometer. For example, alcohol is used instead of mercury in a weather thermometer, because mercury freezes at $-39°C$.

Some thermometers are based on the expansion of solids. However, the thermal expansion rate of a single piece of metal is not large enough for accurate temperature measurements. Therefore, the bending of bimetallic strips is commonly used in thermostats to indicate changes in temperature. The longer the bimetallic strip, the greater the amount of bending. Home heating thermostats typically measure temperatures between 5°C and 40°C, while oven thermostats operate from 100°C to 300°C.

The first thermometers were based on the thermal expansion and contraction of gases. Gas thermometers are still used when great precision is needed. However, the thermal expansion rate of gases is so large that the great length of gas thermometers makes them impractical, unless the temperature range is very limited.

Temperatures such as those reached when iron melts are measured with an optical pyrometer. The functioning of this device is based on the colours produced by glowing objects, rather than on

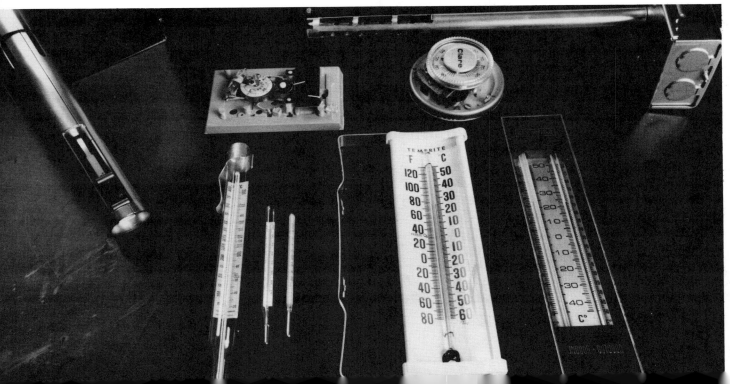

thermal expansion. Similarly, very cold temperatures cannot be measured by thermal expansion: solids become too brittle, and liquids and gases change state. Extremely low temperatures are measured with a thermoelectric device called a thermocouple.

Thermal Expansion and Absolute Zero

Much of the early experimental work on gas expansion was done by the French scientist Jacques Charles towards the end of the eighteenth century. His observations showed that the more a gas was heated, the more it expanded. There seemed to be no upper limit to either gas volume or temperature. However, graphs of thermal contraction for gases did suggest a lower limit. The graph in Figure 11-3 indicates that if a gas could be cooled without liquefying, it would contract until it had "zero volume". This would be reached at a temperature of −273.15°C. This temperature is called **absolute zero**. Scientists believe it is the lowest temperature to which matter can be cooled. At absolute zero, the kinetic energy of the molecules is at a minimum, and heat can no longer be transferred from the matter.

Figure 11-3. The volume of a gas at constant pressure decreases uniformly as the temperature decreases.

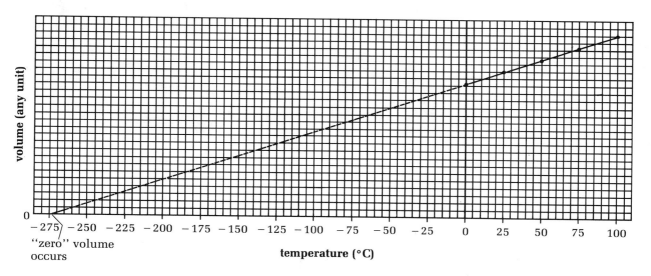

If the graph line is extrapolated until the gas has "zero" volume, it meets the temperature axis at −273.15°C.

Figure 11-4. A comparison of the Celsius and Kelvin temperature scales.

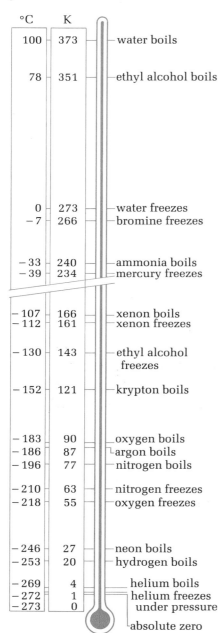

°C	K	
100	373	water boils
78	351	ethyl alcohol boils
0	273	water freezes
−7	266	bromine freezes
−33	240	ammonia boils
−39	234	mercury freezes
−107	166	xenon boils
−112	161	xenon freezes
−130	143	ethyl alcohol freezes
−152	121	krypton boils
−183	90	oxygen boils
−186	87	argon boils
−196	77	nitrogen boils
−210	63	nitrogen freezes
−218	55	oxygen freezes
−246	27	neon boils
−253	20	hydrogen boils
−269	4	helium boils
−272	1	helium freezes under pressure
−273	0	absolute zero

Although absolute zero has not yet been reached, scientists have succeeded in cooling matter to within 0.001°C of the predicted value. Over a century ago, Lord Kelvin (1824-1907) used the concept of absolute zero as the basis for a new temperature scale still employed by scientists around the world. As Figure 11-4 shows, one kelvin equals one Celsius degree. However, zero on the Kelvin scale equals absolute zero; thus, water freezes at 273.15 K. The Kelvin scale is useful to scientists because there are no negative numbers in calculations.

Lord Kelvin

Study Questions

1. a) Define the term thermal expansion.
   b) Explain thermal expansion in terms of the kinetic molecular theory.
2. a) List three different types of problems resulting from the thermal expansion of solids. State an example of each.
   b) Identify two uses of the thermal expansion of solids.
   c) Identify two ways in which the thermal expansion of liquids and gases can cause problems.

3. a) Draw a labelled diagram of i) a liquid thermometer, and ii) a bimetallic strip thermometer, and explain how each thermometer works.
   b) Describe two other devices for measuring temperature.
4. a) Define the term "absolute zero" temperature.
   b) Compare the Celsius and Kelvin temperature scales.
   c) What is the major advantage gained by scientists when using the Kelvin temperature scale?

CHALLENGER

The level of the mercury in a thermometer falls briefly just after the thermometer is placed in a container of hot water. Explain why.

SCIENCE IN ACTION

CRYOGENICS

Cryogenics is the study of effects produced in matter at extremely low temperatures. The coldest naturally occurring temperature recorded is −88°C (185 K) at Vostok Station in the Antarctic. However, scientists do not consider this very cold! The study of cryogenics covers the temperature range from −150°C to −273°C.

Cryogenics has many different applications. One of the most important is the freezing of living cells. If carefully cooled, cells can be thawed later and they will continue to live. (If cells are cooled too rapidly, ice crystals damage their structure and the cells die.) Human blood cells can be frozen and stored for ten years

or more. Cryogenic temperatures are also used to store animal and human sperm (male reproductive cells). Doctors use cryogenic techniques to remove skin growths such as warts. Surgeons use a device called a cannula to kill diseased cells in sensitive areas, such as the human brain. The cannula—a long, thin, hollow probe about 3 mm in diameter—conducts liquid nitrogen to the target cells. Researchers are seeking ways to freeze and store body organs for transplant purposes. Yet another application is the freeze-drying of food using liquid nitrogen.

Gases cooled to cryogenic temperatures can be stored in very small spaces. Millions of litres of liquefied natural gas (LNG) are shipped in refrigerated tankers and trucks. The rockets that launch space vehicles are powered by fuels cooled to cryogenic temperatures.

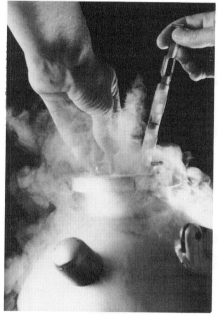

A medical specimen is frozen in a tank containing liquid nitrogen.

The use of heat engines has greatly influenced the development of our cities. What would this landscape look like without them?

Do You Know?
A hot-air balloon with a capacity of approximately 1000 m³ can lift a mass of about 500 kg when filled with air at 100°C.

11.2 Gas Expansion and Heat Engines

If all the machines that operate because of gas expansion stopped working, our lives would change dramatically. Most ships, trains, trucks, buses, and cars would stop moving. No planes would fly, and most power stations would stop producing electricity. Each of these machines contains a *heat engine*, a device that converts thermal energy to mechanical energy. In heat engines, the forces produced by the thermal expansion of gases are used to make parts of the engine move.

Activity 11-2: Expanding Gases and Simple Heat Engines

In this activity you will study the effects produced by gases when heat is added to several different substances. **Note**: Your teacher may wish to demonstrate this entire activity.

Materials

one-hole stopper with
   glass tube inserted
Erlenmeyer flask
wire gauze
clamp
retort stand
ring clamp

Bunsen burner
fan wheel (turbine wheel)
   mounted on a rod
Hiero's engine
lycopodium powder
dust explosion apparatus
candle

Procedure

1. Carefully insert the rubber stopper assembly into an Erlenmeyer flask containing 50 mL of water. Place the flask on the wire gauze, and clamp its neck securely to the retort stand.
2. Gently heat the water in the flask until it boils.
3. Hold the fan wheel in the path of the water vapour, and record what happens.

(*Teacher Demonstrations*)

4. Place 50 mL of water in the Hiero's engine apparatus, and heat the water using a burner flame. Record what happens.
5. Place 1 mL of lycopodium powder in the funnel at the bottom of the dust explosion apparatus. Light the candle and carefully place it in the holder inside the dust explosion apparatus.
6. Place the lid tightly on the dust explosion apparatus, and quickly blow air into the apparatus through the rubber hose. Record what happens.

Discussion

1. a) Describe all the energy transfers and conversions that occurred during step 3.
   b) Explain what happened to the fan wheel in terms of i) the water vapour's thermal energy, and ii) the kinetic molecular theory.
2. Explain the operation of the Hiero's engine in terms of a) the thermal energy of the water, and b) the kinetic molecular theory.
3. Explain what happened during the operation of the dust explosion apparatus in terms of a) the thermal energy of the substances inside the container, and b) the kinetic molecular theory.

CAUTION: Be very careful not to direct the water vapour towards other students. The hot steam can cause painful burns. Do not insert the stopper into the flask too tightly.

CAUTION: Steps 5 and 6 should be attempted only if the proper apparatus and adequate ventilation are available.

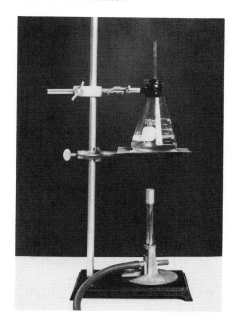

Heat Engines

All heat engines operate on the same principle. When the thermal energy of a gas increases, the gas expands and exerts forces on parts of the heat engine to produce motion. The most common heat engines can be classified as either external combustion engines, or internal combustion engines, depending on whether the fuel is burned outside or inside the engine.

Gas molecules undergo about 5 000 000 000 collisions per second, and about 10 000 000 collisions for every metre travelled. These collisions prevent odours from spreading at several hundred metres per second throughout a room.

Figure 11-5. A cross-sectional view of an external combustion engine.

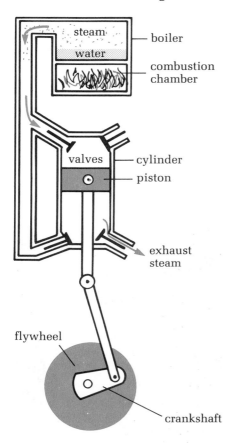

Richard Trevithick (1771-1833) was a Cornish mechanical engineer who invented a compact high-pressure steam engine. In 1803 he constructed the world's first steam railway locomotive.

Steam forces these huge turbine wheels to rotate and drive an electrical generator.

1. **External Combustion Engines**. The first practical external combustion engines were known as reciprocating steam engines (see Figure 11-5). Burning a fuel such as coal heats water in a boiler, which produces steam. The steam flows into the engine and pushes a piston along a cylinder. When the piston reaches the other end of the cylinder, a set of valves changes position. This allows more steam from the boiler to push the cylinder back again. This back-and-forth, or reciprocating, motion is converted into a turning motion by the crankshaft. A heavy flywheel attached to the shaft makes the engine rotate smoothly.

Steam turbine engines, like the one shown in the photograph, are more efficient than reciprocating engines. The steam turbine engine consists of several large discs with curved blades mounted on them. Steam is forced against these blades and rotates the discs. Heat for steam turbine engines is obtained from fossil fuels or nuclear sources. Steam turbines are commonly used in electrical power stations and large ships.

2. **Internal Combustion Engines**. Internal combustion engines (see Figure 11-6) are more compact, because the fuel burns inside the engine itself. Any fuel that can be vaporized can be used to operate such engines. In a typical car engine, a mixture of vaporized gasoline and air flows into the cylinder. A spark then ignites the mixture, and the chemical energy released by the burning fuel rapidly increases the thermal energy of the gases produced during combustion. The force exerted by the expanding gases pushes the piston along the cylinder, causing the crankshaft of the engine to rotate. Most cars, trucks, and trains are driven by internal combustion engines.

Figure 11-6. A cross-sectional view of an internal combustion engine.

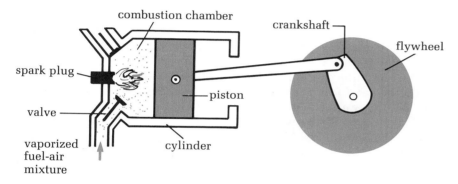

Jet planes, spacecraft, guided weapons, and most forms of transportation are driven by heat engines, as are the electrical generators in most power stations. Even hydroelectric power stations produce electricity using falling water that was originally lifted up by evaporation.

Study Questions

1. a) What is a heat engine, and why are such engines so essential to modern society?
   b) How is the thermal expansion of gases used in heat engines?
2. Describe the operation of a) an external combustion engine, and b) an internal combustion engine.
3. Explain the differences between the two types of heat engines.
4. Explain, in terms of the kinetic molecular theory, what happens to the gases inside an internal combustion engine when the fuel is burned.

CHALLENGER

Car mechanics sometimes use dry ice to cool wheel bearings, which are then fitted onto the car. Explain why. Try to identify some other objects that are cooled for similar purposes.

WEATHER FORECASTS AND EL NIÑO

In 1982-83, Canada experienced one of the mildest winters on record, and unusual weather conditions occurred all around the world. The California coast was hit with massive storms, Peru experienced record rainfalls, and Australia, Africa, and Indonesia were plagued with drought. Meteorological analysis showed that all these unusual conditions had been caused by the same phenomenon—El Niño.

El Niño is the name given to a slight annual warming of a Pacific ocean current just off the coast of Ecuador in South America. This warming is caused by major changes in the normal movements of the water and winds in the tropical Pacific. Usually El Niño's effects on

During one severe storm, the Golden Gate bridge in San Francisco was closed to traffic for several hours.

global weather patterns are minor. Occasionally, however, the change is great enough to affect wind patterns across both the Pacific and Indian Oceans. In 1982-83, the warm equatorial winds that normally blow westwards from South America towards the Philippines reversed themselves. This allowed warm surface water to flow in an easterly direction towards the coast of South America, causing major changes in the heating of the atmosphere.

The problems caused by the 1982-83 El Niño have spurred efforts by scientists around the world to develop more effective models for long-range global weather forecasting. Any successful model must be able to account for the large-scale transfers of heat that occur between the Earth's atmosphere and its oceans.

11.3 Measuring Quantities of Heat

Temperature change is readily measured with a thermometer. However, no simple instrument exists to measure the quantity of heat transferred during a temperature change. Instead, quantities of heat must be calculated.

Calculating Quantities of Heat

Three factors affect the quantity of heat transferred to or from a substance: its mass, the temperature change involved, and the specific heat capacity (S.H.C.) of the substance. A simple mathematical equation relates these factors to the quantity of heat transferred:

$$\frac{\text{heat}}{\text{transferred}} = \frac{\text{mass of}}{\text{substance}} \times \frac{\text{S.H.C. of}}{\text{substance}} \times \frac{\text{temperature}}{\text{change of}}$$
$$\text{substance}$$

Using symbols, the equation becomes:

$$Q = m \times c \times \Delta t$$

where heat transferred (Q) is measured in joules (J); mass (m) is measured in kilograms (kg); specific heat capacity (c) is measured in joules per kilogram degree Celsius (J/(kg·°C)) and temperature change (Δt) is measured in Celsius degrees (°C).

Temperature change is determined using the equation:

$$\frac{\text{temperature}}{\text{change}} = \frac{\text{final}}{\text{temperature}} - \frac{\text{beginning}}{\text{temperature}}$$

Using symbols, the equation becomes:

$$\Delta t = t_2 - t_1$$

These two equations are used to calculate:

1. the heat added or transferred to a substance when its temperature increases;
2. the heat lost by or transferred from a substance when its temperature decreases;
3. how much thermal energy can be stored in or removed from a substance.

Do You Know?
The amount of heat a person gives off each day is sufficient to heat 21 L of water from 0°C to boiling point.

▶ How to Solve Science Problems Involving Equations

The procedure below is a simple application of the scientific method.

Sample problem 1: How much heat is transferred to 200 g of water when it is heated from 20°C to 60°C?

1. *Data*: Read the problem carefully and record all given quantities, using correct symbols and units. Also, record symbols and units for the unknown quantities. (*Note:* Most difficulties can be traced to omissions or errors made in recording given and unknown quantities.)

Data

$$m = 200 \text{ g} = 0.200 \text{ kg}$$
$$c_{\text{water}} = 4200 \text{ J/(kg·°C)}$$
$$t_1 = 20°C$$
$$t_2 = 60°C$$
$$\Delta t = ? \text{ °C}$$
$$Q = ? \text{ J}$$

2. *Equation*: Write the equation(s) related to the problem. Compare the data to the equation(s). Determine how the unknown quantities can be found using the equation(s).

Equation

$$\Delta t = t_2 - t_1$$
$$Q = mc_{water}\,\Delta t$$

3. *Substitute*: Ensure that units for given quantities are the same as those needed in the equation. Substitute given quantities into the equation.

$$\Delta t = 60°C - 20°C = 40°C$$
$$Q = (0.200 \text{ kg})(4200 \text{ J/(kg}\cdot°C))(40°C)$$

4. *Compute*: Compute the numerical answer. Record it with the correct units.

$$Q = 33\ 600 \text{ J} = 3.4 \times 10^4 \text{ J}$$

5. *Answer*: Write an answer statement in sentence form.

The heat transferred to the water is 3.4×10^4 J.

Remember to ensure that the mass of the substance is expressed in kilograms before calculating quantities of heat.

Sample problem 2: What will be the final temperature of 200 g of water at 30°C when 12 600 J of heat is added to it?

Data:

$$m = 200 \text{ g} = 0.200 \text{ kg}$$
$$c_{water} = 4200 \text{ J/(kg}\cdot°C)$$
$$t_1 = 30°C$$
$$t_2 = ?\ °C$$
$$\Delta t = ?\ °C$$
$$Q = 12\ 600 \text{ J}$$

$$\Delta t = t_2 - t_1$$
$$Q = m\,c_{water}\,\Delta t$$

$$Q = m\,c_{water}\,\Delta t$$

$$12\ 600 \text{ J} = (0.200 \text{ kg})(4200 \text{ kJ/(kg}\cdot°C))\,(\Delta t)$$
$$12\ 600 \text{ J} = (840 \text{ J/}°C)\,(\Delta t)$$
$$\frac{12\ 600 \text{ J}}{840\text{J/}°C} = \Delta t$$
$$15°C = \Delta t$$

$$\Delta t = t_2 - t_1$$
$$15°C = t_2 - 30°C$$
$$15°C + 30°C = t_2$$
$$45°C = t_2$$

The final temperature of the 200 g of water when the heat is added will be 45°C.

Sample problem 3: What will be the final temperature of the mixture if 100 g of water at 80°C is mixed with 100 g of water at 20°C?

In this type of problem, note that when the hot and cold water are mixed together, the combined mass of water shares some of the thermal energy of the hot water. This thermal energy shared by the combined samples of water is the heat that could be transferred from the hot water if it was cooled to the temperature of the cold water. This problem can be done in two steps:

i) Calculate the heat that would be transferred from the hot water if it were cooled to the temperature of the cold water.

ii) Calculate the final temperature of the mixture.

Data

$m_{\text{hot water}} = 100 \text{ g} = 0.100 \text{ kg}$ $\Delta t = t_2 - t_1$

$m_{\text{cold water}} = 100 \text{ g} = 0.100 \text{ kg}$ $Q = m \, c_{\text{water}} \, \Delta t$

$c_{\text{water}} = 4200 \text{ J/(kg} \cdot \text{°C)}$ i) Extra heat transferred from

$t_1 = t_{\text{hot water}} = 80\text{°C}$ the hot water to the mixture:

$t_2 = t_{\text{cold water}} = 20\text{°C}$ $\Delta t = t_2 - t_1$

$\Delta t = 20\text{°C} - 80\text{°C} = -60\text{°C}$

$Q = m_{\text{hot water}} \, c_{\text{water}} \, \Delta t$

$Q = (0.100 \text{ kg})(4200 \text{ J/(kg} \cdot \text{°C)}) \, (-60\text{°C})$

$Q = -25\ 200 \text{ J}$

The heat transferred from the hot water is now added to the mixture, which will have a starting temperature of 20°C.

ii) Temperature change of mixture:

$Q = (m_{\text{hw}} + m_{\text{cw}}) \, C\Delta t$

$25\ 200 \text{ J} = (0.100 \text{ kg} + 0.100 \text{ kg})(4200 \text{ J/kg} \cdot \text{°C})(\Delta t)$

$25\ 200 \text{ J} = (840 \text{ J/°C})(\Delta t)$

$\dfrac{25\ 200 \text{ J}}{840 \text{ J/°C}} = \Delta t$

$30 \text{ °C} = \Delta t$

The heat transferred from the hot water increased the temperature of the mixture by 30°C.

Therefore, $t_{\text{m}} = t_1 + \Delta t = 20\text{°C} + 30\text{°C} = 50\text{°C}$

The final temperature of the mixture is 50°C. ◀

Activity 11-3:   The Transfer of Heat in Mixtures

In this activity you will transfer heat by mixing together samples of hot and cold water. Before mixing each sample, you will predict the final temperature of the mixture.

Materials

Bunsen burner	2 250 mL beakers
retort stand	large styrofoam cup
ring clamp	100 mL graduated cylinder
wire gauze	stirring rod
2 thermometers	beaker tongs

Procedure

1. Copy the following table in your notebook.

	Cold Water		Hot Water		
Mixture	Mass (m_{cw})	Temperature (t_{cw})	Mass (m_{hw})	Temperature (t_{hw})	Final Temperature of Mixture (t_m)
1	100 g		100 g	60°C	
2	100 g		100 g	80°C	
3	50 g		100 g	60°C	
4	150 g		50 g	70°C	

You can measure 100 g of water quickly and easily by using an indirect method. Simply pour 100 mL of water into a graduated cylinder. Because the density of water is 1 g/cm³, and 1 cm³ = 1 mL, the mass of 100 mL of water is exactly 100 g.

2. Pour 100 g of cold water into the styrofoam cup. Measure and record the temperature of the cold water.

3. Heat 100 g of water to about 65°C.

4. When the hot water has cooled to 60°C, quickly pour it into the cup containing the cold water. Stir the mixture, then measure and record the highest temperature reached in the last column of the table.

5. **Make a Hypothesis:** Based on your experimental results so far, predict the final temperature of the second mixture in the table. Record your prediction. Test your hypothesis by preparing this mixture and measuring its final temperature.

6. Repeat step 5 for each remaining mixture in the table.

Discussion

1. Compare your predictions with the actual final temperatures. Suggest reasons for any differences.

2. Explain what happens when samples of hot and cold water are mixed together, in terms of the kinetic molecular theory.

3. a) Using the data for the first mixture calculate i) the heat transferred from the hot water as it cooled to the final temperature, and ii) the heat transferred to the cold water as it warmed up to the final temperature. Show all calculations.
   b) Repeat a) using the data for the other three mixtures.

4. Write a general statement summarizing the transfer of heat occurring when two samples of matter at different temperatures are mixed together.

5. Suggest how the procedure for the activity could be changed to reduce any experimental errors.

The Principle of Heat Transfer

When the water in a bathtub is too hot, you turn on the cold water tap and swirl the water around to mix the hot and cold water together. Every time you adjust the temperature of bath water like this, you are using a scientific principle known as the **Principle of Heat Transfer**. This principle states that **whenever two substances at different temperatures are mixed together, the amount of heat lost (transferred) from the hot substance equals the amount of heat gained (transferred to) the cold substance**, provided no heat is lost to the surroundings.

The principle of heat transfer can be expressed in a word equation:

$$\frac{\text{heat lost from}}{\text{hot substance}} = \frac{\text{heat gained by}}{\text{cold substance}}$$

Using symbols, the equation becomes:

$$Q_{lost} = Q_{gained}$$

By mixing hot and cold water together in simple classroom experiments, it is difficult to prove the principle of heat transfer. However, careful research has confirmed its validity. In fact, scientists have used this principle for many years to determine the specific heat capacities of solids, liquids, and gases. The procedure has become known as the "method of mixtures".

List all the examples in the home where we mix hot and cold water together to adjust the water temperature.

In problem 3 on page 325, the final temperature (50°C) of a mixture of hot and cold water was calculated. You checked this value experimentally when you made mixture 2 in Activity 11-3. We will now use the equations introduced on page 327 to check the principle of heat transfer by comparing the heat lost from the hot water to that gained by the cold water in the mixture.

1. Heat Lost (Transferred) from Hot Water

Data

$$m = 100 \text{ g} = 0.100 \text{ kg} \qquad \Delta t = t_2 - t_1$$
$$c_{water} = 4200 \text{ J/(kg} \cdot {}°\text{C)} \qquad Q_{lost} = m \, c_{water} \, \Delta t$$
$$t_1 = 80°\text{C}$$
$$t_2 = 50°\text{C} \qquad \qquad \Delta t = t_2 - t_1$$
$$\Delta t = ? \ °\text{C} \qquad \qquad \Delta t = 50°\text{C} - 80°\text{C} = -30°\text{C}$$
$$Q_{lost} = ? \text{ J}$$

$$Q_{lost} = m \, c_{water} \, \Delta t$$
$$Q_{lost} = (0.100 \text{ kg})(4200 \text{ J/(kg} \cdot {}°\text{C)})(-30°\text{C})$$
$$Q_{lost} = -12 \ 600 \text{ J}$$

The heat lost (transferred) from the hot water was 12 600 J.

2. Heat Gained by (Transferred to) Cold Water

Data

$$m = 100 \text{ g} = 0.100 \text{ kg} \qquad \Delta t = t_2 - t_1$$
$$c_{water} = 4200 \text{ J/(kg} \cdot {}°\text{C)} \qquad Q_{gained} = m \, c_{water} \, \Delta t$$
$$t_1 = 20°\text{C}$$
$$t_2 = 50°\text{C} \qquad \qquad \Delta t = t_2 - t_1$$
$$\Delta t = ? \ °\text{C} \qquad \qquad \Delta t = 50°\text{C} - 20°\text{C} = 30°\text{C}$$
$$Q_{gained} = ? \text{ J}$$

$$Q_{gained} = m \, c_{water} \, \Delta t$$
$$Q_{gained} = (0.100 \text{ kg})(4200 \text{ J/(kg} \cdot {}°\text{C)})(30°\text{C})$$
$$Q_{gained} = 12 \ 600 \text{ J}$$

The heat gained by (transferred to) the cold water was 12 600 J.

As predicted by the principle of heat transfer, the heat released from the hot water equals the heat gained by the cold water. Notice that the negative quantity obtained for the heat transfer from the hot water indicates a loss of heat.

It is also possible to use the principle of heat transfer to calculate the final temperature of a mixture. This can be done by equating the heat lost by the hot substance to that gained by the cold substance, as shown below:

$$Q_{lost} = Q_{gained}$$

Now substitute the heat equation learned earlier:

$$-(m \ c \ \Delta t)_{hot} = (m \ c \ \Delta t)_{cold}$$

The negative sign indicates that heat is lost from the hot substance. To avoid confusion, it is useful to label each symbol with "h" for hot and "c" for cold, as shown below:

$$-(m_h \ c_h \ \Delta t_h) = m_c \ c_c \ \Delta t_c$$

Sample problem: If 500 g of water at 90°C are mixed with 200 g of water at 20°C, calculate the final temperature of the mixture.

Data

Hot Water:

$m_h = 500 \text{ g} = 0.500 \text{ kg}$

$c_{h(water)} = 4200 \text{ J/(kg} \cdot \text{°C)}$

$t_{h1} = 90°C$

$t_{h2} = ?°C$

$\Delta t_h = ? \text{ °C}$

$Q_{lost} = ? \text{ J}$

Cold Water:

$m_c = 200 \text{ g} = 0.200 \text{ kg}$

$c_{c(water)} = 4200 \text{ J/(kg} \cdot \text{°C)}$

$t_{c1} = 20°C$

$t_{c2} = ?°C$

$\Delta t_c = ? \text{ °C}$

$Q_{gained} = ? \text{ J}$

Equation

$$\Delta t_h = t_{h2} - t_{h1} \qquad \Delta t_c = t_{c2} - t_{c1}$$

$$Q_{lost} = Q_{gained}$$

$$-(m_h \ c_{h(water)} \ \Delta t_h) = m_c \ c_{c(water)} \ \Delta t_c$$

Because the specific heat capacity is the same for both substances, the equation can be simplified to:

$$-(m_h \ \Delta t_h) = m_c \ \Delta t_c$$

$$-((0.500 \text{ kg}) (\Delta t_h)) = (0.200 \text{ kg}) (\Delta t_c)$$

$$-2.5 \ \Delta t_h = \Delta t_c$$

Substitute for Δt:

$$-2.5(t_{h2} - 90°C) = t_{c2} - 20°C$$

But $t_{h2} = t_{c2}$ (same final temperature for both samples). Therefore:

$$-2.5t_{h2} + 225°C = t_{h2} - 20°C$$
$$245°C = 3.5t_{h2}$$
$$\frac{245°C}{3.5} = t_{h2}$$
$$70°C = t_{h2}$$

The final temperature of the mixture is 70°C.

The Law of Conservation of Energy

The law of conservation of energy is also known as the first law of thermodynamics.

The principle of heat transfer demonstrates a fundamental law of physics known as the **Law of Conservation of Energy**. This law states that **energy cannot be created or destroyed**; it can only be changed from one form to another.

This means that energy is never really "lost" during an energy transfer or conversion. In a hairdryer, electrical energy is converted to heat, sound, light, and mechanical energy. Careful measurements would show that the total of all forms of energy produced by the hairdryer exactly equals the electrical energy supplied to it. In cases where energy seems to have been lost, it can always be traced to either a new location or a new form of energy. In mixture problems, for example, the "lost" heat from the hot substance has simply been transferred to the cold substance. Eventually, this heat will be transferred to the surrounding air. The same thing happens when a hammer hits a nail. Research shows that whatever energy transfers or conversions occur, all other forms of energy eventually tend to be converted to heat.

What eventually happens to all the different forms of energy produced by a hairdryer?

Study Questions

1. a) In what situations is it necessary to calculate the amount of heat transferred?
   b) Why is heat transfer calculated rather than measured?

2. a) State the principle of heat transfer.
   b) List two cases in which hot and cold substances are mixed together to i) warm one substance, and ii) cool one substance.
   c) How can the principle of heat transfer be used to measure the specific heat capacity of a substance?

3. Calculate the heat required to a) heat 1 kg of water in a kettle at 20°C to boiling point, b) heat 200 g of water for soup from 10°C to boiling point, c) heat 250 kg of water from 10°C to 40°C for a bath, d) heat 50 kg of water in a dishwasher from 10°C to 70°C.

CHALLENGER

In most older types of electric water heaters, the main heating element is located at the bottom of the water tank. In modern water heaters, the main heating element is placed in the upper half of the tank. Why was the location changed?

4. Calculate the final temperature of the mixtures shown in the table below.

Cold Water		Hot Water	
Mass	Temperature	Mass	Temperature
1.5 kg	15 °C	0.6 kg	90 °C
25 kg	5 °C	3.5 kg	100 °C
19 kg	24 °C	45 kg	80 °C
150 g	10 °C	750 g	78 °C
900 g	18 °C	6.5 kg	65 °C
4.8 kg	8 °C	0.7 kg	85 °C

5. State the law of conservation of energy, and explain how it relates to the principle of heat transfer.

HYPOTHERMIA

Every winter in Canada some people die due to severe and continued loss of heat from the body, a condition known as *hypothermia*. Normal human body temperature is 38 °C. In medical terms, a body is hypothermic if its internal temperature falls to 36 °C. When body temperature falls to 33 °C, the victim is semi-conscious. By the time body temperature falls to 30 °C, the victim is unconscious and will die, usually of heart failure, if not given immediate aid.

Cases of hypothermia happen most often during the winter, especially in blizzards and snowstorms. However, hypothermia also occurs when a person accidentally falls into very cold water, often while boating on warm spring days.

The body loses heat 20 times faster when immersed in water than when in air at the same temperature. The colder the water, the more rapid the heat loss. The body responds quickly to protect itself against the rapid cooling; the heart pumps more rapidly and the body begins to shiver violently. Breathing becomes more rapid, inducing the dizziness related to hyperventilation.

Research at the University of Victoria has shown that survival time for adults in water at 10 °C is no more than 3 h. Because of their small size, children may be affected by hypothermia up to three times more rapidly than adults. To increase chances of survival if you should fall into cold water, the Royal Life-Saving Society of Canada recommends these guidelines:

- Avoid movement; rely on the support of a life jacket.

- Hold your arms close to your sides and pull your legs up close to your chest. This is called the Heat Exchange Lessening Posture.

- Unless you are very close to shore, never attempt to swim because this speeds up heat loss.

- Get as much of your body out of the water as possible by climbing onto the overturned boat or any other floating object.

What would happen to the ecosystem of this area if this glacier suddenly changed to water at 0°C?

The word "latent" is from the Latin word meaning "to lie hidden". The term was first used because the heat added during a change of state could not be detected by a change in temperature.

11.4 Latent Heat and Changes of State

Think what might happen if ice changed completely to water as soon as the air temperature rose even slightly above 0°C. On a day when the temperature rises above the freezing point, there would be instant flash floods, followed by a rapid freeze-up as soon as the temperature dropped below 0°C again.

Fortunately, such rapid changes of state do not occur. In fact, when a solid such as ice melts, the heat that is added may seem to disappear because there is a time interval when it has no effect on temperature. However, this added heat does increase the thermal energy of the ice and eventually causes the ice to liquefy.

Specific Latent Heat of Fusion

The quantity of heat required to change a substance from one state to another is called its **latent heat**, l. The **specific latent heat of fusion**, l_f, is **the amount of heat required to melt or "fuse" 1 kg of a substance with no change in temperature**. A characteristic physical property of a substance, specific latent heat of fusion is measured in joules per kilogram (J/kg). Values of the specific latent heat of fusion for some common substances are shown in Table 11-2. For example, melting 1 kg of ice at 0°C requires 3.3×10^5 J of heat.

Table 11-2: Specific Latent Heat of Fusion and of Vaporization

Substance	Melting Point (°C)	Latent heat of fusion (J/kg)	Boiling point (°C)	Latent heat of vaporization (J/kg)
alcohol (ethyl)	−130	1.4×10^4	78	8.5×10^5
alcohol (methyl)	−97.8	6.8×10^4	64.7	1.1×10^6
aluminum	660	9.0×10^4	1800	1.1×10^7
Glauber's salts	32.4	2.2×10^5		
iron	1535	2.5×10^5	3000	6.3×10^6
lead	327	2.5×10^4	1780	8.7×10^5
nitrogen	−209.9	2.5×10^4	−196.8	2.0×10^5
oxygen	−218.9	1.4×10^4	−183	2.1×10^5
silver	961	8.8×10^4	1950	2.3×10^6
water	0	3.3×10^5	100	2.3×10^6

While the ice is melting, there will be no increase in temperature. When 1 kg of water freezes, the same amount of heat is released, i.e., 3.3×10^5 J. Once again, there will be no decrease in temperature until all the water has changed into ice.

The amount of heat required to melt a given mass of a substance can be calculated by using the following equation:

$$\text{heat required} = \text{specific latent heat of fusion of substance} \times \text{mass of substance}$$

Symbolically,

$$Q = l_f m$$

where Q is measured in joules, l_f is measured in joules per kilogram, and m is measured in kilograms.

Sample problem: How much heat is required to melt 2.5 kg of ice cubes placed in a food cooler?

Data

$l_f = 3.3 \times 10^5$ J $Q = l_f m$

$m = 2.5$ kg $Q = (3.3 \times 10^5$ J/kg$)(2.5$ kg$)$

$Q = ?$ J $Q = 8.25 \times 10^5$ J

The heat required to melt 2.5 kg of ice is 8.25×10^5 J.

Applications of Latent Heat of Fusion

So much heat is needed to melt ice that we use it to keep other things cool. We add ice cubes to soft drinks, and pack ice in picnic coolers. Athletes use ice packs to treat certain injuries.

The latent heat absorbed when a solid melts becomes a source of heat when the liquid freezes and gives off the latent heat again. Fruit farmers often spray their crops with water when there is a danger of frost. The large amount of heat released as the water begins to freeze is often sufficient to prevent damage. The heat released when large lakes begin to freeze greatly affects the weather in that region. The range of temperatures experienced near the Great Lakes in winter is much less than in the prairie provinces.

Specific Latent Heat of Vaporization

To control the quality of their products, the food and beverage industries in Canada use millions of litres of distilled water daily. Vaporizing all this water requires huge amounts of heat.

Glauber's salts ($Na_2SO_4 \cdot 10H_2O$) is a substance with a melting point of 32°C and a high latent heat of fusion. Large drums of Glauber's salts are sometimes used to heat solar homes. On sunny days, solar collectors mounted on a house produce temperatures high enough to melt the salts in the drums. The heat absorbed by the salts is released when the temperature in the drums falls to the freezing point (32°C), and the heat is then circulated around the house.

Icicles hang from an orange after growers in Florida had sprayed the orange grove with water to reduce frost damage in unseasonably cold weather.

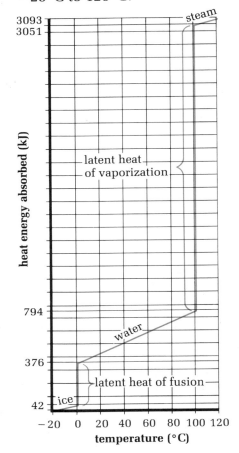

Figure 11-7. A graph of heat absorbed versus temperature for a 1 kg mass of ice as its temperature is raised from −20°C to 120°C.

The **specific latent heat of vaporization**, symbolized by l_v, is **the amount of heat required to vaporize 1 kg of a substance with no change in temperature**. The specific latent heat of vaporization is measured in joules per kilogram (J/kg). It is a characteristic property of a substance, and the values for some common substances are shown in Table 11-2. To change 1 kg of water to steam at 100°C requires 2.3×10^6 J of heat. When steam condenses, the same amount of heat is released and the temperature remains constant until all steam has changed into water.

The amount of heat required to vaporize a given mass of a substance can be calculated by using the following equation:

$$\begin{array}{ccc} \text{heat} \\ \text{required} \end{array} = \begin{array}{c} \text{specific latent heat} \\ \text{of vaporization} \\ \text{of substance} \end{array} \times \begin{array}{c} \text{mass of} \\ \text{substance} \end{array}$$

Symbolically,

$$Q = l_v \, m$$

where Q is measured in joules, l_v is measured in joules per kilogram, and m is measured in kilograms.

Sample problem: How much heat is required to vaporize 0.5 kg of molten silver?

Data

$l_v = 23 \times 10^5$ J/kg	$Q = l_v \, m$
$m = 0.5$ kg	$Q = (23 \times 10^5 \text{ J/kg})(0.5 \text{ kg})$
$Q = ?$ J	$Q = 11.5 \times 10^5$ J

The heat required to vaporize 0.5 kg of silver is 11.5×10^5 J.

Applications of Latent Heat of Vaporization

The refrigerator is an example of cooling produced by vaporization of a gas, usually freon. Liquid freon is sprayed through a small nozzle into the evaporator cooling coils located in the freezer section (see Figure 11-8). As the freon evaporates, it absorbs heat from the copper condenser coils which have already absorbed heat from the food inside the refrigerator. This gas is then compressed by the compressor and passes through a set of condenser coils outside the refrigerator. Here the hot, pressurized vapour condenses to a liquid and gives up the latent heat absorbed when it vaporized. The copper tubing absorbs the heat from the warm liquid, the cooled liquid is then circulated back into the refrigerator, and the process is repeated. An air conditioner in a house or car is basically another form of refrigerator.

When water evaporates at temperatures lower than its boiling point, it still requires approximately 2.6×10^6 J/kg. Hence, whenever water evaporates, the water itself cools because the required heat is obtained from the thermal energy of the water. In humans, evaporation helps to control body temperature. When the body temperature rises, sweating occurs and the heat required to evaporate the water is removed from the body, producing a cooling effect.

Figure 11-8.   The home refrigerator.

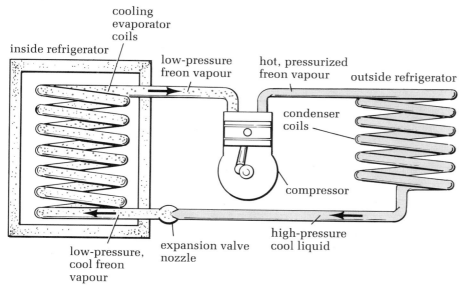

cooling evaporator coils

inside refrigerator

low-pressure freon vapour

hot, pressurized freon vapour

outside refrigerator

condenser coils

compressor

low-pressure, cool freon vapour

expansion valve nozzle

high-pressure cool liquid

A modified form of the refrigerator, called a heat pump, can heat a house in winter and cool it in summer (see Figure 11-9). In a heat pump, the function of the evaporator coils and the condenser coils can be reversed. In winter, the coils outside the house become the evaporator coils and absorb heat from the cold air. As long as the freon gas inside the evaporator coils is cooler than the outside air, it is still possible to transfer heat from the air. The freon gas from the evaporator coils is then compressed and condensed in the condenser coils, and the latent heat released is used to heat the house.

In summer, the process is reversed. The coils inside the house become the evaporator coils, while those outside become the condenser coils. The evaporator coils transfer heat from the house to the outside, and the heat pump functions as an air conditioner. Heat pumps are most economical in regions where winters are mild and summers are hot and humid. The efficiency of heat pumps decreases as the outdoor temperature decreases.

Freon (dichlorodifluoromethane) and ammonia are used as the circulating fluids in refrigerators and heat pumps because they are easily liquefied and are noncombustible.

Figure 11-9. The heat pump.

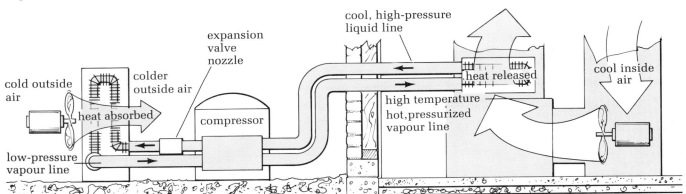

The blue areas are where heat is absorbed or released. The white arrows show where cool air flows through the heat pump.

Do You Know?

It is extremely dangerous to remove the cap from a car radiator when the car engine is hot. The pressurized steam could cause severe burns as it escapes.

Table 11-3.

l_f or l_v of Substance (J/kg)	Heat Energy (J)	Mass (kg)
$l_{f\ water}$	?	4.5
$?\ l_f$	6.25×10^5	25.0
$l_{f\ silver}$	3.6×10^3	?
$l_{v\ oxygen}$	?	0.07
$?\ l_v$	3.45×10^5	0.150
$l_{f\ methyl\ alcohol}$	1.7×10^4	?
$?\ l_f$	3.52×10^7	160
$l_{v\ aluminum}$	?	15.7

Note: Quantities for l_f and l_v can be obtained from Table 11-2.

Hazards of Latent Heat of Vaporization

Most people know that spilling boiling water on the skin causes painful burns. However, the large amounts of heat released when a vapour condenses to a liquid can cause burns far more serious. If 1 g of boiling water at 100°C is cooled to body temperature (38°C), 260 J of heat are released. However, if the same mass of steam (water vapour) at 100°C is cooled to body temperature, about 2560 J of heat are released! Oven mitts should be worn when removing lids from hot saucepans, or when unwrapping the metal foil or transparent wrap covering hot food. The escaping steam can also cause painful burns to your face.

Study Questions

1. a) Define the term specific latent heat of fusion.
   b) Which is better for keeping food in a cooler, 10 kg of ice or 10 kg of ice-cold water? Explain your answer.

2. Calculate the unknown quantities in Table 11-3. Identify the unknown substances using Table 11-2.

3. a) Define the term specific heat of vaporization.
   b) Explain why a burn caused by steam is more serious than a burn caused by the same mass of boiling water.

4. a) Describe how the latent heat of vaporization is used in the operation of i) a refrigerator, and ii) a heat pump.
   b) Why is the climate near the Great Lakes milder in winter than in the prairie provinces?

Meet an Automobile Technician— Satoru Katsuyama

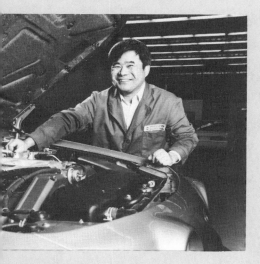

Satoru works in the Technical Centre of the Nissan Automobile Company. His job involves testing new cars, evaluating parts, and sometimes working on customer cars.

Q. AS A CHILD DID YOU PLAN TO BECOME A CAR TECHNICIAN?

A. I played with toy cars a lot, making plastic models and cutting up tin cans to make cars. I also liked physics and science. I still use my basic knowledge of science in the work I do. This job requires a knowledge of physics and electricity.

Q. WHERE DID YOU DO YOUR TRAINING?

A. In Japan I did a three-year machinery course after high school. After I started working, I got my licence as an automobile mechanic. My first job was at Nissan in Japan, working on engines in the service centre of a dealership. I also worked on the side as a racing mechanic for a friend who was a racing car driver. That was very exciting. I learned a lot of things at the track.

Q. WHEN DID YOU COME TO CANADA?

A. In 1967. I joined Nissan in Canada in 1970.

Q. WHERE ARE THE CARS MANUFACTURED?

A. All the cars and parts are made in Japan. This company is just a distributor. However, Nissan buys parts, accessories and supplies in Canada worth about $45 million a year. There are also special Canadian models of most vehicles that we sell in this country.

Q. HOW ARE THE CANADIAN MODELS DIFFERENT?

A. They are made to withstand the extreme weather conditions in Canada. We have a 60° difference in temperature, ranging from $-30°C$ to $+30°C$. Most countries only have a 40° difference. There's a saying that if you can drive a car in Canada, you can drive it anywhere.

Q. WHAT DOES YOUR JOB INVOLVE?

A. I work with our engineering and marketing teams on evaluation of new models before they are introduced for sale. For example, we test cold-weather starting, heater and defroster performance, and other parts that might be affected by extreme cold. We also do tire testing in winter on frozen lakes. We use the same car and try maybe 10 different tires on it to see which ones work best in winter conditions.

Q. DESCRIBE A TYPICAL DAY IN YOUR JOB.

A. I work from 8:30 to 4:30. Every day there is a different problem. That's what makes the job interesting. Sometimes, when I'm working on a customer car, it takes a long time to find the cause of a problem. It's very satisfying to be able to fix these problems.

Q. WHAT TRAINING WOULD A PERSON NEED TO GET A JOB HERE?

A. Nissan dealers will hire students out of high school for apprenticeships. These people then can take the automechanics course at night.

Q. WHAT ADVICE DO YOU HAVE FOR KIDS THINKING OF A CAREER LIKE YOURS?

A. It's not difficult to learn this trade. I tell people that if they have questions, they should go to books for the answer—I do this all the time.

Review Questions

A: Knowledge

1. List four different types of solid thermometers, and state how they are commonly used.

2. a) What liquids are commonly used in thermometers? What are the advantages of each liquid?
   b) List four different types of liquid thermometers, and state how they are commonly used.

3. Describe two types of thermometers in which heat is converted into another form of energy as a means of measuring temperature.

4. What is unusual about the construction of a fever thermometer? Why is it constructed like this?

5. In what ways are the Celsius and Kelvin temperature scales a) the same, and b) different?

6. List as many ways you can think of for estimating the air temperature without a thermometer.

7. Why is it dangerous to sit too close to a fire when wearing synthetic clothing?

8. a) What is meant by the term "permafrost"?
   b) Why does permafrost not disappear each summer?

9. a) Draw a labelled diagram of an external combustion engine and explain how it operates.
   b) List two different types of external combustion engines.

10. a) Draw a labelled diagram of an internal combustion engine and explain how it operates.
    b) List three different types of internal combustion engines.

11. Despite the drastic effects of El Niño that occurred in 1982-83, there was one useful outcome. What was it?

12. List three situations in which the principle of heat transfer is used in the home.

13. What are a) the similarities and b) the differences between the principle of heat transfer and the law of conservation of energy?

14. What might be the safest procedure to follow if you were to fall into icy water about 600 m from shore? Explain your answer.

15. Distinguish between specific heat capacity and specific latent heat.

B: Application

16. a) State what happens to the volume of a solid as it is heated.
    b) Explain what happens, in terms of the kinetic molecular theory.

17. Explain why pouring hot water over a metal lid stuck to a glass jar helps to loosen the lid.

18. What happens to telephone wires strung between poles in hot weather? Explain why.

19. Why does a surveyor record the temperature when making direct measurements of length with a steel chain?

20. Explain what happens to the glass of a thermometer and to the liquid inside the glass when the temperature increases.

21. Some thermometers have the temperature scale marked on a wooden, plastic, or metal backing plate; others have the scale etched on the glass stem. What are the advantages of each type?

22. What part of the body does an adult use when testing the temperature of bath water for a baby? Explain why.

23. Explain, in terms of the kinetic molecular theory, what happens to the gases inside an internal combustion engine when the fuel is burned.

24. Why is it dangerous to throw empty aerosol containers into a fire?

25. What happens to the volume of the air in a car tire in winter? Explain why.

26. How can you determine the quantity of thermal energy shared between a hot and a cold substance mixed together?

27. Calculate the heat required to raise the temperature of:

a) 0.75 kg of water from 5°C to 90°C
b) 300 g of glass from 20°C to 580°C
c) 500 kg of air from −40°C to 21°C
d) 4.5 kg of silver from 20°C to 960°C

28. Explain what happens to the temperature of a piece of ice as it melts, in terms of the motion of its molecules.

29. At one time, people used to put large tubs of water in their cellars to prevent food from freezing on very cold winter nights. Explain why. Describe at least two ways now used to prevent the same problem.

30. Why do farmers sometimes spray their crops and fruit trees with water when there is a danger of severe frost?

31. Why is the latent heat of vaporization of a substance greater than its latent heat of fusion?

32. a) How much heat is released when 25 kg of Glauber's salts freeze?
    b) How much heat is required to melt 1500 kg of iron?

33. a) How much heat is required to vaporize 60 g of ethyl alcohol?
    b) How much heat is released when 1.5 kg of steam condense?

C: Problem Solving

34. Sketch a graph of temperature versus time for each of the following:
    a) Two 200 mL samples of liquid, one water and the other alcohol, being heated from the same beginning temperature to boiling point by the same source of heat.
    b) Two samples of water, one 200 mL and the other 50 mL, being heated from the same beginning temperature to boiling point by the same source of heat.

35. A 1 cm³ piece of dry ice is placed inside an uninflated balloon and the neck of the balloon in clamped shut.
    a) Describe what will happen i) after 10 min, and ii) if the clamp is removed from the neck of the balloon.

b) Explain what is happening in each part of a) in terms of i) the thermal energy of the substances in the balloon, and ii) the kinetic molecular theory.

36. Calculate the final temperature of each of the following mixtures:
    a) 1.6 kg of water at 85°C mixed with 5.0 kg of water at 18°C
    b) 200 g of water at 0°C mixed with 2.4 kg of water at 70°C
    c) 12.0 kg of water at 20°C mixed with 1.5 kg of iron at 400°C

37. a) Calculate the amount of heat required to raise the temperature of 2.0 kg of ice at −25°C to 70°C.
    b) Calculate the amount of heat required to raise the temperature of 500 g of water at 40°C to 150°C.

Try This

1. **Popped Cereals**
   Try testing different kinds of corn kernels to determine which are the best for making popcorn. Suggest reasons why some kinds are better than others. What other kinds of cereal grains can be popped in the same way as corn?

2. **Do Holes Expand?**
   Does the hole in a metal washer become larger as the washer is heated? From a hardware store, obtain a washer that just slides onto the shaft of a steel bolt. Using tongs, heat the washer to a high temperature, and then try to slide it onto the steel bolt. Explain the result.

Chapter 12
Heat Transfer

Six hours after the thermos flask shown in the photograph was filled, the beverage inside is still hot. The flask is designed to minimize the transfer of heat from the hot liquid to its surroundings. When the hot liquid is poured from the flask into a metal mug, the liquid soon cools to room temperature. To understand why some containers lose heat more easily than others, as well as other everyday occurrences related to heat, we need to study how heat is transferred.

Heat is transferred from the metal mug and, to a lesser extent, from the flask by three different methods: conduction, convection, and radiation. In this chapter you will study all three methods of transferring heat, as well as some techniques used to reduce heat transfer. You will also learn how this knowledge can be applied to practical problems such as home heating.

When you finish Chapter 12, you should be able to:

- describe how heat is transferred by conduction, convection, and radiation
- explain each method of heat transfer, in terms of the kinetic molecular theory
- describe some practical applications of heat transfer by conduction, convection, and radiation
- apply a problem-solving model to improve energy conservation in the home

12.1 Heat Transfer by Conduction and Convection

If you stir a hot drink with a metal spoon, the end of the spoon you are holding soon becomes hot. This happens because heat is transferred from the hot liquid to the spoon, along the handle, and finally to your skin. The transfer of heat through a substance, or by direct contact from one substance to another, is called **conduction**. Heat is tranferred by conduction from a hot object to a cold object. Conduction takes place only if there is a temperature difference between the substances in contact, and usually occurs more rapidly in solids than in liquids or gases.

The transfer of heat by conduction can be explained by the kinetic molecular theory. When one end of an object is heated, the kinetic energy of the molecules at the heated end increases. These faster-moving molecules then collide with slower-moving molecules nearby, increasing their kinetic energy. As this process continues, heat is transferred or conducted throughout the substance (see Figure 12-1).

STUDY HINT

When You Get Your Test Back Take some time to review the test. Find out what you should have done to obtain a better mark. If you can find out what went wrong and learn from your mistakes, you may be able to avoid them in the future. If your teacher allows you to keep your returned tests, use them to review the skills and abilities required so that you can apply these to future tests and the final exam.

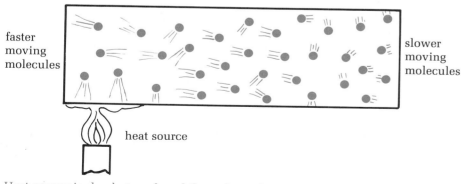

Figure 12-1. The transfer of heat by conduction.

Heat energy is slowly transferred through an object as the faster-moving molecules hit the slower ones, causing them to speed up.

Stirring hot liquids with metal spoons requires the use of oven mitts, while stirring with wooden spoons does not.

Table 12-1: Thermal Conductivity of Common Materials

Material	Relative Thermal Conductivity (compared to air)
silver	18 260
copper	16 520
aluminum	8 700
steel	1 740
glass	37
concrete and brick	37
water	24
human tissue	9
asbestos	7
wood	4 to 7
down (feathers)	1.1
air	1.0

Metal saucepans transfer heat to food rapidly and evenly.

Thermal Conductivity

Substances such as metals conduct heat more rapidly than do materials such as wood. For example, if a wooden spoon is used to stir boiling jam, the handle never gets too hot to hold. The rate at which a substance transfers heat by conduction is called its **thermal conductivity**. A comparison of the thermal conductivity of some common materials is shown in Table 12-1. The quantity of heat transferred by conduction depends on the shape or thickness of the object, its thermal conductivity, and the temperature difference between the two objects in contact.

Heat Conductors and Heat Insulators

Thermal conductivity can be used to classify materials as either **heat conductors** or **heat insulators**. Good heat conductors transfer heat rapidly, especially over short distances. The copper bottoms of some saucepans and the metal radiators that cool car engines are designed to transfer heat rapidly by conduction. Mercury is used in thermometers because it is a good conductor of heat compared to most other liquids. You may have had wet clothing or fingers frozen to metallic objects in very cold weather. The cold metal conducts heat away from the water so rapidly that ice forms almost immediately.

Heat insulators are poor heat conductors. Insulators reduce heat losses from objects which must be kept hot, and slow down the transfer of heat to places where it is not wanted. Layers of fatty tissue beneath your skin act as a natural heat insulator, helping to reduce heat loss from your body. Still air is also an excellent heat insulator. The purpose of cold-weather clothing is to trap still air around the body so that minimal heat is conducted away. If such clothing were not worn, warm air next to the skin would move away and heat would be lost at a much faster rate. The fur on animals serves the same function of trapping air close to the body.

Heat insulators, such as a woollen hat and scarf, are essential during a Canadian winter.

Activity 12-1: Comparing Conduction and Convection

In Part A, you will study the transfer of heat by conduction. In Part B, you will study the transfer of heat by convection. **Note**: Your teacher may demonstrate some procedures.

Materials

candle and candle holder
conductometer
5 metal balls
candle wax
Bunsen burner
stop watch
copper wire (30 cm)
pen
test tube

test tube holder
several crystals of potassium
  permanganate
2 gas bottles
waxed paper (10 cm × 10 cm)
smoke chamber
short candle
smoke paper

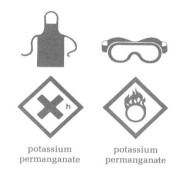

potassium   potassium
permanganate   permanganate

Part A: Heat Transfer by Conduction
Procedure

1. Use candle wax to attach a small metal ball to the end of each rod of the heat conductometer, as shown in the photograph.
2. Place the hub of the conductometer over the centre of the burner flame. Record the time that elapses before each metal ball falls.
3. Place the candle in its holder and light it.
4. Wind a length of copper wire around a pen about 30 times to form a small coil.
5. Remove the pen and slowly lower the coil onto the candle flame. Record what happens. Try it again.
6. Set up the apparatus as shown in Figure 12-2. Fill the test tube about two-thirds full with water at room temperature. Heat the top 4 cm of water with the burner flame. At intervals of 30 s, carefully touch the bottom of the test tube. Record your observations.

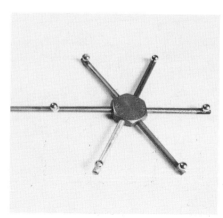

A heat conductometer.

Figure 12-2.

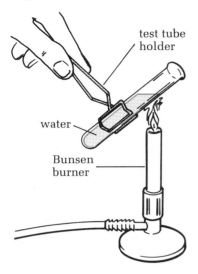

test tube holder

water

Bunsen burner

Discussion

1. a) List the conductometer rod substances in order according to their thermal conductivity (from highest to lowest).
   b) Explain, in terms of the kinetic molecular theory, how heat is transferred in the conductometer.
2. a) Explain the effect produced by the coil of wire on the candle flame.
   b) How could this effect be put to practical use?
3. List three practical uses for a) good heat conductors, and b) good heat insulators.
4. a) What do the observations in step 6 show about the thermal conductivity of liquids? Explain your answer.
   b) Why was it necessary to heat the top of the test tube to demonstrate thermal conductivity in liquids?

Part B: Heat Transfer by Convection

Procedure

1. Place a few crystals of potassium permanganate in a gas bottle. Add enough hot water to dissolve the crystals, then fill the bottle completely with hot water. Fill the other gas bottle with cold water.
2. Place waxed paper on top of the bottle containing hot water, invert the bottle, and carefully place it directly on top of the bottle containing cold water.
3. Gently remove the waxed paper while keeping the two bottles in direct contact. Record your observations during the next 5 min.
4. Repeat steps 1 to 3, this time putting the waxed paper on top of the cold water bottle, inverting the bottle, and placing it on top of the one containing the hot water.
5. Set up the apparatus as shown in Figure 12-3, and light the candle in the smoke chamber.
6. Hold a piece of burning smoke paper first at position A, then at position B. Record what happens in each case.

Discussion

1. a) Explain, in terms of the kinetic molecular theory, what happened to the hot and cold liquids in i) step 3, and ii) step 4.
   b) Draw labelled diagrams to illustrate your answer in a).

Figure 12-3.

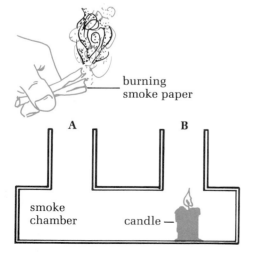

burning smoke paper

A   B

smoke chamber   candle

c) What do you think would happen in step 3 after i) one hour, and ii) one week? Explain why.

2. Explain, in terms of the kinetic molecular theory, what caused the smoke to move as it did in step 6.

3. List three everyday observations from which you can infer that heat transfer by convection is taking place.

Heat Transfer by Convection

Smoke and hot gases always flow upward from a fire. If you hold your hand above a candle flame, your skin will feel much hotter than it would at the same distance to one side of the flame. This happens because heat is transferred upwards by the movement of the hot gases themselves. The transfer of heat by the movement of a fluid from a region at a high temperature to a region at a low temperature is called **convection**. Convection occurs in fluids (liquids or gases), but does not occur in solids because they do not flow. The movements of the fluid are called **convection currents**. When convection occurs, heat is transferred because the thermal energy of the fluid is moved from one place to another by the movement of the fluid itself.

Convection occurs because a fluid expands when heated and becomes less dense than the surrounding unheated fluid. The less dense hot fluid is pushed upward as the denser, unheated fluid around it sinks downward. As the warm fluid rises, it mixes with the cooler fluids it passes through and transfers some heat to them. As the cooler fluids warm up, the heated fluid cools down, becomes more dense, and starts to sink again. This process causes convection currents.

The kinetic molecular theory can explain heat transfer by convection in terms of molecular collisions. When the molecules of a cool fluid strike the molecules of a hot object, the kinetic energy of the fluid molecules is increased. As the fluid molecules speed up, they collide more violently and spread farther apart, increasing the volume of the fluid. Huge numbers of these rapidly-moving molecules produce a less-dense mass of fluid which rises upwards. As these faster-moving fluid molecules move through the slower-moving molecules above, collisions transfer kinetic energy to the slower molecules.

Convection currents help transfer heat in many kinds of heating and cooling systems. In an electric kettle, the heating element first passes heat on to the water by conduction. The resulting increase

Heated air from the candles produce convection currents that rotate the angel chimes.

This huge forced-air heater was invented by Canadian Gerhard Schmidt to melt the ice in a gold mine in Alaska.

Figure 12-4. Convection currents in the atmosphere.

On a sunny day, the temperature of the land surface increases more quickly than that of the water surface. The resulting convection produces breezes that blow from over the water towards the shore.

Do You Know?
Care must be taken in winter when low air temperatures occur at the same time as high wind speeds. For example, if the still air temperature is $-15°C$ and a 30 km/h wind is blowing, there is a danger that exposed flesh will freeze. People driving snowmobiles must be especially careful in very cold weather.

in the water's thermal energy causes it to expand, producing convection currents. In a refrigerator, heat from warm food is conducted to the surrounding air. The heated air then rises to the top of the refrigerator, where it is rapidly cooled by contact with cooling coils in the freezer compartment. The cooled air then sinks back down through the refrigerator.

The human body is cooled primarily by forced convection. Heat is removed from the body by the circulating blood. As the warm blood flows near the skin, heat is transferred by conduction to the skin's outer surface. The heat is then transferred from the skin by conduction to the nearby air, and is finally removed by convection. The forced-air central heating system used in many homes is another example of heat transfer by convection.

The movement of wind illustrates a natural convection process (see Figure 12-4). Winds are the horizontal movements of huge convection currents caused by warmed air as it rises over heated areas, then spreads out and sinks upon cooling. Smoke rising above a campfire, the shimmering effect seen above a hot road surface, and the seasonal recirculation of water in lakes (see the next page) are other examples of natural convection currents.

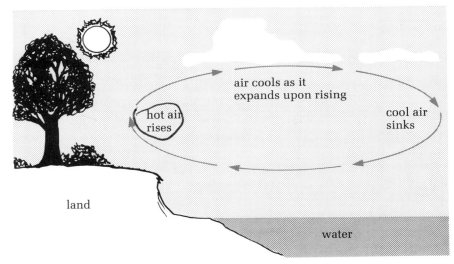

air cools as it expands upon rising

hot air rises

cool air sinks

land

water

Study Questions

1. a) Define the terms conduction, thermal conductivity, and convection.
   b) Explain how heat is transferred i) by conduction, and ii) by convection, in terms of the kinetic molecular theory.

2. a) What are the two main purposes of heat-conducting materials? List two examples for each purpose.

b) What are the two main purposes of heat-insulating materials? List two examples for each purpose.

c) Explain why snow is a better heat insulator than ice.

3. a) What are the two main purposes for which we use convection currents? List two examples for each use.

4. Explain how the transfer of heat by convection produces winds.

5. a) List two examples in which forced convection is used to transfer heat.

b) Why is natural convection not used in these cases?

CHALLENGER

Some yachts on the Great Lakes are left in the water all winter, even though they are surrounded by ice. "Bubbler systems" are often installed around the hulls of these yachts to prevent ice damage. How do the bubbler systems control the formation of ice?

SCIENCE IN ACTION

THE ANOMALOUS BEHAVIOUR OF WATER

Although water is the world's most common liquid, it has an unusual property. If ice at 0°C is heated, its volume decreases as it melts, and then continues to decrease as the liquid is warmed to 4°C. At all other temperatures, both ice and water expand when the temperature rises. The unusual volume change that takes place between 0°C and 4°C is called the **anomalous behaviour of water**.

In the fall, the water at the surface of a freshwater lake is usually warm. As air temperatures begin to decrease, the surface water cools faster than the water below. The volume of the surface water decreases and its density increases, causing it to sink downwards through the warmer water below. Continued cooling of the surface water produces vertical convection currents, which eventually cool all the water in the lake to a temperature of 4°C. The vertical circulation of water helps to distribute dissolved oxygen to the deeper parts of the lake.

With most liquids, this cooling cycle would continue to its freezing point. With water, however, as the liquid at the surface cools to below 4°C, it expands and its density decreases. Because it is now less dense than the water beneath it, the colder water remains on top. Once the surface water freezes, the water temperatures in the lake are as shown in Figure 12-5.

Because water expands as it freezes, ice floats on the surface. Any increase in the thickness of the ice must occur by the conduction of heat from the water beneath the ice. As a result, only very shallow lakes freeze completely solid during the winter. If water behaved as most other substances do, all the liquid in the lake would cool down to 0°C first. Then ice would form on the surface and fall to the bottom. Lakes would freeze from the bottom up to the surface, killing all but the simplest forms of aquatic life.

Figure 12-5. The temperature gradient of an ice-covered pond or lake.

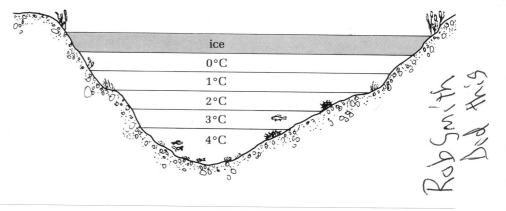

Sunbathers enjoy the transfer of heat by radiation from the Sun on a Toronto beach.

12.2 Heat Transfer by Radiation

When you lie in the Sun on a hot day, the part of your body facing the Sun becomes warmer. But how is the heat being transferred from the Sun? The energy transfer cannot be occurring by conduction or convection because there is no matter between the Sun and the Earth. Instead, a third method of heat transfer called **radiation** is taking place.

Activity 12-2: Investigating Heat Transfer by Radiation

In this activity you will study the transfer of heat by radiation. **Note**: Your teacher may demonstrate this activity.

Materials

heat lamp

metre stick

textbook

piece of window glass

plane mirror

aluminum foil (10 cm × 10 cm)

several small sheets of aluminum painted different colours

Procedure

1. Place your hand 30 cm from a heat lamp. Move your hand slightly closer and then slightly farther away. Compare this with the effect of moving your hand sideways, keeping it 30 cm from the lamp. Record your observations in each case.

2. Place the book in the beam of radiation, 30 cm from the heat lamp. Hold your hand behind the book and record the effect of the beam on your hand. After 2 min, touch the book surface facing the lamp. Record your observations.

3. Repeat step 2, using a piece of window glass instead of the book.

4. Place a mirror in the beam of radiation, 30 cm from the lamp at an angle of 45° to it. Hold your hand as shown in the photograph. Record what you observe when you move your hand parallel to the beam of radiation while facing the mirror.

5. Place the shiny side of the aluminum foil, 30 cm from the lamp in the path of the beam. After 4 min, touch the foil surface facing the lamp. Record your observations.

6. Repeat step 5, using each of the painted sheets of aluminum.

Discussion

1. a) What properties of heat transfer by radiation can be inferred from the observations made in step 1?
   b) Answer a) for steps 2 and 3.

2. What effects can occur when heat transfer by radiation strikes different kinds of matter? What observations support each effect listed?

3. a) Explain what happened in step 4 when the lamp's beam struck the mirror.
   b) How might this effect be applied in a practical device to transfer heat?

4. Which kind of surface showed a) the greatest change in temperature, and b) the least change in temperature when radiation struck it? How can this effect be used in a practical way?

5. In what ways is heat transfer by radiation different from heat transfer by conduction or convection?

Radiation

You have learned that heat is the energy transferred between two objects due to the temperature difference between them. This is true whether heat is transferred by conduction, convection, or radiation. However, the transfer of heat by conduction and convection can only occur through some kind of matter. By contrast, radiation is the transfer of heat between hot and cold objects in the absence

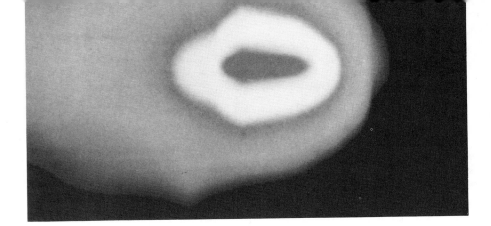

The photograph of the comet was taken by the Infrared Astronomical Satellite (IRAS) in 1984. This satellite's camera scanned the centre of the Milky Way Galaxy for objects that were radiating very small amounts of energy. In order to receive the radiation, the camera had to be colder than the objects it was photographing.

Benjamin Franklin invented the Franklin stove in the 1740s. It was essentially a wood stove fitted into a fireplace. The smoke went up the chimney, and the surfaces of the stove transferred heat throughout the room by conduction, convection, and radiation.

Do You Know?
It is estimated that about 50% of the body heat lost from a person seated in a normal room is due to radiation. Rooms are most comfortable when the walls and floor are warm but the air is not as warm. The Romans and the Japanese heated their houses to be this way thousands of years ago.

of any kind of matter. When you stand facing the Sun, you become warmer because heat is being transferred by radiation through the (near) vacuum of space to your body.

Radiation is given off not only by hot objects such as the Sun. The comet in the photo is giving off radiation, even though its temperature is below −210°C. Every object that has a temperature greater than absolute zero (0 K) is continually giving off energy in the form of radiation. The radiation travels in straight lines in all directions at the speed of light.

When an object gives off radiation, some of its thermal energy is being converted into heat and the kinetic energy of its molecules gradually decreases. The higher the object's temperature, the greater the average kinetic energy of its molecules and the greater the amount of radiation it gives off. For example, a stove element set on "high" radiates more heat than one set on "low".

Any object giving off radiation is also receiving radiation from all the other objects around it. When radiation strikes an object, the radiation may be transmitted, reflected, or absorbed. For example, radiation from the Sun is transmitted through glass windows and is also reflected from mirrors. In most cases when radiation is absorbed, it simply increases the thermal energy of the object. When standing in front of a fire, for example, you become warmer as the radiation is absorbed by your body.

If an object, such as a hot drink, is giving off more radiation than it is absorbing, then its thermal energy and its temperature decrease. This continues until the rate at which heat is being radiated away from the object equals the rate at which it is being absorbed. The object's temperature then remains constant. When all the objects in a room are at the same "room temperature", they are all giving off and absorbing radiation at the same rate.

During the day, the Earth gains thermal energy because it absorbs more heat by radiation from the Sun than it gives off. At night, however, large amounts of heat are radiated out into space from the Earth, and only a small amount is received from the Moon and stars. The temperature change between day and night is produced by this exchange of radiation. On cloudy nights, the heat lost by radiation is less because the clouds absorb some radiation and also reflect some back to the ground.

The nature of an object's surface affects its ability to both radiate and absorb energy. Dark-coloured, rough surfaces are the best absorbers of radiation. Solar collector surfaces are often painted with non-shiny black paint to absorb the maximum amount of radiation from the Sun. Such surfaces are also the best emitters of radiation. Wood stoves are usually painted dull black so they can transfer a maximum amount of heat by radiation. Shiny, light-coloured surfaces reflect most of the radiation striking them and absorb very little. Brightly polished objects, such as silver teapots, therefore, retain the thermal energy of the hot liquids inside for a long time.

Practical Uses of Radiation

The air inside a greenhouse becomes very hot on a sunny day, even in winter. This is known as the greenhouse effect. The Sun's radiation is transmitted through the glass into the greenhouse, where it is absorbed by the soil, plants, and floor. The thermal energy and temperature of these objects increase, and heat the air trapped inside, mainly by conduction and convection. However, because the objects in the greenhouse are still at low temperatures compared to the Sun, the heat radiated and conducted back out through the glass is less than that entering. The temperature inside the greenhouse will continue to increase unless windows are opened to transfer heat by convection. The same effect occurs in homes and cars, especially on hot summer days.

Only one two-thousand-millionth of the energy emitted by the Sun falls on the Earth, and 99% of that is reradiated back into space. The remainder is absorbed by plants through photosynthesis and is the source of our food and fossil fuel energy.

The black metal surfaces of the wood stove are very good emitters of radiation.

Figure 12-6. A thermos flask.

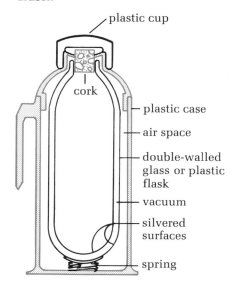

- plastic cup
- cork
- plastic case
- air space
- double-walled glass or plastic flask
- vacuum
- silvered surfaces
- spring

Radiation is reflected by many different kinds of surfaces. The outer walls of houses in very hot countries are often painted white to reflect as much radiation from the Sun as possible. A shiny metallic surface reflects most of the radiation that strikes it. The outer walls of many modern houses in Canada are lined with shiny aluminum foil, which provides a reflective barrier reducing the energy loss due to radiation. People exposed to extremely low temperatures can minimize heat transfer by radiation by wrapping themselves in survival blankets made of shiny metal foil.

In most practical situations, any two, or all three, forms of heat transfer may be occurring at the same time. The thermos flask shown in Figure 12-6 is designed to minimize the transfer of heat by conduction, convection, and radiation. It consists of a double-walled flask made of glass or plastic, with a vacuum between the two walls. This vacuum prevents heat transfer by conduction and convection between the two walls. A small amount of conduction occurs through the thin walls at the top of the flask and through the stopper. Both walls are silvered on the vacuum side. The energy loss by radiation is largely eliminated by these silver coatings. These flasks can be used to keep substances hot or cold.

Solar ovens reflect and concentrate radiation from the Sun to cook food.

Study Questions

1. a) Define the term radiation and list four of its properties.
   b) If an object colder than its surroundings gives off radiation, how can the object's temperature be increased?

2. What problems can result when large amounts of radiation pass through windows?

3. a) Why are thin layers of aluminum sometimes used to cover the surfaces of new buildings, even though aluminum has a high thermal conductivity?
   b) Why do people wear light-coloured clothing in the summer?

4. a) What colour and type of surface i) absorb, and ii) give off radiant energy the best? List two examples for both i) and ii).
   b) Explain why dirty snow melts faster than clean snow.

5. a) Draw a labelled diagram of a thermos flask.
   b) Explain how the construction of a thermos flask reduces heat loss by conduction, convection, and radiation.

12.3 Applications of Heat Transfer in the Home

Every day you make many different decisions in order to function in society. Some are trivial, such as where you will eat lunch. Others, such as the purchase of a stereo or a personal cassette recorder, may entail gathering information to make a wise decision. Making informed decisions to solve problems is known as practical problem solving. There are three kinds of knowledge involved when solving practical problems: scientific knowledge, technological knowledge, and knowledge related to societal implications of the problem (that is, environmental, economic, political, and ethical factors).

Consider the practical problem of reducing the amount of energy used in your home. Such a reduction would benefit both your family and society, for it would save money and conserve a valuable — and limited — resource, energy.

Whether you live in a house or an apartment, you use large amounts of different forms of energy. When you watch TV, for example, you use electrical energy, and light, sound, and heat energy are produced. A washing machine operates on electrical energy and converts it into mechanical energy. The major energy uses in the home are shown in Figure 12-7. Eighty-nine percent of the total energy is used to supply or control the various needs related to heat. Although it is not obvious, the remaining 11% is eventually converted into heat as well.

What kind of information would you gather to make an informed decision about buying a personal cassette recorder?

Figure 12-7. The major energy uses in the home.

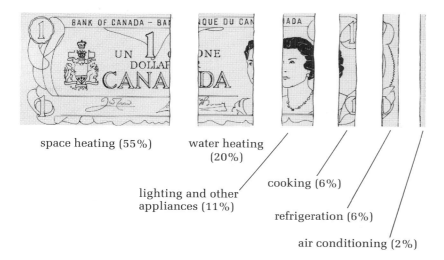

space heating (55%)

water heating (20%)

lighting and other appliances (11%)

cooking (6%)

refrigeration (6%)

air conditioning (2%)

Because of our climate, heating a house requires the largest amount of energy. So, to conserve energy most efficiently, we should investigate ways to reduce the energy needed for space heating. Consider, therefore, the following practical problem: What can be done to reduce the energy *required* for space heating to a *practical* minimum?

This way of stating the problem highlights what is being investigated: we are primarily interested in the heat lost from the house during the heating season. Note that we are not investigating the most efficient source of the heat required. This is another aspect of energy use that can also be approached using the same problem-solving technique.

The major kinds of heat losses in a typical house are shown in Figure 12-8. We will now look at the three kinds of knowledge — scientific, technological, and societal — that relate to our problem.

Figure 12-8. The major kinds of heat losses in a house.

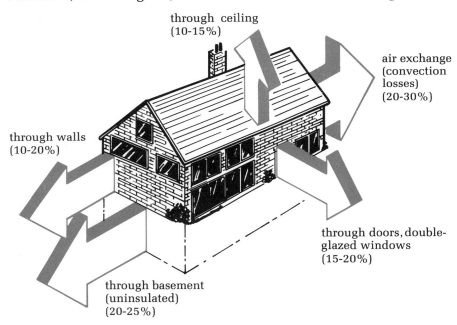

through ceiling (10-15%)

air exchange (convection losses) (20-30%)

through walls (10-20%)

through doors, double-glazed windows (15-20%)

through basement (uninsulated) (20-25%)

1. Scientific Knowledge

The transfer of heat into and out of a house can occur in three ways: by conduction, convection, and radiation. Heat losses through walls, ceilings, roof, doors, windows, and basement occur as a result of both conduction and radiation. Other heat losses occur as a result of convection currents moving into and out of the house. Minimizing heat loss means reducing or eliminating each method of heat transfer wherever possible.

Conduction Heat transfer by conduction depends on the following factors: i) the thermal conductivity of the substance, ii) the thickness of the substance, and iii) the temperature difference between the hot and cold sides of the substance. Heat conduction can be minimized by using substances with low thermal conductivity, increasing the thickness of the substance, and minimizing the temperature difference between the inside and outside of the house.

Convection Heat transfer by convection depends on the following factors: i) the presence of a fluid, either a liquid or a gas, ii) the viscosity of the fluid and its heat capacity, iii) a temperature difference between different regions of the fluid, and iv) the ability of the warm fluid to mix freely with the cold fluid. In a house, heat transfer by convection can be minimized by preventing the warm air from mixing freely with the cold air.

Radiation Heat transfer by radiation depends on the following factors: i) the ability of a substance to transmit, reflect, and absorb radiant energy, and ii) the difference in temperature between the radiating objects. In a house, heat transfer by radiation can be minimized by using materials that reflect, but do not transmit or absorb, radiation. The temperature difference between the inside and outside of the house should also be minimized.

2. Technological Knowledge

Technology is the application of scientific knowledge to make useful products and to improve our lives. The need to provide comfortable temperature levels in Canadian homes and to conserve energy has led to the development of various technological products.

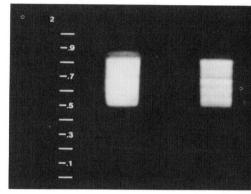

In these photos, the left window has a single pane of glass, while the right window has double panes. The thermograph (heat-sensitive photograph) of the same windows shows that the single-pane window is brighter than the double-pane window, indicating a greater heat loss.

Insulating materials are installed between wall studs of a house.

Table 12-2: Thermal Resistance of Common Building Materials

Material	Thermal Resistance for a Thickness of 1 cm (RSI)
brick	0.008
cellulose fibre	0.229
fibreglass	0.211
gypsum board	0.046
plywood	0.088
rock wool	0.211
styrofoam (Glasclap)	0.305
styrofoam (SM blue)	0.347
styrofoam (white)	0.282
vermiculite	0.159

Conduction Some construction materials reduce heat conduction through the outer shells of buildings. The effectiveness of an insulating material is measured by its **thermal resistance value**, also called **RSI** (for *Résistance Système International*). The greater the RSI value of an insulating material, the less heat is transferred through it. The RSI values of some common building and insulating materials are shown in Table 12-2.

The total RSI value of a wall, or any other part of a building, can be determined by adding the RSI values for all the composite materials in the wall. Figure 12-9 shows how to find the RSI value of an outer wall of a typical house.

Figure 12-9. A cross-sectional view of an outer wall of a house with a brick-and-frame construction.

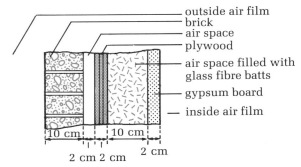

To determine the total thermal resistance of the wall, the RSI value for each material, based on its thickness, is calculated. The values are then added together, as shown below.

Wall material	Thermal resistance (RSI)
10 cm brick	0.08
2 cm air space	0.18
2 cm plywood	0.18
10 cm fibreglass	2.11
2 cm gypsum board	0.09
Total thermal resistance of wall	2.64

The air films on either side of the wall each have an RSI value of 0.08.

Convection   The places where heat losses due to convection occur in a typical house are shown in Figure 12-10. Much of this is heat loss due to infiltration (cold air leaking into the house) and exfiltration (hot air leaking out of the house). These losses can be prevented by sealing the gaps where the air passes in and out of the building, either with caulking or weather-stripping materials. Caulking materials seal fixed gaps between, for example, the concrete foundation and the wooden frame of the house. Weather-stripping seals the moveable parts of the house, such as doors and windows. Some typical caulking and weather-stripping materials are shown in the photograph.

Figure 12-10.   Heat losses due to convection can account for up to 30% of the total heat lost from a house.

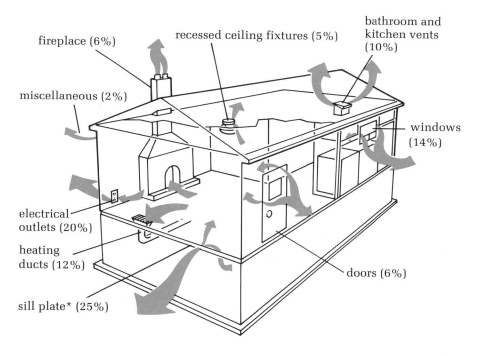

*The sill plate is the piece of wood that rests on the concrete foundation and supports the wooden frame of the house.

Radiation   Radiation losses occur throughout the entire shell of a house. To reduce such losses, thin layers of shiny aluminum foil are sometimes attached to the frame of the house. Thick insulation in the walls also helps reduce the outside temperature of the walls, and thus the amount of radiation.

Do You Know?

To ensure an adequate supply of fresh air, an average family of four requires a complete air change in a house or apartment every four hours. Most Canadian homes are so poorly sealed that they experience more than one air change every hour.

These caulking and weather-stripping materials are used to reduce heat loss due to convection currents from a house.

Do You Know?

A 2 mm air gap around the edge of an outside door is equivalent to having a 160 cm² hole in the outside wall of the house.

Table 12-3: Societal Implications

ethical (values)

economic

health (mental and physical)

safety

environmental

energy conservation

racial

cultural

religious

aesthetic

political

national

In an air-to-air heat exchanger, incoming cold air is heated when it passes through ducts surrounded by outgoing warm air.

It is important to have adequate ventilation in a house or apartment. The various activities of a family of four result in the addition of about 63 L of moisture to the air in a home per week. Over half this amount—about 38 L—is produced by the normal respiration and skin evaporation of the occupants.

3. Societal Implications

Some societal implications to be considered in practical problem solving are shown in Table 12-3. In reducing energy costs for home heating, one critical factor is the cost of the construction itself. Ideally, this cost should be paid for by the savings in energy costs over several years. The occupants' health must also be considered. Both during and after construction, there may be health hazards related to the materials used and to the lower exchange of gases that occurs in a tightly sealed building. Short-term and long-term environmental considerations may also come into play.

By approaching practical problems in a systematic way, it is possible to be more objective about the factors that must be considered. Such an approach helps identify possible negative long-term effects. Many serious environmental problems, such as those related to dioxin, could have been anticipated, and perhaps minimized or avoided, if the potential long-term effects had been studied.

Activity 12-3: Minimizing Heat Losses From a Building

In this activity you will study the effectiveness of your house or school in preventing heat loss. By referring to standards established by the Ministry of Energy, Mines and Natural Resources, you will devise a plan to reduce the heat losses to acceptable levels.

Materials

sample building
metre stick

sheet of plastic food wrap (30 cm × 30 cm) or smoke stick

Procedure

Part A: Conduction and Radiation

1. Determine the total RSI value for each of the following surfaces in the building you have selected: a) an above-ground wall, b) a basement wall, c) a ceiling, d) a floor surface in the basement. Use the data in Table 12-2.

2. Identify any surfaces where reflective metal foil has been installed as part of the wall structure.

3. Determine if any window surfaces have been covered with a reflective film.

Part B: Convection

4. Using either a sheet of plastic food wrap or a smoke stick, determine where air infiltration is occurring around windows, doors, and the other parts of the building where heat losses due to convection occur (see Figure 12-10).

Discussion

Part A

1. Compare the RSI values for the building with those recommended for your geographic location. Identify surfaces in the building that should be upgraded. Using questions 2 and 3, develop a suitable plan of action.

2. Identify the most suitable materials for each surface that requires upgrading.

3. Identify where you might apply reflective coatings in the building to reduce heat loss through radiation.

Part B

4. Identify what materials should be used in each part of the building to reduce heat losses due to infiltration.

5. Suggest some improvements to the doors and windows in the building to reduce heat loss.

6. a) Develop an overall plan to upgrade the structure of the building, and suggest a practical timeline for this plan.
   b) What factors in Table 12-3 should be considered in developing this plan? Why?

Study Questions

1. What three kinds of knowledge should be considered when solving practical problems? Explain why.

2. What is meant by the RSI value of a wall or ceiling?

3. a) What are infiltration and exfiltration?
   b) Why is caulking used on some parts of a building, while weather-stripping is used on others?

4. How can radiation losses from a building be minimized?

5. a) Identify some positive and negative societal aspects of reducing home heating costs.
   b) What long-term advantages are gained by considering all relevant societal factors when developing new technological products?
   c) Identify three products or processes that should have been investigated more fully before being implemented. What should have been done in each case?

SCIENCE IN ACTION

WINDOWS

All outside surfaces of a house lose heat by all three forms of heat transfer. Heat loss through windows can account for 10-25% of the house's total heat loss. The heat loss by convection due to air leakage can be significant, especially for windows that open. Usually, this loss can be reduced by careful caulking and weather-stripping.

Although windows lose some heat by convection, the major losses are due to conduction and radiation. There is a marked heat loss by conduction through windows. Ordinary window glass has an RSI value of only 0.006 compared to 3.51 for a well-insulated wall. The thickness of the glass has very little effect on heat transfer through the window. The insulation value of any window is provided almost entirely by the air films next to the glass surface and by air spaces between multiple panes of glass. The RSI value of a single pane of glass, including air films, is 0.16. A 1 m² pane of glass transfers 22 times as much heat as an equal wall area with an RSI value of 3.51. A double-pane window of the same area loses only 13 times as much heat as the wall.

Nearly half the heat loss through a window is by radiation. In recent years, however, the radiation through windows has been reduced by bonding a layer of metal oxide a few molecules thick onto the surface of the glass. Much of the heat being

radiated from the room through the window is reflected back into the room by this thin, reflective layer. Glass coated with this film is called low-emission, or low-E, glass and has a typical RSI value of 0.75. When this extremely thin transparent layer is added to the glass, the RSI value is increased five times. This thin film also absorbs some ultraviolet light, which helps to reduce fading of curtains, carpets, and upholstery.

Meet a Stationary Engineer — Bernard Villalon

Bernard works at Toronto's O'Keefe Centre, a large auditorium where theatre, ballet, and opera productions are performed. He is in charge of the heating, air conditioning, and general maintenance of the boiler room.

Q. WHAT IS A STATIONARY ENGINEER?
A. A stationary engineer is someone who is in charge of maintaining equipment. It doesn't mean you have an engineering degree from a university.

Q. WHAT DOES YOUR JOB INVOLVE?
A. I'm in charge of the heating and air conditioning, a bit of plumbing, maintaining the pumps — that sort of thing.

Q. WHAT IS YOUR BACKGROUND?

A. I came to Canada from the Philippines in 1973. After various jobs, I decided to study stationary engineering. I went to George Brown College full-time for one year.

Q. HOW DIFFICULT WAS IT TO FIND WORK IN THE FIELD?
A. The only buildings that hire stationary engineers are ones with high-pressure boilers. Very tall buildings, for instance, need high-pressure boilers. There are two oil-fired boilers at the O'Keefe Centre.

Q. HOW LARGE IS THE BUILDING?
A. It sits on 3½ acres (1.4 ha) of land, and the auditorium seats 3200 people. There are also 14 other areas of the building where the heating has to be controlled: the dressing rooms, rehearsal halls, stage, lower refreshment lounge, and so on.

Q. HOW DO YOU CONTROL THE INDIVIDUAL TEMPERATURE OF ALL THESE AREAS?
A. We have a data centre control board that is computerized and controls the whole building. From it we can increase and decrease temperature, start and shut off fans, and control the amount of fresh air coming in.

Q. WHAT DO YOU DO ON A NORMAL SHIFT?
A. When there are two of us on duty, one of us does maintenance. That involves things like changing filters, repairing pumps, and some small plumbing chores. The other person modulates the temperature in each room of the building.

Q. DESCRIBE A TYPICAL AFTERNOON SHIFT.
A. First I check the activity sheet to find out what is going on in the building that day and where the activity is located. For instance, the sheet might indicate that the boutique is open from 4 to 8 p.m., the rehearsal hall is being used by dancers from 2 to 4 p.m., and there is an art show in the lower lounge from 5:30 to 8 p.m. I then go to the control centre and start heating the areas that will be in use. Sometimes I get specific requests, such as to make the rehearsal hall warmer for the dancers because they like to have the room quite warm.

Q. WHAT DO YOU DO ONCE THE HEATING IS SET?
A. I check the boiler and do a water test on it. We have to do these tests constantly because sludge and dissolved solids in the water act as a blanket of dirt between it and the fire, and affect the transfer of heat. Also, if there's a lot of oxygen in the boiler I have to add chemicals to prevent corrosion and pitting. I take samples of the hot water and do tests for alkalinity, chloride, and sulphite.

Q. WHAT DO YOU DO NEXT?
A. I go around to each room, checking for leaks and making sure everything is working all right.

Q. WHAT DO YOU LIKE BEST ABOUT YOUR JOB?
A. Nobody bothers you, and you make good wages. I'm happy here.

Review Questions

A: Knowledge

1. List four practical ways we use the conductivity of heat through metals.

2. List four examples in which heat is transferred by convection.

3. Which kind of cup filled with a hot drink is more comfortable to hold, a paper cup or a styrofoam cup? Explain why.

4. Why does convection not occur in solids?

5. Which substance would be even better than copper for coating the bottoms of saucepans? Why is copper used instead?

6. Why does the wind blow from the sea towards the land on a hot, sunny day?

7. What happens to the density of a substance when it is heated? Why?

8. a) List four properties of radiation.
   b) In what ways does radiation differ from i) conduction, and ii) convection?

9. Why are wood stoves usually painted a dull black?

10. List three examples in which a shiny surface is used to reflect radiation.

11. a) List the RSI values for the insulating materials that should be used in the different parts of a well-insulated house.
    b) In which part of the house should the insulation have the highest RSI value? Explain why.

B: Application

12. Which feels colder at room temperature, a good heat conductor or a poor heat conductor? Explain your answer.

13. Which kind of jar lid, brass or iron, would loosen more when placed in hot water? Explain why.

14. Why is the insulated covering on heating ducts often painted with a shiny metallic-based paint?

15. Why are the bottoms of skis covered with smooth synthetic compounds rather than with smooth metal?

16. Why does a wooden floor feel colder to bare feet than a wool rug at the same temperature?

17. Which type of runner used on sleds and toboggans is better, wooden or steel? Explain your answer.

18. Where are warm-air registers placed in a room? Explain why.

19. Is a fire in a open fireplace an energy-efficient means of heating a room? Explain your answer.

20. Explain why snow melts faster on the south side of a hill than on the north side.

21. Chickens and turkeys are often wrapped in aluminum foil before being roasted in an oven. Is the shiny side of the foil placed against the meat or away from it? Explain your answer.

22. What kinds of heat transfer are involved in each of the following:
    a) A hot stone is dropped into a pan of cold water.
    b) A kettle full of cold water is placed on a hot stove element.
    c) The Sun shines on a black swimming pool cover resting on top of the water surface.

23. The expression "a clear, cold night" is often used to describe a cloudless night. What difference does the presence of clouds make to night-time temperatures? Explain why.

24. Explain how heat transfer by convection affects the weather.

25. How is heat loss by convection prevented in houses?

26. Why do some houses with high ceilings have fans installed close to the ceiling?

27. a) On which parts of a house is it appropriate to use i) caulking, and ii) weatherstripping?
    b) What factors determine whether caulking or weatherstripping should be used in a given location?

28. Explain why the inside of a greenhouse can be warm even on the coldest winter day.

29. Loose insulation and fibreglass batts should not be packed down when installed in a house. Explain why.

30. Which kind of heat transfer can be reduced the most for the least cost? Explain why.

31. Which kind of heat transfer is most difficult to prevent in houses already built? Explain why.

32. a) What problems might occur if all the places where air flows into and out of a house were sealed? Explain why.

    b) What can be done to change the air in a house in a controlled way?

33. Explain why storm windows help to reduce heat loss from a house.

C: Problem Solving

34. Design an investigation to measure the thermal conductivity of a) a liquid, and b) a gas. Identify which factors related to heat transfer are being controlled, and explain how.

35. A family moves into a new house that is very tightly sealed to minimize heat loss. When a fire is lit in the fireplace, the house fills with smoke, even though the chimney damper is open and the smoke can flow freely up the chimney. Explain why this occurs, and suggest ways to solve the problem.

36. Determine the RSI value of the wall shown in the diagram below.

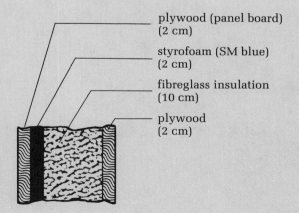

plywood (panel board) (2 cm)

styrofoam (SM blue) (2 cm)

fibreglass insulation (10 cm)

plywood (2 cm)

Try This

1. **Paper Kettles**
   Fill a flat-bottomed paper cup with water, and place the cup on a hot plate. Turn the hot plate on to a high setting. Predict what will happen. Explain what does happen.

2. **Safety Fork**
   Slide a match down between the tines of a fork so that the match is wedged at the bottom at a right angle to the tines. Light another match and use it to light the match wedged in the fork. Explain what happens.

Energy Conservation

The Issue: Could a personal (and family) commitment to energy conservation result in significant energy savings?

When this pool is not in use, it is covered with solar panels that convert the Sun's rays into energy to heat the pool, the home, and the water system.

Until the early 1970s, fossil fuels were in plentiful supply and energy costs were low. In the late 1970s, however, political developments in the Middle East caused the price of oil to increase dramatically. This produced a massive economic recession in those affluent nations whose economies were based on the availability of low-cost energy.

Many countries, including Canada, began searching for ways to conserve energy. Smaller, more fuel-efficient cars became very popular as the price of gaso-line more than tripled. The Canadian government gave grants to homeowners willing to reduce heat losses from their homes by adding insulation and minimizing air loss. In countries which have very limited fossil fuel resources, such as Japan, many electrical appliances were redesigned to make them more energy-efficient.

Efforts such as these did result in significant energy savings. However, in the mid-1980s, further political changes in oil-producing countries around the

world caused a reduction in oil prices. Many energy conservation measures were discontinued. Large cars became popular again.

Regardless of political activity in the oil-producing countries, fossil fuels, a non-renewable resource, will become increasingly scarce. This will likely result in another, and longer-lasting, increase in fossil fuel prices. Other energy sources, such as hydrogen and photovoltaic cells, will have to become economically viable. The increases in energy prices may require a more permanent commitment to energy conservation.

In this activity you will consider ways to conserve energy in all aspects of your daily life. In Chapter 12 we studied a problem-solving technique for deciding how to minimize the heat loss from a building. The same approach can be applied to other ways of saving energy. Some factors—appliances, changes in lifestyle, and forms of transportation—you could consider are listed below.

Appliances: air conditioner, washing machine, clothes dryer, furnace or heating system, heat pump, stereo system, lighting systems, stove, oven, microwave oven, refrigerator, freezer, television, etc.

Changes in lifestyle: water use, clothing, diet, recreation, etc.

Transportation: bicycle, car, subway, bus, moped, motorcycle, etc.

Exploring the Issue

A. Gathering the Data

1. Working on your own or in small groups as directed by your teacher, choose one or more of the factors listed above to research in terms of energy conservation.

2. Use advertising literature, fact sheets, consumer reports, government documents, magazine and newspaper articles, scientific journals, reference books, and library files to obtain information on the factor(s) you are studying.

B. Organizing the Data

1. Classify the information related to the factors into scientific, technological, and societal categories whenever possible.

Scientific: What scientific knowledge is related to the topic?

Technological: What products are or could be involved? How effective are they? How long will they last? How could energy could be saved, and how much? What about the ease of maintenance and quality of construction of different products? Other factors?

Societal: What are the potential energy and economic savings? Any changes in lifestyle required? Are there safety, health-related, and environmental factors to consider? Consult Table 12-3 for other possible societal implications.

2. Determine whether you have enough information of each type to make an informed decision.

C. Making a Decision

1. Evaluate the positive and negative consequences of the energy conservation measure(s) you are considering.

2. Decide which product(s) and course(s) of action are most appropriate. List reasons supporting your decision, and rank them in order of importance.

3. In class, state your decision and provide evidence and reasons to defend it.

4. As a class, summarize the energy savings that could be achieved if a family decided to adopt all the energy conservation measures proposed.

D. Identifying Your Personal Position on the Issue

What energy conservation measures would you be prepared to follow if:

a) energy costs increase significantly?

b) energy costs remain the same?

Justify your position in each case.

Unit 4 Wrap-Up

Unit Summary

Heat was once thought to be a massless, invisible fluid called caloric. Since about 1850 heat effects have been explained by the *kinetic molecular theory*. *Heat* is that form of energy which is transferred from a hot substance to a cold substance. The transfer of heat is related to the motion (*kinetic energy*) of particles of matter.

Temperature is a measure of the average kinetic energy of the molecules in a substance. The two fixed points of the *Celsius temperature scale* are based on the freezing point and boiling point of water.

When heat is added to a substance, the *thermal energy* of the substance increases. Thermal energy is the only direct source of heat. Electrical, chemical, nuclear, and mechanical energy are first converted into thermal energy, and then transferred as heat.

The three factors affecting the heat capacity of a substance are the substance itself, its mass, and its temperature. Each substance has a specific ability to absorb heat, known as its *specific heat capacity*.

Solids, liquids, and gases expand when heated and contract when cooled. The design of various types of thermometers is based on the differing thermal expansion rates of solids and gases. *Absolute zero* is the lowest temperature to which matter can be cooled.

All gases expand and contract at the same rate. The expansion of gases is used to operate both external combustion engines and internal combustion engines.

The quantity of heat transferred to and from a substance is calculated by multiplying mass, specific heat capacity, and temperature change. The *principle of heat transfer* applies when hot and cold substances are mixed together. This principle demonstrates the *law of conservation of energy*.

Each substance has a specific *latent heat of fusion* and a specific *latent heat of vaporization*. The sub-stance absorbs its latent heat of fusion when it changes from solid to liquid. The latent heat of vaporization is absorbed when the substance changes from liquid to gas.

Heat is transferred by *conduction* in solids. Thermal conductivity is used to classify substances as *heat conductors* or *heat insulators*. In fluids, heat transfer occurs by natural or forced *convection*.

Radiation is the heat transfer that occurs in the absence of matter. All matter above absolute zero transfers heat by radiation. The nature of an object's surface affects its ability to absorb or transfer radiation. If a substance absorbs more radiation than it gives off, its temperature increases.

Practical problems such as minimizing the heat loss from a building can be approached by considering *scientific knowledge*, *technological knowledge*, and *societal implications*.

Key Terms

absolute zero
caloric theory
conduction
convection
energy
fixed points
heat capacity
heat energy
heat engine
heat transfer
kinetic energy
kinetic molecular
 theory
latent heat of fusion

latent heat of
 vaporization
law of conservation of
 energy
principle of heat
 transfer
radiation
specific heat capacity
technology
temperature
thermal conductivity
thermal energy
thermal expansion

Unit Practice and Review

A: Short Answer

True or False

State whether each statement is true or false. Correct each false statement.

1. The fixed points on a laboratory thermometer are based on the melting point and boiling point of mercury.

2. Electrical energy is a direct source of heat.

3. All fluids expand at the same rate for the same change in temperature.

4. If two unequal masses of hot and cold water are mixed together, the heat transferred to the cold water equals the heat lost from the hot water.

5. Heat transfer by conduction is faster than heat transfer by radiation.

Multiple Choice

In each question below, select the best answer.

1. The bore of a laboratory thermometer is very narrow because:
   a) this makes the thermometer easier to read.
   b) a slight expansion of the mercury causes a large change in the mercury level.
   c) mercury is toxic.
   d) the thermometer would break too easily if the bore were larger.

2. The amount of heat needed to raise the temperature of 1 kg of a substance by 1°C is called:
   a) latent heat of vaporization
   b) latent heat of fusion
   c) specific heat capacity
   d) heat capacity

3. Compared to most other liquids, water requires more heat to increase its temperature by 1°C because water:
   a) has a high boiling point
   b) cannot absorb heat easily
   c) has a low specific heat capacity
   d) has a high specific heat capacity

4. When 1 kg of hot iron is mixed with 1 kg of cold water:
   a) the heat gained by the water equals the heat lost by the iron.
   b) the temperature change of the iron equals the temperature change of the water.
   c) the volume change of the iron equals the volume change of the water.
   d) the density change of the iron equals the density change of the water.

Complete the Statement

Complete each of the following statements with the correct word or phrase. Do not write in this book.

1. Heat is a form of ___?___ .

2. When heat is added to a substance, its ___?___ energy increases.

3. A bimetallic strip bends because the two metals have different ___?___ .

4. The amount of heat required to change 1 kg of a boiling liquid to vapour is called its ___?___ .

5. The single major cause of heat loss in a house is ___?___ .

Matching Items

Match each item in Column A with the appropriate item in Column B.

1. *Column A*
   i) measure of the average kinetic energy of the molecules in a substance
   ii) energy possessed by molecules due to motion
   iii) the total energy of the molecules in a substance
   iv) when molecules have minimum kinetic energy

   Column B
   a) heat
   b) thermal energy
   c) temperature
   d) absolute zero
   e) latent heat
   f) kinetic energy

2. *Column A*
   i) heat transfer through a vacuum
   ii) heat transfer used to heat many homes
   iii) heat transfer by vertical movement of water in lakes
   iv) heat transfer from liquid freon to copper tubing in a refrigerator

   Column B
   a) conduction
   b) natural convection
   c) radiation
   d) forced convection
   e) infiltration

B: Knowledge and Application

1. Which effect of heat could not be explained by the caloric theory? Explain why.

2. Give examples of two objects that have the same temperature but different quantities of thermal energy.

3. Explain why heat is considered a form of energy, using two examples.

4. Would it be necessary to change a scientific model if it could explain all but one of the experimental observations related to it? Explain your answer.

5. Which contains more thermal energy, a cup of hot coffee or a swimming pool on a summer day? Explain your answer.

6. Why does the space shuttle have only parts of its surface covered with special tiles?

7. Explain, in terms of the kinetic molecular theory, why your hands become warmer when you rub them together.

8. Why is a steel bridge built with expansion joints at various intervals along its length?

9. What liquids are commonly used in liquid thermometers? What are the advantages of each?

10. Most houses have several thermostats. Where are three of them located?

11. a) Explain why concrete sidewalks are poured in sections that have spaces between them.
    b) What material is used to fill the spaces between the concrete? Explain why.

12. Why are slightly oversized patterns or moulds used in a foundry?

13. What might happen if a bicycle tire were pumped up hard, and the bicycle were then left in the Sun? Explain why.

14. When a large mass of hot water is mixed with a small mass of cold water, which sample will have the greatest change in temperature? Explain why, in terms of the kinetic molecular theory.

15. Why is more heat required to boil 1 kg of water into steam than to melt 1 kg of ice into water? Explain why, in terms of the kinetic molecular theory.

16. Why is it necessary to drain water pipes and toilet bowls in cottages that are not used in the winter in Canada?

17. In which state(s) of matter is heat transferred i) by conduction, and ii) by convection? Explain why, in terms of the kinetic molecular theory.

18. a) Define radiation.
    b) List four sources of radiation.

19. When you touch a metal object, it feels much colder than a piece of wood at the same temperature. Explain why, in terms of the kinetic molecular theory.

20. Which is a better heat insulator, solid wood or sawdust? Explain your answer.

21. Why do deep lakes remain unfrozen throughout the winter?

22. Why are thin layers of aluminum used to prevent heat loss from buildings, even though aluminum has a high heat conductivity?

C: Problem Solving

1. Calculate the heat required to heat:
   a) 2.5 kg of water from 13°C to 76°C
   b) 500 g of water from 8°C to 95°C
   c) 4.8 kg of cooling oil from 18°C to 130°C
   d) 2500 kg of bricks from 5°C to 40°C

2. If you were able to add exactly 1000 J of heat to an unknown substance, how could you determine its specific heat capacity?

3. Calculate the final temperature of the mixtures shown in the table below.

Cold Water		Hot Water	
Mass	Temperature	Mass	Temperature
75 g	10°C	2 kg	75°C
150 kg	15°C	2.5 kg	100°C
700 g	30°C	5.5 kg	90°C
15 kg	20°C	600 kg	95°C

4. Calculate the unknown quantities in the table below.

l_f or l_v of Substance (J/kg)	Heat Energy (J)	Mass (kg)
? l_f	3.62×10^4	1.45
l_f water	2.75×10^7	?
? l_v	1.40×10^8	165
l_v nitrogen	?	21.6

Note: Quantities for l_f and l_v can be obtained from Table 11-2.

D: Challengers

1. What change in length would occur in an iron bridge 150 m long if the temperature changed from $-45°C$ to $30°C$?

2. A Florida fruit grower sprays water over a 6 ha orange grove all night to reduce the damage caused by freezing temperatures. If a total depth of 6 cm of water at $12°C$ was sprayed over the area and the water was cooled to $-2°C$, calculate how much heat was released by the water.

3. What mass of water at $10°C$ would be required to cool 4.5 kg of water at $100°C$ to a final temperature of $35°C$?

4. Which method would cool a large soft drink bottle more rapidly, immersing the bottle in a bucketful of ice-cold water or wrapping a wet towel around it? Explain your answer.

Project Ideas

1. Four different fluid theories were used to explain the effects of heat, light, electricity, and magnetism in the eighteenth century. Research each theory and identify i) why it was finally abandoned, and ii) the modern theory that has replaced it. Write a report summarizing your findings.

2. Select one form of energy that is commonly converted into heat, and identify one (or more) unusual sources. Research possible ways each unusual source of heat could be put to practical use. Write a report discussing your ideas.

3. Identify the major types of thermometers and the method(s) of heat transfer that occur(s) in each case. Write a report explaining how the design of each thermometer is related to the method of heat transfer used.

4. Research the major kinds of heat engines and write an in-depth report on one example of i) an external combustion engine, and ii) an internal combustion engine.

5. Design and draw plans for an energy-efficient house. Explain in a written report how each feature of the house contributes to energy conservation.

Readings

Brown, Bob. 666 *Science Tricks and Experiments.* Blue Ridge Summit, Pa.: TAB Books, 1978. (Contains an interesting chapter on activities related to heat.)

How Things Work (Volumes 1 and 2). London, England: Granada Publishing (Palladin Books), 1972. (An invaluable resource for both student and teacher. Contains information on many devices that use heat energy.)

Spooner, M. *Sunpower Experiments.* New York: Sterling Publishing Co., 1979. (A collection of useful and interesting projects related to solar energy.)

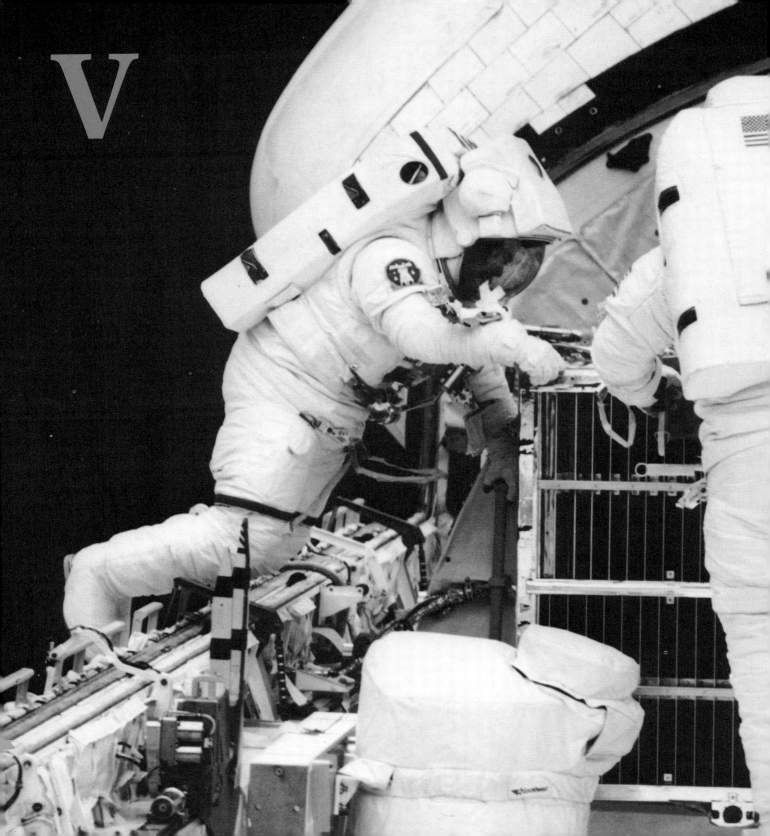

V

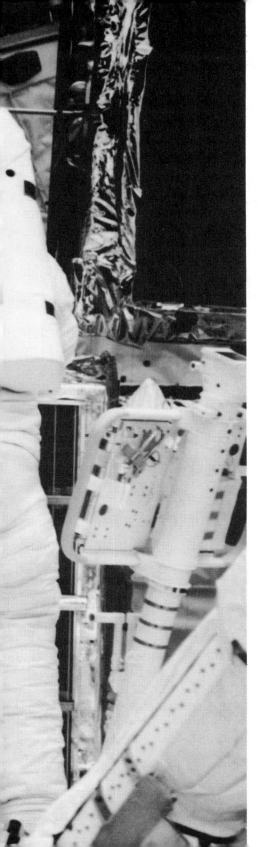

Applied Chemistry

We live in a chemical world. Thousands of chemical compounds occur naturally all around us—in air, water, salt, mineral ores, and petroleum. Applied chemistry transforms these compounds into an incredible array of products ranging from nylon to aspirin to detergents to cosmetics. Through such products, the science of applied chemistry helps to prolong life and to make it more enjoyable. Nevertheless, the image of chemistry has become tarnished in the eyes of the public. Newspaper and television reports of harmful chemicals abound, yet little attention is paid to the fact that most manufactured chemicals are put to beneficial uses. Through applied chemistry, we have learned to combine nature's basic ingredients in new ways to make products we want and need.

The principles of chemistry and the products of chemical engineering touch every facet of our daily lives, from the time we wash our hands and faces with soap in the morning to the time we crawl between our permanent-press sheets at night.

Chapter 13
Acids, Bases, and Applied Chemistry

Acids and bases are frequently encountered both in the home and in industry. Most of us know that an acid is something found in automobile batteries, that it causes heartburn, and that it is neutralized by antacids advertised on television. Common knowledge suggests that a "strong" acid will burn the skin. Bases are not as commonly known in everyday life, but you may have heard that a base also can burn the skin, that it can be used to unclog drains, and that it feels soapy.

Acids and bases play an important role in many industrial and biological products and processes. Whether a solution is acidic or basic affects the efficiency of some drugs, the formulation of shampoos and conditioners, the quality of wines, the suitability of commercial detergents and cleaning products, and the pollution of streams and rivers.

In this chapter you will broaden your knowledge of acids and bases as they are defined in chemistry and applied chemistry. You will also study the use of certain acids and bases in some medicines.

When you finish Chapter 13, you should be able to:

- define the properties of acids and bases
- use the pH scale to identify a substance as acidic, basic, or neutral
- describe how indicators are used
- describe how acids and bases are important in some medicines

13.1 Acids and Bases

Acids

The term **acid** is familiar to almost everyone. You may associate it with the sour taste of vinegar and lemon juice. Vinegar contains acetic acid. Citrus fruits contain citric acid, which gives these fruits their pleasant tang. Many other foods also contain acids. Your stomach produces hydrochloric acid to help digest your food. Doctors use mild, dilute, boric acid solutions to wash out patients' eyes. Other acids, like the acid in an automobile battery, can be dangerous and must be handled with great care. Certain acids can destroy metal, clothing, and your skin if you should accidentally spill any.

In this snack, acids are found in the Coke, vinegar, the orange, and the ketchup on the fries.

The English word "acid" is derived from the Latin word *acidus*, meaning "sour". Sometimes we say that someone cutting and harsh has an acid tongue, meaning sour, biting, sharp, or tart. Acid compounds in nature also have characteristics that are sour, harsh, and cutting.

The origin of the term "base" is not clear. The word probably came from the ancients' attempts to classify substances that reacted with, and so destroyed, an acid in solution. "Noble" metals such as gold and silver do not react with acids, whereas "base" metals like lead and iron do.

Bases

The less-familiar term **base** applies to a class of compounds that are the chemical opposites of acids. "Antacid", meaning "against acid", is a familiar term in television advertising. Bases are antacids.

Some bases are used regularly in the home. Household ammonia is a base used in many cleaning products because it loosens grease and grime. Lye, or sodium hydroxide, is a very active base found in many drain cleaners and used to unclog plugged drains. Antacid tablets are milder than lye and ammonia, and can be taken to relieve excess stomach acid or indigestion.

To the general public, the term **alkali** is a more common synonym for "base". Toothpaste is mildly alkaline. It neutralizes the acids, harmful to your teeth, that are formed when bacteria in saliva act on the sugars in food.

Many bases are used for household cleaning tasks.

Activity 13-1: Properties of Acids and Bases

In this activity, you will look for several characteristics of both acids and bases to help derive definitions. Then you will react an acid with a base and examine the product.

Materials

test solutions (1% except as noted):
- hydrochloric acid solution
- sulphuric acid solution
- acetic acid solution
- sodium hydroxide solution
- aqueous ammonia solution
- limewater solution (saturated)

sodium hydrogen carbonate

phenolphthalein solution

magnesium powder

6 test tubes

25 mL graduated cylinder

glass stirring rod

red litmus paper

blue litmus paper

rubber stopper

wood splint

evaporating dish

medicine dropper

Bunsen burner

support stand assembly

scoopula

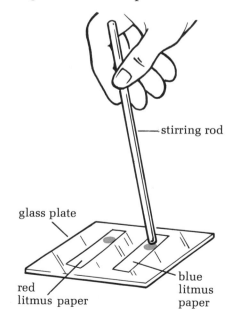

hydrochloric acid   sodium hydroxide

phenolphthalein

CAUTION: Wear goggles and an apron. Avoid contact with acids and bases.

Procedure

Part A: Acids

1. Draw the following table in your lab report. Tabulate your results in the table.

	Hydrochloric Acid	Sulphuric Acid	Acetic Acid
formula	HCl	H_2SO_4	$HC_2H_3O_2$
action with:			
red litmus			
blue litmus			
sodium hydrogen carbonate			
magnesium powder			

2. Pour 10 mL of hydrochloric acid solution into a test tube in a test tube rack.

3. With a stirring rod, place a drop of the acid on a piece of red litmus paper and another drop on blue litmus paper. (Save the paper for step 6 and Part B.)

4. Pour half the acid solution into another test tube to obtain two 5 mL portions. Add a small amount (0.25 mL) of sodium hydrogen carbonate (baking soda) to the acid in one test tube. Carefully pour the resulting gas (but not the liquid) into 2 cm of limewater in a third test tube. Stopper and shake the tube of limewater. Observe what happens.

Figure 13-1. Step 3.

stirring rod

glass plate

red litmus paper

blue litmus paper

5. Use a scoopula to add a small amount (0.25 mL) of magnesium powder to the acid in the second test tube standing in the test tube rack. Stir for 2 s. After 20 s, insert a blazing splint down into the test tube. Observe.

6. Completely wash out the three test tubes. Repeat steps 2 to 5 with each of the other two acids. Complete your table.

Part B: Bases

7. Draw the following table in your lab report. Tabulate your results in the table.

	Sodium Hydroxide	Ammonia Water	Limewater
formula	NaOH	NH_4OH	$Ca(OH)_2$
action with:			
red litmus			
blue litmus			
magnesium powder			

8. Pour 5 mL of sodium hydroxide solution into a test tube.

9. Place a drop of the base on the piece of red litmus paper and another drop on the blue litmus paper.

10. Add a small amount (0.25 mL) of magnesium powder to the base in the test tube.

11. Using clean test tubes, repeat steps 8 to 10 first with aqueous ammonia, then with limewater. Complete your table.

Part C: Reacting an Acid with a Base

12. Pour 5 mL of sodium hydroxide solution into a clean evaporating dish. Use a stirring rod to add two drops of phenolphthalein solution, stir, and note any observable change. As you stir the mixture, use a medicine dropper to slowly add hydrochloric acid solution, drop by drop, to the dish. When the pink colour *just* disappears, stop adding acid.

13. Set up the apparatus as shown in Figure 13-2, and be sure you are wearing your safety goggles. Evaporate the solution to dryness. Allow the dish to cool.

14. Examine the solid substance that forms in the evaporating dish.

Do You Know?
Phenolphthalein is the compound used in Ex-Lax to provide the laxative effect.

CAUTION: Hot solid may spatter out of the evaporating dish as the solution dries.

Discussion

1. Look at the formulas for the acids you used. (See the table in Part A.) What do they have in common?

2. Look at the formulas for the bases you used. (See the table in Part B.) What do they have in common?

3. How do acids and bases differ in their effect on red and blue litmus paper?

4. a) What happens when a metal such as magnesium is placed in an acid?
   b) What happens when such a metal is placed in a base?
   c) Name any gases produced in a) or b).

5. a) What happens when sodium hydrogen carbonate is placed in an acid?
   b) What gas is produced?

6. a) What product was formed when hydrochloric acid reacted with sodium hydroxide?
   b) The reaction between an acid and a base is called **neutralization**. Water and a salt are formed in every neutralization reaction. Write a word equation for the neutralization reaction that occurred in Part C.

7. a) List all properties common to acids *and* bases.
   b) List all properties possessed *only* by acids.
   c) List all properties possessed *only* by bases.

8. Considering the properties you listed in 7 above, write a definition for an acid and a base.

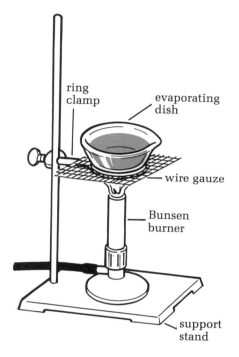

Figure 13-2. The evaporating dish contains the dilute acid and base solutions, as well as a few drops of phenolphthalein solution.

ring clamp
evaporating dish
wire gauze
Bunsen burner
support stand

Defining Acids and Bases

If asked to describe acids, most people would probably say, "Acids have a sour taste." You can safely verify the taste of lemon juice and vinegar. But this is not a very useful definition because it is dangerous to taste unknown substances. If you tasted prussic acid (hydrogen cyanide solution), for example, you would hardly have time to report your findings before you turned blue and died in agony.

One safer test involves combining acids with certain metals. In the previous activity you saw that gas bubbles formed in such a reaction. Tests show that the gas is hydrogen. This means that hydrogen atoms must be part of an acid. It is important to note, however, that not all hydrogen-containing compounds are acids. Gasoline and sugar contain hydrogen atoms, for example, but they do not behave like acids.

It can be shown that solutions of acids conduct electricity easily. This means that these solutions contain ions. When an electric current is passed through an acid solution, hydrogen, which is common to all acids, is attracted to the negative electrode. This suggests that hydrogen is present in the form of positively charged ions (H^+), and leads to a more detailed description of an acid. **An acid is a compound which dissolves in water to produce hydrogen ions in the solution**.

Recall that an ion is an atom or a group of atoms that has a positive or a negative electrical charge.

$$\text{hydrochloric acid} \longrightarrow \text{hydrogen ions} + \text{chloride ions}$$
$$(+) \qquad\qquad (-)$$

In general, bases have properties opposite to those of acids. Bases have a bitter taste and do not react with metals to form hydrogen gas. Base solutions, however, also conduct electricity. This means that an alkaline solution contains many ions. Each base contains one or more hydroxide or OH^- groups. In a water solution, the base forms hydroxide ions (OH^-), which have a negative charge. **A base is a compound which dissolves in water to produce hydroxide ions in the solution**.

$$\text{sodium hydroxide} \longrightarrow \text{sodium ions} + \text{hydroxide ions}$$
$$(+) \qquad\qquad (-)$$

Neutralization occurs when a base reacts with an acid to form a salt and water.

$$\text{sodium hydroxide} + \text{hydrochloric acid} \longrightarrow \text{sodium chloride}$$
$$+ \text{ water}$$

In the early 1800s chemists began to designate as **organic** compounds those which could be found only in living organisms, either plants or animals. They referred to as **inorganic** all other substances found in soil, seawater, air, and rocks. In time it was found that organic compounds could be prepared from nonliving material. Chemists then realized that the one element *always* present in organic compounds, either natural or synthetic, is carbon. Thus a simple, accurate definition still used is: *organic compounds contain carbon*. They may also contain hydrogen, oxygen, nitrogen, sulphur and/or other elements.

▶ **How to Prepare Acids and Bases**

There are many different ways of preparing acids. One of the most important ways involves the reaction of a nonmetal oxide with water.

$$\text{sulphur trioxide} + \text{water} \longrightarrow \text{sulphuric acid}$$
$$\text{carbon dioxide} + \text{water} \longrightarrow \text{carbonic acid}$$

Acids that can be prepared in this way are sometimes called mineral acids because they come from mineral sources rather than from organic ones.

Bases can also be prepared in many ways. One of the main methods involves the reaction of metal oxides with water.

sodium oxide + water ⟶ sodium hydroxide

calcium oxide + water ⟶ calcium hydroxide

Uses of Some Common Acids

Hydrochloric acid, a strong corrosive mineral acid known commercially as muriatic acid, is used industrially to clean metals that are about to be coated or plated. Cleaning with hydrochloric acid is known as the **pickling** process. This acid is so strong that it is used to clean brick and cement.

Nitric acid, another mineral acid, is very reactive. A spill turns fair skin yellow. This colour change is caused by a reaction between the nitric acid and the protein in the skin. Nitric acid is used mainly in the production of fertilizers, but it is also used to make plastics, dyes, and explosives.

Sulphuric acid, a very strong corrosive mineral acid, is used in fertilizers, gunpowder, and nitroglycerine. Car batteries contain dilute sulphuric acid. In a battery a chemical reaction between the acid and the metal plates creates an electric current.

Phosphoric acid is a weak mineral acid. Its uses range from flavouring soft drinks to producing superphosphates for fertilizers. Dental cements holding false teeth in place contain phosphoric acid.

Acetic acid is found in vinegar. By law vinegar must contain no less than 4% acetic acid. Until recently, all vinegar was made by fermenting plant material such as apples. Acetic acid was then obtained by distilling the vinegar. Because of its original connection with living things, acetic acid is often called an organic acid. Nowadays, it is made in chemical factories from raw materials such as petroleum. It is also used in chemical factories. Concentrated acetic acid is used in manufacturing some plastics, and in making synthetic fibres called acetates.

Uses of Some Common Bases

Sodium hydroxide, commonly called lye, is a base used in drain and oven cleaners. It is also used to make soaps and cellophane. The petroleum industry uses sodium hydroxide to neutralize acids in the oil refining process.

Calcium hydroxide, often called slaked lime, is important in the

The base, ammonia, and acids such as sulphuric, nitric, and phosphoric are used in the manufacture of agricultural fertilizers.

Firefighters dressed in protective suits neutralize spilled acid on a city street by pouring lime (calcium hydroxide) on the acid.

construction industry. It is used in mortar, plaster, cement, and many other building and paving materials.

Ammonia is a gas. When dissolved in water it forms a solution sometimes called ammonia water or ammonium hydroxide. Ammonia water is commonly used as a household cleaner. Besides removing stains effectively, ammonia is used in manufacturing textiles such as rayon, and in making plastics and fertilizers. Because of its sharp odour, it is used in smelling salts.

Magnesium hydroxide, commonly called milk of magnesia, has many uses as a medicine. In small doses it acts as an antacid, in larger doses as a laxative.

Table 13-1: Acids in Commercial Products

Product	Contents
battery acid	sulphuric acid
vinegar	acetic acid
soda water	carbonic acid
pop	carbonic acid
	phosphoric acid
	citric acid
rust remover (naval jelly)	phosphoric acid
Saniflush (solid toilet bowl cleaner)	sodium hydrogen sulphate
Vanish (solid toilet bowl cleaner)	sodium hydrogen sulphate
	potassium monopersulphate
Saniflush, Lysol (liquid toilet bowl cleaner)	hydrochloric acid
pH down (for swimming pools)	hydrochloric acid (liquid)
	sodium hydrogen sulphate (solid)
Ajax, Comet, Old Dutch Cleanser	chlorinated cyanuric acid
chlorine stabilizer (pools)	cyanuric acid
Murine (eye drops)	boric acid, sodium borate

Acids are used in these household products.

Table 13-2:   Bases in Commercial Products

Product	Contents
Liquid Plumr (drain opener)	sodium hydroxide
	sodium hypochlorite
Easy-Off Oven Cleaner	sodium hydroxide (aerosol solution)
Drano (solid) (drain opener)	sodium hydroxide, aluminum chips
Windex, Glass Plus (glass cleaner)	ammonia
Amex (powdered ammonia)	ammonium carbonate
baking soda	sodium hydrogen carbonate
washing soda (detergent booster)	sodium carbonate
Sanifoam (bathroom cleaner)	trisodium phosphate (aerosol solution)
pH up (for swimming pools)	sodium hydrogen carbonate
	sodium carbonate

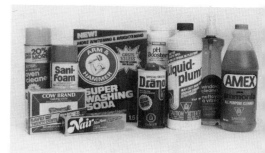

Bases are used in these household products.

Study Questions

1. Give several examples of common acids.
2. Give several examples of common bases.
3. a) Define the terms "acid" and "base".
   b) What is meant by neutralization?
4. Give five examples of household products that contain acids and five that contain bases.
5. Formic acid (from the Latin *formicus*, meaning "ant") was first prepared in 1670 by the distillation of red ants. This acid is partially responsible for the irritation that results from ant bites. A colourless liquid of pungent odour, formic acid is now used in dyeing wool, dehairing hides, tanning leather, and removing calcium deposits. Describe three tests you could do to prove to someone else that this substance is an acid. State clearly what you would expect to observe in each test.

From a very early age, Svante Arrhenius showed signs of a brilliant intellect. He taught himself to read at the age of three, and graduated from high school at age 17 as the youngest and brightest in his class. While attending university in Sweden, he began to study how electricity passed through solutions. From his work on the lowering of the freezing point of salt solutions, Arrhenius decided that the only way to explain the results was to assume that table salt, for example, broke up into two kinds of particles, sodium ions and chloride ions. Since the table salt solution did not contain metallic sodium or gaseous chlorine, he concluded that the sodium and chlorine particles must carry electric charges.

His teachers and most of the chemists of the time found this theory too wild to believe. Electrically charged atoms were inconceivable to those who accepted Dalton's model of the atom.

Nevertheless, in 1884 Arrhenius prepared his ionic theory. It defined an acid as a compound that dissolves in water to yield hydrogen ions, and a base as a compound that dissolves in water to yield hydroxide ions. He underwent an oral exam on the theory, but was awarded only a bare passing mark by his examiners who thought the theory too far-fetched.

In the 1890s, however, upheavals in science began to occur. J.J. Thomson discovered the electron and Becquerel discovered radioactivity. It soon became clear that the atom was made up of charged particles such as the negatively charged electron. Suddenly Arrhenius' ionic theory made sense. In 1903 he won the Nobel prize in chemistry for the same theory that had earned him only a passing grade just nineteen years earlier.

13.2 Indicators and Acid-Base Strength

In order to compare the strength of one acidic or basic solution to another, chemists have developed what is known as the **pH scale**. Often it is more convenient to estimate the pH of a solution than to determine it precisely. To achieve such estimates, acid-base indicators are used.

Acid-Base Indicators

Acid-base indicators are weak organic acids or bases that change colour when added to acids and bases. Many dyes from plants, for example, change colour as the pH of a solution changes. For example, **litmus**, a dye obtained from a species of lichen, dissolves in water to form a purple solution. Litmus solution turns red when

Figure 13-3. Which solution is acidic, and which is basic?

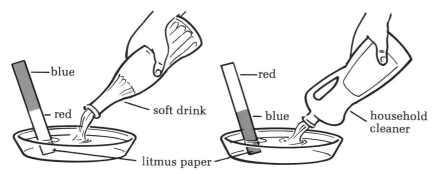

an acid is added, and blue when a base is added. Using an indicator is the safest way to determine whether a solution contains an acid or a base.

Synthetic dyes have replaced plant materials as indicators. Some of the more common of these dyes are methyl orange, phenolphthalein, methyl red, and bromthymol blue. You used phenolphthalein in the neutralization of an acid and a base in Activity 13-1. The colours shown by some indicators when added to acidic or alkaline solutions are given in Table 13-3.

The pH Scale

An indicator such as litmus does not tell us how acidic or basic a solution is. Whether 5 mL of dilute sulphuric acid is added to 5 mL or 100 mL of water, the mixture will turn purple litmus red. The second solution would be more dilute than the first one, however, and therefore not as acidic. The difference between the two solutions can be expressed by using pH.

Numbers on the pH scale are given to indicate the level of acidity of a solution. The "p" stands for the Danish word *portenz*, meaning "strength", so "pH" means "the strength of the hydrogen ion". The scale generally covers a range from a pH of 0 to a pH of 14. All solutions that contain equal numbers of hydrogen ions (H^+) and hydroxide ions (OH^-) are **neutral** and have a pH of 7. The pH of pure water is 7. Acidic solutions have a pH between 0 and 7. For example, the pH of orange juice is about 3. Basic solutions, however, have a pH greater than 7. The pH of oven cleaners is about 14.

You may have noticed how the colour of some jellies, such as grape or blackberry, changes when a dish smeared with jelly is washed in soap or detergent. Jelly is slightly acidic. Dishwater is usually slightly basic, due to the added soap or detergent. Washing the dish neutralizes the acid in the jelly. In this process, the colouring matter in the jelly changes from purple to dark blue.

Table 13-3: Colours of Some Acid-Base Indicators at Various pH Levels

Indicator	pH														
	0	1	2	3	4	5	6	7	8	9	10	11	12	13	14
thymol blue*	red	transition	yellow												
methyl orange			red	transition	yellow										
methyl red					red	transition	yellow								
litmus							red	transition	blue						
bromthymol blue							yellow	transition	blue						
metacresol purple								yellow	transition	purple					
thymol blue*									yellow	transition	blue				
phenolphthalein									colourless	transition	red				

*Thymol blue indicator undergoes two colour changes—one in the acid range and one in the base range.

Figure 13-4. The pH scale.

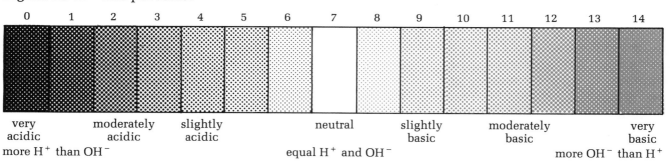

| 0 | 1 | 2 | 3 | 4 | 5 | 6 | 7 | 8 | 9 | 10 | 11 | 12 | 13 | 14 |

very acidic   moderately acidic   slightly acidic   neutral   slightly basic   moderately basic   very basic

more H$^+$ than OH$^-$ equal H$^+$ and OH$^-$ more OH$^-$ than H$^+$

Activity 13-2: Making an Indicator from Red Cabbage

You can use certain plants to prepare some indicators. Indicators can be extracted from red cabbage leaves, tea, red beets, and red cherries. In this activity you will prepare a cabbage indicator and use it to test some common substances for acid-base properties.

Materials

red (purple) cabbage
graduated cylinder
250 mL beaker
100 mL beaker
distilled water
2 ring clamps
support stand
wire gauze
Bunsen burner

5 test tubes
test tube rack
test substances:
  vinegar
  lemon juice
  detergent
  ammonia solution
  drain cleaner
tweezers

ammonia solution   drain cleaner
(sodium hydroxide)

Procedure

1. Tear a leaf of red cabbage into very small pieces. Place the pieces of cabbage in the bottom of a 250 mL beaker.
2. Cover the cabbage pieces with 50 mL of distilled water.
3. Boil the cabbage until the liquid is a deep purple colour.
4. Cool the contents of the beaker and pour off the coloured liquid into a 100 mL beaker.
5. Draw a table to record the test substances and the colour of the cabbage indicator for each.
6. Pour the coloured liquid to a depth of about 1 cm in each of five test tubes. Add a small amount of vinegar to one of the test tubes. Repeat this procedure with each of the other test substances. For the drain cleaner, use only one pellet and handle it with tweezers. Record your observations in your table.
7. Using tweezers, add one pellet of drain cleaner to the test tube containing the indicator and the vinegar. Observe.

Discussion

1. What evidence do you have that a) red cabbage solution is an indicator, b) the indicator is not consumed?
2. For approximate pH values, the dye in red cabbage has the colours shown in Table 13-4. Use this table to determine the approximate pH of each test solution in this activity. Why is it difficult to determine pH by this method?

CAUTION: Drain cleaner is very corrosive. Do not let it get on your skin or clothing.

Figure 13-5.

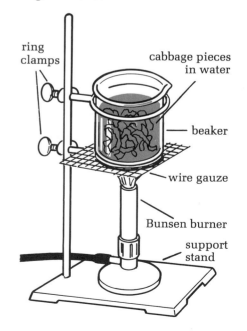

ring clamps

cabbage pieces in water

beaker

wire gauze

Bunsen burner

support stand

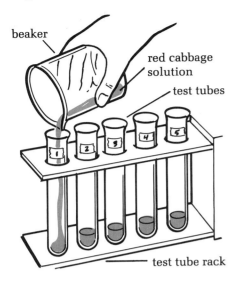

beaker

red cabbage solution

test tubes

test tube rack

Figure 13-6.

Some pH paper indicators.

Table 13-4: pH and the Colour of Red Cabbage Dye

2	3	4	5	6	7		8	9	10	11	12	13	14
red		red-purple		purple	blue-purple	blue	blue-green		green			yellow	

Activity 13-3: Finding the pH of Common Substances

One way of finding the pH of a solution is to use a mixture of indicators called a "universal indicator". Such an indicator shows different colours at different pH levels. Paper that has been soaked in such a solution and then dried is called **universal indicator paper**, or **pH paper**. The manufacturer of the indicator paper supplies a chart showing the colour the indicator turns at a particular pH. To find the pH of a solution, you simply add a drop of the solution to the pH paper and then compare the colour produced with those on the standard chart provided.

In this activity you will use universal indicator paper to determine the pH of a variety of solutions.

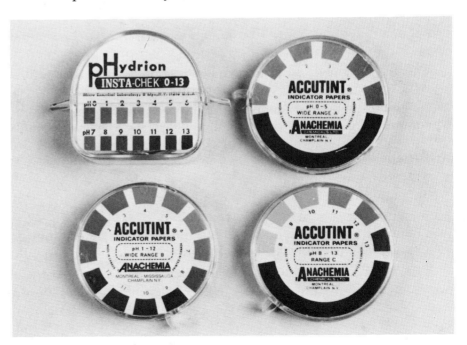

Materials

8 test tubes

test tube rack

10 mL graduated cylinder

hydrochloric acid solution (1%)

sodium hydroxide solution (0.4%)

distilled water

pH paper with colour chart

materials to be tested:
tap water
milk
distilled water
sour milk
orange juice
borax solution
lemon slice
milk of magnesia
tomato slice
limewater
vinegar
sodium chloride solution
red vinegar

hydrochloric   sodium hydroxide
acid

Procedure

Part A: Acid and Base Solutions

1. Set up 8 test tubes in a rack and label them 1 to 8.

2. In tubes 1 to 4 prepare a series of four hydrochloric acid solutions as follows. Pour about 10 mL of hydrochloric acid solution into test tube 1. Using a graduated cylinder, add exactly 9 mL of distilled water to each of test tubes 2, 3, and 4. Transfer exactly 1 mL of the solution in test tube 1 to test tube 2. Stir to mix well. Transfer 1 mL of liquid from test tube 2 to test tube 3. Stir to mix well. Transfer 1 mL of liquid from test tube 3 to test tube 4. Again, stir to mix well.

3. Pour 10 mL of the sodium hydroxide solution into test tube 5. Add 9 mL of distilled water to each of test tubes 6, 7, and 8. Prepare a series of dilutions (in test tubes 6, 7, and 8) just like the dilutions of hydrochloric acid.

4. Draw a table to record the test tube numbers and pH values you will obtain in step 5.

5. Measure the pH of the solution in test tube 1 by tearing off a small piece of pH paper and dipping it into the liquid. Compare the resulting colour with the standard chart and record the pH value in your table.

6. Similarly, use small pieces of pH paper to find the pH values of the other solutions.

Figure 13-7.

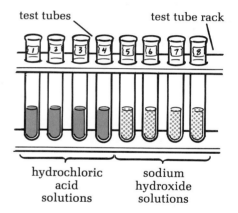

test tubes   test tube rack

hydrochloric   sodium
acid   hydroxide
solutions   solutions

CAUTION: Always add acid to water and never the reverse. This prevents any acid from splashing back at you. Remember this rule by thinking "AAA" for "always add acid".

Part B: Common Substances

7. Draw a table to record your observations in step 8.

Substance	pH	Acid, Base, or Neutral

8. Use small pieces of pH paper to find the pH of the various test substances listed in the Materials list (or of other substances provided by your teacher). In your table, record the pH for each substance. Record also whether the substance is acidic, basic, or neutral.

Discussion

1. As the hydrochloric acid solution is diluted, what kind of change takes place in the pH?
2. As the sodium hydroxide solution, a base, is diluted, what kind of change takes place in the pH?
3. If you spilled acid on the kitchen floor, what could you use to neutralize it? Why would you not use sodium hydroxide?

The Importance of pH

Maintaining a certain pH value or range of values is often important in biological systems. For example, our blood maintains a pH of between 7.35 and 7.45. If blood changes more than a few tenths of a pH unit from the normal range, the results can be fatal. Too much acid or base interferes with the ability of the blood to pick up, carry, and release oxygen.

Most plants grow best in soil with a pH value between 6 and 7. Higher or lower values prevent plants from absorbing nutrients from the soil. A too acidic soil, for instance, can prevent plants from absorbing nutrient phosphate properly.

Even bacteria have an ideal pH range. Pickling foods in vinegar is an effective way to preserve them because most bacteria that cause food spoilage cannot grow in solutions having the low pH value of vinegar.

Shampoos normally have a pH of about 8. Your scalp, on the other hand, is on the acidic side, with a pH of around 6. Rinsing your hair with vinegar after shampooing neutralizes the base left by the shampoo. This restores the acid condition of the scalp. An alkaline scalp results in a dry, flaky condition resembling dandruff.

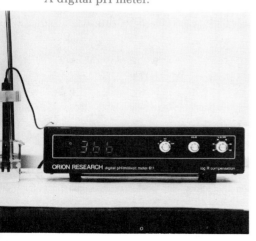

A digital pH meter.

Many modern shampoos, therefore, are advertised as "pH-adjusted". This means that various mild acids have been added to the shampoo to lower the pH to about 6.

Figure 13-8 shows the approximate pH values of some common solutions, as determined with acid-base indicators. For more accurate pH determinations, pH meters are used.

Study Questions

1. a) What is an acid-base indicator?
   b) Why is litmus paper commonly used as an indicator?
   c) Name some common indicators found at home.
2. a) What is meant by pH?
   b) Which indicates an acid, a low pH or a high pH?
   c) Is a solution with a pH value of 4 more acidic or less acidic than a solution with a pH value of 6?
3. How could you determine the level of acidity in tea, coffee, and Coca-Cola?
4. a) How can pH be measured to obtain approximate values?
   b) How can pH be measured if a high degree of accuracy is required?
5. Sodium benzoate is commonly used as an additive to minimize the bacterial spoilage of food. It is not effective at a pH higher than 4. In what types of foods could sodium benzoate be used?

Figure 13-9.

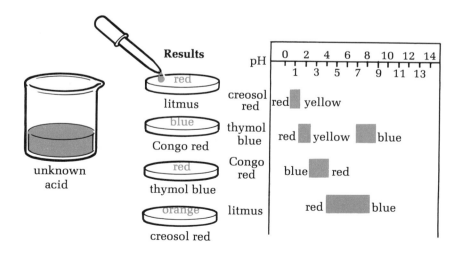

Figure 13-8. The pH values of familiar water solutions.

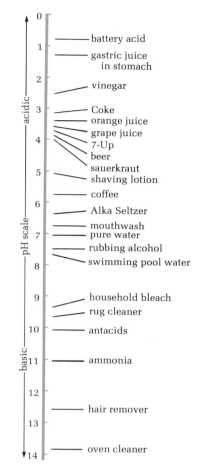

CHALLENGER

Can You Find the pH?
An unknown acid solution was tested with four different indicators. The results and the pH ranges of the indicators are shown in Figure 13-9. State what can be concluded about the pH of the unknown acid solution after each test. What is your best final estimate of the pH of the acid solution?

pH CAN BE A PAIN!

The sensation of pain in humans and animals comes from the response of nerve endings to changes in the pH of solutions surrounding the nerves. The pH of blood and cell fluids in tissues is 7.4. This pH is close to the value of "neutral" pure water. If you spill vinegar or lemon juice on a cut finger, you feel a sharp sting. This indicates that the nerve endings have come in contact with a more acidic solution of much lower pH than normal.

For a similar reason, insect stings are felt when the insect forces a solution of formic or other acid into the tissues. Solutions of formic acid have pH values between 2 and 3.

The fluids inside the cells in flesh also contain weak acids. The pH of these acids is much lower than in the fluids outside the cells. When injuries such as cutting or burning break the walls of cells in the flesh, the acidic fluid normally held inside the cells escapes. When this low-pH fluid comes in contact with nerve endings, it causes the sensation of pain. Studies have shown that a drop in pH as slight as from 7.4 to 6.2 can be detected by the irritation it causes.

If the solution causing the irritation or pain in the tissues can be neutralized, pain is relieved. Salves or creams used to treat skin problems such as poison ivy rash or sunburn use slightly basic solutions. This ensures a pain-relieving neutralization reaction. Many "after bite" products for easing the itch of mosquito bites contain ammonia, a base.

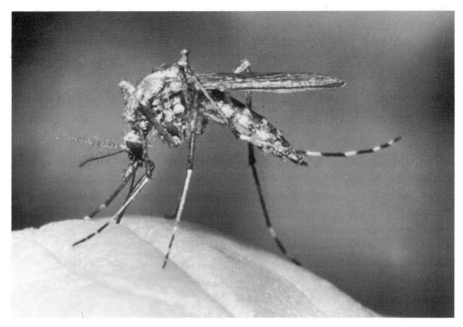

A female mosquito withdraws human blood to aid in the development of her eggs.

13.3 Applied Chemistry and Medicines

Chemistry is applied to biological systems in order to understand how chemicals and medicines affect life processes. On the basis of this understanding, drugs or medicines can be developed to help combat illness and disease.

Medicines

The average life expectancy in Canada was only 49 years in 1900. It is expected to reach 79 plus by the year 2000. An increase in sanitation and the availability of a large assortment of new medicinal compounds are in large part responsible. High blood pressure, tuberculosis, pneumonia, diabetes, and some forms of mental illness are a few of the many common afflictions that now respond successfully to drugs.

Due to chemical research, improved drugs appear constantly to replace less effective ones. Drugs for reducing fever, relieving pain, and fighting infection top the list. Thorough research is required to ensure that a new drug is safe to use. Of the thousands of new drugs produced each year, only a handful are approved and released to consumers.

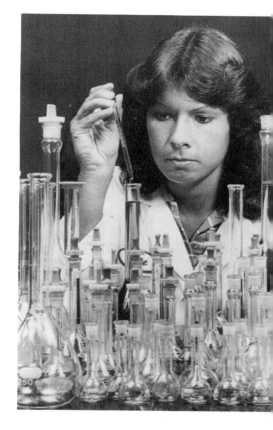

Antacids

One of the simplest medicines to understand in terms of its chemical action is the antacid tablet. Commercial antacids are advertised as a means of relieving upset stomach. One brand claims that it consumes 47 times its own weight in excess stomach acid. This claim raises several questions: What is stomach acid? What is excess stomach acid? What does "consumes" mean?

Your stomach contains hydrochloric acid to prepare protein for digestion and to kill bacteria entering the stomach. The digestive juices normally have a pH of 3, but they can become too acidic. Excess acid exists when the pH value of the stomach contents falls below 3, causing symptoms such as heartburn and indigestion. An

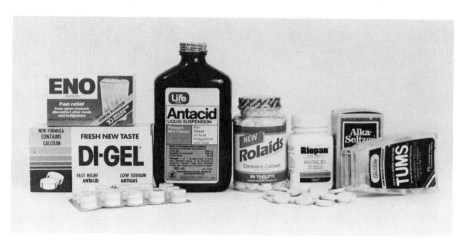

Common antacids.

antacid is a weak base that "consumes", or neutralizes, excess stomach acid. It is not healthy to take a lot of antacid tablets, particularly strong ones, because if you neutralize too much acid, your body will supply *more* acid to the stomach. Therefore, too much antacid can cause a vicious cycle and produce ulcers.

▶ How to Use a Mortar and Pestle

Figure 13-10.

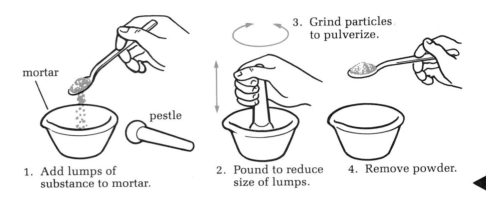

mortar

pestle

1. Add lumps of substance to mortar.

2. Pound to reduce size of lumps.

3. Grind particles to pulverize.

4. Remove powder.

Activity 13-4: Which Antacid is the Best Buy?

In this activity you will use titration to test different antacids to see which can neutralize the most acid. The antacid that neutralizes the most acid for the lowest price is called the "best buy". **Titration** is an important laboratory procedure used in performing chemical analyses. In this acid-base titration, an acid is added to a weakly basic antacid tablet; the titration is stopped when the indicator changes colour, showing that the neutralization reaction is complete. Congo red indicator turns colour at a pH of 3, the normal pH in your stomach.

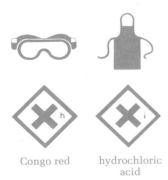

Congo red

hydrochloric acid

Materials

various antacid tablets	large medicine dropper
mortar and pestle	graduated cylinder
100 mL graduated cylinder	hydrochloric acid (10%)
stirring rod	white paper
250 mL flask	balance
Congo red indicator (0.1%)	

Procedure

1. Copy the chart in the margin into your lab report.
2. Record the mass of an antacid tablet.
3. Use a clean pestle to crush an antacid tablet in a clean mortar.
4. Add 50 mL of water to the mortar. Stir to dissolve the tablet, then pour the contents of the mortar into a 250 mL flask. Rinse the mortar with another 50 mL of water. Again, pour the contents into the flask.
5. Add 6 drops of Congo red indicator to the flask.
6. Carefully add hydrochloric acid, drop by drop, while gently swirling the flask over a sheet of white paper until the contents of the flask turn a light purplish blue. Record the number of drops of acid neutralized by the tablet.
7. Repeat steps 2 to 6 for a different brand of antacid as directed by your teacher.
8. Your teacher will provide price information for the different brands of tablets investigated by the class.

Discussion

1. Which antacid tablet neutralized the most acid?
2. Calculate the number of drops of acid neutralized per gram of tablet. Which brand of tablet was the most effective *per gram*? Rank the tablets in order of effectiveness, with the most effective at the top of the list.
3. Calculate the number of drops of acid neutralized per penny spent. Which tablet was the most effective *per penny*? Rank the tablets in order of cost with the most economical at the top of the list.
4. Considering both your lists, which antacid tablet would you rate as the "best buy" (high effectiveness coupled with low cost)?

Study Questions

1. Give two reasons for the increase in average life expectancy in Canada.
2. Why is drug research so costly?

Comparison of Antacids

	Tablet 1	Tablet 2 . . .
brand name		
mass of tablet used		
drops of acid required		
cost per tablet (cents)		

Figure 13-11.

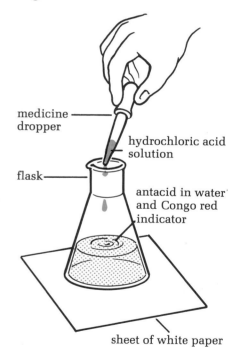

medicine dropper

hydrochloric acid solution

flask

antacid in water and Congo red indicator

sheet of white paper

3. What is an antacid, and why do we use antacids so often?

4. For drugs that are almost identical in composition and performance, how would you determine the best buy?

5. There are many kinds of drug classifications. One scheme classifies drugs according to usage: i) to fight disease, ii) to prevent disease, iii) to aid body functions, iv) to ease pain.

   a) Do you think a drug could fit into more than one of these categories? Explain.

   b) Where would you place antacids in this classification scheme? Explain.

PAINKILLERS CAN KILL

One of the largest groups of medicinal compounds are the **analgesics**, or "painkillers". When we suffer a headache we take an analgesic. When we have a tooth filled or extracted, the dentist gives us Novocain. For very intense suffering, the physician may prescribe a strong painkiller like codeine or morphine. Most analgesics are acids or bases of one sort or another. And while these compounds are very useful, they can kill if an overdose is taken.

Early civilizations probably used **opium** as a painkiller. Opium is obtained by scarring the opium seed pod with a sharp knife. From the scar flows a sticky mass containing about 20 different compounds called **alkaloids**. These are organic bases that usually contain

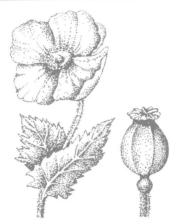

Figure 13-12. An opium poppy and seed pod.

nitrogen. The alkaloid **morphine** is primarily responsible for opium's effects. Two derivatives of morphine are **codeine**, which is as powerful as morphine but less addicting, and **heroin**, which is extremely addictive and therefore rarely used in medical treatment.

When a mild analgesic is required, most of us use acetylsalicylic acid (ASA, Aspirin, Anacin). The history of

ASA began in 1763 with the discovery that the bark of the willow when chewed helped relieve the symptoms of malaria. Seventy-five years later salicylic acid was identified as the active ingredient in the willow. Unfortunately, this acid has a very disagreeable taste. By 1893, Felix Hofmann, a chemist working for the Bayer Company in Germany, had discovered a way to convert salicylic acid into acetylsalicylic acid, which is relatively tasteless. The acidity of this aspirin was low enough that it could be taken orally.

The fact that some people are sensitive to the side effects (stomach irritation) of ASA led to the development of **acetaminophen**. Acetaminophen (Tylenol, Excedrin, Anacin-3) is as effective as ASA in relieving pain and reducing fever, but, unlike ASA, it does not reduce inflammation. Tests show that there is no real difference among competing brands of analgesics except for their price.

Meet a Lab Technician— George Gomes

George is a lab technician who came to Canada from India 13 years ago. He works in the quality control laboratory of Revlon, a large cosmetics firm, where he tests the product line that includes mascara, body lotion, shampoo, and hair conditioner.

Q. WHAT DO YOU LOOK FOR WHEN YOU TEST PRODUCTS?
A. We look mainly for four things: colour and appearance, odour, pH level, and viscosity. We have a set of specifications for every product, and we do tests to see that these specifications are met. We also test for the percentage of water and the percentage of solids in a product.

Q. WHAT KIND OF INSTRUMENTS DO YOU USE?
A. Well, for instance, if we're testing the pH level of a product, which shows whether it is acidic, alkaline, or neutral, we use a pH meter. All products have a certain pH level that must be maintained.

Q. WHAT HAPPENS WHEN YOU FIND THE pH LEVEL IS WRONG?
A. I notify my boss who's in charge of quality control, and we have more samples brought in. Body lotion, for example, is alkaline and normally over pH 7 —if it tests at pH 5 we correct it in the lab. Once we've made the adjustment, we give the necessary instructions to the compounding department where the product is made.

Q. WHAT OTHER INSTRUMENTS DO YOU USE?
A. For testing viscosity, we use a viscometer which measures the thickness or thinness of a product. We use a karlfischer to determine how much water is in a product, an ultraviolet spectrophotometer to measure different types of acid, and a nitrogen distillation unit to determine the percentage of nitrogen in raw materials.

Q. HOW MANY PRODUCTS DO YOU TEST IN A DAY?
A. It varies, depending on the production schedule. Every day I get samples from the assembly line to test. We have 10 or 12 product lines, and in one day I might test an average of about 15 samples. Some days I test many different products. I also check the lot numbers, labels, and make sure the right product is going into the right container and that the number of millilitres listed is correct. The aesthetic appearance of the product is important, too— for instance, if the bottle used is transparent, I make sure it doesn't look half-full.

Q. DO YOU NEED A BACKGROUND IN CHEMISTRY TO DO THIS WORK?
A. I have a chemistry degree from the University of Bombay, but we hire a lot of high school graduates and train them on the job. I use my knowledge of chemistry when I get involved with testing raw materials.

Q. HOW DOES TESTING RAW MATERIALS DIFFER FROM PRODUCT TESTING?
A. There's more analyzing of chemical composition. Revlon has a set standard for all raw materials used in its products, so we run a graph to see if the materials used in a product match our standard. We test powders, liquids, waxes, detergents—that sort of thing. We use an infrared spectrophotometer, a device that shows all the ingredients. I find this work more interesting because it involves chemical reactions, not just testing.

Q. WHAT DO YOU LIKE BEST ABOUT YOUR JOB?
A. I believe in the company's concern for the quality of its products. There's a great deal of emphasis put on this and on meeting the customer's demands. I like being involved in maintaining this quality.

Review Questions

A: Knowledge

1. Name some common acids used in the home.
2. Name some ways in which acids differ from each other.
3. Explain why a person can safely drink large quantities of carbonic acid in soft drinks.
4. Give the chemical and common names for the bases used in the home.
5. Suggest reasons why more acids than bases were familiar to early chemists.
6. How are salts formed?
7. In what ways are acids and bases important in our economy?
8. A certain solution contains equal numbers of hydrogen ions and hydroxide ions. What term can be used to describe the solution? What is the pH value of the solution?
9. The pH values of several solutions are given below. In each case, tell whether the solution is acidic, basic, or neutral.
   a) 2.3 b) 9.6 c) 7.3 d) 7.0
   e) 6.8 f) 13.7
10. State whether each of the following substances is acidic, basic, or neutral.
    a) turns red litmus paper blue
    b) has a pH of 7
    c) produces hydroxide ions in water solution
    d) has no effect on either red or blue litmus paper
    e) has a pH of 12
    f) is made from the juice of lemons
    g) has a pH of 3
11. State whether each of the following statements is true or false. If false, rewrite the statement to make it correct.
    a) Vinegar is an acid that turns blue litmus paper red.
    b) Acidic and basic solutions conduct electricity because they contain electrons.
    c) A solution used to clean household drains is acidic and turns red litmus paper blue.
    d) "Antacid" means "against acid", and most acids are antacids.
    e) The term "alkali" is a common name for a base.
    f) The reaction between an antacid and a base is called neutralization.
    g) A base is a compound which dissolves in water to produce hydrogen ions in solution.

B: Application

12. In some laboratories, large bottles are labelled: "FIRST AID FOR ACID BURNS— Rinse area of burn thoroughly with water. Then rinse with 5% baking soda solution. Rinse again with water. Seek medical attention."
    "FIRST AID FOR BASE BURNS—Rinse area of burn thoroughly with water. Then rinse with 5% acetic acid solution. Rinse again with water. Seek medical attention."
    a) What is the purpose of rinsing thoroughly with water?
    b) What is the purpose of the baking soda rinse?
    c) What is the purpose of the acetic acid rinse?
    d) What is the purpose of the second rinse with water?
    e) Why are baking soda and acetic acid solutions recommended, rather than sodium hydroxide and hydrochloric acid solutions?
    f) Why should the burns be reported, and additional medical attention sought?
13. Lactic acid is the sour ingredient in sour milk and buttermilk. A recipe that calls for sour milk or buttermilk usually also calls for baking soda. Why?
14. Fresh milk has a pH of 6.4, while milk that has gone sour has a pH of between 3 and 4. What kind of chemical substances have been produced in the milk by bacterial action, causing it to go sour?
15. Using indicator paper, a student determined the pH values of a variety of different solutions. These are the results.

Solution	A	B	C	D	E	F	G	H
pH	7	3	2	4	8	6	9	5

Vol. (mL)	0	2	4	6	8	10
Temp. (°C)	18	21.6	24.8	28.0	31.2	34.0

Vol. (mL)	12	14	16	18	20
Temp. (°C)	33.2	32.4	31.4	30.1	28.8

a) Which solution is the most acidic?
b) Which solution is the most basic?
c) Which solution is closest to neutral?
d) Which action would increase the pH of
D: i) adding water, ii) adding C,
iii) adding G?

16. a) Suggest a reason why the pH of a swimming pool might become i) too high, ii) too low.
b) Could exhaust fumes from a nearby highway (mainly oxides of carbon, nitrogen, and sulphur) affect the water in the pool? In what way?

17. The pH of a cosmetic is in the 4.5 to 5.5 range. The label states that the product is "pH-balanced" to be compatible with the pH of human skin.

a) Is skin slightly basic, very basic, slightly acidic, or very acidic?
b) Is the cosmetic claim valid?
c) Why would skin need balance?

C: Problem Solving

18. In photography, a print is developed by placing it in a basic developer solution. The print is then placed into a solution containing acetic acid called a "stop bath".

a) What type of chemical reaction occurs in the stop bath solution?
b) Some stop bath solutions turn blue when they are exhausted. This warns you to prepare a fresh solution. How is this colour change accomplished?

19. A student added portions of a sodium hydroxide solution to 20 mL of hydrochloric acid in a styrofoam cup. The temperature of the solution was measured after each portion was added.

a) Draw a temperature-volume graph.
b) Why does the temperature first increase, then decrease?

20. A typical hair spray has the formula:
resin, 3.0%
plasticizer, 0.2%
ethyl alcohol, 26.0%
propellant, 70.8%
perfume, negligible percentage
Assume the resin costs are:
resin, $2.00/kg
plasticizer, $2.50/kg
ethyl alcohol, $3.30/kg
propellant, $1.00/kg
Calculate the cost of the ingredients in a 500-g can of hair spray.

Try This

Who's Got Special Breath?
Half fill a 500 mL Erlenmeyer flask with ethyl alcohol. Add 5 drops of bromthymol blue indicator to the alcohol. Add a drop of dilute sodium hydroxide solution to just turn the alcohol blue. Stopper the flask. Have some of your friends remove the stopper, breathe once into the flask, restopper the flask, and then swirl the liquid in the flask. Tell your friends that special breath is needed to change the blue colour. Why does this happen with some friends but not others? What's in some people's breath?

Chapter 14
Chemistry in the Home

Chemistry is important in the manufacture of a wide range of household consumer products, including detergents, cosmetics, medicines, and synthetic fibres. Household products also include disinfectants, cleansers, deodorizers, floor waxes, furniture polish, and many other items. Soaps and synthetic detergents are by far the most widely sold household chemicals.

The markets for all these products have been enlarged by massive advertising campaigns. Widespread use has caused some harmful side effects, however. For example, Freon from aerosol sprays damages the upper atmosphere, drain cleaners and polishes can harm humans, and detergents pollute water.

In this chapter we will look at consumer chemistry. We will also study soap and synthetic detergent, two of the most common household products, and examine the effect of hard water on each.

When you finish Chapter 14, you should be able to:

- discuss the connection between chemistry and consumer products
- prepare and describe the properties of a soap and a synthetic detergent
- describe the differences between soaps and synthetic detergents
- explain the causes of hard water and possible ways to soften it

14.1   Consumer Chemistry

Consumer chemistry is the application of chemistry to meet the needs of consumers. Wise consumers always try to get the best value for their money. To do this, they must be able to evaluate both consumer products and industry advertising. The emphasis in this unit is on the *product* and the chemistry necessary to understand it, rather than on the chemistry with the product as an illustration. This is the essence of consumer chemistry.

Market Research and Product Personality

Market research is a dialogue between the manufacturer and the consumer of a product. Much consumer-related information is gained through surveys conducted by market research firms. Market research provides the manufacturer of a product with feedback on consumer needs, attitudes, and behaviour. The consumer's

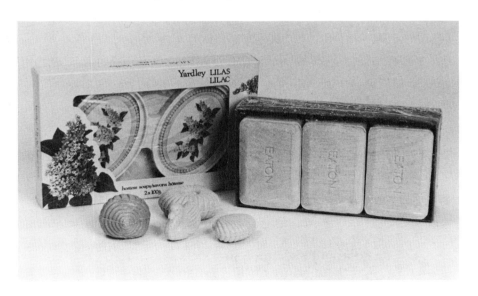

Different soap shapes and packaging.

Technicians at Consumers' Union, publisher of *Consumer Reports*, soil dishes prior to a test of dishwashers.

Canada's Ministry of Consumer and Corporate Affairs publishes a variety of ratings and guidelines on product safety. Information is available, for example, on infant cribs and car seats.

overall impression of a product is a combination of the product's properties, performance, brand name, packaging, price, and advertising. All toilet soaps do much the same thing. What determines whether you purchase one or the other? Manufacturers try to give each of their products a particular personality, which they communicate through advertising. This **personality** may be the strongest factor in attracting a person to buy a product. Market research determines consumer reaction to a product and its personality.

People are more likely to buy a product if they like its personality. We tend to buy products that we trust, feel comfortable with, and that enhance our own self-image. Product personality is a definite influence in the choice of many food and toiletry products, as well as *social products* such as cars, cosmetics, and alcohol. We tend to buy the brand that reinforces a desirable impression of ourselves.

There is an old saying, *caveat emptor*, or "let the buyer beware". Because many modern products are so complex, however, it is often difficult for the average consumer to make meaningful comparisons. Wise consumers buy the best product at the best price regardless of the image projected by an advertiser. Impartial and nonprofit organizations such as consumer advocacy groups test products to see how they compare, regardless of their personalities. Monthly consumer magazines such as *Canadian Consumer* and *Consumer Reports* try to tell us which is the best hair conditioner, furniture polish, coffee, bath soap, bicycle, or car for the price, depending on our individual preferences. A product that is both high in quality and relatively low in price is called a "best buy".

Study Questions

1. Which products of the chemical industry are the most widely advertised?

2. a) What is market research?
   b) Why is market research important?

3. a) How do we gain an overall impression of a product?
   b) What is meant by the "personality" of a product?
   c) What are "social products" and why are they so named?

4. Advertisements often compare brand-name products with competing products, which the advertisers refer to as "Brand X". Select one product that you see advertised in this way, and design a set of experimental procedures to test it against one of its competitors. Some products you might consider are lawn fertilizers, window cleaners, paper towels, popcorn, and detergents.

WORKING FOR THE CONSUMER

In 1947, a coalition of women's groups, angered at postwar inflation and questionable marketing practices, met in Ottawa to form an association to act as a watchdog on prices and consumer goods. The association expanded in 1961 to include men in its membership.

The organization, which eventually became the Consumers' Association of Canada, fought and won many battles. Results included: packaging that indicated the fat content of bacon; a ban on the use of DDT; the removal of federal tax on prescription drugs; new safety standards for school buses; the development of safety closures for drug containers; the establishment of standard clothing sizes; and the securing of better and safer labelling for household chemicals.

As modern technology produced a flood of new items from fabric softener to textiles, the CAC decided to extend its efforts in providing consumer information. By 1976, the CAC had begun purchasing and testing consumer products in independent laboratories. Test results are published monthly in *Canadian Consumer* which, with a circulation of 150 000, is the

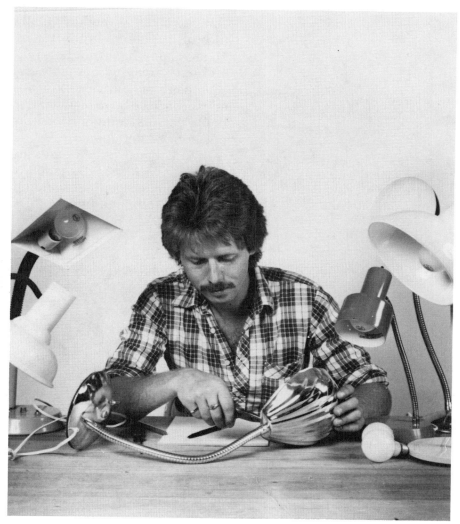

Study lamps are tested in a Consumers' Association of Canada lab.

most visible product of the CAC's efforts.

Today the CAC continues to take up consumers' rights, wherever and under whatever circumstances they seem to have been violated. Although consumers have become more aware, they still want an

independent and honest organization such as the CAC to speak for them and to check the multitude of consumer products that continue to appear in the marketplace.

14.2 Soaps and Detergents

Dirt has been defined as "matter in the wrong place". Mustard is nice on a hot dog, but if it lands on your T-shirt it's a dirty stain. Today, many household cleaning products remove dirt and stains without damaging our clothes. The time-tested recipe for making soap has changed very little since A.D. 100. However, significant advances have been made in the purity of soap, the use of additives to increase cleaning power, and the relatively recent development of synthetic detergents.

In broad terms, **detergents** are substances that remove dirt from a surface. Thus, many materials can be called detergents. Even water is a detergent, although it is not a particularly efficient one. Natural detergents included Fuller's Earth, soap berries, and the leaves and sap of the Soapwort plant. Modern detergents include soap and the synthetic detergents.

Large kettles were used to manufacture soap in mid-nineteenth century France.

Soaps

Until the 1900s, most soap was made at home. Fats from cooking and butchering were saved until there was enough to make a batch of soap. Ashes were collected and "leached" by pouring hot water through them to get a base. Then the fat and the base were boiled together to make soap, which, once cooled, was cut into rough bars.

While soap remains popular for personal hygiene, its use in laundering has decreased greatly. The problem with soap is that it combines with minerals dissolved in water to form a sticky, insoluble material called "soap curd". Soap curd clings as a scum to whatever it comes in contact with, and does not rinse away easily.

During the early twentieth century, scientists began searching for materials that would clean as well as soap but would not form soap curd. In 1933, the first synthetic household detergents were introduced in North America. Made from petroleum, these synthetic detergents are commonly known as **syndets** (for *synthetic detergents*). Early syndets did not have the cleaning power required for the family wash, however.

Detergent manufacturers worked for over ten years to boost the cleaning power of these detergents. The result was heavy-duty washing products that were as good as soaps at removing dirt and more soluble in water. They also prevented dirt from being redeposited into clothes, did not form soap curd, were mild to hands, and were safe for fine fabrics. However, soaps are still less expensive, and are made from renewable resources such as plant oils and animal fats, rather than from nonrenewable petroleum.

Activity 14-1: Making Soap

Soap is made by boiling fat or vegetable oil with a concentrated, aqueous solution of a base. In this activity you will use castor oil and the base sodium hydroxide to make soap the old-fashioned way. The word equation for the reaction is:

$$\text{fat } + \text{ base} \longrightarrow \text{soap } + \text{ glycerol}$$

(The soap produced here is called sodium ricinoleate.)

An advertisement for Pears' soap at the turn of the century.

In 1933, the first "light-duty" detergent, named Dreft, was introduced in North America. The first "heavy-duty" laundry detergent was introduced in 1946. It was named Tide.

Glycerol belongs to a class of compounds called alcohols. It is a sweet-tasting syrupy liquid used in cough medicines and candies to keep sugar crystals from forming. It is also used to make nitroglycerine, an explosive.

sodium hydroxide

Figure 14-1.

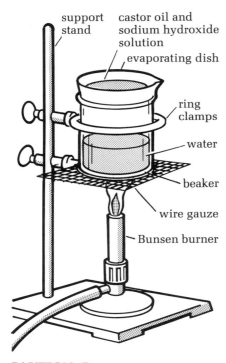

support stand
castor oil and sodium hydroxide solution
evaporating dish
ring clamps
water
beaker
wire gauze
Bunsen burner

Materials

castor oil	Bunsen burner
sodium hydroxide solution (20%)	boiling chips
sodium chloride	stirring rod
measuring spoon (5 mL)	tongs
graduated cylinder	funnel
evaporating dish (75 cm)	filter paper
250 mL beaker	clay triangle
support stand	test tube and solid stopper
2 ring clamps	paper towels
wire gauze	

Procedure

1. Pour 5 mL of castor oil into an evaporating dish.
2. Add 20 mL of sodium hydroxide solution and stir well.
3. Set up the apparatus as shown in Figure 14-1.
4. Heat for 10 min over a boiling water bath. Stir the mixture in the evaporating dish during the heating. Hold the dish with tongs in order not to tip the dish while stirring.
5. Add 5 mL of sodium chloride and stir well. Continue heating and stirring for another 3 min.
6. Turn off the Bunsen burner. Use tongs to carefully remove the evaporating dish from the steam bath. Allow to cool for a few minutes.
7. Filter the contents of the evaporating dish using a funnel and filter paper. Wash the soap by pouring 15 mL of cool tap water over the soap in the funnel.
8. Dry the soap by pressing it between paper towels.
9. Make a hypothesis to predict the result of adding a small piece of your soap to water in a test tube and then shaking the mixture. Test your hypothesis.
10. Dispose of your soap as directed by your teacher.

Discussion

1. Name two other sources of fat that could be used to make soap in place of castor oil.
2. What was the purpose of a) adding the salt? b) washing the soap with cold water?

3. What could you do to your soap to make it more attractive to a consumer?

4. Comment on the validity of the hypothesis you made in step 9.

The Industrial Manufacture of Soap

Soap makers today use as raw materials a variety of fats and oils, including mutton and cattle fat, olive oil, coconut oil, soya bean oil, palm kernel oil, cottonseed oil, and peanut oil. There are two industrial soap making methods. In the **kettle process,** soap is made in separate batches in a huge kettle. Fats and oils and a base are placed in the kettle, where steam is passed upwards into the mixture to heat and stir in one operation. When the reaction is complete, salt is added, causing the soap to separate and form a top layer. The soap is then mixed and blended with other ingredients such as dyes and perfumes to make the finished product. This is similar to the method used to make soap at home before commercial production began.

Figure 14-2. The kettle process of soap making.

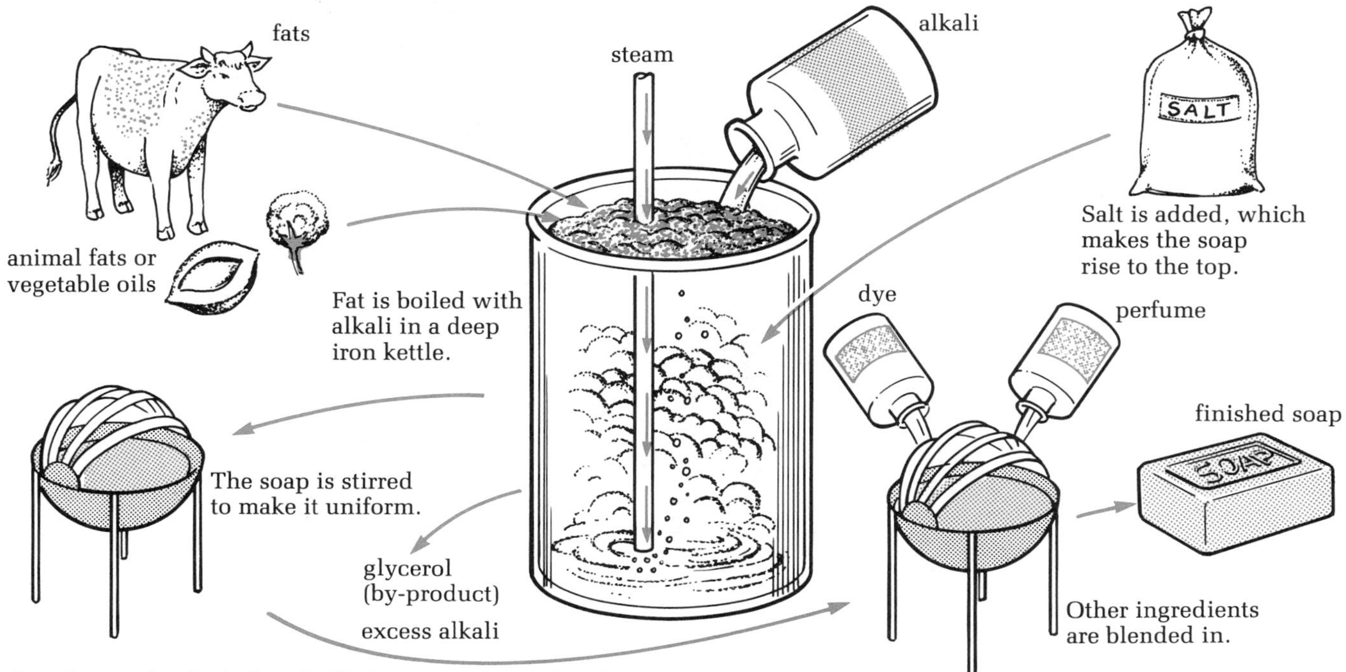

fats
steam
alkali
SALT

animal fats or vegetable oils

Salt is added, which makes the soap rise to the top.

Fat is boiled with alkali in a deep iron kettle.

dye
perfume

finished soap

The soap is stirred to make it uniform.

glycerol (by-product)

excess alkali

Other ingredients are blended in.

When fat or oil is boiled with alkali, soap is formed. Salt is then added to separate the soap from the excess alkali and the by-product, glycerol.

The **continuous process** is an improvement over basic soap making. Hot steam is forced into the top of a large column about 1 m in diameter by 25 m high. Hot fat enters near the bottom of the column, where it is broken down into fatty acids and glycerol through a chemical reaction. While the glycerol flows out of the bottom of the column, the fatty acids are mixed with bases to make soap. This is a complete continuous process. Raw materials are fed into one end of the system at the same time as the finished product emerges from the other. This process makes it easy for soap makers to blend different kinds of fats and oils, along with other ingredients, in order to make a wide range of soaps according to their special formulas.

Figure 14-3. The continuous process of soap making.

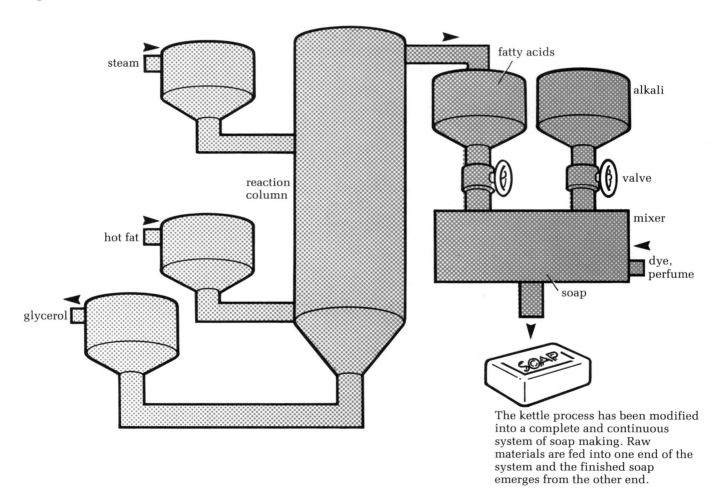

The kettle process has been modified into a complete and continuous system of soap making. Raw materials are fed into one end of the system and the finished soap emerges from the other end.

Special Soaps

Some soaps are made for special purposes. A **hand soap** may contain pumice as an abrasive to remove heavy dirt and grime from the skin. Pumice, a gritty powder of volcanic origin, helps rub dirt away but does not dissolve it. **Shaving soaps** must lather easily, and must not contain excess alkali that can irritate the skin. **Liquid soaps** are usually mixtures of potassium and sodium soaps dissolved in water containing small amounts of glycerol. Liquid soaps for personal use are often made from coconut oil. **Floating soaps** are made by whipping melted soap to fill it with tiny air bubbles. The trapped air decreases the soap's density so that it floats in water. **Mottled** or **streaked soaps** are made by mixing soaps to which different colouring substances have been added. **Transparent soaps** are made by dissolving solid soap in alcohol, which removes impurities. The alcohol is distilled, leaving behind a transparent jellylike mass. This is allowed to dry in moulds of desired shapes. **Medicated soaps** contain certain drugs and should only be used on the advice of a physician.

A variety of household soaps.

► How to Carefully Pour One Liquid Into Another

Figure 14-4.

1. Hold the stopper between two fingers.

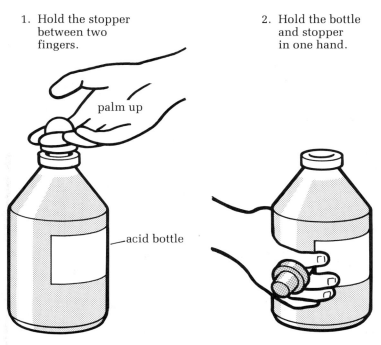

palm up

acid bottle

2. Hold the bottle and stopper in one hand.

3. Slowly and carefully pour the liquid along the stirring rod.

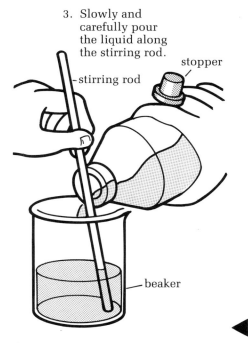

stirring rod

stopper

beaker

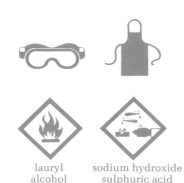

lauryl   sodium hydroxide
alcohol   sulphuric acid

CAUTION: Concentrated
sulphuric acid is very corrosive.
Be sure to wear safety goggles
and an apron.

Step 4.

Activity 14-2:   Making a Synthetic Detergent

By the mid 1950s, sales of detergents had surpassed those of soap
in Canada. Detergents have now largely replaced soap-based products for laundering and home care. In this activity you will make
the synthetic detergent, sodium lauryl sulphate.

Materials

lauryl alcohol (dodecanol)   250 mL beaker
4 mL concentrated sulphuric acid   stirring rod
sodium hydroxide solution (8%)   filter paper
25 mL graduated cylinder   test tube and solid stopper
150 mL beaker

Procedure

1. Your teacher will premix the lauryl alcohol and sulphuric acid
   for you before class. To do this your teacher will measure out
   13 mL of lauryl alcohol and pour it into a 150 mL beaker. Then
   carefully and *very slowly* your teacher will add 4 mL of sulphuric acid to the alcohol. (See "How to Carefully Pour One
   Liquid Into Another" on the previous page.)

2. From your teacher obtain 17 mL of the alcohol-acid mixture in a 150 mL beaker.

3. Pour 20 mL of the sodium hydroxide solution into the 250 mL beaker.

4. With constant stirring, carefully and slowly pour the acid-alcohol solution from step 2 into the sodium hydroxide solution. Observe the thick solid that forms.

5. Place the product on an open piece of filter paper on top of several thicknesses of paper towel to absorb excess moisture.

6. Make a hypothesis to predict the results of adding a small amount of your detergent to water in a test tube and shaking the mixture. Test your hypothesis.

7. Dispose of your detergent as directed by your teacher.

CAUTION: Do not use your detergent for washing. It still contains corrosive acid.

Discussion

1. What compound did you use in making both the soap and the synthetic detergent?

2. Compare your soap and synthetic detergent. List some similarities and some differences.

3. Why is a "lemon-fresh" scent or some other perfume usually added to detergents?

4. Comment on the validity of your hypothesis.

How Soaps and Detergents Work

Water is traditionally thought of as the best way to get things clean. It is cheap and readily available, and it dissolves more substances than any other known liquid. Unfortunately, water by itself does not usually work very well in cleaning things. Why?

If you were to examine closely a tiny speck of dirt, you would see that it is surrounded by a thin film of oil. Figure 14-5 shows a typical piece of dirt, no matter what its origin. To get rid of the dirt using water, we must find some way to get oil and water to mix — something they do not normally do. Detergents (soaps and syndets) provide an answer.

Detergent molecules consist of two distinct parts — a head and a long tail section. The head is water soluble or **hydrophilic** ("water-loving"), while the tail is oil-soluble or **hydrophobic** ("water-hating"). Thus, the same soap molecule can dissolve in both water

Figure 14-5. A typical dirt particle is surrounded by a thin film of oil.

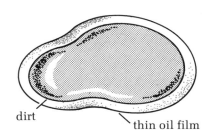

dirt
thin oil film

Figure 14-6. A typical detergent molecule.

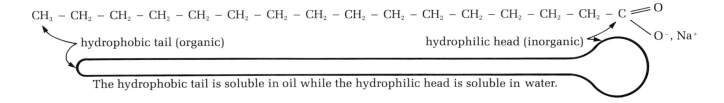

$$CH_3 - CH_2 - CH_2 - CH_2 - CH_2 - CH_2 - CH_2 - CH_2 - CH_2 - CH_2 - CH_2 - CH_2 - CH_2 - CH_2 - CH_2 - C \genfrac{}{}{0pt}{}{}{} O$$

hydrophobic tail (organic)   hydrophilic head (inorganic) O^-, Na^+

The hydrophobic tail is soluble in oil while the hydrophilic head is soluble in water.

and oil. Figure 14-6 shows the structure of a typical detergent molecule.

When a pair of dirty jeans is placed in water in a washing machine, the oil-covered dirt particles on the jeans will not mix with the water. (See Figure 14-7a).) When detergent is added to the washing machine, the dirt particles are surrounded by detergent molecules, as shown in Figures 14-7b) and 14-7c). The detergent molecules become attached to the film of oil by their hydrophobic tails. The opposite hydrophilic heads become attached to the water. Agitation by the washing machine helps to carry the dirt particles away from the fabric. These dirt particles, surrounded by detergent molecules, are small enough to remain suspended in the water. Therefore, they can be removed from the washing machine in the drain cycle along with the waste wash water. A rinse cycle removes any remaining dirt particles.

Figure 14-7. Removing dirt from fabric in a washing machine.

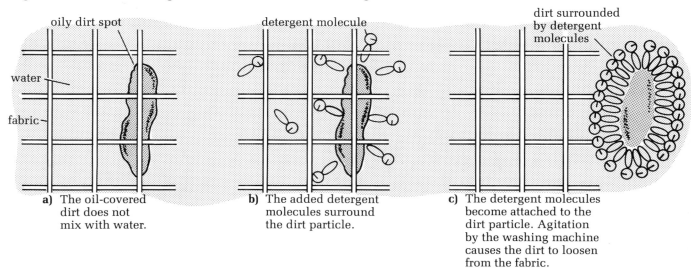

a) The oil-covered dirt does not mix with water.

b) The added detergent molecules surround the dirt particle.

c) The detergent molecules become attached to the dirt particle. Agitation by the washing machine causes the dirt to loosen from the fabric.

Problems with Syndets

As useful as synthetic detergents proved to be, they created two major problems. The first problem was excessive foaming in rivers, lakes, and sewage treatment plants. Also, unlike soaps, the early syndets were not **biodegradable**. That is, they could not be broken down by bacteria or other microorganisms in the environment. The tail end of the syndet molecule was modified to solve this problem.

The second problem had to do with the phosphates added to syndets to boost their cleaning power. Phosphate, a fertilizer, greatly increased the nutrient quality of water. This caused overgrowth of aquatic plant life, which robbed the water of oxygen, thereby killing fish. This problem was solved by reducing or eliminating the phosphate and replacing it with a nonnutrient substance.

Effective January 1973, a revision of the Canada Water Act reduced the acceptable phosphate level in detergents from 20% to 5%, so that all detergents had to be redesigned.

These dead fish suffocated due to a lack of oxygen in the polluted Kaministik River in Thunder Bay, Ontario.

Study Questions

1. a) Define "detergent".
   b) Why can both soaps and synthetic detergents be classified as detergents?

2. Compare the advantages and disadvantages of soaps and synthetic detergents.

3. a) Describe the typical structure of a detergent molecule.
   b) How do detergents remove dirt from clothes?

4. If you spill maple syrup on your clothes or hands, you can easily wash it away with water alone. However, if you spill cooking oil or get butter on your clothes or hands, it does not wash away easily unless you use soap. Briefly explain the difference.

THE HISTORY OF SOAP MAKING

The home manufacture of soap was common throughout Europe by the ninth century. Soap was not "wasted" on personal cleanliness but was used instead to remove grease and dirt from wool and other fibres. By the early eighteenth century, the textile industry's demands for cleansing alkalis and soaps were far exceeding the supply.

It seems that industrial and commercial demands have always had a way of inspiring inventors. In 1775, the French Academy of Sciences offered a prize of 12 000 francs to anyone who developed a practical method of manufacturing sodium carbonate (a compound necessary for soap making) from salt (sodium chloride).

Nicolas Leblanc (1742-1806) developed such a process, and set up a factory to make sodium carbonate—commonly called soda ash—from which sodium hydroxide could easily be made for soap manufacture. Unfortunately, the French Revolution was in full swing at the time. Instead of receiving the prize, Leblanc had his factory confiscated, and he was forced to publicize his secret method.

This was the first chemical discovery that had an immediate commercial application, and the chemical industry as we know it today was born. The Leblanc process dominated the soap industry in Europe for 75 years until it was replaced by a simpler method in 1861.

At the same time, another French chemist, Michel Chevreul (1786-1889), was studying the chemical nature of fats. He discovered the most common constituents of fats and oils. As a result of the work of Leblanc and Chevreul, the large-scale manufacture of soap became possible. This ultimately had important effects on personal health and hygiene throughout the world.

Nicholas Leblanc (1742-1806)

Chevreul in his laboratory.

14.3 Water Hardness

If you bathe in tap water using solid soap, you may notice that it is difficult to form a lather, and that a greyish-white scum appears. The amount of scum and the difficulty in forming the lather depend on your community's water supply. Water that does not easily form a lather with soap is called **hard water**. Water hardness is caused by dissolved minerals. Hard tap water is pure in the sense that it is safe to drink, but it is chemically impure in that it contains substances other than water. Water containing few or no dissolved minerals is called **soft water**.

"Next time, I'll use hard water!"

Activity 14-3:   What Causes Water Hardness?

In hard water any lather that does form breaks down quickly and a scum appears. In this activity you will try to discover which of a variety of substances can make water hard.

Materials

test solutions (1%):
   sodium chloride
   calcium chloride
   magnesium chloride
   potassium nitrate
   magnesium nitrate
   calcium nitrate
   sodium sulphate
   magnesium sulphate

soap solution
10 mL graduated cylinder
medicine dropper
8 test tubes
test tube rack
solid rubber stopper

Procedure

1. Draw a table in which to record results in your lab report. Record your observations as you do the experiments.

Test Solution	Appearance of Lather		
	Scum formation	Amount formed (mm)	Stability

Figure 14-8a).

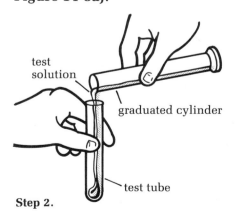

test solution

graduated cylinder

test tube

Step 2.

2. Measure 5 mL of sodium chloride solution, and pour it into a test tube.

Figure 14-8b).

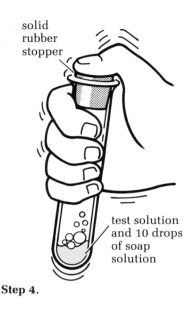

solid rubber stopper

test solution and 10 drops of soap solution

Step 4.

3. Add 10 drops of soap solution. Look for evidence of scum formation.

4. Stopper the test tube and shake it vigorously for 15 s.

5. Observe how well the soap forms a lather. Measure and record the height of the lather that forms. Stand the test tube and contents in a test tube rack and save for step 7.

6. Repeat steps 2 to 5 with each of the other test solutions. Complete the table.

7. Now examine the lather in each tube. Is it unstable or stable (that is, does it break down quickly or last a long time)?

Discussion

1. Name a) the metal chlorides, b) the metal nitrates, and c) the metal sulphates, that made the water hard.

2. Does the hardness depend upon the metal ion or the nonmetal ion? How do you know?

3. Which two ions cause water hardness in this activity?

4. How could you change this experiment to compare the hardness of different samples of water?

5. List the important variables in this activity. How did you control each?

Figure 14-9.

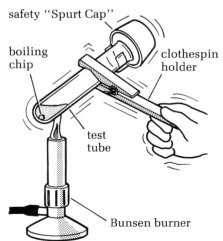

safety "Spurt Cap"

boiling chip

clothespin holder

test tube

Bunsen burner

▶ How To Safely Heat a Liquid in a Test Tube

1. Wear safety goggles and an apron. Remain standing with lab stools cleared out of the way.

2. Add a boiling chip to the liquid to be heated.

3. Place a safety "Spurt Cap" on top of the test tube containing the liquid to be heated. If liquid should spurt out, it will hit the cap and flow downwards.

4. Use a test tube holder or a clamp to hold the test tube at arm's length, at about a 45° angle. Long wooden clothespin holders are much safer than wire holders.

5. Heat near the top of the liquid. Keep moving the test tube back and forth over the flame. Do not heat the bottom of the test tube! ◀

Heating liquid in a test tube with a Spurt Cap.

Activity 14-4: Softening Hard Water

Water hardness can be classified as temporary or permanent. An indicator of water hardness is the amount of soap solution needed to make a stable lather. In this activity you will examine ways to soften both types of hard water.

Materials

25 mL graduated cylinder

limewater

distilled water

100 mL beaker

straw

test solutions:
  calcium chloride solution (5%)
  calcium hydrogen carbonate
    solution (as prepared in step 2)
  distilled water
  tap water

12 test tubes (19 mm × 150 mm)

test tube rack

soap solution

medicine dropper

solid rubber stopper

boiling chips

Bunsen burner

safety "Spurt Cap"

test tube holder

sodium carbonate solution
  (20%)

stirring rod

Procedure

1. Draw the following observation table in your report.

Treatment Used	Calcium Chloride		Calcium Hydrogen Carbonate		Distilled Water		Tap Water	
	No. of drops	scum (yes/no)	No. of drops	scum (yes/no)	No. of drops	scum (yes/no)	No. of drops	scum (yes/no)
untreated								
boiled								
sodium carbonate added								

2. Add 10 mL of limewater to 20 mL of distilled water in a small beaker. Using a straw, blow through this solution until it becomes cloudy. Continue blowing through the solution until it becomes clear again. The resulting solution contains calcium hydrogen carbonate.

3. Place 10 mL of each test solution in a separate test tube. Carry out the Soap Test procedure (see below) on each of the four untreated test solutions.

4. *Your teacher may wish to demonstrate this part.* Place 10 mL of each test solution in a separate test tube. Add a boiling chip to each test tube. Boil each solution for about 20 s. See "How To Safely Heat a Liquid in a Test Tube" on page 414. Continue with step 5 while you allow the contents of the four test tubes to cool in a test tube rack. Carry out the Soap Test procedure on each of the four boiled solutions when they have cooled.

5. Place 10 mL of each test solution in a separate test tube. Add 5 mL of sodium carbonate solution to each test tube. Stir each solution, taking care to wipe off the stirring rod between solutions. Carry out the Soap Test procedure on each of the four chemically treated solutions.

Soap Test

a) Add 3 drops of soap solution using a medicine dropper. Examine the solution for the presence of any solid (scum). Record your results. Stopper the test tube and shake vigourously for 15 s.

b) Continue to add 3 drops of soap solution, followed by shaking each time, until you produce at least 1.5 to 2 cm of lather. Record the number of drops of soap required. Wash and rinse out the test tubes with distilled water.

Discussion

1. a) Which untreated solution produced lather most readily?
   b) In which untreated test tubes did solid scums form?
2. What effect do calcium chloride and calcium hydrogen carbonate have on the formation of a lather?
3. Why is hardness caused by calcium hydrogen carbonate called "temporary", and that caused by calcium chloride called "permanent"?
4. What effect did sodium carbonate have on the hardness of the solutions?
5. Was the behaviour of tap water similar to the behaviour of solutions of calcium chloride and calcium hydrogen carbonate? Explain.
6. Of the methods investigated in this activity, which is likely the least expensive method for softening hard water?

Figure 14-10.

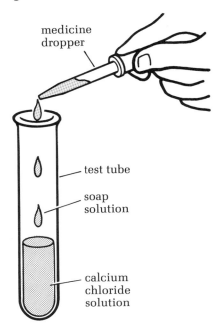

medicine dropper

test tube

soap solution

calcium chloride solution

Permanent and Temporary Water Hardness

The substances present in natural water vary from place to place. Water content depends on the type of rocks and soil through which the water flows on its way to reservoirs. One important type of rock is *gypsum* (calcium sulphate), which is slightly soluble in water. Water that flows through gypsum rock will dissolve a little calcium sulphate and become hard.

Another rock that contributes to hardness is *limestone* or chalk (calcium carbonate). If tap water is collected in a limestone area it will likely be hard. But limestone, which is mainly calcium carbonate, does not dissolve in pure water. So how can calcium ions from the limestone get into the water to make it hard?

Whether tap water is collected in a reservoir or pumped from a deep well, it all comes from the same source — rain. As rain falls, it dissolves some of the carbon dioxide in the air to form carbonic acid.

water + carbon dioxide $\longrightarrow$ carbonic acid

When this acidic water falls on or runs through limestone, it dissolves the calcium carbonate. A solution of calcium hydrogen carbonate forms.

calcium carbonate + carbonic acid $\longrightarrow$ calcium hydrogen carbonate

This solution contains calcium ions. If it forms part of the water supply for a particular community, the water will be hard.

Water hardness due to calcium hydrogen carbonate can be removed by boiling the water. With heat, the calcium hydrogen carbonate decomposes, liberating carbon dioxide and water to form solid calcium carbonate. Hardness removed simply by boiling the water is called **temporary hardness**.

Hard water is obvious when boiled in a kettle. The calcium hydrogen carbonate decomposes to form the rocklike calcium carbonate that sticks to the inside of the kettle.

Boiling will have no effect on anything other than hydrogen carbonates. For example, water containing calcium, magnesium, or iron in salts such as sulphates will not be softened by boiling. Hardness that cannot be removed by boiling the water is called **permanent hardness**.

Tap water often contains both types of hardness, so that boiling will soften it partially, but not completely. Adding washing soda (sodium carbonate) will, however, remove all hardness.

Advantages and Disadvantages of Hard Water

The human body, which contains 1000 g to 1500 g of calcium in bones and teeth, requires regular calcium intake to replace what is lost by daily use. Studies have shown a lower incidence of heart disease in hard water areas of Canada. Some industries benefit from being located in hard water areas. Breweries, for example, often use hard water to improve the quality and taste of beer.

Other industries, however, find hard water a disadvantage. In paper and textile manufacturing, the minerals in hard water interfere with the production of glossy paper and yarn, and with the dyeing of cloth in uniform shades of colour. Hard water solids that form inside the boiler and hot water pipes of a heating system reduce both the water flow and the transfer of heat. Industries that require large amounts of hot water must first soften the water in some way.

Do You Know?

In large dishwashing machines, laundries, and heating plants, special water-softening equipment is used continuously. Water softeners are also installed in homes located in areas where the water is especially hard. In such devices, the hard water passes over chemicals such as zeolite, which removes the minerals causing hardness. Every so often the flow of water is stopped and salt water is released through the zeolite instead. This salt water and a backwash eliminate the minerals so that the zeolite can soften more hard water.

AMAZING UNDERGROUND CAVE FORMATIONS

Incredibly beautiful and varied formations may occur in underground cave systems. They are created by a process of precipitation and dissolving that takes place over many centuries. Tightly packed limestone of varying composition is most suitable for such formations. A composition of soluble and relatively less soluble substances results in the development of caverns strong enough to resist collapse.

Most limestone formations are jointed and cracked. This allows rain water to flow downward from the surface until it becomes saturated with calcium carbonate. As the limestone dissolves, large channels and vast underground chambers form. When water drops from a cave ceiling, solid calcium carbonate may be deposited on the ceiling and the floor below as the water evaporates. The cylindrical "icicle" that forms on the ceiling as water falls drop by drop is called a *stalactite*. If the water flows too quickly to evaporate entirely on the ceiling, it falls to the floor. The small domes of stone that begin to rise from the floor are called *stalagmites*. In time, stalactites and stalagmites may meet to form a single column. The tiny calcite crystals in these rock formations sparkle in colours that greatly enhance the cave's natural beauty.

The tri-level Carlsbad Caverns in New Mexico in the United States possess the largest natural cave room in the world. The Big Room is 1220 m long, 190 m wide, and 107 m high. The longest cavern in the world is probably Mammoth Cave in Kentucky, which contains more than 300 km of interconnected passages. Castleguard Cave in Banff National Park is Canada's longest known cave. It extends 18 km and passes far beneath the Columbia icefields. The exploration of such caves as a hobby is called spelunking, or simply "caving".

Paul Griffiths, president of the Canadian Speleological Society, makes a mid-air inspection of a cave near Nimpkish Camp, B.C.

Study Questions

1. Explain the difference between hard and soft water.
2. a) What is temporary hardness?
   b) How can it be removed?
3. a) What is permanent hardness?
   b) How can it be removed?
4. a) What are the disadvantages of hard water?
   b) What are the advantages of hard water?
5. One sample of water contains dissolved calcium hydrogen carbonate. A second sample contains calcium sulphate.
   a) What procedure could you use to soften the first solution but not the second?
   b) How could you soften both solutions?
   c) What undesirable effect does water softening by soap cause?
   d) Why are synthetic detergents better for laundering in hard water?
6. A certain mineral compound is composed of calcium carbonate (limestone), sodium carbonate (soda ash), and water. Describe how you could separate each of these substances from the rock. The following table gives some properties of the two carbonates.

Property	Calcium carbonate	Sodium carbonate
melting point	decomposes at 825°C	851°C
solubility:		
in alcohol	insoluble	insoluble
in acid	soluble	soluble
in water (0°C)	insoluble	slightly soluble
(100°C)	insoluble	soluble

14.4 Household Chemical Products

There are many household products on the market that either promote cleaning and disinfecting, or that enhance the desirable properties of other goods. In each case a variety of materials is combined to accomplish a particular type of job.

Drain Cleaners

Drain cleaners contain a mixture of sodium hydroxide and aluminum filings. This mixture reacts with water to produce heat that melts fat and grease. It then reacts with the fat to change it to a soap. This strong solution can also decompose hair caught in the drain. Drain cleaners are very corrosive to skin. They should never be mixed with other cleaners.

Household Bleach

Sodium hypochlorite solutions serve as disinfectants, bleaches, and deodorizers. Through a chemical reaction, the bleach produces substances that attack coloured dyes and destroy microorganisms.

Typical household cleaners.

Stain Removers

Most stain removal procedures are based on solubility or chemical reactions. Rust stains, for example, can be removed by using oxalic acid and water. The oxalic acid reacts with rust to produce a soluble substance which can then be rinsed away.

Scouring Powders

About 80% of a scouring powder is an abrasive powder, usually fine sand, calcite, or limestone. The rest is washing soda with a bit of bleach as a disinfectant. The washing soda reacts with water to produce a basic solution. This basic solution has the cleaning properties of a detergent cleanser.

Ammonia Cleansers

Household ammonia reacts with fats and greases and breaks them down partly to form soaps. A basic solution, household ammonia has the properties of a detergent cleanser also.

Toilet Bowl Cleaners

These cleaners contain a strong acid solution that dissolves encrusted calcium carbonate that can build up from the surface evaporation of hard water. They usually contain a disinfectant and a fragrance chemical, too.

Chemical Oven Cleaners

Modern aerosol oven cleaners use sodium hydroxide as a cleaning agent, along with thickeners and a gaseous propellant. The sodium hydroxide reacts with burnt-on grease to form a soap that is easily wiped from the oven's surface.

Fabric Softeners

Fabric softeners reduce static electricity and its clinging effect by adding a film that attracts moisture. Most of today's softeners contain electrically charged ions that have a positive end to attach to the fibre. A long (hydrocarbon) tail provides softness, water repellancy, antistatic ability, and lubrication, so that the fibres resist abrasion.

Soil Repellants

The best-known treatment for repelling water- and air-borne soil from fabrics is Scotchgard. There are many compounds called Scotchgard, most containing from 4 to 18 carbon atoms surrounded by fluorine atoms. Such compounds bond strongly to most fabrics and do not deteriorate with repeated washings.

Activity 14-5: Preparing Some Household Products at Home

In this activity intended for home use you will find directions for making a few common household products. They are easy to make, work well, and cost much less than commercial products.

A. Window Cleaner

You will be surprised at how well this inexpensive window cleaner works and how little it costs to make. Store-bought brands cost ten times as much.

Materials

alcohol

ammonia

"sudsy" ammonia

rubbing alcohol (isopropyl alcohol)

liquid dishwashing detergent

4 L plastic jug

spray bottle

Procedure

1. Mix together 125 mL of sudsy ammonia, 450 mL of rubbing alcohol, and 10 mL of dishwashing detergent in a clean 4 L plastic jug.
2. Fill the jug with water and shake gently to mix. Pour into a spray bottle.
3. To use, spray lightly on glass and wipe clean with paper towels. (On large surfaces, work from the bottom up.)

B. Lemon Oil Furniture Polish

This has a pleasant citrus fragrance, and is similar to commercial lemon oil polishes. It is easy and economical to make.

Materials

lemon oil	plastic jug	spray bottle
mineral oil	stirring device	

Procedure

1. Add 20 mL of lemon oil to 1 L of mineral oil in a plastic jug. Stir to mix.
2. Pour into a spray bottle.
3. Spray lightly on furniture and wipe off with a clean dry cloth.

C. Fabric Softening Sheets

These are easy to prepare, cost a fraction of the ready-made sheets, and reduce static cling in your laundry. The cost saving is even greater if the homemade sheets are used again and again.

Materials

liquid fabric softener   J-cloth

Procedure

1. Pour about 10 mL of liquid fabric softener onto half a J-cloth and squeeze it in.
2. Place the J-cloth in a dryer with a load of clothes to dry.
   Note: Some dryer warranties may be invalidated by the use of homemade softeners.

D. Metal Cleaner

This is a simple, all-purpose metal cleaner and polish. The ingredients are available in hardware and grocery stores.

Materials

washing soda	baking soda	covered container
trisodium phosphate (TSP)	plastic jug	

trisodium
phosphate

Procedure

1. Mix together 400 mL of washing soda, 100 mL of TSP, and 150 mL of baking soda in a plastic jug.
2. Rub the mixture on tarnished metal with a damp cloth, then rinse clean with water.
3. Store in a covered container.

Study Questions

1. List and describe five cleaning products for the home.

2. a) Why would people make their own household products?
   b) Why do so few bother?

3. a) Where can you find information that compares one product brand to another?
   b) How do such comparisons help consumers?

4. A consumer comparison report of powdered all-fabric bleaches revealed the following information.

Product	Cost per use (cents)	Whitening Ability	Stain Removal		
			Wine	Oil	Blood
A	20	◔	◕	◕	◕
B	10	◔	◒	◕	◒
C	11	◔	◕	○	○
D	23	◔	○	●	◕
E	16	●	◒	●	○
F	6	◔	◒	◒	◕

Rating Code:

Better ⟵⟶ Worse

● ◕ ○ ◒ ●

For each of the following tasks, choose the best product and give reasons for your choice.
a) low-cost oil stain removal and whitening in a garage
b) low-cost blood stain removal in a butcher shop
c) general all-purpose home use

Meet a Market Researcher— Joan Chapman

Joan has been in the field of market research since graduating from university with a degree in psychology. After taking a few years off to raise her family, she now works for Commins Wingrove, a market research company.

Q. WHAT IS MARKET RESEARCH?
A. It is the systematic collection, organization, and interpretation of information relating to problems and opportunities in the marketing of products or services. Market researchers act as middlemen between the consumer and the company making the product or providing the service. We get information that will assist people in making decisions.

Q. WHAT DO YOU FIND THE MOST INTERESTING PART OF YOUR WORK?
A. The introduction of new products. Every year companies are under pressure to look at new products. Many companies have product development managers who spend all their time looking at new ideas, not just in products but in packaging.

Q. WHEN DO YOU BECOME INVOLVED IN A PROJECT?
A. A company comes to us with ideas for a new product and asks us to find out if consumers will be interested in it or if it can be profitable. Even before developing a new product concept we do what is called qualitative research.

Q. WHAT IS QUALITATIVE RESEARCH?
A. In market research we do both qualitative and quantitative research, and the differences are similar to the use of these terms in chemistry. Qualitative research is exploratory and designed to determine what elements exist, just as in chemistry. For instance, if we were studying a new fruit juice product, we would find out things like how people drink juice, when they drink it, how much they drink, and so on.

Q. WHAT HAPPENS AFTER YOU GATHER THIS INFORMATION?
A. Sometimes, the idea is scrapped if there doesn't seem to be a future for it. But if it still seems like a good idea we go on to do some quantitative research.

Q. WHAT IS QUANTITATIVE RESEARCH?
A. Again, just as in chemistry, we measure how much of each element exists. In quantitative research the results consist of answers supplied by a relatively large number of individuals. In the juice example we would try to determine what percentage of the population really wants a new fruit juice. There are many different methods to obtain the information, such as by telephone interviews, personal interviews (often conducted in shopping malls), and mailed questionnaires. Deciding which is the most effective research tool to get the information required is also part of a market researcher's job.

Q. WHAT QUALITIES MAKE A GOOD MARKET RESEARCHER?
A. You have to be creative because there's a new problem to solve every day. Often, the solutions involve common sense. A background in science and math is good because the methodological procedures used require that kind of discipline. Flexibility is important because this is a high-pressured job—time is always an issue. I sometimes have 50 jobs on the go, so it's also important to be organized. Good communication skills are needed because you often have to make presentations to groups of people and write lengthy reports.

Q. DO YOU THINK THERE WILL CONTINUE TO BE A LOT OF JOBS IN THIS FIELD?
A. Yes. It's an expanding field, and a good one for anyone willing to work hard.

Review Questions

A: Knowledge

1. a) What is a detergent?
    b) Name three natural detergents.
    c) Name the two types of modern detergents.

2. a) What two basic raw materials are needed to make soap?
    b) Write a word equation for the preparation of soap.
    c) Name the common fats and oils used to make soap.
    d) Why is steam passed through the mixture in the kettle process?
    e) Why is salt added to the soap?

3. a) Describe the kettle process of soap-making.
    b) Describe the continuous method of soap-making.

4. Explain how detergents clean a dirty surface.

5. What evidence led to a reduction of phosphates in detergents?

6. a) Name compounds that can cause i) temporary hardness and ii) permanent hardness in water.
    b) Describe what you would see if a soap solution were added to both temporary and permanent hard water. Contrast this with the action of a soapless detergent on a sample of hard water.
    c) Describe how two types of water hardness arise in nature.
    d) Why is it necessary in hard water areas to check domestic hot water pipes and old central-heating water pipes on a regular basis?

7. Temporary hard water is usually thought to contain calcium hydrogen carbonate, and permanent hard water is usually thought to contain calcium sulphate.

    a) Assuming that newly-formed raindrops are totally pure water, explain the natural processes by which these two kinds of hard water are formed.
    b) Describe experiments to show why these kinds of hard water are called "temporary" and "permanent".
    c) Describe one method that can be used to soften both temporary and permanent hard water.

8. In your notes correct each of the following sentences by replacing the italicized error with another word.

    a) All substances that remove dirt from a surface are called *soaps*.
    b) Soap combines with water hardness to form a sticky *soluble* material called soap curd.
    c) Fats and *acids* are boiled together to make soap.
    d) The main function of detergents is to reduce surface *washing* and to allow the water to wet thoroughly.
    e) The *hydrophilic* or "water-hating" tail of a detergent molecule is soluble in oil.
    f) Water that does not form a lather with soap is called *soft* water.
    g) *Permanent* hardness can be removed by boiling.

B: Application

9. Describe some advertisements on television or in magazines that you think are misleading or make dubious claims. Suggest how a chemist might determine the validity of the claims made for the products advertised.

10. How has the manufacture of soap changed over the years?

11. Explain:

    a) why distilled water is used in ships' boilers.
    b) why bath salts are made of sodium carbonate.
    c) why stalactites and stalagmites are often found in caves in limestone districts.

12. Describe the process by which limestone caverns, stalactites, and stalagmites are formed. How is the formation of stalactites and

stalagmites related to the formation of boiler scale from temporary hard water?

13. Suppose a home hot-water tank is heated with an electric immersion rod. Is a scale of calcium carbonate more likely to form in the water entry pipe, on the rod, on the walls of the tank, or in the water exit pipe? Explain.

14. A sample of water was found to exhibit both temporary and permanent hardness. After boiling, or adding a small quantity of calcium hydroxide to it, the water was found to be less hard than at first. After adding sodium carbonate in excess of that in the original water, the water was found to be softened completely.

a) Explain why the water was not as hard after i) boiling, ii) adding a small quantity of calcium hydroxide.

b) When calcium hydroxide was added, the products were a white solid (commonly called chalk) and a clear colourless liquid (with a density of 1000 kg/m³ that boils at 100°C and freezes at 0°C). Write a word equation for the reaction.

c) Calcium hydroxide is a slightly soluble calcium compound. Why was it important to add only a small amount of it to the water?

d) Explain why all hardness was removed when excess sodium carbonate was added to the water.

e) The use of sodium carbonate leaves sodium compounds in the water. Why is this of no concern in washing laundry?

f) With the aid of a diagram, explain how you could obtain chemically pure water from some of the original samples.

C: Problem Solving

15. An automobile wax company decided to compare their wax to other brands. They divided the roof of a car into four areas. They used their wax on area A. On areas B and C, they used competitors' waxes. Area D was left untouched.

a) What is the variable in this experiment?

b) Which area is the control?

c) How might the company continue this experiment to find out which wax is the most durable and the most protective?

16. In order to determine the relative hardness of a tap water sample, a soap solution was prepared. It was found that to produce a permanent lather lasting for 2 min, 25 mL of distilled water required 0.6 mL of the soap solution, 25 mL of the tap water required 10.6 mL of the soap solution, and 25 mL of the tap water after boiling required 6.6 mL. Calculate the percentage of the total hardness that is only temporary.

Try This

1. **The Magic Touch**
   Sprinkle powdered sulphur or pepper on the surface of water in a large beaker. Dip your finger into liquid detergent and allow it to dry. Now ask your friends to touch the surface of the water. When you touch the surface with your magic finger, something quite different happens. Can you explain why? Can your friends figure out what happened?

2. **Mysterious Soap Bubbles**
   Place a 600 mL beaker in the bottom of a plastic bucket. Add 100 g of baking soda to the beaker, and then pour 200 mL of dilute 10% hydrochloric acid into the baking soda. This will generate and fill the bucket with carbon dioxide. Use commercial bubble solution and its wand to make a bubble. Lower the bubble into the carbon dioxide. What happens unexpectedly? Why does the colour pattern in the soap film change? Try to explain your observations. (*Hint*: Compare the solubilities of carbon dioxide and air in water.)

A petrochemical plant in Sarnia, Ontario.

Chapter 15
Chemistry in Industry

Look at photographs in an album or the picture on a television screen. Listen to your radio or the compact discs on your stereo. Feel the smooth surface of a polished table or the rough texture of a carpet. Test a new fragrance at the perfume counter. Eat a chocolate bar or a bag of potato chips. What are you doing in each case? Enjoying the products of applied chemistry. Somewhere along the line, chemistry played a role in making each one possible.

In this chapter we will look at the importance of crude oil as the initial raw material for the chemical industry. Nearly all the chemicals from crude oil are used to make consumer products. Nylon, textile fibres, and dyes are a few byproducts of the petrochemical industry that we will examine.

When you finish Chapter 15, you should be able to:

- discuss how applied chemistry affects our lives
- explain the importance of crude oil to the chemical industry
- describe the fractional distillation of crude oil
- make a synthetic polymer (nylon)
- compare natural and synthetic dyes, and various dyeing processes

15.1   Petroleum

The modern chemical industry depends heavily on raw materials made from coal and petroleum. These so-called fossil fuels were formed millions of years ago from plant and animal materials that decayed and were covered by many layers of sediment. High temperature, pressure, and time slowly changed them into the fuels we know today. Coal is a solid. Petroleum may consist either of small, gaseous molecules known as natural gas, or of a mixture of large molecules known as crude oil.

Huge offshore drilling rigs are used in oil exploration off the Canadian coast.

Keeping the Petrochemical Industry Well Oiled

Crude oils don't always look alike. Some are almost colourless, while some are pitch black. Others can be amber, brown, or green. They may flow like water or creep like molasses. Some crude oils contain over one per cent sulphur and other mineral impurities. These are called sour crudes. Sweet crudes have a sulphur and mineral content below one per cent.

Petroleum pumped from the earth as crude oil may be a black, smelly, sticky liquid. What can we do with one cubic metre of it? You are probably thinking we could make motor oil and gasoline from it. You're right. But that cubic metre of oil could be used for much more. We could make 122 polyester shirts, 34 garbage cans, 122 sweaters, 965 lingerie items, 5 tires, 21 tire tubes — and still have enough fuel left over to last a household two and a half months.

Most crude oil is refined into fuel and then burned. Only 5% is used in the manufacture of consumer products. Plastics, aspirin, shampoo, soaps and detergents, dyes, furniture polish, paint, glue, ink, replacement parts for the human body, and more than half the fibres for everything from carpets to coats all come from crude oil. So does the fertilizer that increases the world's food crop yield.

Chemicals derived from petroleum to make such consumer products are called **petrochemicals**. How important are petrochemicals? Just think how different our lives would be without the products that come from crude oil.

After chemical industries and others have processed it, a cubic metre of oil, worth $150, can zoom to over $60 000 worth of finished products.

Each worker in the petrochemical industry provides jobs for three more people in related industries, such as the synthetic rubber or fibre industries. These workers provide another 12 to 30 jobs when the materials are used to make consumer products. Thus the applied chemical industry not only increases the value of that cubic metre of oil, but also creates a lot of jobs.

The supply of fossil fuels is limited. Although petroleum is still being formed, the amount produced each year is probably very small compared to the amount we take out of the earth. For this reason, fossil fuels are called "nonrenewable resources".

Fractional Distillation

Water can be purified by removing the solids in it, or, in other words, distilling it. In distillation, the water boils, vaporizes, and then turns back to liquid water in a condenser. The dissolved solids in the water remain in the flask.

A similar process can be used to separate several liquids that have different boiling points, such as the hydrocarbon molecules in crude oil. **Hydrocarbons** are compounds containing only carbon and hydrogen. When a mixture of hydrocarbons is heated slowly, the compound with the lowest boiling point boils first and leaves the boiling mixture as a vapour. It condenses to a liquid in a cooler part of the distillation apparatus. The temperature of the boiling mixture is then raised, and the compound with the next highest boiling point is also distilled and collected in a separate container. This process is repeated until none of the original liquid is left. In this way the original mixture is separated into a number of **fractions**, or parts. Such a process is called **fractional distillation**.

Figure 15-1. A common distillation apparatus.

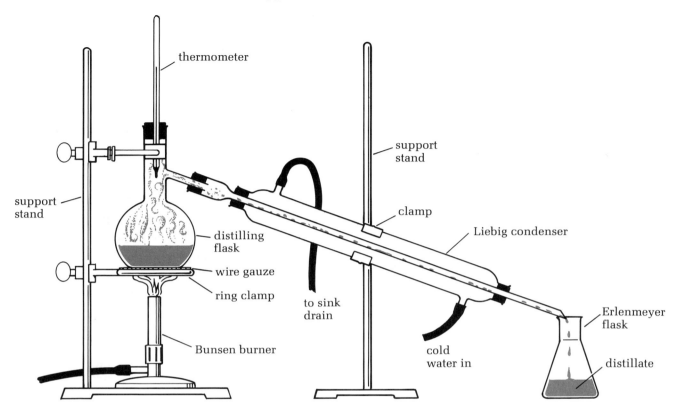

Fractional distillation is commonly used to separate liquid mixtures such as petroleum in which the boiling points of the components differ by less than 30 to 40°C. In this situation a fractionating column is used to provide a better separation of the components in the liquid mixture. A laboratory fractionating column is a vertical condenser packed with stainless steel wire gauze, glass beads, glass tubing pieces, or other suitable material. Each component in the liquid mixture, beginning with the one with the lowest boiling point, goes through a series of condensations and vaporizations on the packing material in the column. Each time this happens, the rising vapour in the column becomes more concentrated in the lower boiling component. By the time the vapour reaches the top of the column it is very rich in the lowest boiling component. As the vapour leaves the column it is condensed and collected as separate fractions.

Activity 15-1:   Fractional Distillation
(Teacher Demonstration)

In this activity, your teacher will demonstrate fractional distillation by distilling a mixture of distilled water and isopropanol (rubbing alcohol). The properties of the fractions collected will be examined to verify that a separation has occurred.

isopropanol

Materials

isopropanol	test tubes
distilled water	test tube rack
thermometer	cold tap water
250 mL round bottom flask	filter paper
boiling chip	large glass plate
fractionating column	wood splint
condenser	sugar
rubber tubing	test tube brush
one-hole rubber stoppers	support stands and clamps
solid rubber stoppers	heat source: heating mantle, hot plate, or Bunsen burner with wire gauze pad
beaker	
graduated cylinder	

Procedure

Part A: Collecting the Fractions

1. Your teacher will set up the apparatus as shown in Figure 15-2 using appropriate support stands, clamps, and heat source, and then carry out the following procedure.

2. Place a mixture consisting of 10 mL of isopropanol and 15 mL of distilled water in the round bottom flask. Add a boiling chip and turn on the cooling water to the condenser.

3. Label three test tubes 1, 2, and 3. Stand these in a test tube rack.

4. Heat the liquid mixture so that it distills at a rate no faster than 2 mL per minute. Collect the distillate in test tube 1. Record the temperature at which the distillate first appears.

5. When the thermometer reads 82°C, remove test tube 1 and replace it at once with test tube 2. Continue to collect liquid in test tube 2 until the temperature reaches 98°C. Then replace test tube 2 with test tube 3.

Figure 15-2. Fractional distillation of isopropanol.

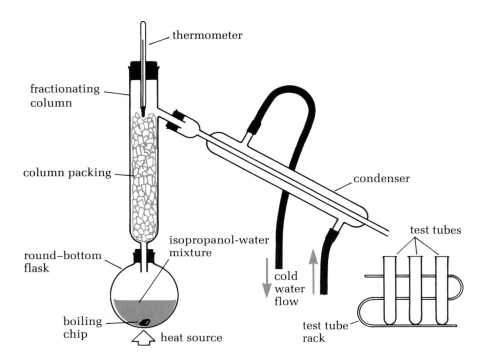

6. Continue to collect liquid until only about 5 mL of mixture remains in the flask. Do not boil the flask to dryness. Read and record the final temperature on the thermometer.

Part B: Testing the Fractions

7. Draw the following table in your lab report for your observations.

	Fraction		
Property	1	2	3
boiling range			
odour			
flammability			
sugar solubility			

8. Record the boiling range for each fraction in your table.

9. Smell each of the fractions for degree of odour.
10. Place three pieces of filter paper on a glass plate. Pour a small amount of each fraction onto a different filter paper so that each becomes moistened. Light a wood splint and bring the flame to each piece of filter paper. Observe how readily each fraction catches fire and burns.
11. Test the sugar solubility of each fraction by adding 0.5 mL of sugar to 2 mL of the fraction in a test tube. Stopper and shake vigorously for two minutes. Observe whether or not the sugar dissolves.

Discussion

1. What evidence do you have that the original mixture was separated into different fractions?
2. How could you find the density of each fraction? Why might this information be useful?
3. In which characteristic property must two liquids differ before you can consider separating a mixture of them by fractional distillation?

A crude oil distillation unit at a Shell oil refinery in Montreal, Quebec.

Refining Petroleum

Petroleum refineries operate day and night all year long. A refinery is a continuous-flow operation. Crude oil is continually fed in at one end, and separated liquids are removed at various points in the process.

When delivered to a refinery, crude oil is a mixture of hundreds of different hydrocarbons. The mixture varies widely from one oil field to another. In a series of processes, petroleum refining separates crude oil into various hydrocarbon groups. These are then combined, broken up, or rearranged, and other ingredients are sometimes added. The three major processes in modern refinery operations are separation, conversion, and treating.

Separation

The first step in separating the hydrocarbon groups is fractional distillation. You have already done this on a small scale in the laboratory. Refineries use a special kind of distillation apparatus called a fractionating column, or "bubble" tower, that functions

Figure 15-3. Fractional distillation of crude oil.

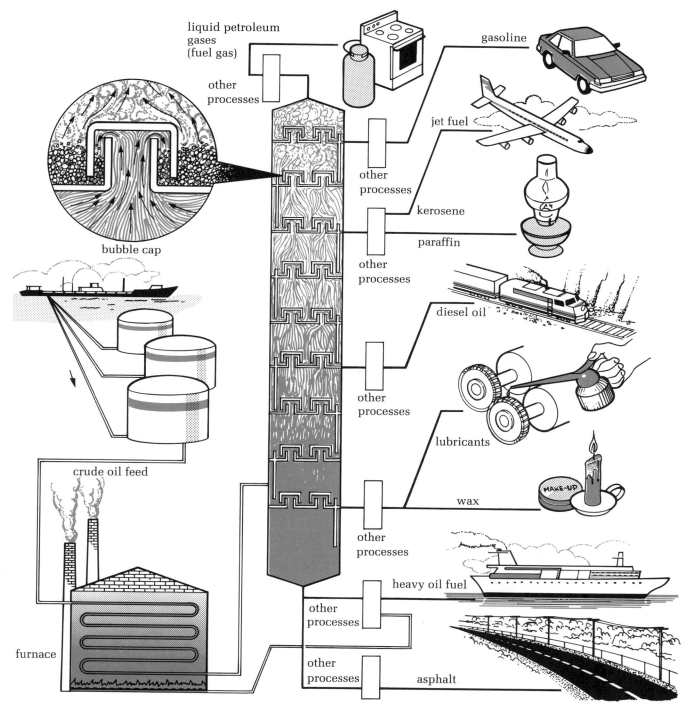

liquid petroleum gases (fuel gas)

other processes

bubble cap

gasoline

jet fuel

kerosene

paraffin

other processes

other processes

diesel oil

other processes

lubricants

wax

other processes

crude oil feed

heavy oil fuel

other processes

furnace

other processes

asphalt

continuously. The crude oil is pumped into steel tubes in a furnace. Almost all of the petroleum boils and passes as vapour into the bottom of the column. As the vapours rise in the column they cool, condense, and are drawn off at various levels in the tower.

The liquid residue remaining is drawn off at the bottom of the tower to be used as asphalt and heavy fuel oil. Higher up in the column, lubricating oil is drawn off. Next come the heating oils, then kerosene and gasoline condense near the top. Those gases which do not condense flow out of the top of the column.

Figure 15-4. Uses of oil products.

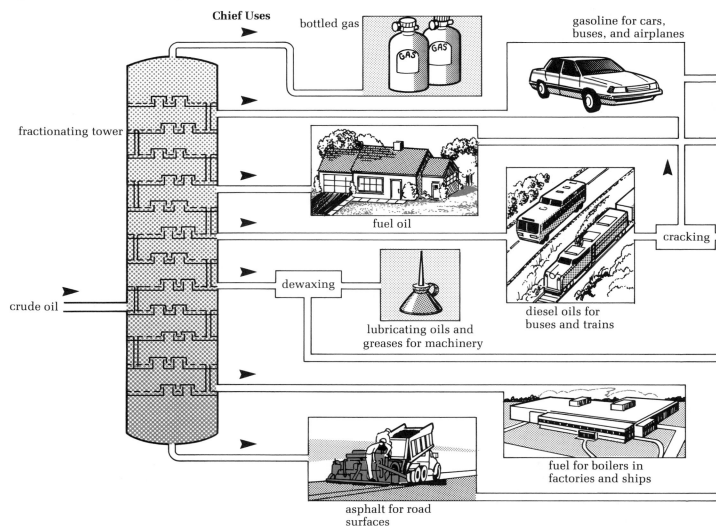

Other Uses

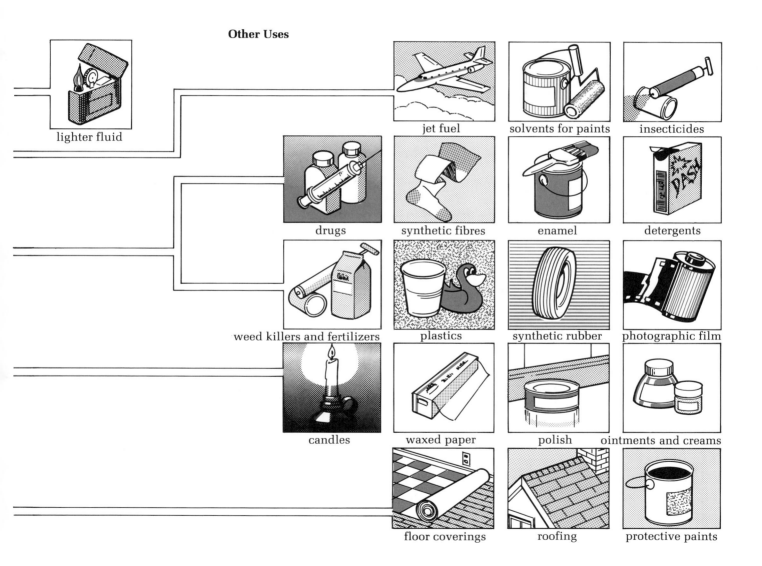

lighter fluid

jet fuel

solvents for paints

insecticides

drugs

synthetic fibres

enamel

detergents

weed killers and fertilizers

plastics

synthetic rubber

photographic film

candles

waxed paper

polish

ointments and creams

floor coverings

roofing

protective paints

Conversion

In the summer there is more demand for gasoline than for heating oil. Heating oil molecules are larger than gasoline molecules. To make more gasoline, a refinery breaks the large heating oil molecules into small gasoline molecules. This conversion process is called **cracking**. Cracking not only increases the amount of gasoline but also improves its quality, making a car engine run more smoothly.

Sometimes the refinery has more compounds with small molecules than it can sell, but these small molecules may be joined together to produce a larger molecule. This process (to be discussed later in the chapter) is called **polymerization**.

Treating

For a definition of "antiknock", see "Getting the Lead Out" on the following page.

Crude oils with high sulphur content produce fuels that have an unpleasant odour and smoke heavily when burned. Such crude oils are **treated** to remove sulphur and other impurities before the fractional distillation process occurs. Sulphur compounds in gasoline limit the effectiveness of antiknock additives, and increase wear and maintenance problems. Most important of all, sulphur compounds are removed in order to reduce sulphur dioxide levels in the atmosphere. Sulphur dioxide in the atmosphere forms the acid rain so damaging to our environment.

Study Questions

1. Explain why crude oil is much more valuable as a raw material for the chemical industry than as a source of fuels to be burned.

2. a) List the physical properties of crude oils.
   b) How were fossil fuels formed?
   c) Why is the supply of fossil fuels limited?

3. Briefly explain the meaning of each term: separation, conversion, cracking, polymerization, treating, fractional distillation.

4. Name at least a dozen common products derived from petroleum.

5. a) Draw a labelled diagram of the apparatus you would use to carry out a fractional distillation.
   b) i) Before the mixture is heated, boiling chips are added to it. Why?
      ii) Chemists collect "fractions" during a fractional distillation. Explain what is meant by a "fraction".

iii) Name two liquid mixtures that could be separated by fractional distillation in the laboratory.

c) Give one important industrial application of fractional distillation.

GETTING THE LEAD OUT

Gasoline is a mixture of several hydrocarbons. Each burns at a different temperature. For a car engine to operate properly, all of the gasoline must burn at the right moment. If the gas ignites before it should (pre-ignition), a small explosion is heard as a "knock" in the engine. Knocking will eventually cause the internal parts of the engine to break down.

Antiknock agents can be added to gasoline to reduce knocking. Gasolines containing such compounds are called leaded gas. Tetraethyl lead is the best-known antiknock additive, but it is very toxic. Cars burning leaded fuels release poisonous lead compounds that pollute the air and are dangerous to humans.

Concern about such problems has forced governments to encourage auto makers to modify engines so that they run on unleaded gasoline. When no lead is used, knocking can be controlled by using a higher-grade mixture of hydrocarbons, such as those obtained from cracking.

The octane number posted on gasoline pumps is a measure of the antiknock quality of the gasoline. Using a higher octane grade than a car needs to prevent knocking wastes money, however, and does not improve the car's performance.

15.2 Polymers

When many small molecules are linked together, they form a long chainlike molecule called a **polymer**. The small molecules are called **monomers**, and the chemical reaction that links many monomers together to form a giant polymer is called **polymerization**. There are both synthetic and natural polymers.

Figure 15-5. Just as railway boxcars are linked together to form a freight train, so many small molecules (monomers) can be linked together to form a long chainlike molecule (a polymer).

Natural Polymers

A number of natural polymers are vital to life. The genes that determine what and who you are, the protein that builds your body's muscle tissue, and the starch in the food you eat are all natural polymers.

Cellulose is an important natural polymer. Cellulose fibres give wood its strength. Books, magazines, and newspapers are printed on paper made largely of cellulose fibres. As the photograph shows, **fibres** are threadlike substances which can be seen clearly under a microscope.

Cotton and linen fabrics are made of cellulose. The properties of these natural fabrics are different from synthetics. Cotton and linen shrink on the first washing and need ironing, but are more comfortable in warm weather because they absorb moisture.

Wool, like all animal hair, is made of long protein molecules. It is a good insulator, and protects the body from temperature changes. Silk is a protein fibre made by silkworms. Silk is strong, elastic, and smooth, which prevents dirt from clinging to it.

Newsprint magnified 260 times.

Synthetic Polymers

Most clothes today contain synthetic fibres. These materials are usually cheaper and easier to care for than natural products. Polyester fabrics wrinkle less than cotton or wool. Gloves, gasoline hoses, and shoe soles made of a synthetic rubber such as neoprene last longer than those made from natural rubber. Plastics are synthetic polymers that are lightweight, can be shaped easily into different forms, and are often very strong. Plastic garden hose is lighter in mass, yet lasts longer in sun and weather than hoses made from natural rubber.

Many synthetic polymers are made from petroleum products. Thus, as petroleum prices increase, so do the prices of synthetic polymers and the chemicals from which they are made.

Nylon — A Synthetic Polymer

The first completely synthetic polymer fibre, called "nylon", was marketed by the Du Pont Company beginning in 1939. Nylon was an instant and enormous success. Manufacturers could not meet the demand for nylon stockings, and huge quantities of nylon were used during World War II for parachutes. Today, nylon is used in clothing, draperies, upholstery, rugs, ropes, and many other products that require a strong fibre.

There are many types of nylon. Each of these is similar to protein in structure. The properties of each type depend on the starting materials used and the length of the nylon chain.

Nylon was discovered by Wallace Carothers as he studied many types of large molecules while working for the Du Pont Company. When Carothers pulled a stirring rod from one of his mixtures one day, he observed that long tough threads had formed. After several years of trial and error, a satisfactory commercial process was developed to make nylon fibre.

After initial winding on paper sleeves, the nylon fibre is stretched and twisted to develop its full strength.

hexamethylene diamine
sebacoyl chloride

sodium hydroxide

hexane

CAUTION: Wear safety goggles and an apron.

Figure 15-6.

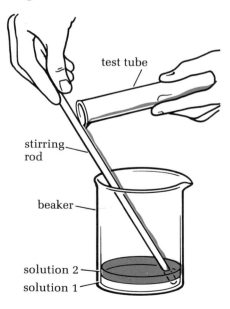

Activity 15-2: Making Nylon

We continually try to improve the quality of our clothes and the furnishings in our homes. To meet this need the textile industry develops both natural and synthetic fibres. In this activity you will make a sample of nylon, the first synthetic polymer to be manufactured and marketed to consumers.

Materials

solution 1: hexamethylene diamine in sodium hydroxide solution (12 g/200 mL of 2% NaOH)

solution 2: sebacoyl chloride in hexane solution (8 g/200 mL)

test tube (19 mm x 180 mm)

100 mL beaker

stirring rod

paper clip

paper towel

Procedure

1. Pour 10 mL of each solution into separate test tubes. Label each tube.
2. Pour solution 1 into the 100 mL beaker.
3. Place a stirring rod in the beaker and hold it at an angle. Pour solution 2 so that it runs *slowly* down the stirring rod and onto solution 1. Try to keep the solutions from mixing as much as possible.
4. Bend a paper clip to form a small hook. Use the hook to grasp the centre of the film that forms between the two layers of liquid in the beaker. Carefully lift the nylon "rope" from the beaker.
5. Loop the rope around the stirring rod and slowly wind up the string of nylon. Continue until the solution is almost used up. If the nylon rope breaks, use the paper clip to start a new rope.
6. Wash the nylon thoroughly under running tap water to remove the corrosive sodium hydroxide that remains.
7. Examine the nylon and describe some of its properties.
8. Dispose of the nylon and any remaining solution as directed by your teacher.

Discussion

1. Which of the two solutions has the lower density? Explain how you know.
2. What evidence is there that a chemical change occurred?
3. Why were the two solutions mixed so carefully, instead of just being stirred together to form nylon?
4. Why is nylon called a synthetic material?

Fibres

Some polymers are useful for making long strands or fibres. The fibre can then be formed into a yarn from which a fabric is woven. To produce a fibre useful for fabric formation, the molecules of the polymer used must be long and thin.

To make a fibre strong, as many long thin molecules as possible must be lined up in the same direction. In the previous activity you made nylon fibres that were weak and unsuitable for making things like nylon stockings.

When nylon is warmed, however, and a thread drawn out of the mass, a very strong fibre forms. This is because the randomly oriented molecules become lined up when the hot substance is pulled out. A polymer, then, is of no practical use for fibre formation unless its molecules are long and thin and can be drawn out into regular parallel lines, as shown in Figure 15-7.

Figure 15-7. Nylon fibres.

a) The polymer molecules show no regular pattern.

b) The long, thin polymer molecules have been drawn out into regular, parallel lines, making a much stronger fibre.

Table 15-1:   Some Common Textile Fibres and Fabrics

Textile	Type	Source	Properties	Examples
acetate	synthetic	wood pulp or cotton fibres treated with acetic acid	weaker than cotton, drapes well, silklike, fair crease recovery, warm, soft, mothproof	
acrylic	synthetic	chemicals derived from coal or petroleum	warm, soft, strong, hard-wearing, shrink- and stretch-proof, resistant to attack by moths and mildew, often blended with wool or cotton	Acrilan Orlon
cashmere	natural (animal)	Tibetan mountain goat	soft, mats quickly, needs careful washing	
cotton	natural (plant)	cellulose	cheap, strong, hard-wearing, stronger wet than dry, hardy to all washing processes, wrinkles, shrinks	
fibreglass	natural (mineral)	woven from glass filaments	resistant to bacteria, completely flame-proof, drapes well, nonstretch, nonsag	
linen	natural (plant)	flax	strong, washes and wears well, can be boiled	
mohair	natural (animal)	Angora goat	long-haired, provides exceptional warmth even when wet	
nylon	synthetic	petrochemicals	slightly absorbent, attracts dirt, increases the strength of a fabric	Antron Cordura
polyester	synthetic	petrochemicals	strong, hard-wearing, shrink-proof, nonabsorbent, good sunlight resistance, mothproof, often mixed with natural fibres	Dacron Fortrel Terylene
rayon	synthetic	cellulose	highly absorbent, pleasant feel, drapes well, dyes well	
wool	natural (animal)	sheep	available in several different qualities for making fabrics with a warm soft feel, shrinks	

Study Questions

1. Distinguish between "monomer" and "polymer".

2. Name three natural polymers and what each is used for.

3. a) What is a synthetic polymer?
   b) What was the first synthetic polymer to be marketed?
   c) What is this synthetic polymer used for today?

4. a) What is required of a molecule so that it can be used in fibre production?
   b) How is a fibre strengthened?

5. Read the following list of substances: Orlon, ethylene, cellulose, Dacron, water. From this list name:
   a) a naturally occurring polymer
   b) two synthetic polymers
   c) a substance which is not a polymer but can readily be converted into one
   d) a substance which is not a polymer and which could not be polymerized

A magnified view of a cotton stocking.

GOODBYE WRINKLES, HELLO CREASE

Clothes that lose their crease or that wrinkle when washed are common. These problems can be solved by ironing, but some people do not enjoy this task. To find a solution, scientists have focused on what causes a wrinkle and what ironing does to remove it.

The layers of a fibre are held together by strong attractive forces called bonds. The layers can slip and bond to other layers to produce a wrinkle when material is placed under strain. During ironing, when material is dampened or a steam iron is

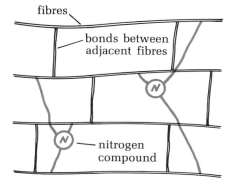

used, the water spreads the fibres apart and weakens the bonds. The heavy iron then pushes the fibres back into place and dries them so that the proper bonds are formed again.

Chemical substances, such as special nitrogen compounds, may be used to connect the layers and hold the fibres in place to

Figure 15-8. Special nitrogen compounds fit between the fibres, forming a strong link, or bridge, between two or more fibres. These hold the fibres in place, preventing wrinkles.

prevent wrinkles. These substances fit between the fibres so that each molecule forms a bridge between two or more fibres to strengthen them.

To put a permanent crease in a pair of slacks, the treated fabric is heated much more than in normal ironing. The additional bonds that form make the crease permanent, hence the term "permanent press".

15.3 Dyes and Dyeing

Dyes were originally extracted from natural sources such as berries and plants. The first synthetic dye was produced more than 100 years ago, and thousands are now in use. Not all of these dyes and pigments are useful. Many are deficient in one way or another.

Labelled cans of dyes ready for use in textile dyeing.

Old clothing, such as socks and underwear, is used to make hooked rugs after it is dyed in natural dyes made from walnut shells, onion skins, and cranberries.

Approximately 150 000 insects are needed to produce a kilogram of the beautiful red dye, cochineal. These insects are found only on certain cacti in Mexico. Because they must be hand-picked, the collection process is time-consuming and expensive.

Natural and Synthetic Dyes

Natural dyes

Many plants yield dyes that can colour fibres, but only a few produce bright shades. Those that do are difficult to obtain or extract.

Although still used by craftspeople in various parts of the world, natural dyes now have little economic importance. Artists are enthusiastic about natural dyes because of the one-of-a-kind colours that are possible. Each batch of dye has subtle differences because of impurities in given plant materials.

Synthetic dyes

The first synthetic dye was discovered accidentally by Sir William Perkin in 1856. The then 18-year-old Perkin was experimenting with a black tarry substance called coal tar. While trying to make an antimalaria drug, he discovered a compound that produced the colour mauve when dissolved in alcohol. Recognizing the significance of his find, Perkin quit his job at the Royal College of Chemistry in England, and the following year opened a plant for making the dye. Soon after Perkin's discovery, similar dyes were discovered and the synthetic dye industry was born.

Success in the manufacture of dyes and the chemical knowledge derived from those efforts influenced many other chemical endeavours, such as studies of medical drugs, plastics, and synthetic rubber.

Now more than 8000 dyes are produced, and new dyes are developed each year. The dye industry is one of the largest in the world, manufacturing a variety of dyes for foods, cosmetics, and textiles. Environmental laws govern the use and disposal of dyes, as they present hazards to both consumers and the environment. Because dyes and pigments are intensely coloured, for example, even small quantities that escape into rivers and streams become immediately obvious.

Classification of Dyes

Dyes can be classified either by chemical structure or by the way in which they are used. The former classification is difficult as chemical structures are extremely complex. There are now 31 different chemical classes of dyes.

There are many ways to use dyes, but all dyeing methods involve dipping cloth into a dye solution. When removed, the cloth should be evenly coloured by the dye. However, fabrics dipped in some dye solutions lose this colour when they are washed. Such colouring materials are useless as dyes. How well a dye remains attached

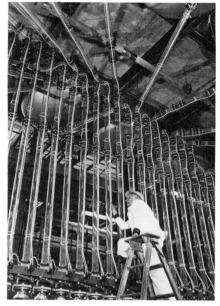

Dye is conveyed through 22 glass pipes to a rotary carpet printer at this plant located in Brantford, Ontario.

Spools of fabric are lowered into a dye vat.

to the fibres of a material is an indication of its **fastness**. Some dyes attach, or fix readily, to one type of fibre and will not attach to another.

Dyes must keep their colour, and must not fade when exposed to air and bright sunlight. They must also be unaffected by perspiration and cleaning materials. The first synthetic dyes were much more brilliant than the earlier natural dyes, but their fastness when exposed to sunlight and washing was poor. While these dyes worked well for animal fibres such as wool and silk, they quickly washed out of cellulose fibres such as cotton and linen.

True dyeing, and not merely surface staining, depends on the ability of a dye to reach and stay in the interior of a fibre. This happens when there is a chemical attraction between the fibre and the dye when the dye is soluble. Or, the insoluble dye particle is unable to get out of the fibre because of the fibre's narrow and tangled structure.

Mordant dyes

Fastness may be improved by using a substance called a **mordant**, which fixes the dye in the fibre to make it insoluble. The mordant is deposited in the material, and links to both the fibre and the dye molecules. The insoluble compounds that form are retained in the fine tangled spaces of the fibres. Common mordants include tannic acid and metal salts such as alum. Mordants can often change the colour of a particular dye considerably.

Direct dyes

The first direct dye for cotton, Congo red, was discovered in 1884. Because of its natural affinity for cotton, it could dye cellulose fibres without the use of a mordant. This class of water-soluble dyes is the largest in existence. Colours generally are bright and have good fastness.

Vat dyes

Vat dyes are among those with the best fastness. Natural vat dyes have been used for nearly 4000 years. They are insoluble in water but react in a basic solution to produce a soluble form that is attracted to fibres. Once applied, a vat dye can be made insoluble again so that the large dye molecule becomes trapped within the fibre. While vat dyes have excellent fastness, their colours are somewhat muted.

Disperse dyes

Many synthetic fibres are difficult to dye because their molecules are unreactive. One way to colour such fibres is to disperse, or mingle, the dye molecules among those of the fabric. This is done by heating the material so that its molecules move apart slightly, allowing the insoluble dye molecules to move in between the fibres. As the material cools, the dye molecules become trapped when the fibre molecules move back together. Disperse dyes are widely used to colour polyesters. They provide very even colouring and fair-to-good fastness.

The dyed fabric is wound on a roll.

Reactive dyes

Reactive dyes were developed most recently. Their chemical structure enables them to react directly with fabric molecules. Because the linkage between dye and fibre is so strong, these dyes are very fast when washed. Reactive dyes compete strongly with vat dyes because of their brilliance, fastness, and ease of application.

All-purpose dyes

All-purpose household dyes are so called because they can be used effectively with almost all fibres—protein, cellulose, or synthetic. They are actually a mixture of different dyes. When used to dye a single fibre such as wool, only the portion of the dye that colours wool reacts. Although the rest of the dye is wasted, which is expensive, this is a convenient method for small household jobs.

Tie dyeing at home.

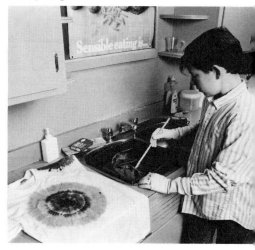

Pigment dyes

Very insoluble, finely-divided, and coloured mineral compounds known as **pigments** are dispersed either in a solution of the synthetic polymer or in the melted synthetic polymer before it is spun into fibre. The pigment particles become dispersed throughout the fibre and, because of their insolubility, are locked in so that colour is very fast. The most important pigment, titanium dioxide, dulls the shiny appearance of synthetic fibres so that they appear more natural.

Activity 15-3:   Dyeing Fabrics

In this activity you will dye several samples of white material in various ways, and compare the intensity and evenness of colour.

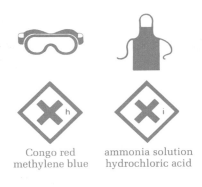

Congo red
methylene blue

ammonia solution
hydrochloric acid

Materials

three 5 cm × 15 cm white strips of one of the following fabrics, as assigned by your teacher: wool, silk, cotton, nylon, polyester, acetate

hydrochloric acid solution (1%)

distilled water

Congo red or methylene blue

sodium sulphate

sodium carbonate

alum (potassium aluminum sulphate)

cream of tartar

ammonia solution (10%)

indelible pencil

250 mL beaker

two 600 mL beakers

boiling chip

Bunsen burner

support stand

ring clamp

wire gauze

stirring rod

instant coffee

Procedure

Part A: Direct Dyeing

Note: Each of the fabrics will be assigned to a few groups.

1. Use an indelible pencil to number each fabric sample for later identification.

2. Place fabric sample 1 in a 250 mL beaker. Add enough hydrochloric acid solution to cover the fabric. The hydrochloric acid removes any "size" (material that makes the fabric less absorbent). Stir the solution for a few minutes. Pour off the acid and rinse the fabric in tap water. Remove excess moisture and keep the fabric for step 4.

3. Place 250 mL of distilled water in a 600 mL beaker. Add 1 g of synthetic dyestuff (Congo red or methylene blue), 2 g of sodium sulphate, and 4 g of sodium carbonate. Add a boiling chip, stir, and heat to boiling.

4. Add the fabric from step 2 to the boiling dye bath. Boil gently for 10 min. Remove the dyed sample and let it dry. Keep the dye bath for step 8.

Part B: Mordant Dyeing

5. Dissolve 2 g of alum and 0.5 g of cream of tartar in 250 mL of distilled water to prepare the mordant.

6. Add fabric samples 2 and 3 to the mordant solution. Stir and heat to the boiling point. Boil gently for about 15 min.

Figure 15-9.

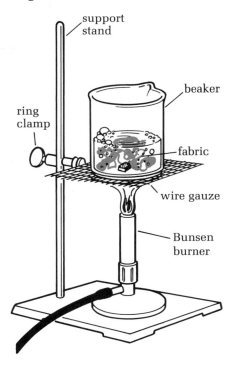

support stand

beaker

ring clamp

fabric

wire gauze

Bunsen burner

7. Remove the two samples and place them in the dilute ammonia solution for 2 to 3 min. Remove and rinse well in tap water.

8. Place either sample 2 or 3 in the dye bath saved from step 4. Save the other sample for step 10. Boil the fabric in the dye bath for about 5 min. Remove the sample and let it dry.

9. Heat 250 mL of water to boiling in a 600 mL beaker. Add 25 mL of instant coffee and stir.

10. Add the other fabric sample from step 7 to the (natural) coffee dye bath. Boil the fabric in the coffee dye bath for about 5 min. Remove the dyed sample and allow it to dry.

Part C: Comparing the Dyed Samples

11. Draw the following tables in your lab report.

	Intensity of Colour					
	Wool	Silk	Cotton	Nylon	Polyester	Acetate
direct dye						
mordant dye:						
a) synthetic						
b) natural						

	Evenness of Colour					
	Wool	Silk	Cotton	Nylon	Polyester	Acetate
direct dye						
mordant dye:						
a) synthetic						
b) natural						

12. Your teacher may wish to tape the samples to a sheet of bristol board for the comparison. Examine the samples for intensity and evenness of colour. Use this code to record your findings.

xxx high colour intensity   xxx very even colouring
xx fair colour intensity   xx fair evenness of colour
x poor colour intensity   x poor evenness of colour

13. Save all of the dyed samples for Activity 15-4.

Discussion

1. Which method provides the best "all-round" results?
2. Which method is the most suitable for the "difficult-to-dye" fabrics?
3. Why are some fibres easier to dye than others?
4. Why is the colour sometimes different, even when the same dyestuff is used?
5. What methods, other than those used, might give better results for some of the samples?
6. Which stage is most important in the dyeing process?

Activity 15-4:   Fastness and Dye Retention

In this activity, previously-dyed material is washed and exposed to sunlight. The samples are then compared to the originals so that you can estimate the degree of dye fastness and retention.

Materials

3 previously dyed samples
   from Activity 15-3

scissors

indelible pencil

synthetic detergent

warm wash water

ultraviolet lamp (optional)

Procedure

1. Arrange your previously dyed fabric samples in a logical pattern on your desk. Cut each into three equal pieces, and identify and number all the pieces using an indelible pencil. Keep one piece of each fabric sample as a comparison control.
2. Test one piece of each sample for washing fastness and dye retention. Use a synthetic detergent to wash each sample separately in warm water, then rinse and let the samples dry. Note the colour of the wash water in each case for evidence of dye loss.
3. Test one piece of each sample for light fastness. Expose the samples to sunlight for three weeks, or place them under an ultraviolet lamp overnight.

4. To make comparison easier, the treated class samples may be mounted alongside the control samples on a sheet of bristol board.

5. Draw the following table in your lab report. Examine the samples and report your results in the table, using the code given.

	Wool	Silk	Cotton	Nylon	Polyester	Acetate
direct dye:						
washed						
sunlight						
mordant — synthetic:						
washed						
sunlight						
mordant — natural:						
washed						
sunlight						

Code:

xxx distinct loss of colour   x slight loss of colour   + dye fast

Dyed fabric samples are tested for colour fastness.

Discussion

1. Which dyeing method produces the fastest colours?
2. Which fabric(s) retain(s) the dyestuffs most successfully?
3. Which of the two treatments is the most detrimental to the dye?
4. Why are some dyestuffs faster with certain fabrics than others?

Study Questions

1. a) What are dyes?
   b) How do natural and synthetic dyes differ?
2. a) What are the sources of natural dyes?
   b) Why are natural dyes still used today?
3. a) What is meant by the "fastness" of a dye?
   b) What is a mordant and why is it used?
4. Describe the dyeing action of each of the seven types of dye.
5. Experiments were carried out on four dyes, A, B, C, and D. Use

the following information to classify each dye into one of the seven dye types.

A: insoluble in water, excellent fastness, muted colours, used for a long time, applied using alkaline solution

B: insoluble in water, average fastness, used for polyesters, provides even colouring, applied in hot solution

C: insoluble in water, excellent fastness, mineral composition, applied to molten polymer before fibre formation

D: made insoluble in water, connected to the fibre by means of another substance, dye colour can vary

BETTER JEANS THROUGH CHEMISTRY

In 1850, a young Bavarian-born merchant, destined to revolutionize our concept of clothing, arrived in San Francisco. His name was Levi Strauss. He had originally intended to sell canvas for tenting, but then he recognized the need of American miners for rugged, dependable clothing. The first Levis were born. They were very stiff and uncomfortable at first, so Strauss soon switched to a softer all-cotton denim strengthened with copper rivets and dyed in indigo vats.

Indigo is a blue colouring matter that comes from a delicate shrub of the pea family and is native to India and Egypt. Indigo vat dyeing is a fascinating process. As yellow fabric is lifted from the indigo vat and exposed to oxygen, it turns to green and then blue. The dipping and airing process is continued until the desired shade of blue is obtained.

Today, denim appears in a variety of weights, from chambrays to heavier bottom weights, and in dozens of clothing items, particularly jeans and jackets. Special finishes are produced by washing the garments in acids or in machines containing chemically-soaked stones.

Blue jeans are popular with high school students.

Meet a Chemical Engineer— Tony Joseph

Tony is a project engineer at the Canadian Gas Research Institute. After attending university in Trinidad, Tony emigrated to Canada and completed a Master's degree in chemical engineering at the University of Waterloo.

Q. WHAT IS NATURAL GAS?
A. Natural gas is not a liquid, as many people think, but a gas that occurs naturally underground hundreds of metres below the earth's surface. Its chemical composition is 96% methane, 2% ethane, 1½% nitrogen, and the balance propane and carbon dioxide. It has to be moved in a pipeline and needs little refining.

Q. WHAT SORT OF PROJECTS DO YOU WORK ON AT THE CGRI?

A. There are two aspects to our work: natural gas research and development. We are funded by 21 companies in the gas distribution and transmission business across Canada, so we work to meet their needs. We research new designs in gas furnaces, water heaters, and industrial burners and venting systems. We also develop technology to improve efficiency.

Q. WHAT'S AN EXAMPLE OF YOUR RESEARCH?
A. Lately, we've done a lot of work on problems related to corrosion in furnace heat exchangers. In high-efficiency condensing furnaces, the moisture is condensed out of the combustion gases. The moist air condensed is acidic, and this was causing corrosion in the heat exchanger units that were built of low-grade stainless steel.

In this case, we found that chlorides and some fluorides in the air—often the result of using aerosol sprays in the home— were causing the corrosion. We had to find a material that could withstand this corrosion. We came up with two stainless steel alloys that are the most resistant to corrosion, and we recommend their use in the manufacture of condensing furnace heat-exchangers.

Q. WHAT KIND OF DEVELOPMENT WORK DO YOU DO?
A. Right now, I'm working on a fuelling device for cars that would run on compressed natural gas. I'm designing a nozzle that will dispense natural gas into the tank of a car at a self-service station.

Q. ARE THERE ANY CARS NOW THAT RUN ON NATURAL GAS?
A. In Ontario, there are about 600 vehicles in the Consumers Gas fleet that have dual fuel tanks, but they mainly operate on natural gas. It's far cheaper to run a car on natural gas than on gasoline. Because there is an abundance of natural gas in Canada,it will become the fuel of the future.

Q. HOW DO YOU DESIGN THIS KIND OF FUELLING DEVICE?
A. I start by collecting all the available information, and then I do rough drawings. The next stage is to make a final engineering drawing. Then we have prototypes made. This is a long process. I keep refining, getting new information, redesigning the prototype. In designing something like this for public use, we have to make sure it's easy to manipulate. Normally we make many prototypes before arriving at the final design.

Q. WHAT PART OF YOUR JOB DO YOU LIKE BEST?
A. I like the design aspect because it's quite creative. In the end, you actually have a finished product, and that is very satisfying.

Q. WHAT QUALITIES MAKE A GOOD ENGINEER?
A. A creative ability and perseverance. Things don't always go right and you have to be able to cope with failure. Often, in design, you have more failures than successes. The best way to learn is to get in there and get your hands dirty. Experience is the best teacher.

Review Questions

A: Knowledge

1. Gasoline that comes straight from the fractionating tower can no longer be used in automobile engines. Describe today's methods of producing synthetic gasoline.

2. State how fractional distillation and cracking can provide a range of hydrocarbon fuels.

3. a) What is a natural polymer?
   b) What is a synthetic polymer?
   c) How are polymers important to us?

4. What clothing fabrics come from animals? Why is woollen clothing warm?

5. What advantages do synthetic dyes have over natural dyes?

6. Describe the differences between direct and mordant dyes.

7. Describe how mordants are used in dyeing fabric.

8. State whether each of the following statements is true or false. If false, rewrite the statement to correct it.
   a) Hydrocarbons are compounds that contain hydrogen and carbon.
   b) Petroleum is the only fossil fuel.
   c) Fractional distillation separates a liquid mixture into different fractions.
   d) Cracking is the joining of small molecules to produce larger molecules.
   e) Nylon is the only synthetic polymer in widespread use.
   f) The first synthetic dye was discovered accidentally by Sir William Perkin.
   g) A mordant fixes a dye in the fibre by making the dye soluble.

B: Application

9. Use the pie chart below to answer the following questions.
   a) What information is presented?
   b) Which energy sources are presented?
   c) What fossil fuels are shown?
   d) What percentage of fossil fuels make up world energy consumption?
   e) Which source provided the greatest portion of our energy in 1985?
   f) What energy sources might be included in "other"?
   g) As supplies of fossil fuels diminish, which known energy sources are most likely to replace them?

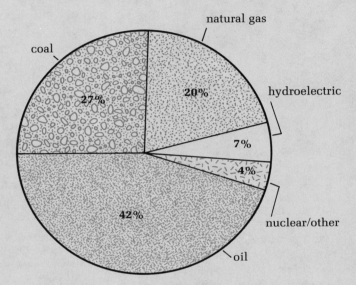

World energy consumption (1985)

10. In 1964, the total world energy consumption was the equivalent of 71 million barrels of oil a day. By 1974, this figure had reached 116, and by 1984, the figure was 142.
    a) By what percentage did world energy consumption increase between i) 1964 and 1984, ii) 1964 and 1974, iii) 1974 and 1984?
    b) What change in the growth rate of world energy consumption occurred during the decade 1964 to 1974, compared with 1974 to 1984?
    c) Give some possible reasons for this change in world energy consumption.

d) Do you think the chemical industry is responsible for a portion of this increased energy consumption? Explain.

11. Oil, natural gas, and coal are used in many ways other than as sources of energy. The most common use is in the preparation of synthetic chemical compounds. List some synthetic compounds that can be produced from petroleum, and give one use for each.

12. What information about construction, fibre content, colour, and durability is printed on clothing labels?

13. Making, dyeing, and finishing fibres account for about 10% of the retail cost of fabrics. Spinning, weaving, designing, and manufacturing account for about 50%. This means that production costs are five times higher than those of preparing the fibres. Should an increase or decrease in petroleum prices have much effect on fabric costs?

14. If everyone decided to reject synthetic fabrics in favour of natural fabrics, what would be the advantages and disadvantages?

C: Problem Solving

15. It has often been suggested that oil should be used less as a fuel and reserved mainly for the petrochemical industry, while coal should be used more as a fuel. Consider the following facts supporting this argument. It takes 1.5 times more oil (as fuel) to produce a paper bag than to make a plastic bag from petrochemicals. It takes 2.5 times more oil (as fuel) to make a glass bottle than to make a plastic container of the same size from petrochemicals. What are some strengths and weaknesses in this argument?

16. Lead is only one of several pollutants that automobile engines emit. Exhaust gases include 6% carbon monoxide, 0.04% nitrogen oxides, and 0.006% sulphur dioxide. In Canada alone, millions of tonnes of these exhaust gases are discharged into the atmosphere every year.

    a) Why are lead compounds added to gasoline?

    b) Why is lead in the atmosphere considered dangerous?

    c) How could the oil industry avoid using lead compounds in gasoline? Would this be expensive?

    d) Which is the most common pollutant in exhaust fumes (excluding lead), and in what proportion is it found?

    e) What is the current price difference between leaded and unleaded gasoline in your area? Is this pricing justified? Explain.

17. Most clothing labels give fabric information and cleaning recommendations. Survey at least six items of your own clothing and state the fibres of which they are made. Divide the list into natural and synthetic fibres.

18. Three different dyes are used to colour three samples of nylon drapery fabric. Which of the following methods is faster for discovering which dye will fade the least in sunlight?

    a) Leave the samples in sunlight with half of each sample covered.

    b) Shine an ultraviolet light on the samples with half of each sample covered.

    Explain your answer.

19. How do you feel about the possibility of using up fossil fuels within a few decades? Do you think we owe future generations a supply of these resources to provide fuels and consumer goods? Would you agree to give up air conditioning in the summer and to turn down the thermostat in the winter so that fossil fuels would be available to your grandchildren?

Try This

Plant, Animal, or Synthetic?
Collect fabrics of plant, animal, and synthetic origin. Try burning a few fibres of each fabric and observe what happens. Heat a small sample of each fabric in a test tube. Test the resulting vapours with moist litmus paper. Based on your findings and research, suggest how to determine a fibre's origin.

Acid Rain and Our Environment

The Issue: How can governments work with one another to control the problem of acid rain.

Acid rain begins in the towering smokestacks of smelters and fossil-fueled power plants, in oil refineries and other industries, and in the exhaust pipes of millions of cars. Each day thousands of tonnes of invisible gas — mainly the oxides of sulphur and nitrogen — stream into the atmosphere, where winds carry them on a journey that can last from a few days to a few weeks, sometimes taking them thousands of kilometres from their source.

While these invisible clouds of sulphur dioxide and nitrogen oxides are carried aloft, sufficient time passes for chemical reactions to convert them into sulphuric and nitric acids. Of course, what goes up must come down. For these sulphuric and nitric acids, the trip back to the earth's surface occurs with each rain and snowfall. These acids that have mixed with water vapour in clouds return as acid rain and acid snow.

Sulphur dioxide contributes about 70% of the acid rain problem, while the oxides of nitrogen account for most of the rest. About half of the nitrogen oxides come from the tailpipes of moving vehicles.

In the spring of 1982, Farley Mowat, the famed Canadian author and environmentalist, urged Canadians to form a coalition to fight acid rain. Here are the facts that prompted

Limestone and marble buildings are damaged by the sulphur dioxide in acid rain.

Lime is dusted over an Ontario lake to restore the acidic water to a more neutral condition.

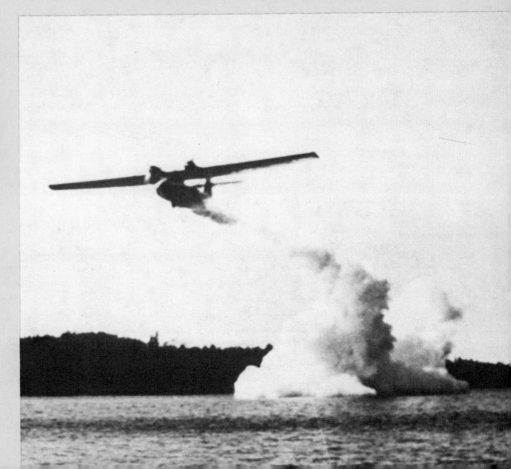

Mowat's call for action.

1. Rain is now as acid as vinegar in some places. Rain in parts of Eastern Canada is routinely 40 to 50 times more acid than normal.

2. Acid rain contributes to the health problems of asthmatics and others with respiratory ailments. Moreover, acid leaches the poisonous heavy metals out of the soil, thus risking contamination of our drinking supplies.

3. Nature's delicate balance is being disrupted, and many of our most valuable species of sportfish are disappearing. Over 140 lakes in Ontario are now completely dead, and 48 000 may die soon. Cottagers and campers may see the deterioration of their favourite recreational spots within their own lifetimes.

4. Taxpayers face a shocking expense, totalling hundreds of millions of dollars, as acid rain destroys the economy in regions where people's livelihoods depend on fishing, forestry, or tourism.

5. Historic buildings, homes, cars, and even gravestones are actually being eaten away by acid rain.

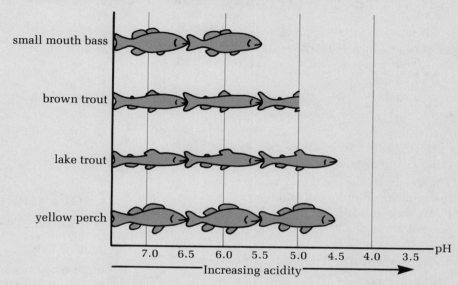

Figure 15-10. Fish vary in sensitivity to the acidity of the water in which they live. Acid rain, which decreases the pH of lake and pond water, is thought to be a major factor in the death of the entire fish population in some lakes.

Exploring the Issue

A. Gathering the Evidence

1. Examine each of the facts presented by Mowat in 1982. Is each fact still relevant? What additional information has surfaced in the meantime?

2. Find out whether the acid rain situation has improved or worsened since 1982.

3. How acid is acid rain today? Try to find out pH values for specific areas and rainfalls.

B. Examining Courses of Action

4. Make a list of government actions taken since 1982 to reduce acid rain. If possible, include the actions of other countries besides Canada.

5. What steps could be taken to reduce acid rain? Discuss the costs of each action in terms of dollars, jobs, etc.

6. Why does it take so long to solve problems like this when the solutions seem so simple on the surface?

Unit 5 Wrap-Up

Unit Summary

Acids and *bases* are common in both industry and the home.

Acids are *compounds* that taste sour, *neutralize* bases to produce salts and water, turn blue litmus paper red, and react with some metals to form hydrogen gas.

Bases taste bitter, neutralize acids, turn red litmus paper blue, and feel slippery.

Arrhenius defined an acid as a substance that produces *hydrogen ions*, and a base as a substance that produces *hydroxide ions* in water.

The strength of an acid and a base is determined by the number of hydrogen and hydroxide ions, respectively, in solution. The *pH scale* is commonly used to measure acid and base strength.

Chemistry can be applied to industrial processes, and to the household needs of consumers.

Soaps and *syndets* are the most common household products. Synthetic detergents have largely replaced laundry soaps since they are unaffected by hard water.

Hard water can contain both permanent and temporary hardness. *Temporary hardness* can be removed by boiling, but *permanent hardness* requires chemical treatment.

The petroleum industry supplies raw materials for the petrochemical industry. The resulting chemicals are sources for a multitude of consumer products.

Fractional distillation can be used to separate a mixture of compounds with different boiling points. Petroleum refineries use tall fractionating columns to distill petroleum into its *hydrocarbon fractions*.

Large molecules can be broken into smaller ones, and small molecules can be combined to form large ones.

Polymers are large molecules made from many small molecules called *monomers*. Nylon was the first completely synthetic polymer produced by industry.

Petrochemicals and coal tar chemicals are the main sources of *dyes*. In dyeing, *mordants* can help "fasten" the dye to the fabric.

Key Terms

acid
base
biodegradable
cracking
detergent
dye
fastness
hard water
hydrocarbon
hydrophilic
hydrophobic

indicator
monomer
mordant
neutralization
organic compound
polymer
polymerization
pH scale
soap
synthetic
treating

Unit Practice and Review

A. Short Answer

True or False

State whether each statement is true or false. Correct each false statement.

1. All crude oils are black, tarry, smelly liquids.
2. To make gasoline, a refinery can break oil molecules into gasoline molecules.
3. To make a strong fibre, long thin molecules must be lined up in the same direction.
4. In true dyeing, the dye is not allowed to reach the interior of the fibre.
5. All soaps are detergents, but all detergents are not soaps.

Multiple Choice

In each question below, select the best answer.

1. A natural polymer is:
   a) sodium hydroxide
   b) polyester
   c) cellulose
   d) plastic

2. Which of the following substances is a mordant?

   a) sodium hydroxide
   b) sulphuric acid
   c) aluminum sulphate
   d) ammonia solution

3. Detergents tend to:

   a) loosen and remove dirt.
   b) dissolve in both oil and water.
   c) suspend dirt in the water.
   d) do all of the above.

4. A weak acid:

   a) has a pH of 7.
   b) produces few hydrogen ions in solution.
   c) does not conduct electricity.
   d) does not affect blue litmus paper.

5. A solution with a pH of 7.4 is:

   a) slightly acidic
   b) very acidic
   c) slightly basic
   d) very basic

Complete the Sentence

Complete each of the following statements with the correct word or phrase. Do not write in this book.

1. Crude oil is a mixture of thousands of different compounds of hydrogen and carbon. These compounds are called __?__ .

2. In fractional distillation the liquid is separated into different parts, or __?__ .

3. Today, instead of nylon, synthetic fibre called __?__ is used in permanent-press fabrics.

4. Water that does not form a lather with soap is called __?__ water.

5. A(n) __?__ is a compound that dissolves in water and produces positive hydrogen ions.

Matching Items

Match each item in Column A with the appropriate item in Column B.

1. *Column A*

   i) removal of sulphur from oil impurities
   ii) many small molecules joined to form a large molecule
   iii) fossil fuel

   Column B

   a) petroleum
   b) treatment
   c) cracking
   d) polymeri-zation
   e) fractional distillation

iv) oil molecules converted to gasoline molecules

2. *Column A*

   i) ability of a dye to remain on a fibre
   ii) insoluble substance that adds colour
   iii) more brilliant than natural dyes
   iv) helps fix the dye to the fibre

   Column B

   a) fastness
   b) mordant
   c) dye
   d) pigment
   e) synthetic dyes

3. *Column A*

   i) product of neutrali-zation
   ii) acidic solution
   iii) basic solution
   iv) neutral solution

   Column B

   a) pH = 4
   b) soap
   c) pH = 7
   d) salt
   e) pH = 9

B: Knowledge and Application

1. a) Alcohol and salt can be separated by distillation. What substance will be found in the distillate, and what substance (the residue) will remain in the distilling flask?

   b) What conditions are required for two or more liquids to be separated using the process of distillation?

   c) Name this type of distillation.

   d) Explain why the name in c) is an appropriate one.

2. a) Distinguish between hydrocarbons and organic compounds.

   b) Describe the appearance of crude oil.

   c) Why can petroleum be separated by fractional distillation?

   d) Describe the fractional distillation of petroleum.

3. A mixture of liquids X, Y, and Z undergoes fractional distillation. The boiling points are: X, 100°C; Y, 80°C; Z, 160°C.

   a) Of which liquid does most of the first fraction consist?

   b) Sketch a temperature-time graph to show the change in temperature with time.

4. Classify the following processes into those that involve a) breaking large molecules into several smaller molecules, b) building up a larger molecule from a few or many smaller molecules, and c) neither building up nor breaking down molecules.

condensation   polymerization
neutralization   cracking
fractional   treating
   distillation

5. a) How does hard water form in nature?
   b) How would a chemist i) explain the properties of this liquid, and ii) remove hardness from water?

6. You can ease the pain of a burn by covering it with a baking soda paste. Why?

7. Consider the following changes.

   a) the action of carbonic acid on limestone
   b) the formation of nylon from sebacoyl chloride and hexamethylene diamine
   c) the formation of gasoline from heating oil
   d) the formation of soap from castor oil

   i) Which of the above changes occur naturally?
   ii) Which of the changes can be achieved by the cracking process?
   iii) Which change requires the use of an alkali?
   iv) In which change do the products consist of much larger molecules than those of the reactants?

8. In terms of molecules, ions, and the forces that may act between them, how would you account for the following?

   a) Gasoline molecules are made from oil molecules.
   b) If nylon is warmed and a thread is drawn from it, a very strong fibre forms.
   c) Detergents remove greasy dirt.
   d) Reactive dyes in nylon produce brilliant, fast colours.
   e) A vinegar solution conducts an electric current.

9. Explain the following observations.

   a) A thin film of nylon is formed where the two solutions used in its preparation come in contact.
   b) A hydrochloric acid solution reacts rapidly with zinc, but an acetic acid solution of the same concentration reacts slowly with the same metal.
   c) A dog and its owner enter a cave containing more than the usual amount of carbon dioxide; the dog suffocates but the owner is unharmed.
   d) A brown ring forms in a bathtub when soap is used for bathing.
   e) A stalactite forms on a cave ceiling.

C: Problem Solving

1. Gasoline consists partly of octane, C_8H_{18}. When octane is burned in an excess of air, carbon dioxide and water vapour are the only products.

   a) Write a word equation for the reaction.
   b) If 100 g of liquid octane is burned, will the mass of the products formed be i) 100 g, ii) more than 100 g, or iii) less than 100 g?
   c) If 100 mL of liquid octane is burned, will the volume of the products be i) 100 mL, ii) more than 100 mL, or iii) less than 100 mL?

2. A universal indicator changes colour as pH changes, in the following sequence:

Colour	pH	Colour	pH
red	4 or less	blue	8
orange	5	indigo	9
yellow	6	violet	10 or more
green	7		

The pH values of a series of solutions were determined by adding a few drops of indicator to each solution. The results were:

Solution	Colour	Solution	Colour
nitric acid	red	sodium bi-sulphite	blue
baking soda	green	distilled water	yellow
washing soda	violet	sodium sulphite	indigo
carbonic acid	orange	distilled water	yellow

List the solutions in order of acidity, beginning with the most acid solution.

3. A Grade 10 science class was asked to find a method to soften a sample of hard water. To produce a lather lasting 2 min, 20 mL of the original untreated sample required 25 mL of soap solution. After completing the experiments, each student took 20 mL of the resulting water and added soap solution until a 2-min lather was obtained by vigorous shaking. The methods used and the results obtained were:

Technique	Soap Volume
boiling	25 mL
distilling	1.5 mL
filtration	25 mL
washing soda	1.5 mL

a) Which techniques softened the water?
b) Was the original sample temporarily or permanently hard? Explain.
c) What chemical might have caused the hardness?
d) Why did boiling and filtration produce a similar result?
e) Why did distillation and filtration produce different results?

D: Challengers

1. To produce chemicals on a large scale, cheap and abundant supplies of raw materials are needed.

Such raw materials include: air, sea water, petroleum, fats, metal oxides.

a) Select one of these raw materials and describe a process by which it is converted into another chemical substance (technical details are not required).
b) Comment briefly on the importance to society of the chemical substance(s) made from the raw material you selected. Suggest what could happen if the raw material became unobtainable.

Project Ideas

1. Fossil fuels also occur in nature as tar sands and oil shale. Find out more about these two materials. What practical importance does each have for Canada's current energy program? Under what future circumstances might this value change?

2. Examine several brands of liquid dishwashing detergent, laundry detergent, and bar soap. List the ingredients of each brand, and try to find out the function of each component.

3. Select a consumer product discussed in this unit. Look through current and past issues of magazines in your school resource centre. Try to find at least six different advertisements for the selected product. Do the ads give factual information? Can you find any false or misleading claims? Does each ad make a strong or an understated sales pitch? Prepare an evaluation of each ad. If possible, identify one that is particularly good and one that is especially offensive.

Readings

Korchin, Florence G. *Science in the Marketplace*. Red Bank, New Jersey: Tiger Publications, 1986. (Includes many laboratory activities related to consumer product chemistry.)

Selinger, Ben. *Chemistry in the Marketplace* (3rd ed.). Sydney, Australia: Harcourt Brace Jovanovich, 1986. (Interesting information on consumer products.)

VI

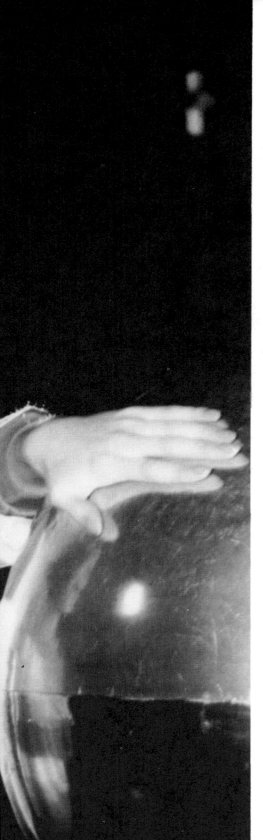

Electricity and Magnetism

Think what life would be like if electricity had not been put to practical use. Electricity operates televisions, sound systems, cooking and heating appliances, telephones, and lights. Many of these devices convert electrical energy into the four forms of energy we use most: sound, light, heat, and mechanical energy.

Light bulbs and stove elements operate using electricity alone. However, a television uses both electricity and magnetism to produce both the picture on the screen and the sound from the loudspeaker. The design of many household devices is based on a special relationship which exists between electricity and magnetism.

In this unit we will investigate electricity and some basic electric circuits. We will then study magnetism and the combined effects of electricity and magnetism (known as electromagnetism). Finally, we will look at electromagnetism's many practical uses.

Chapter 16
Electrostatics

Electricity is a general term referring to electric charge. When objects are rubbed together, they often become "electrified", or charged with "electricity". These objects can remain electrically charged for minutes or even hours. Because the electric charge remains "static", or stationary, on the object and does not move away, the phenomenon is called **static electricity**. The study of static electric charge is called **electrostatics**.

One of the most common effects of static electricity occurs when you comb your hair on a day when the air is very dry. Your hair stands on end, and there may be a crackling noise. Static electricity causes clothes to cling together in the dryer. It also causes the surfaces of records and magnetic tapes to attract dust as they are played.

In this chapter you will learn about some properties of electric charges, and how charges are produced and transferred. You will also study some benefits and drawbacks of static electricity.

When you finish Chapter 16, you should be able to:

- explain the behaviour of charged objects when placed near other charged or uncharged objects
- explain, using the electrical model for matter, several methods of charging and discharging objects
- describe some problems caused by static electricity and how they can be overcome
- describe the operation of some practical devices that use static electricity

16.1   The Electrical Nature of Matter

Scientists believe that all matter is made up of atoms, and that these atoms contain particles that possess electric charges. To develop a more complete understanding of electricity, the properties of electric charges will now be studied in more detail.

Activity 16-1:   The Properties of Electric Charges

In this activity you will electrically charge a variety of substances and identify some properties of electric charges. You will also demonstrate the Law of Electric Charges.

Materials

plastic comb

fur

wool and cotton fibres

2 polyethylene strips (ebonite rods)

balloon

evaporating dish (and plasticine)

2 acetate strips (glass rods)

silk

Procedure

As you perform the procedure, record your observations.

Part A: The Effects of Static Electricity

1. Rub a plastic comb on a piece of fur. Bring first the comb, then the fur, near some small fibres of wool and cotton.
2. Rub a polyethylene strip with fur, then hold the strip near a fine stream of tap water.
3. Rub an inflated balloon against your hair, then place the balloon against several vertical surfaces.

Do You Know?
A Greek philosopher named Thales is reputed to have studied static electricity around 600 B.C. He found that when amber was rubbed with fur it attracted small pieces of cloth or leaves. The Greeks called this attraction the "amber effect". (Amber is a clear yellow-orange solid produced naturally from the sap of pine trees.)
    Around 1600, William Gilbert (1540-1603), personal physician to Queen Elizabeth I, found that many other materials, including glass, also showed the amber effect. Because the Greek word for amber is "elektron", Gilbert called this effect "electric".

Part B: The Law of Electric Charges

4. Rub one end of the polyethylene strip with fur. Mount the strip on an evaporating dish, as shown in Figure 16-1.

Figure 16-1.

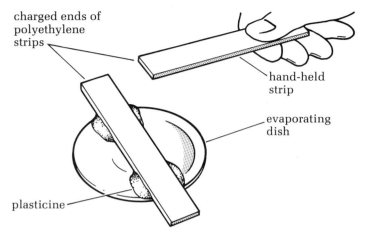

5. Rub one end of another polyethylene strip with fur. Bring this charged end of the strip close to, but not touching, the charged end of the strip on the dish.

6. Bring the uncharged end of the polyethylene strip close to the charged end of the polyethylene strip on the dish.

7. Repeat steps 4, 5, and 6, but substitute acetate strips which have been rubbed with silk.

8. Charge a polyethylene strip with fur and mount it on the dish. Charge an acetate strip with silk, and bring it near the charged end of the polyethylene strip on the dish.

Discussion

Part A

1. a) What can you infer about the behaviour of uncharged objects placed near charged objects?
   b) Does an uncharged object always move towards a charged object? Explain your answer.

2. What happens to the force exerted between charged and uncharged objects as the distance between them increases? Support your answer with evidence from this activity.

3. a) List three everyday examples of static electricity.
   b) List some ways to control static electricity.

4. What evidence suggests that there are two kinds of electric charge?

5. From your observations, what can you infer about the behaviour of objects brought close to one another a) if they have like charges? b) if they have unlike charges?

6. What test could you perform to determine a) whether an object is charged or uncharged, and b) the kind of charge present on a charged object?

Electric Charge

The polyethylene strip and the piece of wool shown in the photograph are both electrically uncharged. The small uncharged pieces of paper on the desk are not attracted towards either the uncharged polyethylene or the wool when they are held above the paper. Electrically uncharged objects are said to be **neutral**.

Neutral (electrically uncharged) objects are not attracted to each other.

When the polyethylene strip is rubbed with wool, however, the strip becomes electrically charged. As the photograph on the next page shows, the charged polyethylene strip now attracts the small uncharged pieces of paper. It can be inferred that electrically charged objects exert forces on nearby uncharged objects, even when the objects are not touching.

Do You Know?
Benjamin Franklin (1706-1790)
Benjamin Franklin's major scientific accomplishment was a better understanding of the fundamental aspects of electricity. In 1752, this American statesman and scientist performed his famous kite experiment, proving that lightning is an example of the discharge of static electricity. Franklin was extremely fortunate to survive the experiment; several scientists who tried to duplicate his results were killed by lightning strikes.

It is important to realize that electric charges cannot move by themselves. Only charged *particles* can move from one place to another. Physicists use the term "moving electric charges" for convenience, because it is easier to say and write. Always remember it means "moving electrically charged *particles*".

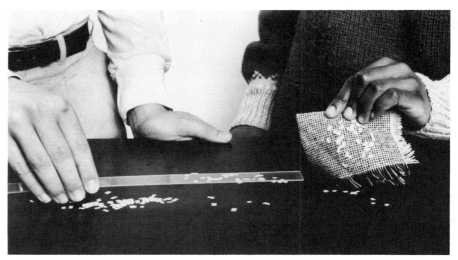

The positively charged wool and the negatively charged strip attract the uncharged pieces of paper to the areas where the wool and strip were rubbed together.

Note that the pieces of paper stick only to the part of the polyethylene strip that was rubbed with wool. The unrubbed part of the strip is still uncharged. Because the electrically charged particles do not move from their original positions on the strip, the electric charge is said to be **static** (stationary).

In the photograph, you can see small pieces of paper clinging to the wool and to the strip. This shows that both the wool and the strip became charged when they were rubbed together. You probably recall from earlier studies that there are two kinds of electric charge: negative and positive. When two different substances are rubbed together, one substance always becomes negatively charged while the other one becomes positively charged. For example, when polyethylene is rubbed with wool, the polyethylene is said to have a negative charge, while the wool is said to have a positive charge. Both positively charged and negatively charged objects attract most neutral objects, including liquids and gases.

Do You Know?

Experiments by the French chemist Charles DuFay (1698-1739) showed that there were two kinds of electric charges. In 1747, Benjamin Franklin named the kind of charge found on a polyethylene strip the "negative" charge, and that found on wool the "positive" charge. Although Franklin used different materials, the charges were of the same kind, and the names have remained the same ever since.

When testing to identify the kind of charge on an object, the repulsion test must always be used. Why?

The Law of Electric Charges

When two negatively charged polyethylene strips are brought close together, they repel one another (Figure 16-2a). When two positively charged acetate strips are brought close together, they also repel one another (Figure 16-2b). Two objects with like charges, whether positive or negative, always repel one another. However, when a positively charged acetate strip is brought near a negatively

Figure 16-2.

a)

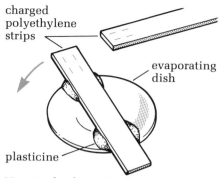

charged polyethylene strips

evaporating dish

plasticine

Negatively charged polyethylene strips repel one another.

b)

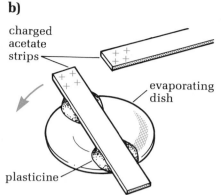

charged acetate strips

evaporating dish

plasticine

Positively charged acetate strips repel one another.

c)

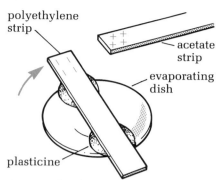

polyethylene strip

acetate strip

evaporating dish

plasticine

Oppositely charged strips attract one another.

charged polyethylene strip, the two strips attract one another (Figure 16-2c)). Two objects with unlike charges always attract one another. This constancy of behaviour is known as the **Law of Electric Charges**, which states that:

Like charges repel one another, and unlike charges attract one another.

A Model for the Electrical Nature of Matter

In earlier studies you became familiar with the Rutherford-Bohr model of the atom as shown in Figure 16-3. This model provides a basis both for explaining observations and for making predictions about the structure of matter and chemical change. The same model can also be used to explain and predict electrical effects. The main postulates of the model related to electric charge are outlined in Table 16-1 on the next page.

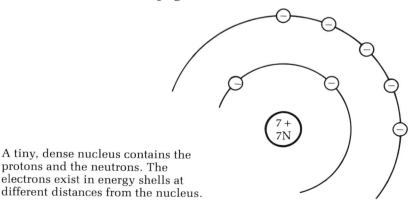

A tiny, dense nucleus contains the protons and the neutrons. The electrons exist in energy shells at different distances from the nucleus.

Do You Know?
The formation of chemical compounds, the shapes of crystals, and properties such as melting and boiling points, hardness, and density are affected by the electrical forces between atoms and molecules. Scientists think that the action of enzymes, the formation of protein in cells, and the reproduction of cells are all based on the attraction and repulsion of electrically charged molecules.

Figure 16-3. The Rutherford-Bohr model.

Neutral and charged objects may be represented by sketches with positive and negative signs marked on them.

Table 16-1: A Model for the Electrical Nature of Matter (based on the Rutherford-Bohr Model of the Atom)

1. All matter is made up of submicroscopic particles, called atoms.

2. At the centre of each atom is a region called the nucleus (Figure 16-3). In the nucleus are two kinds of particles: the proton, which is positively charged, and the neutron, which has no charge and is therefore electrically neutral. Protons are strongly attracted to, and do not move from, the nucleus when an atom becomes charged.

3. Surrounding the nucleus at different energy levels is a cloud of particles called electrons, which are negatively charged. The amount of electric charge on an electron is the same as that on a proton, but the kind of charge is opposite. When atoms become charged, only the electrons move from atom to atom.

4. Like charges repel one another; unlike charges attract one another. The electric force decreases as the distance from a charged object increases.

5. In some elements, the nucleus has a weaker attraction for its electrons than in others. In elements such as copper and silver, electrons are able to move freely from atom to atom. In elements such as sulphur and oxygen the electrons are strongly bound to each atom.

6. The identity of an element is determined by the number of protons in an atom. The number of electrons surrounding the nucleus equals the number of protons in the nucleus. A single atom is always electrically neutral.

7. If an atom gains an extra electron, the net charge on the atom is negative. Such an atom is called a **negative ion**. If an atom loses an electron, the net charge on the atom is positive. Such an atom is called a **positive ion**.

Do You Know?
We live in a "sea" of air consisting of huge numbers of gas atoms, gas molecules, and dust particles. There are also from 1000 to 2000 ions in every cubic centimetre of "normal" air over open land. Ions are produced mostly by radiation from the Sun and from minute quantities of radioactive materials in soil and rocks. Many different human activities such as the operation of heavy machinery in factories also produce large quantities of ions.

Measurements have shown that normal air usually contains approximately five positive ions for every four negative ions. Some scientists think that the ratio of positive to negative ions in the air may affect the health of both plants and animals.

Do You Know?
The rubbing produced by sliding across a car seat and stepping to the ground may charge you to an electric potential of fifteen thousand volts. You may experience a small electric shock, but the amount of electric charge is too small to be dangerous.

Transferring Electric Charge

Many of the electrical effects you will study in this chapter occur when electric charges are transferred from one substance to another. There are three basic ways in which objects become electrically charged: by friction, by contact, and by induction.

Charging by Friction

You have already seen that electric charges can be transferred by some kind of rubbing action, or friction. Charging by friction causes many of the effects produced by static electricity. Large amounts of electric charge build up on clothes in a dryer because the tumbling motion is a kind of rubbing action. Transparent plastic food wraps stick to bowls because of static charges. When someone walks across a carpet, the friction between the carpet and the person's shoes produces a charge on both the person and the carpet.

Sometimes substances rub against one another in a less obvious way. For example, when gasoline rushes out of a hose at a gas station, or when dry air rushes over the surface of a car or an airplane travelling at high speeds, large amounts of electric charge can be transferred. You can receive an electric shock when you touch the surface of a car charged this way. Even wearing clothes made of different materials can cause a build-up of electric charge. As the different materials rub together, each piece of clothing develops its own electric charge.

Figure 16-4 shows how the model for the electrical nature of matter (Table 16-1) can be used to explain charging by friction. When a polyethylene strip is rubbed with fur, the polyethylene becomes negatively charged, and the fur becomes positively charged. In terms of the model, this occurs because polyethylene molecules attract their electrons more strongly than the fur molecules attract theirs. When the polyethylene is rubbed against the fur, some of the electrons in the fur molecules are strongly attracted by the polyethylene molecules, and transfer over to them. This causes excess negative charge to build up on the polyethylene strip. Because the fur loses some electrons, it becomes positively charged.

Figure 16-4. Charging objects by friction. When a polyethylene strip is rubbed with fur, the polyethylene becomes negatively charged, and the fur becomes positively charged.

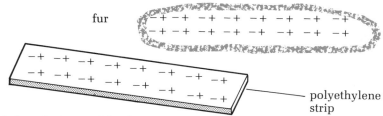

fur

polyethylene strip

a) Before being rubbed together.

In terms of the model for the electrical nature of matter, only electrons move during the transfer of electric charge on an atom. The protons remain in their original locations, at the centre of the atom.

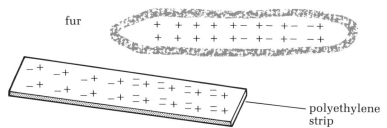

fur

polyethylene strip

b) After being rubbed together at one end.

Table 16-2: The Electrostatic Series

[*Weak hold on electrons*]

acetate

glass

wool

cat's fur, human hair

calcium, magnesium, lead

silk

aluminum, zinc

cotton

paraffin wax

ebonite

polyethylene (plastic)

carbon, copper, nickel

rubber

sulphur

platinum, gold

[*Strong hold on electrons*]

CHALLENGER

The Rutherford-Bohr model for the structure of the atom was developed after much careful experimentation and thought by many brilliant scientists. An interesting problem arises if you think about the structure of the nucleus itself. Based on the Law of Electric Charges, what *should* happen to the protons in the nucleus? What *does* happen? Try to develop a theory to explain why the protons behave as they do.

The Electrostatic Series

Scientists have developed a list known as the **Electrostatic Series** (Table 16-2) to determine the kind of electric charge produced on each substance when any two substances are rubbed together. When charging by friction occurs, the substance higher in the list (for example, acetate) always loses electrons and becomes positively charged, while the substance lower in the list (for example, silk) becomes negatively charged.

Study Questions

1. What major forms of energy are produced from electrical energy?
2. a) Why is the term *static* electricity used?
   b) List six effects caused by static electricity.
3. a) State the Law of Electric Charges.
   b) Explain in detail how you could demonstrate this law.
4. List the key ideas in the model for the electrical nature of matter.
5. a) Explain, in terms of the electrical model for matter, how objects become charged by friction.
   b) Describe the function of the Electrostatic Series.
   c) Predict what will happen when acetate is rubbed with fur.
   d) By mistake, a silk blouse and a pair of wool socks are put into a clothes dryer. What charge will appear on the blouse when it rubs against the socks? Explain why.

16.2 Transferring Electric Charge to Insulators and Conductors

If you have ever polished furniture or glass on a dry winter day, you may have noticed that the surfaces quickly become charged with static electricity due to friction. Such objects attract dust as soon as they are cleaned. Other objects, such as the metal taps on sinks, never remain charged no matter how hard you rub them. The next activity will help you to understand why some materials become charged by friction while others do not. It will also introduce a second method of transferring charge from one object to another. To detect whether charge has been transferred, you will use a device called an electroscope.

Activity 16-2: Charging Different Substances

In Part A of this activity you will use a pith-ball electroscope to study how electric charge is transferred by contact. In Part B, you will observe what can happen to electric charges once they have been transferred to two different kinds of substances.

Materials

fur

silk

pith-ball electroscope

polyethylene strip

acetate strip

iron rod

30 cm piece of plastic-coated copper wire

glass rod

evaporating dish (and plasticine)

objects supplied by the teacher

Part A: Charging by Contact

Procedure

1. Bring a negatively charged polyethylene strip close to the uncharged pith ball, and then remove it. (Do not allow the pith ball to touch the strip.)
2. Repeat step 1 using a positively charged acetate strip.
3. Touch the uncharged pith ball with the charged polyethylene strip, remove the strip, and then approach the pith ball with the charged strip again. Then approach but do not touch the pith ball with a charged acetate strip.
4. Repeat step 3, but first touch the uncharged pith ball with the charged acetate strip.

A pith-ball electroscope consists of a small ball suspended by a thin cotton thread. Originally pith balls were made from the soft centre, or pith, of elderberry stalks. Now they are more commonly made of plastic foam. Because the ball is very light, it moves in response to the electric forces produced by very small amounts of electric charge.

Note: If the pith ball does touch the rod, the pith ball may become charged. To remove the charge, simply hold the ball gently in your fingers and repeat the step of the procedure.

Discussion

1. What can you infer about the transfer of electric charge when a charged object is placed near, but does not touch, the pith ball electroscope? Explain why.
2. What can you infer about the transfer of charge when the pith ball is touched by a) a negatively charged object, and b) a positively charged object? Explain why.
3. Write a summary statement identifying the kind of charge transferred to an uncharged object when it contacts a charged object.

Figure 16-5.

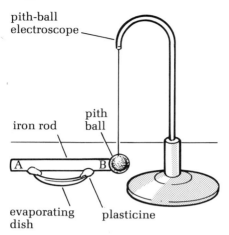

pith-ball
electroscope

iron rod

pith
ball

A   B

evaporating
dish

plasticine

Part B: Transferring Electric Charge through Substances

Procedure

1. Set up the equipment as shown in Figure 16-5.

2. Touch a negatively charged polyethylene strip against end A of the iron rod, then remove it. After 3 s, move the pith ball slowly along each side of the rod and around the ends. Do not allow the pith ball to touch the rod. Record what happens.

3. Recharge the polyethylene strip and bring it close to the pith ball. Observe, and then remove any charge from the pith ball (see note on page 475).

4. Connect one end of the copper wire to a water tap, and, as you hold the wire by the plastic coating, touch the iron rod with the other end.

5. Hold the *uncharged* pith ball close to the iron rod. Record what happens.

6. Repeat step 2, and then touch the metal rod with your finger. Repeat step 5.

7. Repeat steps 2 to 5, replacing the iron rod with a glass rod.

8. Replace the glass rod with each of the other objects supplied by the teacher. Repeat steps 2 to 5 for each object.

Discussion

1. a) What kind of charge is on the pith ball in step 2?
   b) Explain what happened when the polyethylene strip touched the end of the iron rod in step 2.

2. a) What kind of charge is on the pith ball in step 7?
   b) Explain what happened when the polyethylene strip touched the end of the glass rod in step 7.

3. a) Compare the movement of electric charge in the iron rod to that in the glass rod.
   b) Classify the objects used in the activity into two groups: i) those that transfer electric charge, and ii) those that do not transfer electric charge.

4. List, in order, the inferences you made as you answered discussion questions 1 and 2.

5. State two reasons why plastic materials are used to cover the copper wires in electrical equipment.

Insulators and Conductors

The continuous build-up of static charge on furniture and glass during cleaning can be explained by considering what can happen to electric charges when they are transferred to an object. Wooden furniture and glass are both electrical **insulators**. An insulator is a substance in which electrons cannot move freely from atom to atom. If some atoms of an insulator become negatively charged with extra electrons, these electrons remain on the same atoms until removed. An insulator that has positively charged atoms on its surface behaves in a similar manner. When you polish furniture, the electric charges remain on the surfaces and attract dust particles.

Kitchen and bathroom taps are made of substances called electrical **conductors**. A conductor is a substance in which electrons can move freely from one atom to another. If a conductor becomes negatively charged with extra electrons, they move freely along its surface. When taps are charged negatively by friction, the extra electrons repel one another and are conducted away from the taps along metal water pipes throughout the house. Some excess electrons may be conducted out of the house through the main water supply pipe, where they transfer into the ground. Because the electric charge is conducted away as it is produced, the taps remain uncharged. Table 16-3 lists common insulators and conductors.

Table 16-3: Common Insulators and Conductors

Good Conductors	Fair Conductors	Good Insulators
silver	carbon	oil
copper	nichrome	fur
gold	human body	silk
aluminum	moist human skin	wool
magnesium	acid solutions	sulphur
tungsten	salt water	porcelain
nickel	the Earth	plastic
mercury	water vapour (in air)	wood
platinum		paper
iron		wax
		glass
		rubber
		ebonite

Many materials we use and wear every day are electrical insulators. Because these materials often become charged with static electricity, they can be irritating, especially in winter. However, because electrons cannot pass through electrical insulators, these materials can protect us from electric shocks. Insulating materials cover many household tools and appliances. Electrical cords, plugs, wall sockets, and switches are actually metal conductors covered by some kind of insulating material.

Transferring Charge by Contact

The first way you learned to transfer charge, by friction, is difficult to avoid. The second way to transfer charge, by contact, is the one we try to avoid because it can be painful. When you touch a doorknob after walking across a carpet, you often get a shock (see Figure 16-6). Electric charges have been transferred by contact between you and the doorknob. After walking across the carpet, you may be charged negatively, due to friction. The doorknob, which is often a conductor, is usually uncharged. When you touch the doorknob, some of the extra electrons on your body transfer to it. Thus, the total electric charge on your body is shared between you and the doorknob, and the charge transferred to the doorknob is also negative. The pith ball on the pith-ball electroscope becomes charged in the same way. An object that becomes charged by contact always receives the same kind of charge as that on the object giving the charge.

Figure 16-6. a)

The student is charged negatively after walking across the carpet. The door knob is uncharged.

b)

door knob

carpet

When the student touches the door knob, it becomes negatively charged by contact. When a charge is transferred by contact in this way, the result is often a painful shock.

Besides giving irritating shocks, transferring electric charge by contact can also cause dangerous accidents. A single spark produced through charging by contact can cause fires and explosions. Special safety precautions are followed in grain elevators, flour mills, coal mines, hospital operating theatres, and oil refineries to prevent or control sparks produced by static electricity.

Do You Know?
The splashing water in a shower produces negative charges in bathroom air. Similarly, the high-speed water jets used to clean large crude-oil supertankers produce large amounts of negative charge. The resulting sparks have caused serious explosions on the ships.

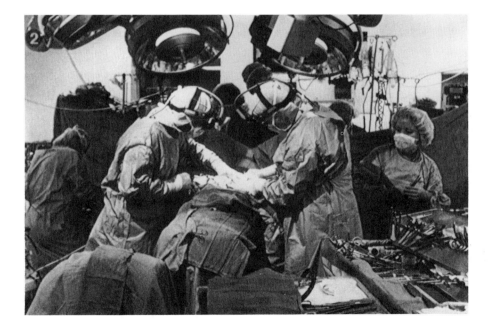

The clothing worn by doctors and nurses in operating theatres is woven with electrical conducting fibres in order to eliminate sparks caused by static electricity.

Discharging or Neutralizing Electrically Charged Objects

Charged objects can be discharged by simple exposure to the air. On a humid summer day, the charge leaks away so rapidly that many of the problems caused by static electricity are not noticeable. However, on a cold dry winter day when the humidity is low, the charge leaks away so slowly that combing your hair can be difficult. Other ways to discharge an object are to shine a light on it or to expose it to radioactivity.

When the electric charges on a charged object are removed, the object is said to be **discharged** or **neutralized**. Because of the dangers caused by sparks, certain objects must be continually discharged. This can be done by connecting these objects to the Earth by means of a conductor. The Earth itself is a fairly good conductor. When a charged object is connected, or **grounded**, to the Earth, it shares its charge with the Earth. The Earth is so large that it effectively removes all the charge from the object. Assembly-line workers who connect microchips to the circuit boards of computers and other electronic equipment often wear metal straps on their wrists. The strap is connected by a wire to the metal workbench. Why must they wear this strap?

The surface shape of a charged conductor affects the rate at which it becomes discharged. Smooth, spherical shapes retain charges indefinitely, because the charges spread themselves evenly over the surface. However, conductors pointed at the ends lose charges rapidly. Scientists think that electrons concentrate near the point of the conductor and attract positive ions from the air nearby (see Figure 16-7). A positively charged conductor attracts negative ions. This method of discharging charged objects, called **discharge at a point**, is the basic principle on which the lightning rod operates (see page 490).

Figure 16-7.

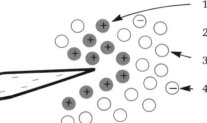

A negatively charged conductor attracts positively charged ions in the air, and neutralization occurs rapidly.

1. Positively charged ions are attracted to the rod.
2. Electrons jump from the rod to the ions, forming neutral molecules.
3. Electron transfer forms neutral molecules.
4. Negatively charged ions are repelled from the rod.

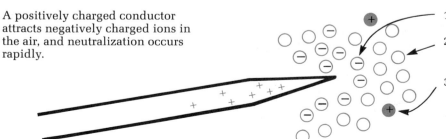

A positively charged conductor attracts negatively charged ions in the air, and neutralization occurs rapidly.

1. Negatively charged ions are attracted to the rod.
2. Electrons jump from the ions to the rod, forming neutral molecules.
3. Positively charged ions are repelled from the rod.

Study Questions

1. a) Explain the difference between a conductor and an insulator, in terms of the transfer of electrons.
   b) List three practical uses for i) electrical conductors, and ii) electrical insulators.

2. What happens when a negatively charged object touches an uncharged pith ball on an electroscope? Explain why.

3. When an object is charged by contact, how does the kind of charge transferred compare to that on the object giving the charge? Explain.

4. a) List three situations in which charging by contact can be dangerous. Explain why in each case.
   b) Describe three ways in which charged objects can be discharged.

CHALLENGER

On dry winter days, the problem of flyaway hair can be reduced by using aluminum combs rather than plastic ones. What two factors help to reduce problems with static electricity? (Hint: Review Tables 16-2 and 16-3.)

SCIENCE IN ACTION

SUPERCONDUCTORS

What single scientific discovery could eventually lead to practical electric cars; trains that travel at hundreds of kilometres per hour supported by powerful magnets; smaller, but more powerful computers; and a 20% reduction in energy losses when electricity is transmitted by overhead power lines? The answer is high-temperature "superconductors".

When an electric current flows through a normal conductor such as copper wire, some of the electrical energy is converted into heat energy. It is thought that the electrons collide with one another as they move through the conductor, and the energy loss is released as heat. However, at extremely low temperatures near absolute zero (0 K), some metals suddenly become "superconductors", and the electrons flow through the substance without losing any energy at all. In fact, electric currents that have been started in ring-shaped superconducting materials have been observed to flow for years without any added energy, and with no decrease in the amount of current.

The potential benefits of superconductivity have been known for many years. It was first observed by Dutch physicist H.K. Onnes (1853-1926) in 1911, when he cooled mercury below 4.2 K. However, the high cost of keeping temperatures near absolute zero using liquid hydrogen or helium limited its usefulness. In December 1985, at the IBM Zurich Research Lab in Switzerland, two physicists, K.A. Muller and J.G. Bednorz, discovered a compound of barium, lanthanum, copper, and oxygen that became

American high school student Heidi Grant demonstrates how to make a superconductor at the National Science Foundation in Washington, D.C.

superconductive at 35 K. By February 1987, researchers discovered a new compound that became superconductive at a temperature of 98 K. Such compounds can be kept at superconducting temperatures using inexpensive liquid nitrogen (b.p. 77 K). Scientists worldwide are trying to develop substances that will be superconducting at even higher temperatures.

16.3 Charging by Induction

What do lint sticking to your clothes and the operation of a TV aerial have in common? They are both examples of the third way of charging an object, charging by induction. In physics, the term induction suggests that something is made to happen without direct contact.

Activity 16-3: Charging by Induction

In this activity you will investigate two different methods of charging objects by induction. In Part B you will test your understanding by making predictions and testing them.

Materials

fur	polyethylene strip
silk	acetate strip
metal rod	metal-leaf electroscope
evaporating dish (and plasticine)	insulated wire conductor

Part A: Induced Charge Separation on Uncharged Objects
Procedure

1. Place the uncharged metal rod on the evaporating dish, and approach it with a negatively charged polyethylene strip. (Do not transfer any charge to the metal rod.)
2. Repeat step 1, using a positively charged acetate strip.
3. Approach the uncharged metal-leaf electroscope with a negatively charged polyethylene strip. (Do not transfer any charge to the electroscope.)
4. Repeat step 3, using a positively charged acetate strip.

Discussion

1. According to the Law of Electric Charges, what can you infer about the kind of charge that appears to be induced on the metal rod i) in step 1, and ii) in step 2? Explain your answers.
2. a) In terms of the movement of electrons, explain what happened to the electroscope i) in step 3, and ii) in step 4.
   b) In terms of the movement of electrons, explain what happened to the metal rod i) in step 1, and ii) in step 2.

A metal-leaf electroscope consists of a small metal ball connected to a metal rod. Hanging from the rod are two thin metal strips, or leaves. To prevent the leaves from being disturbed by air currents, they are usually enclosed in a glass-sided, insulated container. Because the parts of the electroscope are made of metal, which is a conductor, negatively charged electrons are able to move freely. When charged objects are brought near the ball, electrons move onto or out of the metal leaves. The resulting charge on the leaves causes them to repel one another.

3. a) Write a summary statement identifying the kind of charge that is induced on a neutral object when it is near a charged object.
   b) Why is it possible for the uncharged object to appear charged if no charge has been transferred to it?

Part B: Charging Uncharged Objects by Induction

Procedure

1. Place the uncharged metal rod on the evaporating dish, and attach an insulated wire conductor from one end of the metal rod to the water tap, as shown in Figure 16-8.
2. Bring a negatively charged polyethylene strip near (but not touching) the other end of the metal rod. While the charged strip is near the one end of the metal rod, remove the wire conductor from the other end. Then remove the charged strip.
3. **Make a Hypothesis:** Predict the kind of charge that has been induced on the metal rod. Then test for the charge you have predicted, using the appropriate test.
4. Attach an insulated wire conductor from the rod of the metal-leaf electroscope to the water tap, as shown in Figure 16-9.
5. Repeat steps 2 and 3, using the metal-leaf electroscope.
6. **Make a Hypothesis:** Predict what will happen if steps 1 to 5 are repeated using a positively charged acetate strip. Then test your prediction.

Discussion

1. a) What kind of charge was induced on i) the metal rod and ii) the metal-leaf electroscope by the polyethylene strip? Comment on the validity of your predictions.
   b) Explain what happened in step 2, in terms of the movement of electrons.
2. a) What kind of charge was induced on i) the metal rod, and ii) the metal-leaf electroscope, by the positively charged acetate strip? Comment on the validity of your predictions.
   b) Explain what happened in step 6 to i) the metal rod, and ii) the metal-leaf electroscope, in terms of the movement of electrons.
3. Write a summary statement identifying the kind of charge transferred to an object that is charged by induction.

Figure 16-8.

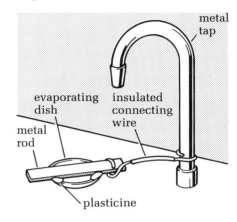

Figure 16-9.

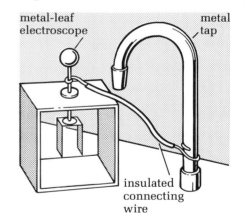

Effects Produced by Induced Charge Separation

Certain annoying effects of static electricity, such as dust and lint clinging to clothes, furniture, and records, are caused by an effect known as induced charge separation. Earlier you learned that uncharged objects are attracted to charged objects. This attraction occurs because of a slight movement of the electric charges on the uncharged object.

Consider the uncharged dust particle in Figure 16-10a). It has equal numbers of negative and positive charges spread evenly over it. Now, if the dust particle is brought near a piece of negatively charged magnetic tape (see Figure 16-10b), the negative charges on the dust particle are repelled slightly. This slight shift in the position of the electrons makes the side of the dust particle nearest the magnetic tape appear positively charged. We say that a positive charge has been induced on one side of the dust particle. Because positive charges are attracted to negative charges, the dust particle is attracted to the magnetic tape. Even though the dust particle is actually still neutral, the slight shift or movement of the electrons makes it appear positively charged on one side. The charges on the dust particle have been forced, or induced, to separate slightly.

Figure 16-10c) shows what happens to a dust particle near a positively charged object. Whether an object is charged positively or negatively, the dust particle is still attracted to it. A neutral object always has an opposite charge induced on it when placed near a charged object. This is why there is an attractive force between charged objects and neutral objects.

If you walk through a carpeted room and touch a doorknob, you can experience all three ways of transferring electric charge. First, as you walk your shoes rub against the carpet fibres, and your body becomes charged by friction. Then, as you continue across the room, the electric charge on your body attracts dust, lint, and hairs to your clothes by induction. Finally, when you touch the doorknob, you transfer an electric charge to it by contact.

Figure 16-10.

a) In an uncharged dust particle, the positive and negative charges are evenly distributed.

b) An uncharged dust particle near a negatively charged magnetic tape.

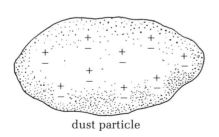

dust particle

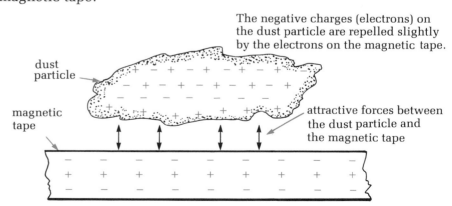

The negative charges (electrons) on the dust particle are repelled slightly by the electrons on the magnetic tape.

dust particle

magnetic tape

attractive forces between the dust particle and the magnetic tape

c) An uncharged dust particle near a positively charged table top.

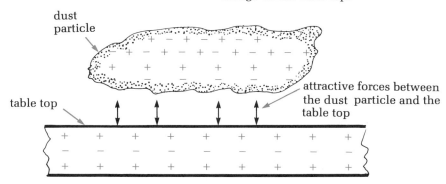

Electrons are attracted by the positive charge on the table top.

dust particle

table top

attractive forces between the dust particle and the table top

Charging Uncharged Objects by Induction

Another way of charging by induction actually causes the transfer of charged particles from one object to another. Suppose a negatively charged strip is brought near one end of an uncharged metal rod. The electrons at that end of the metal rod are repelled. This movement of electrons induces a negative charge on the other end of the metal rod, as shown in Figure 16-11a). When the negatively charged strip is removed, the electrons redistribute themselves evenly along the rod again (Figure 16-11b)).

However, if a conducting wire is connected from the metal rod to a "ground", such as a water tap, something quite different happens. When the negatively charged strip is brought close to the metal rod, some of the electrons repelled along the metal rod are conducted into the wire (see Figure 16-12a)) on the next page). If the wire is now removed from the metal rod, the metal rod will have lost some electrons and will be positively charged (Figure 16-12b)). When the negatively charged strip is removed, the remaining electrons spread evenly along the metal rod again, but the rod stays positively charged (Figure 16-12c)). The charging of a metal-leaf electroscope by induction is shown in Figure 16-13.

When objects are charged by induction in this way, a permanent charge is induced on the uncharged object (in this case, the metal rod). The induced charge is always opposite to that of the charged object producing the charge. For example, a negative charge can be induced on a metal rod by placing a positively charged strip near the metal rod when the conducting wire is connected to it.

Figure 16-11.

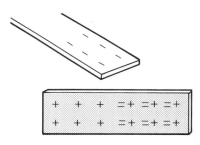

a) Electrons in the metal rod are repelled by the negatively charged strip.

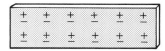

b) When the negatively charged strip is removed, the electrons redistribute themselves evenly throughout the metal rod.

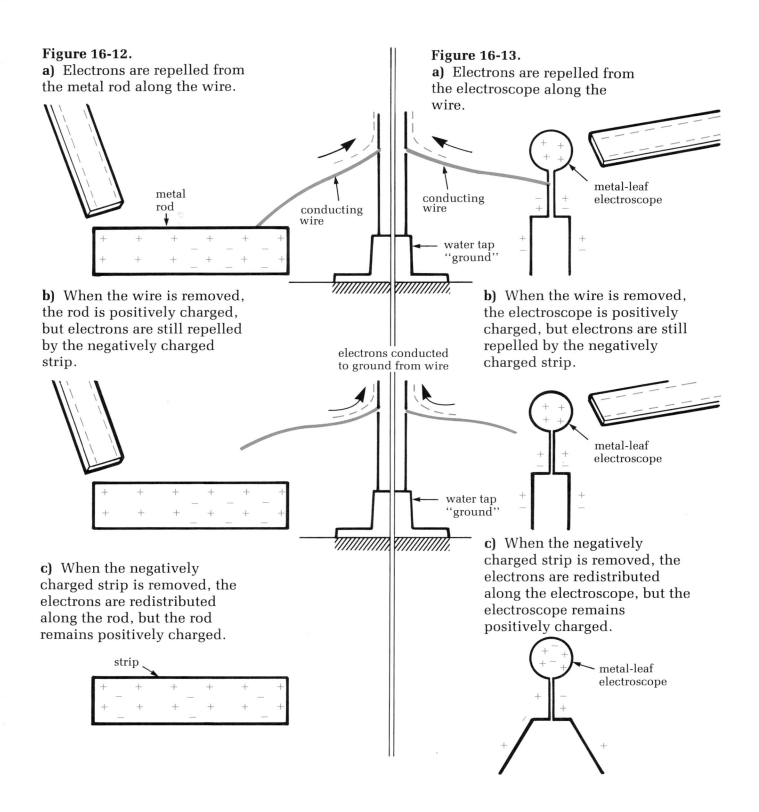

Figure 16-12.
a) Electrons are repelled from the metal rod along the wire.

metal rod

conducting wire

b) When the wire is removed, the rod is positively charged, but electrons are still repelled by the negatively charged strip.

c) When the negatively charged strip is removed, the electrons are redistributed along the rod, but the rod remains positively charged.

strip

Figure 16-13.
a) Electrons are repelled from the electroscope along the wire.

conducting wire

water tap "ground"

metal-leaf electroscope

electrons conducted to ground from wire

water tap "ground"

metal-leaf electroscope

b) When the wire is removed, the electroscope is positively charged, but electrons are still repelled by the negatively charged strip.

c) When the negatively charged strip is removed, the electrons are redistributed along the electroscope, but the electroscope remains positively charged.

metal-leaf electroscope

In this explanation, the conducting wire was connected and disconnected to show that a charge was induced on the metal rod. However, in practical applications of charging by induction, the wire is usually connected permanently. The induced charge can then move on and off the object freely whenever electric forces act on the object. Devices such as electrostatic microphones, television aerials, and lightning rods all work on the principle of induced charges.

Practical Uses of Static Electricity

Although static electricity can be annoying and even dangerous, it also has practical uses. Three main kinds of applications of electrostatic devices are:

1. Pollution and Dust Control

The electrostatic air cleaners installed in homes and hospitals use static electricity. Dust is removed from the air by applying the attraction between unlike charges. The dirty air is usually sprayed with positively charged ions as it passes into the air cleaner. The positive ions are attracted to the dust particles by induction. This produces positively charged dust particles that are then forced through a set of negatively charged flat plates. These attract the oppositely charged dust particles. The cleaned air passes through. A similar method removes most of the pollutants travelling up industrial chimney stacks.

The small portable air cleaners used to get rid of cigarette smoke and dust emit electrically charged particles that first attach themselves to the smoke and dust particles; the charges then deposit the particles on various surfaces by induction.

The smokestacks at this Ontario Hydro generating station are equipped with electrostatic air cleaners, which remove many air pollutants before they enter the atmosphere.

Figure 16-14. An
electrostatic spray-painting
machine. It is possible to
spray the back of an object,
even though the spray gun is
pointed at the sides. Explain
why.

2. Coating Surfaces with Particles

An electrostatic process is used to spray-paint objects. The tiny
paint particles from the spray gun are electrically charged as they
pass an electrode attached to the gun. The object to be painted is
given a charge opposite to that on the paint. If the object is made
of an insulating material, it is first coated or dipped in a conducting
substance. The charged paint particles are attracted towards the
oppositely-charged object. Paint droplets that would normally have
missed the object are pulled towards it by the attractive electric
forces.

A similar method is used to control the spraying of insecticides
on plants. Using the same principle, other machines have been
developed to make sandpaper, to coat wallpaper and greeting cards
with fibres, and to produce fabrics with a velvet-like coating.

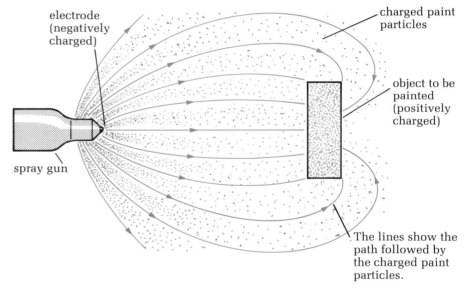

3. Copying Printed Materials

A copying machine uses the scientific principle that electric
charges can be removed from a surface by light. First, a special
kind of selenium-coated flat plate is positively charged (step 1).
Light shone through a lens then projects an image of the page to
be copied onto the charged plate. Wherever the light falls on the
plate, the positive charge is removed (step 2). Only the dark areas,
representing the printed material on the page, remain charged.
Particles of negatively charged powdered ink are then sprinkled
over the plate, and these particles are attracted to the charged areas
(step 3). Next, a positively charged piece of paper is brought in

contact with the plate, and the negative ink particles transfer to the paper (step 4). A lamp rapidly heats the paper, causing the ink to fuse or melt onto it, making a permanent copy of the original page (step 5). This process, shown in Figure 16-15, is called **xerography**.

Xerography is derived from two Greek words, *xeros* meaning "dry", and *graphein* meaning "to write".

Figure 16-15. The operation of a photocopying machine.

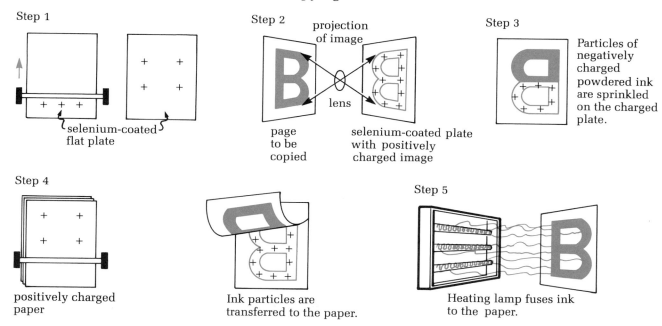

Step 1

selenium-coated flat plate

Step 2
projection of image
lens
page to be copied
selenium-coated plate with positively charged image

Step 3
Particles of negatively charged powdered ink are sprinkled on the charged plate.

Step 4
positively charged paper

Ink particles are transferred to the paper.

Step 5
Heating lamp fuses ink to the paper.

Study Questions

1. a) Why is a dust particle attracted to a charged object?
   b) Draw a diagram to show what happens to the charges on the dust particle in 1 a).
2. a) Describe how the movement of charge on a pith-ball electroscope differs from that on a metal-leaf electroscope.
   b) What is the essential difference between the two types of electroscopes?
3. When an object is charged by induction, how does the kind of charge transferred compare to that on the object inducing the charge? Explain.
4. a) Describe how to charge a metal-leaf electroscope with a negative charge by induction.
   b) Draw a series of diagrams to show the movement of electrons as the electroscope in 4 a) is charged.

CHALLENGER

When pieces of paper are attracted to a charged rod, some remain stuck to the surface. Other pieces of paper, however, are initially attracted, and then fall off. Why does this happen?

LIGHTNING

Lightning is simply an enormous spark caused by huge amounts of static electricity. Most lightning occurs between thunderclouds; this kind is called sheet lightning. Scientists estimate that the Earth is struck by lightning about 100 times every second. Most of these lightning strikes return negative charges to the Earth.

The diagram in Figure 16-16 shows how a lightning rod can protect a house from a lightning strike. A pointed metal rod is attached to the highest point of the building. A thick conductor, usually copper, is connected from the pointed rod to a metal plate buried in the ground. The plate is used to conduct the electric charges from the rod to the ground. If the base of the cloud above the house is charged negatively, the pointed rod, the house, and the ground immediately beneath the cloud become positively charged by induction.

The air in the lower atmosphere contains huge numbers of both positive and negative ions. The movement of these ions is shown in Figure 16-16. Most of the time this movement of the ions above the pointed rod is sufficient to prevent a lightning strike from occurring at all. However, if a lightning strike does occur, the copper conductor carries the negative charges safely to the plate in the ground.

Lightning is spectacular, but it is also very dangerous. Lightning causes most of the forest fires in Canada, and kills and injures dozens of people every year. The Canada Safety Council recommends the following actions if you are caught in a thunderstorm.

- Seek shelter indoors, or in a car, bus, or truck with a metal roof.
- Get away from the water. If boating, get to shore.
- Avoid exposed metal objects, such as bicycles, golf clubs, and fences.
- Stay away from tall trees, open spaces, hilltops, overhead wires, and transmission towers.
- In an open area, crouch in a fetal position with only the feet touching the ground to minimize exposure. If possible, do so in a low place such as a ditch. In a forest, seek shelter under small trees in a low area.
- If in a group of people, spread out to reduce risk.
- Do not use the telephone. Lightning can travel along the line.

Figure 16-16. The protection of a building by a lightning rod.

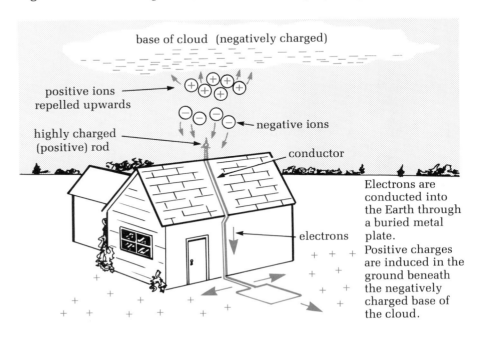

base of cloud (negatively charged)

positive ions repelled upwards

negative ions

highly charged (positive) rod

conductor

electrons

Electrons are conducted into the Earth through a buried metal plate. Positive charges are induced in the ground beneath the negatively charged base of the cloud.

Meet an Electrical Design Engineer — Arthur Radacz

Since 1984 Arthur has worked at Spar Aerospace Limited, a company that designs products for the aerospace industry and industrial robotics.

Q. WHEN DID YOU FIRST THINK OF ENGINEERING AS A CAREER?
A. In high school I started in the music program, but then I got sidetracked into computer programming in Grade 10. This was when computers were first being introduced into schools and certain students with high math marks were selected. Later I went into electrical engineering at university.

Q. WHAT KINDS OF ENGINEERS WORK AT SPAR?
A. We have mostly mechanical and electrical engineers working in various divisions. My time is divided between electrical design duties in the aerospace field and in the industrial section which is a newer division of the company. Some of the aerospace work is classified as secret.

Q. WHAT SORT OF PROJECTS DO YOU DO IN THE INDUSTRIAL DIVISION?
A. In the last 10 to 15 years, a lot of mass production operations have been integrated with computers. We use the term "robotics" to mean the upgrading of a machine so that a robot simulates operations formerly done by a person. This applies particularly to assembly line work like drilling operations, metal punching, and welding.

Q. DO THESE MACHINES REPLACE PEOPLE?
A. Not really, because the machine needs three people to run it: a programmer, a maintenance person, and a person who operates the machine on a regular basis. The advantage is that the machine doesn't get tired, so there's a guarantee of better quality. Also, because the machine can be left alone, the operator can work on several different machines at the same time.

Q. DO YOU WORK ALONE ON AN INDUSTRIAL DESIGN SYSTEM?
A. No, I'm nearly always part of a team. For instance, if a customer contacts the company with a problem, a group of us will meet with the customer. There may be a mechanical engineer, an electrical designer like myself, someone in controls or software, and a draughtsperson. We all work together to develop a proposal that will meet the client's requirements.

Q. WHAT IS YOUR MOST MEMORABLE ACCOMPLISHMENT?
A. I tend to remember my catastrophes rather than accomplishments. Once I was working on a mechanical arm for Ontario Hydro that could lift one tonne and had about a ten-metre reach. It went out of control and headed toward a wall because the protection systems didn't work. I'll never forget that near-catastrophe.

Q. WHAT DO YOU LIKE BEST ABOUT YOUR JOB?
A. It's easier to answer that what I don't like is the paperwork. One of the big problems for engineers is that you eventually end up in a management type of position. It's hard to keep up-to-date, with technology changing as fast as it does. Very few people stay design engineers forever — they get squeezed into management and more paperwork. I work constantly at keeping up with new technology because I want to stay in design.

Q. WHAT ADVICE DO YOU HAVE FOR STUDENTS INTERESTED IN AN ENGINEERING CAREER?
A. Most important is "don't close any doors". Take a variety of courses.

Review Questions

A: Knowledge

1. a) Draw a labelled diagram showing the structure of an atom.
    b) Indicate the kind of charge on each of the particles that make up the atom.

2. Why do some atoms lose electrons when rubbed against atoms of a different substance?

3. What is:
    a) a negatively charged ion?
    b) a positively charged ion?

4. Which particles in the atom move when electric charge is transferred from one atom to another? Explain why.

5. a) List three ways of changing the charge on an uncharged object.
    b) List two examples of each way of changing the charge.

6. Describe three methods of discharging a charged object.

7. List three safety precautions that should be taken if you are outside during a lightning storm.

8. What does it mean to electrically "ground" an object?

9. List six materials that are electrical conductors and six that are electrical insulators.

10. Explain why an electric charge quickly builds up on the surface of furniture when it is being polished, but not on water taps.

11. Determine, using the Electrostatic Series, the charge on each object when the following materials are rubbed together:
    a) glass and cotton
    b) copper and silk
    c) sulphur and fur
    d) acetate and wool

B: Application

12. a) What is the function of an electroscope?
    b) Name the kind of electroscope that can be recognized as being charged, just by observation.
    c) Explain how to identify the kind of charge present on i) a charged pith-ball electroscope and ii) a charged metal-leaf electroscope.

13. Why is pith used for the ball on the pith-ball electroscope?

14. How is an electroscope used to determine if a substance is a conductor or an insulator?

15. Describe and explain what happens when a) a negatively charged, and b) a positively charged object is brought up to an uncharged pith-ball electroscope.

16. Explain how to identify the unknown charge on an object, using a pith-ball electroscope.

17. Explain the purpose of the Electrostatic Series. List a practical example to illustrate your answer.

18. What kind of electric charge remains on your hair after you comb it with a plastic comb? Explain why this happens.

19. Why is it necessary to place an electrical conductor on an electrical insulator to be able to electrically charge the conductor?

20. Use the Electrostatic Series to explain what happens when you rub a balloon against your hair.

21. Why are metallic fibres woven into the pile of some types of carpets?

22. Identify four objects in the home that consist of electrical insulators and conductors combined together. Explain why these combinations are used.

23. When you polish a metal ornament in the kitchen, dust particles are attracted to it. However, when you polish a nearby metal water tap, it does not attract dust particles. Explain these two situations.

24. a) What happens when you comb your hair on a dry day in winter?
    b) Explain why this happens, in terms of the model for the electrical nature of matter.

25. Why do some cars and trucks have wires and chains hanging underneath them?

26. If you were given only a negatively charged strip, how could you charge a metal-leaf electroscope a) positively, and b) negatively?

27. How does the charge produced by contact differ from the charge produced by induction?

28. Why is lint attracted to your clothes in winter?

29. a) How does a lightning rod protect a house during a thunderstorm?
    b) List three safety precautions that should be taken inside a house during a lightning storm.

30. Which has more need of lightning protection, a wooden barn or a tall steel skyscraper? Explain why.

31. a) List four major areas of application in which electrostatic devices are used.
    b) State the properties of electric charges that are used to advantage in each area of application.

32. When static electricity is discharged rapidly, what forms of energy can be produced? List examples to support your answer.

33. Why is dust attracted to records while they are being played?

C: Problem Solving

34. Consider the following interactions between various combinations of four pith balls, A, B, C, and D. The force between B and A is repulsion. D attracts C and A. If D is attracted to an acetate strip that has been rubbed with silk, what are the charges on A, B, and C?

35. a) Describe what happens when a negatively charged object is touched to a metal-leaf electroscope, and then removed.
    b) Draw a series of diagrams to show what happens to the movement of electric charges on the electroscope.

36. a) Suppose you have a positively charged acetate strip, and two uncharged metal spheres mounted on insulating stands. Describe how to use the charged strip to charge one sphere positively and one sphere negatively by electrostatic induction.
    b) Explain what happened to the charges on the two spheres. Draw a series of diagrams to illustrate your answer.
    c) How can you check the kind of charge on each sphere?

Try This

1. **Your Personal Electrostatic Series**
   When two different substances are rubbed together, they become charged. Using the Electrostatic Series in Table 16-2 as a reference, try rubbing together a number of different substances commonly found in the home. By analyzing the results, develop your own version of the Electrostatic Series.

2. **Kitchen Electroscopes**
   Study the electroscopes used in your classroom. Try to make an electroscope from materials available in your home. Test your electroscope and compare its performance with those in the classroom.

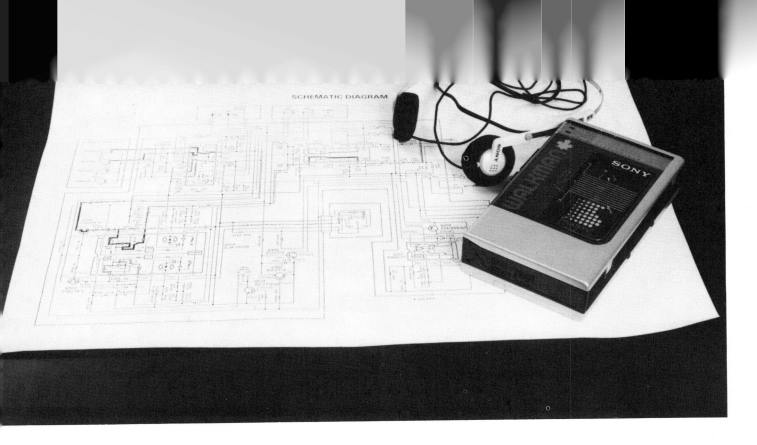

Chapter 17
Electricity and Electric Circuits

When lightning strikes, or a spark jumps from your hand to a door knob, electric charges are moving through the air. Electrical energy is transferred by the movement of electric charge. The movement, or flow, of electric charges from one place to another is called an **electric current**.

The path taken by the electric current flowing during a lightning stroke is not controlled. However, when electricity is used in the home (for example), the electric current flows in a controlled path called an **electric circuit**. We use electric circuits to produce electrical energy, and to convert it into other forms of energy needed in our modern society.

In this chapter, we will examine the basic parts of an electric circuit. We will also learn about electric current, electric potential (voltage), and sources of electrical energy. Finally, we will study the characteristics of two basic kinds of electric circuits.

Always remember that "moving electric charges" is a shortened form for "moving electrically charged *particles*".

When you finish Chapter 17, you should be able to:

- explain the function of each part of an electric circuit
- construct and describe the operation of an electrochemical cell (a source of electrical energy)
- draw and construct simple electric circuits, and measure electric potentials (voltages) related to the circuits
- describe the characteristics of two basic kinds of electric circuits

17.1   The Electric Circuit

Electrical energy is a major source of energy in our homes. Every time you plug in an electric kettle, turn on the TV, or switch on a light, you are using electrical energy in an electric circuit of some kind.

Activity 17-1:   The Electric Circuit

In this activity you will construct a simple electric circuit, and determine the function of each of its parts.

Materials

dry cell   light bulb (screwed into holder)
switch   connecting wires (conductors)

Procedure

1. Draw the diagram of the electric circuit shown in Figure 17-1 in your notebook.

Figure 17-1.

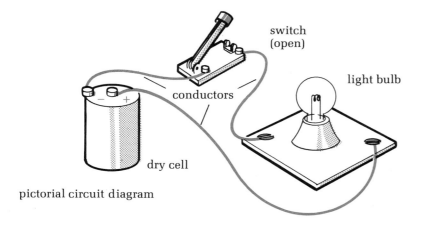

switch (open)

light bulb

conductors

dry cell

pictorial circuit diagram

Do You Know?
We often use the term "battery" instead of "cell". A battery is actually a combination of two or more cells.

CAUTION: Ensure that the switch is "open", as shown in Figure 17-1, before connecting the wires in the electric circuit. When the arm on the switch is pushed down, the switch is said to be "closed".

2. Place the dry cell, the (open) switch, and the light bulb on your desk, in the positions shown in Figure 17-1.

3. Connect a wire from the negative terminal of the dry cell to one side of the switch. Draw a line on the circuit diagram in your notebook to show which wire has been connected. (See Figure 17-2.)

Figure 17-2.

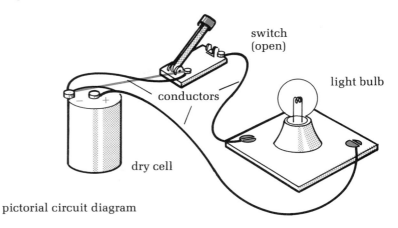

pictorial circuit diagram

4. Connect a wire from the other side of the switch to the bulb. Draw the appropriate line on your circuit diagram.

5. Connect a wire from the other side of the bulb to the positive terminal of the cell. Draw the appropriate line on your circuit diagram.

6. Close and open the switch several times. Record what happens. Touch the light bulb.

7. Close the switch. Disconnect and then reconnect each end of all three wires in turn. Record what happens.

8. Close the switch. Unscrew the bulb, and then screw it in again. Record what happens.

9. Remove the switch from the circuit, and connect the bulb to the dry cell. Find as many ways as possible to turn the light bulb on and off. Record each method.

Discussion

1. What happens to the stored chemical energy in the dry cell when the switch is closed?

2. What energy changes occur in the light bulb?

3. What is the function of a) the dry cell, b) the switch, c) the light bulb, d) the wires?

4. Which one of the four parts of the circuit can be omitted? Why is it usually included in a circuit?

5. List three different ways of turning the light bulb on and off.

6. Would the circuit operate differently if a) the connections on the switch were reversed, b) the switch were connected on the other side of the light bulb? Explain your answers.

7. List three simple electric circuits used in the home that have the four parts identified in this activity.

The Parts of an Electric Circuit

Although the flashlight and the light bulb shown in the photograph in the margin look quite different, the electric circuits which operate both of them are basically the same. There are four basic parts in a simple electric circuit. These four parts are:

1. A Source of Electrical Energy

In the home a number of different types of electrical outlets supply electrical energy to desk lamps, washers, and television sets. In many flashlights, cameras, and toys, dry cells supply the electrical energy. Dry cells and other sources of electrical energy are discussed in Section 17.2.

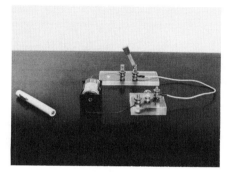

Although different in form, both the flashlight and the light bulb use the same type of electric circuit.

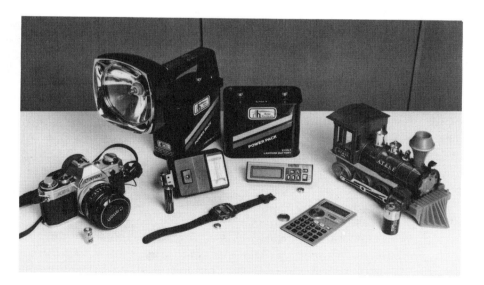

The shape and size of dry cells and batteries vary greatly, depending on the electrical devices they operate.

Electrical energy is usually converted into heat, light, sound, or mechanical energy. Try to think of devices operated by electricity that produce these forms of energy.

2. An Electrical Load

All electric circuits include a device to convert electrical energy into another form of energy. In a flashlight, the energy converter is the light bulb; in a washing machine, it is an electric motor. The energy converter in any electric circuit is usually called the load. Electrical loads are discussed in Section 17.4.

3. Devices to Control the Electric Current

In a flashlight, a **switch** controls the electric current. Switches are perhaps the most common control devices used in electric circuits. Other control devices are electrical fuses (p. 520), circuit breakers (p. 522), and the control knobs on home appliances.

Electrical fuses and circuit breakers are automatic safety switches that open if the current exceeds a safe level. Light switches and dimmers are operated by hand.

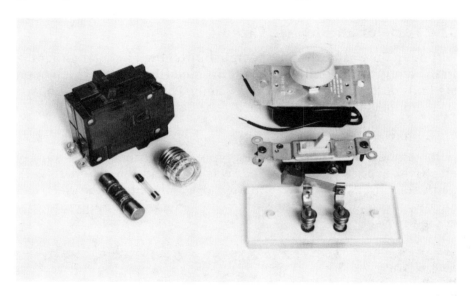

4. Electrical Conductors for Connectors

Wires or pieces of metal that are good electrical conductors are generally used to connect the other three parts of an electric circuit. The conducting wires provide a controlled path for the flow of electric current (electrons) in the circuit. The wires are usually covered with an insulating material to ensure that the electric current flows only in the circuit.

In the photograph of the light bulb circuit, the light bulb is not glowing because the switch is in the "off" position. When the switch is in the "off" position, it is said to be "open". When the switch is open, and no electric current can flow, there is said to be an **open circuit**. When the switch is pushed to the "on" position,

Some electric circuits can operate without a switch. An electric kettle is an electrical load that is not usually connected by a switch to the source of electrical energy. Electric current can flow in the circuit only when you insert the plug (or "connecting leads") into a wall outlet.

it is said to be "closed". An electric current can flow in the electric circuit only if the switch is closed. When an electric current flows in a circuit there is said to be a **closed circuit**. The electric current flows from the **negative terminal** of the cell, through the wires, the switch, and the light bulb, and returns to the cell's **positive terminal**.

Electric Circuit Diagrams and Symbols

To show how the various parts of a simple light bulb's electric circuit are connected, it was necessary to draw a simple sketch of each part. To avoid having to do such time-consuming pictorial diagrams of electric circuits, special symbols are used instead. Some of the most commonly used symbols are shown in Figure 17-3.

Figure 17-3. Symbols for schematic circuit diagrams.

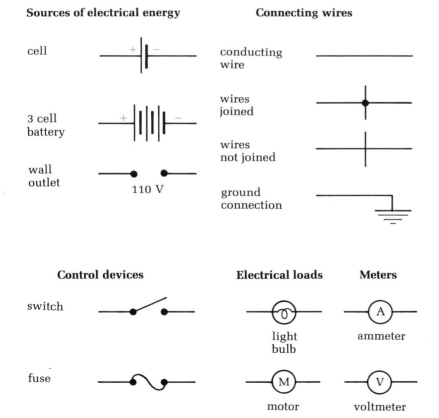

Drawings of circuits using these symbols are called **schematic circuit diagrams**. In these diagrams, the connecting wires are usually drawn as straight lines, with right-angled corners. This makes it easier to understand complicated circuits. However, when you connect an electric circuit, you simply connect the wires between the devices. The actual connecting wires do not have to be laid out in the straight lines shown in the circuit diagram.

André Marie Ampère (1775-1836) Long before the existence of the electron was even suggested, Ampère proposed that tiny electrical currents exist within the atom.

In electric arc welding, the electric current flowing between the welding rod and the pieces of metal produces so much heat that the metals actually melt together.

Electric Current: Moving Electrons

To develop a better understanding of electric circuits, you will first learn about two fundamental electrical quantities: electric current and electric potential (voltage).

An electric current is made up of moving electric charges. In solids, the moving charges are electrons. Electric current is a measure of the rate at which electric charges (electrons) move past a given point in a circuit per second. The metric SI unit used to measure electric current is the **ampere**. The symbol for the ampere is A. An electric current of about one ampere (1 A) flows through a 100 W light bulb. Table 17-1 lists some electrical loads and the electric currents required to operate them.

Table 17-1: The Electric Current Ratings of Some Common Electrical Loads

Electrical Device	Electric Current (amperes)	Electrical Device	Electric Current (amperes)
electronic wrist watch	0.00013	vacuum cleaner	6.5
electronic calculator	0.002	stove element	6.8
electric clock	0.16	oven element	11.4
light bulb (100 W)	0.91	toaster	13.6
television (colour)	4.1	water heater element	27.3
electric drill	4.5	car starter motor (V-8)	500.0

When the switch on a flashlight is closed, an electric current flows through the bulb and the filament produces light immediately. As each electron leaves the negative terminal of the cell and enters the electric circuit, another one moves from the circuit into the positive terminal of the cell.

Measuring Electric Current — The Ammeter

An ammeter is a device that measures the amount of electric current flowing in a circuit. When an electric current flows through the ammeter, the needle of the ammeter indicates the amount of current in amperes. An ammeter measures the rate at which electrons flow past a point in the circuit.

Electric Potential (Voltage)

If you put your fingers across the two terminals of a small dry cell, you would not feel anything. However, you must never touch the terminals of an electrical wall outlet. You would receive a severe electric shock.

A dry cell and a wall outlet are both sources of electrical energy, and each releases electrons into its electric circuit. What is the difference between the two sources of electrical energy? The difference is in the *amount* of energy that each electron receives from the energy source before moving into the electric circuit. The energy given to each electron leaving the terminal of the wall outlet is about 75 times greater than the energy given to each electron leaving the terminal of the dry cell. In fact, the energy of the electrons leaving the terminals of a wall outlet is great enough to cause a dangerous amount of electric current to flow through your body. When this happens you feel an electric shock.

When electric current flows from a dry cell, chemical energy is converted into electrical energy. The chemical energy separates electrons from atoms in the cell. The energy given to each electron is called **electric potential (energy)**. The electric potential gained by electrons can be compared to the gravitational potential energy gained by objects lifted above the Earth's surface. The larger the electric potential, the greater the amount of energy possessed by each electron at the terminal of a source of electrical energy.

The SI unit used to measure electric potential is the **volt**, and the symbol for this unit is V. Electric potential is often called **voltage**. Table 17-2 lists some sources of electrical potential, with typical voltage values.

Table 17-2: Some Sources of Electric Potential (Voltage)

Source of Electric Potential	Voltage (volts)	Source of Electric Potential	Voltage (volts)
record player pickup head	0.01	electrochemical battery	3.0 to 28
tape playback head	0.015	electric eel	650
human cell	0.08	portable generators	24, 110, 220
microphone	0.1	wall outlets in house	110, 220
photocell	0.8	generators in power stations	550
electrochemical cell	1.1 to 2.9		

Measuring Electric Potential — The Voltmeter

A voltmeter is a device that measures the electric potential of a source of electrical energy. When a voltmeter is connected across the terminals of a source of electrical energy, it indicates the electric potential in volts. A typical voltmeter is shown in the photograph.

CHALLENGER

To appreciate just how many electrons flow through a wire when a current of 1 A is flowing, consider the following. Suppose that an electron is equivalent to one grain of sand, and that the grain of sand has a volume of 1 mm³.

1. Now, imagine a large dump truck filled with sand. If the container measured 2 m × 3 m × 5 m, how many grains of sand would be required to fill a truck level with the top?

2. There are approximately 6 000 000 000 000 000 000 electrons moving past a given point in 1 s when 1 A flows in an electric circuit. To have as many grains of sand as there are electrons flowing in 1 A, how many filled dump trucks would have to pass you in one 1 s?

Study Questions

1. Define the following terms: electric circuit, open circuit, closed circuit, load, switch.

2. a) Name the four basic parts of an electric circuit.
   b) Explain the function of each part.

3. a) What is an electric current? State the SI unit and the symbol used for electric current.
   b) Name the two main factors that determine the amount of electric current flowing in a circuit.

4. a) What is electric potential? State the SI unit and the symbol used for electric potential.
   b) Explain, in terms of the energy of the electrons, why someone would receive a severe electric shock from a 120 V source, yet hardly notice the electric shock from a 6 V battery.

5. Why are schematic, rather than pictorial circuit diagrams, used?

HUMAN RESPONSE TO ELECTRIC SHOCK

There are many misconceptions about the effects of electricity upon the human body. It is important to realize that it is the *amount* of electric current that flows through the body that is the critical factor. The electric potentials that cause muscle movement in the human body are produced by nerve cells, and are typically about 0.08 V. When muscles are stimulated by electrochemical impulses from the nerve cells, the fibres in the muscle cells contract. The larger the electric current, the more strongly the muscles contract.

When a person touches an external source of electricity, an electric current passes through the body. If the current is large enough, the muscles in the part of the body in which the electric current is flowing automatically contract, and remain contracted until the electric current ceases. The chart in Figure 17-5 shows the effects produced by varying amounts of electric current. The amounts of electric current listed are average values.

Most people do not feel anything if the current is below 0.001 A, but feel a tingling sensation if the current is about 0.002 A. When the electric current is about 0.016 A, the muscles convulse. This level of electric current is sometimes referred to as the "let go" threshold, because the person cannot let go of the object giving the electric shock. If the electric current is flowing from one hand to the other through the chest, the breathing muscles may become paralyzed and the victim will suffocate unless the current is stopped.

If a current of 0.050 A or more passes through the chest, the heart muscles stop their regular pumping action and merely flutter. This fluttering of the heart muscles is called *ventricular fibrillation*. After a few seconds, the victim will become unconscious. The only way to stop ventricular fibrillation is to restart the pumping of the heart muscles by means of another *controlled* electric shock, administered as soon as possible. Electric currents above 0.200 A usually cause severe burns.

Before helping a victim of electric shock, ensure that you cannot receive a shock yourself. The electric current must be turned off, or the victim must be pulled from the danger zone with a nonconducting object, such as a piece of wood.

Figure 17-4. The effects of different levels of electric shock on the human body.

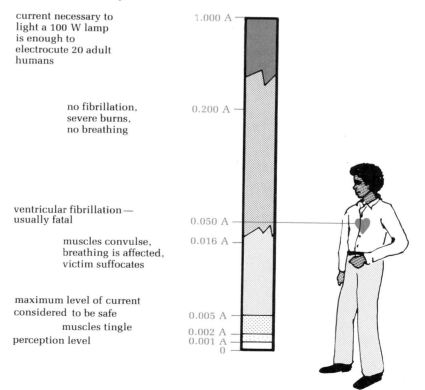

current necessary to light a 100 W lamp is enough to electrocute 20 adult humans — 1.000 A

no fibrillation, severe burns, no breathing — 0.200 A

ventricular fibrillation— usually fatal — 0.050 A

muscles convulse, breathing is affected, victim suffocates — 0.016 A

maximum level of current considered to be safe — 0.005 A

muscles tingle — 0.002 A

perception level — 0.001 A

0

17.2   Sources of Electrical Energy

A surprising number of everyday devices convert different forms of energy into electrical energy. Examples are the mouthpiece on a telephone, the pickup head on a record player, and the solar cells in a pocket calculator. Although most of these devices produce only a small amount of electrical energy, many of them play an essential role in our everyday lives.

▶ How to Read the Scale on a Voltmeter

Usually, the needle on a voltmeter moves from left to right. The zero voltage value is on the left, and the maximum value is on the right. If the voltmeter scale has only one set of numbers, use the following procedure to measure the voltage.

A. Determine the voltage value of the smallest division on the scale.

1. Record both the maximum voltage value on the scale and the units used.

2. Identify the smallest division on the scale, and record how many there are on the entire scale.

3. Divide the maximum voltage value by the number of smallest divisions. This number is the voltage value of the smallest division.

B. Read the voltage value indicated by the needle.

Figure 17-5.

Example: (see Figure 17-5a))
A. Voltage value of smallest division
1. Maximum voltage on scale = 1 V
2. Number of smallest divisions = 50
3. Voltage value of smallest division

$$= \frac{\text{Maximum voltage value}}{\text{Number of divisions}}$$

$$= \frac{1 \text{ V}}{50}$$

$$= 0.02 \text{ V}$$

B. Voltmeter reading = 0.76 V

a)

b)

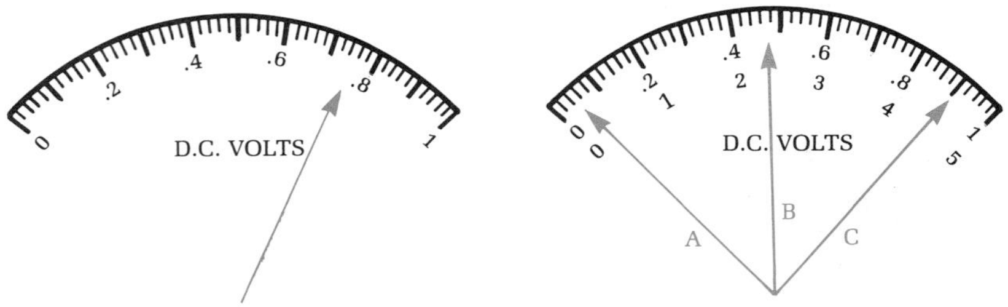

If the voltmeter scale has several sets of numbers, identify which set of numbers matches the voltage range on the voltmeter that is connected to the circuit. Then follow the procedure outlined on this page.

C. Determine the two values of electric potential indicated by each of the needle positions A and B shown on the voltmeter scale in Figure 17-5b).

Activity 17-2:   Electrochemical Cells

In this activity you will study the structure and operation of a simple source of electrical energy, the voltaic cell.

Materials

zinc plate	voltmeter
copper plate	connecting wires
steel wool	dilute sulphuric acid
beaker	small brush
light bulb	

sulphuric acid

Procedure

1. Polish the metal plates using steel wool.
2. Place the zinc and copper plates in the beaker.
3. Connect the light bulb and the voltmeter to the two metal plates as shown in the schematic circuit diagram in Figure 17-6. Record what happens. Record the voltmeter readings each time observations are made during steps 3 to 5.
4. Pour about 200 mL of dilute sulphuric acid into the beaker. Record what happens a) immediately, and b) after 4 min.
5. Using the brush, sweep the bubbles off the plates. Record what happens.

Figure 17-6. Schematic circuit diagram for Activity 17-2.

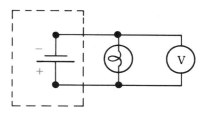

schematic circuit diagram

Discussion

1. List the energy changes that take place a) in the cell, and b) in the bulb.
2. Draw the schematic circuit diagram shown in figure 17-6 and draw an arrow on your circuit diagram to indicate the direction of current flow in the circuit.
3. a) Why does the brightness of the light from the bulb change in step 4?
    b) How can this be overcome?
4. Explain the voltage readings observed in steps 3 to 5.
5. List two disadvantages of a voltaic cell, compared to a dry cell.

Ways of Producing Electrical Energy

The amounts of electrical energy produced by the many different kinds of energy converters range from fractions of a microjoule to many megajoules. Some of these sources of electrical energy are listed in Tables 17-3 and 17-4.

Table 17-3: Sources of Electrical Energy in which Another Form of Energy is Directly Converted into Electrical Energy

Forms of Energy	Sources of Electrical Energy
chemical	*electrochemical*: dry cell, battery, biological cell (human, electric eel)
heat	*thermoelectric*: thermocouple
radiant	*photoelectric*: photocell, light meter, video camera, compact disc player, aerial on a television or radio
mechanical	*piezoelectric*: crystal needle on pickup head of a record player
magnetic	*electromagnetic*: cassette tape, video playback head, computer disc drive, electromagnetic pickup head of a record player

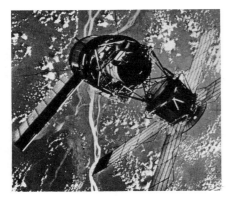

Photovoltaic cells convert solar energy into the electrical energy used to operate the satellite Skylab.

Table 17-4: Sources of Electrical Energy in which More Than One Energy Conversion is Required to Produce Electrical Energy

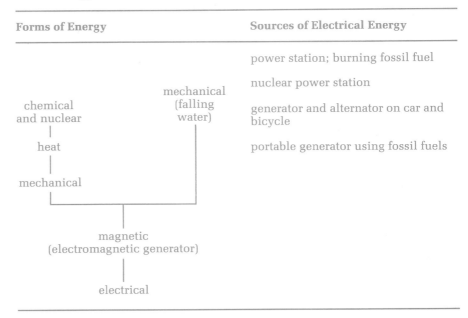

Forms of Energy	Sources of Electrical Energy
	power station; burning fossil fuel
mechanical (falling water)	nuclear power station
chemical and nuclear	generator and alternator on car and bicycle
heat	portable generator using fossil fuels
mechanical	
magnetic (electromagnetic generator)	
electrical	

Electrochemical Cells

In an **electrochemical cell**, stored chemical energy is converted into electrical energy. There are many different types of electrochemical cells but they can all be divided into two main groups: **primary cells** and **secondary cells**.

The Primary Cell: A Disposable Energy Source

Some common primary cells are shown in the photograph. As the electric current flows from a primary cell, chemical reactions occur which use up some of the materials in the cell. When these materials have been used up, the cell is said to be **discharged**, and cannot be recharged again. They are called primary cells because only the chemical reactions related to discharging the cell take place. Two kinds of primary cells are described below.

Primary cells.

The Voltaic Cell

The **voltaic cell** was first developed by an Italian scientist, Alessandro Volta, in 1800. This simple primary cell can be made easily out of common household materials. The voltaic cell shown in the photograph is called a **wet primary cell** because it is made of two pieces of metal placed in a *liquid*. The zinc and copper metal plates are called **electrodes**. The liquid in the cell, a solution of dilute sulphuric acid, is called the **electrolyte**. An electrolyte is any liquid that conducts an electric current.

When the two electrodes are placed in the electrolyte, the zinc electrode reacts chemically with the sulphuric acid. The chemical energy released separates electrons from the zinc atoms. The electrons collect on the zinc plate, which is called the **negative terminal** of the cell. At the same time, positive charges collect on the copper plate, which is called the **positive terminal** of the cell. These elec-

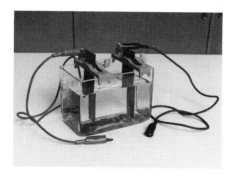

A zinc-copper voltaic cell produces an electric potential of 1.1 V.

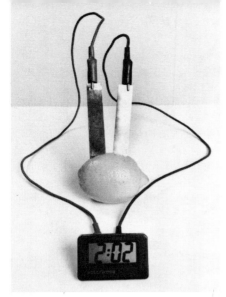

Batteries can be made from even the simplest materials, like the "lemon cell" shown here. The liquid of the lemon provides the electrolyte, and the copper and zinc strips provide the electrodes.

The electrodes in both wet (voltaic) cells and dry cells can be made from any two different substances provided they are both electrical conductors. Each combination of substances produces a different electric potential.

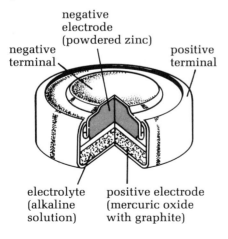

negative electrode (powdered zinc)

negative terminal

positive terminal

electrolyte (alkaline solution)

positive electrode (mercuric oxide with graphite)

tric charges remain static on each electrode. Cells discharge only when connected to a closed electric circuit.

When the cell is connected to a closed electric circuit, electrons are attracted from the negative terminal, through the circuit, towards the positive terminal. These moving electrons form an electric current. The energy lost by the electrons as they pass through the circuit is the electric potential energy that was obtained from the chemical energy released in the cell. The electric potential (voltage) of a new zinc-copper cell is always 1.1 V. As electrons leave the zinc electrode, the zinc reacts with the sulphuric acid, and more electrons are released into the circuit. The copper electrode is not affected by the chemical reaction.

Two major disadvantages of the voltaic cell are the danger of spilling the electrolyte, and the continual need to replace the zinc plate and the electrolyte. Another problem is that the chemical reaction produces hydrogen, which forms as bubbles on the copper plate (positive electrode). This problem can be solved by adding potassium dichromate to the electrolyte, where it reacts with the hydrogen to form water.

The Dry Cell

A **dry primary cell** functions in the same way as a wet primary cell, but the electrolyte is a moist paste rather than a liquid. Two of the more common types of dry primary cells are shown in Figure 17-7. When most of the negative electrode has been used up by the chemical reaction, the electric current stops, and the cell is discharged.

Figure 17-7. A cross-section of two kinds of primary cells: a mercury cell (left) and a carbon-zinc cell (right).

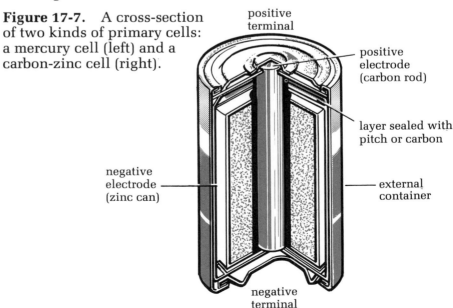

positive terminal

positive electrode (carbon rod)

layer sealed with pitch or carbon

negative electrode (zinc can)

external container

negative terminal

The Secondary Cell — A Reuseable Energy Source

The secondary cell was developed to provide larger amounts of electrical energy economically. A secondary cell can be discharged and recharged hundreds of times. A car battery consists of a group of secondary cells connected together. Two kinds of secondary cells are described below.

The Lead-Acid Cell

Although new types of secondary cells have been developed in recent years, the **lead-acid cell** is still one of the most useful sources of portable electrical energy. It has been used for many years in car batteries. This cell was developed by Gaston Plante in 1859. A typical lead-acid secondary cell is shown in Figure 17-8.

Figure 17-8. A fully charged lead-acid cell produces an electrical potential (voltage) of 2.2 V.

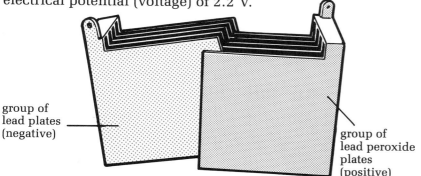

group of lead plates (negative)

group of lead peroxide plates (positive)

To recharge the cell, the chemical change is reversed, by connecting the cell to a source of electrical energy, such as a battery charger (or the alternator in a car). As the cell is recharged, the electrical energy from the charger changes the electrodes to their original state. The electrical energy is converted to chemical energy.

The Nickel-Cadmium Cell

One of the most reliable portable sources of electrical energy, the **nickel-cadmium cell** may be charged and discharged hundreds of times while still providing a constant electric potential. In terms of cost per hour of use, it is perhaps the most economical secondary cell. Needing no routine maintenance, this highly reliable cell is often permanently wired into equipment. Nickel-cadmium cells are used in portable devices such as pocket calculators, electric shavers, electronic flash units for cameras, "Walkmans", portable TVs, and many kinds of power tools.

In new secondary cells, the electrolyte is a jelly-like substance instead of dilute sulphuric acid. These cells are sealed units; some can be operated in any position, even upside-down.

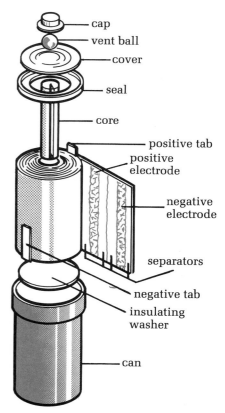

cap
vent ball
cover
seal
core
positive tab
positive electrode
negative electrode
separators
negative tab
insulating washer
can

Figure 17-9. A fully charged nickel-cadmium cell produces an electric potential of 1.2 V.

Select a size of dry cell that is available in both throw-away and rechargeable versions. Determine how many times such a rechargeable cell would have to be recharged for it to be an economical purchase.

Study Questions

1. Define the following terms: primary cell, secondary cell, voltaic cell, electrode, electrolyte, positive terminal, negative terminal.
2. a) List five sources of electrical energy, each deriving from a different form of energy.
   b) List three different sources of electrical energy used in the home.
3. a) What energy changes occur in an electrochemical cell when electric current flows from it?
   b) Describe the conditions necessary in a voltaic cell to produce a steady supply of electrons.
   c) Draw a labelled diagram of a voltaic cell.
4. a) Explain why dry primary cells were developed.
   b) Explain the difference between a primary cell and a secondary cell.

17.3   Cells and Batteries

There is not much chemical energy stored in one dry cell. The cell in a small flashlight will operate for only a few hours before it is completely discharged. One way to increase the amount of energy available is to make a larger cell. Another way is to connect several small cells to one another electrically so that the energy in all of the cells is added together.

Activity 17-3:   Connecting Cells in Parallel and in Series Circuits

When two or more cells are connected to provide more electrical energy, the combination of cells is called a "battery". There are two basic kinds of electric circuits used to form batteries. In this activity you will investigate the characteristics of each kind of circuit.

Materials

4 dry cells	switch
light bulb	voltmeter
connecting wires	

Part A: Connecting Cells in Parallel
Procedure
1. Connect the circuit as shown in Figure 17-10a).

a)

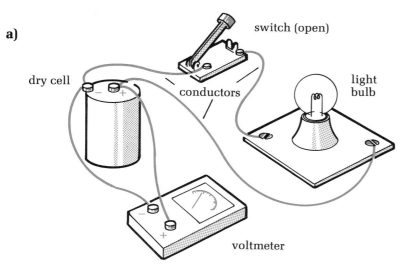

pictorial circuit diagram

Figure 17-10. Three cells connected in parallel.

2. Close the switch, record the voltage across the cell, and note the brightness of the bulb. Then open the switch.
3. Connect the second cell in "parallel" with the first cell, as shown in Figure 17-10b). Repeat step 2.

b)

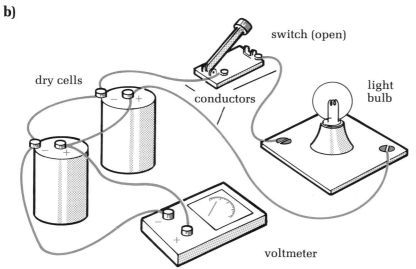

pictorial circuit diagram

CAUTION: Be careful not to connect a wire from the positive terminal to the negative terminal on the same cell. When there is no light bulb to act as an electrical load, a connecting wire provides a "short" circuit for the electric current. When a short-circuit occurs, very large currents flow from the cell which may cause it to explode.

4. Connect the third cell in parallel with the other two cells, as shown in Figure 17-10c). Repeat step 2. Draw the schematic circuit diagram shown in Figure 17-10d).

c)

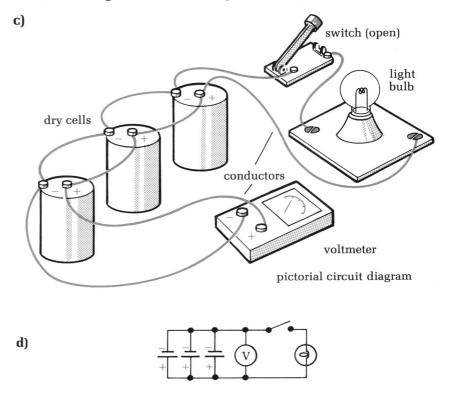

dry cells

switch (open)

light bulb

conductors

voltmeter

pictorial circuit diagram

d)

schematic circuit diagram

Discussion

1. a) What happens to the total electric potential (voltage) of the battery as each new cell is connected in parallel?
   b) What can be inferred about the amount of electric potential energy of the electrons leaving the negative terminal of the battery as each new cell is connected?

2. a) What happens to the brightness of the bulb as more cells are added in parallel?
   b) What can you infer about the amount of electric current flowing through the bulb as the cells are added in parallel? Explain your answer.

3. What advantage is gained by connecting cells in parallel? State a practical use for this kind of battery.

Part B: Connecting Cells in Series

Procedure

1. Connect the positive terminal of a dry cell to the positive terminal of the voltmeter.

2. Connect the negative terminal of the cell to the negative terminal of the voltmeter. Record the voltmeter reading.

3. Disconnect the wire attached to the negative terminal of the cell. Connect the negative terminal of the first cell to the positive terminal of the second cell. Cells connected in this way are said to be connected in "series". (See Figure 17-11 a) and b).)

Figure 17-11.   Two cells connected in series.

a)

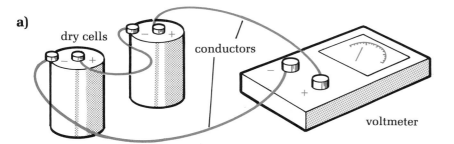

pictorial circuit diagram

b)

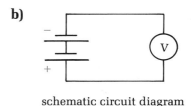

schematic circuit diagram

4. Reconnect the wire from the negative terminal of the voltmeter to the negative terminal of the second cell, and record the voltmeter reading.

5. Repeat steps 3 and 4, this time connecting a third cell to the second one.

6. Repeat steps 3 and 4, this time connecting a fourth cell to the third one.

7. Connect the cells as shown in Figure 17-12. Record the voltmeter reading.

Figure 17-12.

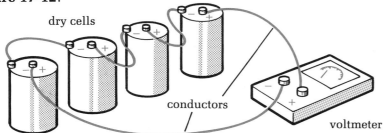

pictorial circuit diagram

Discussion

1. Draw a separate schematic circuit diagram for each arrangement of cells in the activity. Record the electric potential produced by the cell(s) beside each circuit diagram.

2. What happens to the total electric potential of a battery when its cells are connected in series with one another?

3. a) Explain how to connect 1.5 V cells to obtain an electric potential of 9 V. Draw a schematic circuit diagram showing the arrangement of the cells.
   b) What will happen to the electric potential of the 9 V battery if one of the cells is reversed?
   c) What effect will reversing the cell have on the cell itself?

4. Draw a schematic circuit diagram to show how 0 V could be obtained by connecting four cells in series.

5. Some toys and calculators could be damaged if the cells are inserted the wrong way around. What is done to prevent this?

Cells in Parallel and in Series

1. Cells in Parallel—Increasing the Amount of Electric Charge

Some electrical devices operate on small values of electric potential. The flashlight shown in the photograph operates using only a single 1.5 V dry cell. The amount of electric charge in the cell will keep the bulb glowing for several hours. When the store of electric charge in the cell is depleted, the bulb will stop glowing and the cell needs replacement. To keep the bulb glowing longer, the store of electric charge must be increased. This can be done by increasing the size of the cell or by connecting several cells together to form a battery.

If two cells are connected together, as shown in Figure 17-13a), the bulb will glow twice as long as with just one cell. Cells connected in this way are said to be connected **in parallel**. The circuit diagram for the two dry cells in parallel is shown in Figure 17-13b). To connect cells in parallel, the positive terminal of one cell is connected to the positive terminal of the next cell. The negative terminals of the two cells are also connected to each other. The electric potential (voltage) of the two cells in parallel is the same as that of a single cell; however, the total amount of stored electric charge has doubled. The amount of electric charge stored in a battery can be increased even more simply by adding more cells in parallel.

Figure 17-13. Two cells in parallel.

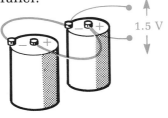

a) pictorial circuit diagram

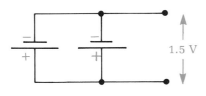

1.5 V

b) schematic circuit diagram

2. Cells in Series — Increasing Electric Charge *and* Electric Potential

Sometimes the operation of an electrical device requires a higher electric potential than can be supplied by just one cell. The flashlight shown in the photograph needs an electric potential of 4.5 V for its bulb to glow brightly. An electric potential of 4.5 V is obtained by connecting three 1.5 V dry cells together, as shown in Figure 17-14a). Cells connected in this way are said to be connected **in series**. When cells are connected in series, the positive terminal of one cell is connected to the negative terminal of the next cell. The electric potentials (voltages) of all the cells in series add together. The schematic circuit diagram of the complete flashlight is shown in Figure 17-14b).

When replacing discharged flashlight cells, the new cells must be properly positioned inside the hollow handle. If one of the cells faces the wrong way, the flashlight will emit only a little light. The electric potential of the reversed cell is subtracted from the two properly connected cells so that, instead of a combined electric potential of 4.5 V, there is only 1.5 V.

In some batteries, cells are connected both in series and in parallel. The lantern battery shown in the photograph has two sets of four cells. Each set of four cells is connected in series, to produce an electric potential of 6 V. The two sets of four cells are connected in parallel, so that the battery will last twice as long as with just one set of four cells.

Figure 17-14. A flashlight with three 1.5 V cells connected in series produces an electric potential of 4.5 V.

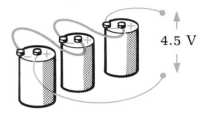

4.5 V

a) pictorial circuit diagram

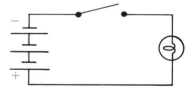

b) schematic circuit diagram

Do You Know?
In car batteries, six 2 V cells are connected in series to produce an electric potential of 12 V. These batteries can supply the starter motor in a car with over 500 A of electric current for short periods of time.

Study Questions

1. Explain the difference between a cell and a battery.
2. a) Why are cells connected in parallel?
   b) Describe how the terminals on the cells are wired together to connect cells in parallel.
   c) Draw a schematic circuit diagram showing four cells connected in parallel.
3. a) Why are cells connected in series?
   b) Describe how the terminals on the cells are wired together to connect cells in series.
   c) Draw a schematic circuit diagram showing five cells connected to produce i) the highest, and ii) the lowest electric potential.
4. Draw a schematic circuit diagram showing how to connect a voltmeter to the battery in 3c), to measure electric potential.

LIVING SOURCES OF ELECTRICAL ENERGY

Several different kinds of fish possess organs capable of producing electric currents. These organs consist of masses of flattened cells, called *electroplates* or *electroplaques*, which are stacked in neat rows along the sides of the fish. When one of these biological cells is activated by a nerve impulse, a momentary flow of ions—in effect, an electric current—moves across the cell's membrane. During the time the electric current flows across the membrane, the cell behaves just like one of the electrochemical cells discussed in this chapter. Each electroplate cell produces an electric potential of about 0.1 V.

The arrangement of the electroplate cells along the sides of the fish is such that the cells are electrically connected in series with one another. Fishes such as the electric eel and the giant sea ray, which have thousands of electroplates connected in series, can generate electric potentials of over 600 V. Freshwater electric fish have even greater numbers of electroplates in series, because fresh water does not conduct electricity as well as sea water.

A mature electric eel can produce pulses of electric current of 0.5 A or more. These pulses of electric current can be repeated several hundreds of times per second. If this much current were to flow through just one set of electroplate cells in series, the cells themselves would be destroyed. So, to produce large pulses of current without causing

The three electric eels in this aquarium in Vancouver generate enough electrical energy to light a set of Christmas tree lights.

damage, the sets of cells connected in series along the sides of the fish are also connected in parallel with one another. In this type of electric fish the biological cells, the electroplates, are electrically connected in series to increase the electric potential, and in parallel to increase the amount of electric current.

17.4 Electrical Loads

The main reason for producing electrical energy is to convert it back into *other* forms of energy, using devices called **energy converters**. A light bulb is an energy converter; it converts electrical energy into light energy and heat energy. Clothes dryers, toasters, ovens, television sets, and electric motors are all energy converters. As the electric current flows through the wires in the hair dryer, heat energy is produced. An energy converter connected to an electric circuit is usually called an **electrical load**. The electrical load affects the amount of electric current flowing in the circuit.

The cells and batteries in some electrical devices, such as calculators, cameras, and flashlights, operate only one electrical load at a time. However, when Christmas tree lights or the lights on a car are turned on, several electrical loads operate simultaneously. Two basic kinds of electric circuits are used to connect these loads: the series circuit and the parallel circuit. Both are investigated in the following activity.

Many electrical loads are used in a kitchen.

Activity 17-4: Electrical Loads in Series and Parallel Circuits

In Part A you will first study the characteristics of an electric circuit with the electrical loads connected in series. In Part B you will study the characteristics of an electric circuit with the electrical loads connected in parallel.

Materials

3 bulbs
3 bulb holders
1 D dry cell
1 D dry cell holder

voltmeter
9 connecting wires
switch

Part A: Electrical Loads in a Series Circuit
Procedure

1. Draw the schematic circuit diagram shown in Figure 17-15a).

2. Construct the circuit shown in Figure 17-15a). Ask your teacher to inspect your circuit before continuing.

3. Close the switch and record what happens.

4. Connect the voltmeter a) across the cell and b) across the bulb. Record the reading in each case.

Figure 17-15.
a)

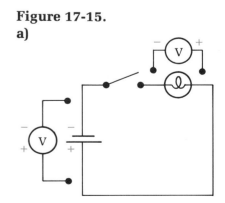

schematic circuit diagram

Figure 17-15.

b)

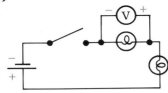

schematic circuit diagram

c)

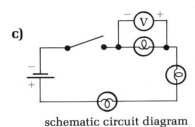

schematic circuit diagram

Figure 17-16.

a)

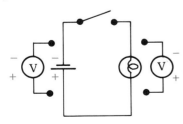

schematic circuit diagram

5. Open the switch. Repeat step 4 with the switch open.

6. Leaving the voltmeter connected across the first bulb, connect a second bulb in series with the first bulb, as shown in Figure 17-15b). Close the switch. Record what happens. Open the switch.

7. Connect a third light bulb in series with the other two bulbs, as shown in Figure 17-15c). Close the switch. Record what happens. Open the switch.

8. Close the switch. Unscrew the first light bulb, then screw it back into the socket. Record what happens.

9. Repeat step 8 for each of the other two bulbs. Open the switch.

10. **Make a Hypothesis:** Predict the voltages that would be measured across each of the bulbs a) in step 6, and b) in step 7. Check your prediction.

Discussion

1. a) What happens to the brightness of the light from the bulbs as each bulb is added?
   b) What can you infer about the amount of electric current flowing through each bulb in the circuit as each bulb is added? Explain.

2. a) What happens when one of the bulbs is unscrewed? Explain why.
   b) How many paths for current flow are there in a series circuit?

3. What would you find if you measured the electric current flowing in each part of the circuit?

4. For each of the three series circuits, compare the voltage of the dry cell to the voltages measured across the bulb(s). What general relationship seems to exist?

Part B: Electrical Loads in a Parallel Circuit

Procedure

1. Draw the schematic circuit diagram shown in Figure 17-16a).

2. Construct the circuit shown in Figure 17-16a).

3. Close the switch. Note the brightness of the bulb. Connect the voltmeter a) across the cell, and b) across the bulb. Record the reading in each case. Open the switch.

4. Connect the second bulb to the circuit, as shown in Figure 17-16b) on the next page. Repeat step 3.

5. Connect the third bulb to the circuit, as shown in Figure 17-16c). Repeat step 3.

6. Close the switch, then unscrew one bulb. Record what happens. Open the switch, and screw in the bulb.

7. Repeat step 6 for each of the other two bulbs in turn.

Figure 17-16.

b)

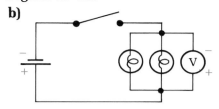

schematic circuit diagram

c)

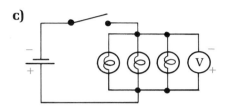

schematic circuit diagram

Discussion

1. How does the voltage measured across the dry cell compare to that measured across the three bulbs? Explain why.

2. a) What happens to the brightness of the light from each bulb as each new bulb is added?
   b) What can be inferred about the amount of electric current flowing through each bulb? Explain why.
   c) What can be inferred about the total current flowing from the cell, compared to the current flowing through each of the three bulbs?

3. Explain what happens when the bulbs are unscrewed.

4. a) Suppose 15 light bulbs were connected in series, and one bulb burned out. How could you find the defective bulb?
   b) How could you identify one defective bulb if the 15 bulbs are connected in parallel? Explain.

5. Are the electrical wall outlets in your home wired in series or in parallel? Explain your answer.

The Series Circuit

In Section 17.3 you learned how to connect dry cells in series to obtain a larger electric potential (voltage). Actually, the term "series" applies to any electric circuit in which the parts of the circuit are wired to one another in a single path.

The three light bulbs in the photograph are connected in a series circuit. The schematic circuit diagram is shown in Figure 17-17 on the next page. When the switch is closed, all three bulbs produce light. When the switch is open, the three bulbs stop producing light. Notice that the three bulbs and the switch are all wired together, one after the other, to provide a single path for the electric current. The same electric current flows through the cell, the bulbs, and the switch. One characteristic of a series circuit is that the electric current is the same in all parts of the circuit.

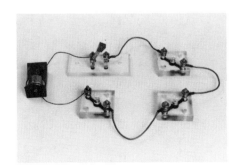

Figure 17-17.

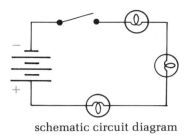

schematic circuit diagram

Sets of Christmas tree lights connected in series may contain as many as 30 bulbs in the one circuit. If one bulb burns out, all the bulbs have to be checked to find the defective one.

All the electric circuits in a car are wired in parallel. There is only one 12 V battery, but you can operate any electrical device in the car without affecting any of the others.

An electric circuit showing four light bulbs connected in parallel.

A single switch controls the electric current in all parts of a series circuit. When the switch is open, the only path that the current can flow through in the circuit is also open. The current can flow only when the switch is closed. But a burnt-out bulb prevents current from flowing, just as if a switch were open. Unscrewing a bulb has the same effect. Because there is only one path for the current to flow through, the other two bulbs will also stop glowing. If the path of the current in a series circuit is broken at any point, the current stops flowing. This is another characteristic of a series circuit.

Most electric circuits have a safety device called a fuse which is connected in series with the rest of the circuit. A fuse is a thin piece of metal which melts, or "blows", when the current through it exceeds a certain safe value (the fuse rating). Because the fuse is connected in series, the current in the circuit stops flowing when the fuse blows.

The Parallel Circuit

The first photograph shows four light bulbs in a bathroom light fixture. Three of the bulbs will light up, even if the other one remains unlit. Therefore, these bulbs cannot be connected in a series circuit. If they were, either all or none of the bulbs would have lit up. The bulbs are connected in a **parallel circuit**, in which the current passes through a separate circuit to each bulb. Each separate circuit is called a **branch circuit**. Because each bulb is connected to its own branch circuit, it does not affect the other bulbs. If any one of the bulbs is unscrewed, the other bulbs remain lit. The second photograph on the next page shows how the wires are connected to three bulbs in a parallel circuit.

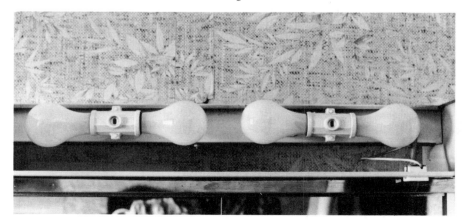

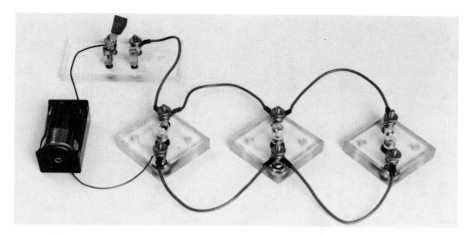

In the simple series circuit shown in Figure 17-18a), only one bulb is connected to a switch and a dry cell. When the switch is closed, the bulb lights up.

In Figure 17-18b), a second bulb is connected beside, or in parallel with, the first bulb. Notice that the current can now flow through two separate paths or branch circuits. Assuming that the two bulbs are identical, the same amount of current will flow through each bulb, because the electric potential (voltage) is the same in each case. The current flowing from the dry cell will now be twice the amount it was with only one bulb. Half the total current flows through the first bulb and half through the second bulb. After passing through the bulbs, the two currents combine again and return to the dry cell. If either bulb is unscrewed the other one stays lit because each bulb has a separate branch circuit connected to the cell.

In Figure 17-18c), a third bulb is connected in parallel. The current can now flow in three separate paths around the circuit, so the current flowing from the dry cell will be three times what it was when only one bulb was connected. One third of the total current flowing from the cell passes through each bulb. In this circuit as well, each bulb can be switched on and off or unscrewed without affecting the other bulbs. Note that each time another bulb is added in parallel to the circuit, the current from the cell increases. In a parallel circuit, the total current flowing from the source of electrical energy equals the sum of all the separate branch currents in the circuit. The electric potential across each branch circuit is the same as that produced by the source of electrical energy.

The parallel electric circuit shown in Figure 17-18c) is basically the same as the circuit operating the four bathroom fixture lights. All the electric circuits in your home are connected in parallel.

Figure 17-18.
a) A simple series circuit.

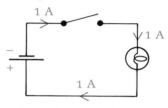

schematic circuit diagram

b) Two light bulbs connected in parallel.

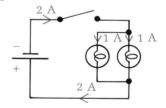

schematic circuit diagram

c) Three light bulbs connected in parallel.

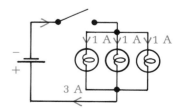

schematic circuit diagram

Practical Uses of Series and Parallel Circuits

The electrical energy for each house on a street is supplied by a set of wires usually brought in by an overhead or underground cable. Each house is really a separate branch in a parallel circuit. The wires entering a house are connected to a large switch called the main breaker. The wires from the main breaker switch are connected in series to the main electrical control panel. When the main breaker is switched off, all the electrical circuits in the home are also switched off. Inside the main control panel, the single set of wires is connected in parallel to all the branch circuits operating electrical devices in the house.

Large appliances such as the refrigerator, stove, and electric water heater are each connected to a separate branch circuit. On other branch circuits, as many as ten different lighting fixtures and wall outlets may be connected together in parallel. Because all the circuits are wired in parallel, any appliance, light, or wall outlet can be used without affecting the others.

Each parallel circuit connected to the main control panel is controlled by a fuse or a circuit breaker connected in series with the circuit. If too many appliances and lights on one branch circuit are switched on at the same time, the fuse controlling that circuit will melt and the current will stop.

Figure 17-19. A combination of series and parallel circuits is
used to distribute electrical energy throughout a house.

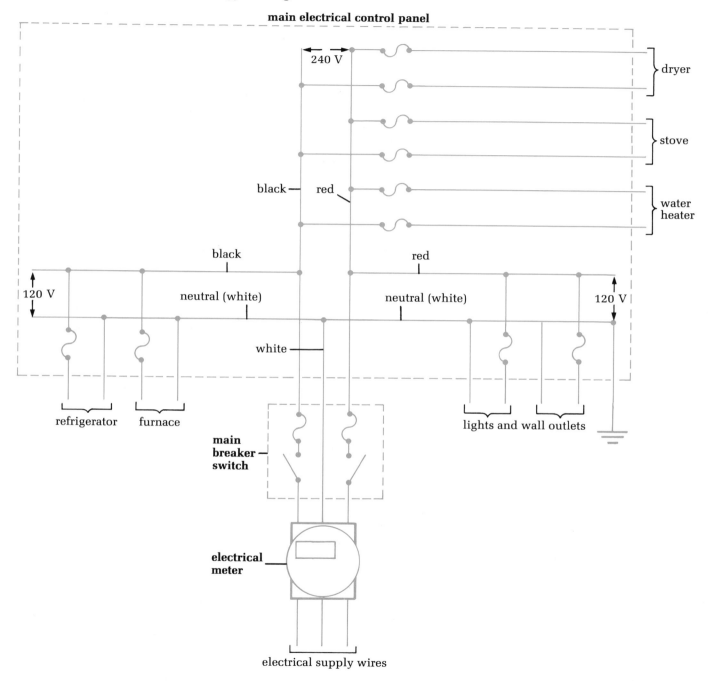

Study Questions

1. a) What is the function of an electrical load in a circuit?
   b) List four electrical loads used in the home, and state the forms of energy each load produces.

2. a) State two characteristics of i) a series circuit and ii) a parallel circuit.
   b) What happens when one of a set of light bulbs burns out in i) a series circuit, and ii) a parallel circuit? Explain why in each case.

3. a) Why are the electric circuits in a house wired in parallel with one another?
   b) What is the function of a fuse?

4. Draw a schematic circuit diagram for each of the following.
   a) Three cells are connected in series, which in turn are connected to two light bulbs, a motor, and a switch, also connected in series. A voltmeter is connected to the battery to measure its electric potential.
   b) Two cells are connected in parallel, which in turn are connected to three light bulbs connected in parallel. A switch is connected in series with just one of the light bulbs.

SCIENCE IN ACTION

ELECTRICAL SAFETY IN THE HOME

Next to motor vehicles, the home is where most fatal accidents occur in Canada each year. The electrical safety suggestions listed below should be followed when using electricity in the home.

1. Never operate space heaters, radios, and other electrical appliances when you are in the bathtub or shower, or near a water-filled sink in the kitchen or laundry room.

2. Keep floors dry around washers and dryers to reduce the hazards of electric shock.

3. Never use water to put out an electrical fire.

4. Never try to conceal extension cords under rugs.

5. Pull on the plug, rather than the electrical cord, when disconnecting an appliance.

6. Replace damaged or frayed appliance cords, or damaged wiring on appliances, as soon as damage is observed.

7. Disconnect appliances such as toasters and irons as soon as you have finished using them.

8. Cover unused electrical outlets to prevent young children from inserting objects into them.

9. Do not overload an electrical circuit by using a multiple socket device in an outlet intended for only two electrical loads.

10. Always turn off the main electrical switch before replacing a blown fuse.

11. If a fuse blows repeatedly, have a qualified electrician identify the cause of the problem.

12. Never replace a blown fuse with a fuse of higher rating to prevent further blow outs. Never use a penny or foil to replace a fuse.

Meet an Avionics Technician— Rachelle Boudreau

Rachelle is one of two female avionics technicians who work for Air Canada at Toronto's Pearson International Airport. She was the first woman to graduate in avionics at Centennial College in Toronto.

Q. WHAT DID YOU WANT TO BE WHEN YOU WERE A CHILD?
A. I always wanted to be an airline pilot. Everyone used to laugh at me when I was little. When I was in high school, I still wanted to be a pilot but the guidance counsellors discouraged me, saying it was a man's job. I still regret listening to them.

Q. WHAT IS AVIONICS?
A. It is the maintenance of the electrical and electronic systems of an aircraft, such as communications, navigation, auto pilot, flight recording, and entertainment systems. Wherever there's a wire, it's my responsibility. In a modern commercial plane, there are miles of wires.

Q. WHAT IS YOUR WORKING ENVIRONMENT?
A. My time is divided about equally between two locations: the hangar and the terminal. I prefer working in the terminal where there are more people around. The planes that are in the hangar usually have problems that can't be solved at the terminal.

Q. WHAT'S A TYPICAL SHIFT LIKE?
A. When I come in, I check at the avionics shop to find out what needs to be done. For instance, there might be a Boeing 727 in the hangar that has fuel problems. I would check the work board to see if anything has been done before I arrived. Then I would check the logbooks to see how many times that particular fuel tank has developed problems. Afterwards I would decide what action to take. The problem could be solved in half an hour, or it might take eight hours.

Q. DO YOU WORK ON A SPECIFIC TYPE OF AIRCRAFT?
A. No, I work on the whole airline fleet, which includes B-747, B-767, B-727, L-1011, DC-8, and DC-9. I am licensed on the 727 and 767, which means I have written the appropriate examinations for those types of aircraft. With these particular aircraft, I am in charge and people work for me.

Q. WERE THE EXAMS DIFFICULT?
A. Very. I didn't feel ready to try them until I'd been working for five years. I had to study the whole aircraft from nose to tail. The exams have to be tough because you have to know your material. After all, I have the final say on whether an aircraft can be released for flying.

Q. WHY ARE THERE SO FEW WOMEN IN THIS FIELD?
A. Electronics is hard for a lot of people. It's very abstract. You don't see it working. It's not like plumbing, where you can see water running through a pipe.

Q. WHAT'S THE MOST DIFFICULT PART OF YOUR JOB?
A. Making a decision on whether an airplane can be fixed and released, or whether it has to be taken off the line and to the hangar. There's a lot of pressure, and it's often difficult to estimate exactly how long it will take to fix a problem.

Q. WHAT DO YOU LIKE BEST ABOUT BEING AN AVIONICS TECHNICIAN?
A. I like the challenge. When I come to work, I never know what's waiting. The problems are always different.

Review Questions

A: Knowledge

1. Describe the difference between static electricity and current electricity.

2. a) List six different electrical loads used in a car.
   b) For each electrical load, name the forms of energy produced when electric current is flowing in the circuit.

3. a) Draw a pictorial circuit diagram of a single cell flashlight.
   b) Draw a schematic circuit diagram of the same single cell flashlight.

4. a) What is an electrochemical cell?
   b) What is an electrolyte? Explain its purpose.
   c) List three examples of i) a primary cell, and ii) a secondary cell.

5. a) How is the production of hydrogen gas controlled in a primary cell?
   b) Which of the two electrodes controls the effective operating life of a primary cell? Explain why.

6. Why should a burnt-out fuse never be replaced by one with a higher current rating?

7. Explain why electrical insulators are used to cover the conducting wires in electrical cords attached to appliances.

8. a) What happens when a short-circuit occurs in an electric circuit?
   b) Why can a short-circuit be dangerous?

9. a) What effect does an electric current have on human muscles?
   b) Explain what is meant by the term "let-go threshold"?

10. State the characteristics related to electric current and electric potential in a) a series circuit, and b) a parallel circuit.

11. a) What kind of circuit connection is used to connect cells to produce the highest electric potential?
    b) List three electrical loads that use batteries with cells connected this way.

12. What is the major advantage of a secondary cell compared to a primary cell?

13. List three safety precautions related to the use of electricity that should be observed in the home.

14. What precautions should you take, before you try to help someone who is experiencing an electric shock?

B: Application

15. List three ways to stop the electric current from flowing in a simple single-bulb circuit.

16. Name six different uses for switches in a) the home, b) a car, c) the garden.

17. What source of electrical energy is most appropriate for the following electrical loads:
    a) a personal cassette recorder
    b) a pocket calculator
    c) a cellular telephone
    d) the playback head on a tape recorder
    e) a communications satellite
    f) a blender
    g) a car lighting system
    h) the lighting system on a deep-sea oil rig

18. Determine the values of electric potential indicated by the meter needle position C shown in Figure 17-5b).

19. Why is it dangerous to place electrical appliances, such as fans or radios, near bathtubs or showers?

20. Explain what happens when one bulb burns out in a circuit made up of six bulbs connected in series with one another?

21. a) What electric potential is produced when five 1.8 V cells are connected in series?
    b) Draw a schematic circuit diagram of this battery.
    c) What is the lowest electric potential that can be obtained by connecting the five cells in series? Draw a schematic circuit diagram to show how to obtain this value.

22. a) What electric potential is produced when three 1.3 V cells are connected in parallel? Explain why.
    b) Draw a schematic circuit diagram of this battery.

23. a) List three practical uses for photocells.
    b) If photocells could be mass-produced at a low price, in what practical ways could they be used?

24. Why should care be taken not to short-circuit cells or batteries?

25. Explain how using an appliance with a damaged electrical cord could cause a fire.

26. a) To measure the electric current flowing through a bulb, should an ammeter be connected in series or in parallel with the bulb? Explain your answer.
    b) To measure the electric potential of a battery, should a voltmeter be connected in series or in parallel with the battery? Explain your answer.

27. List three electrical loads designed to produce a) sound energy, b) light energy, c) heat energy, and d) both sound and light energy.

C: Problem Solving

28. How could people living in remote areas use the different sources of electrical energy to provide them with the energy they need both day and night?

29. As the electric current rating of a fuse increases, what happens to the thickness of the fuse wire? Explain why this happens.

30. Draw a schematic circuit diagram consisting of a 110 V source of electrical energy and two light bulbs connected in series, which in turn are connected to two light bulbs and a motor, all connected in parallel with each other. The complete circuit should be controlled by a switch and protected by a fuse. An ammeter should measure the current through the motor and a voltmeter should measure the electric potential of the 110 V supply.

31. Describe and explain what would happen in the circuit diagram shown below if:

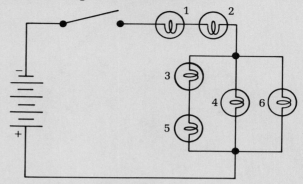

a) the switch is closed
b) the switch is closed and light bulb number 2 is unscrewed
c) the switch is closed and light bulb number 5 is unscrewed
d) the switch is closed, and light bulb number 4 is removed and replaced by a copper wire

Try This

1. **Six-Cent Cell**
   The inside of your mouth is very sensitive to small amounts of electric current. Clean a nickel and a penny with a detergent and rinse them thoroughly. Then connect them together with a wire. Place one coin on top of your tongue and the other one underneath it. Describe and explain what happens.

2. **Food Cells**
   Try to make a simple voltaic cell at home, using different kinds of fruits and vegetables. You can use coins or pieces of wire made of different metals for the electrodes. Test your cell with a bulb from a flashlight.

3. **Electrochemical Series**
   Research the term "electrochemical series". Then design and complete an investigation to determine the electric potential produced in a voltaic cell by several different combinations of metals.

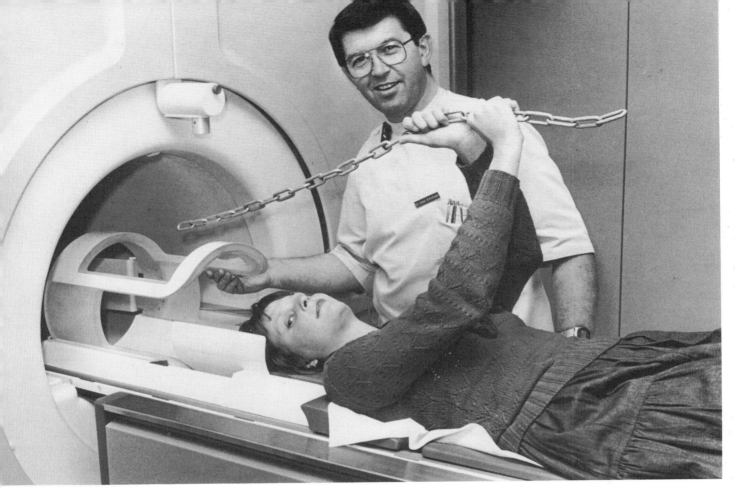

The magnet in this nuclear magnetic resonance (NMR) imager, a new medical diagnostic instrument, exerts enough force to support the full length of the steel chain.

Chapter 18
Magnetism and Electromagnetism

We use many kinds of magnets in our daily lives. Every time we watch TV, listen to the stereo, talk on the telephone, or turn on an electric motor, we are using magnetic forces. In some of these devices, the magnetic forces are produced by electricity. In others, the reverse occurs—electricity is produced by magnetic forces.

In this chapter we study the properties of magnetism, and the special relationship between electricity and magnetism. We learn about the domain theory of magnetism, and extend the Rutherford-Bohr model of the atom to develop an explanation of electromagnetism. We then study the patterns produced by magnetic force fields. Finally, we investigate how magnetic forces can produce electricity.

When you finish Chapter 18, you should be able to:

- describe how to measure magnetic forces
- explain the behaviour of magnets placed near other magnets and magnetic materials, using the domain theory of magnetism
- draw two-dimensional diagrams of the magnetic force fields around magnets, and describe the characteristics of magnetic fields
- describe how to construct an electromagnet
- explain the relationship between electricity and magnetism

18.1   Magnetism

Inside the soft rubber gasket seal on the door of your refrigerator is a long thin magnet. The attracting force exerted by the magnet pulls the rubber gasket tightly against the metal case of the refrigerator to prevent air leakage. The seals on metal freezer lids and the weatherstripping on metal doors also contain magnets. Some of the more common uses of magnets are shown in the photograph.

Memorizing versus Thinking
Memorizing is an important part of any education. Certain types of information are used over and over and must be remembered. However, memorizing is not the same as thinking. Some students believe that they simply have to memorize what they have learned and be ready to recall that information at test time. This is not true. You must be able to use information, and to apply facts and skills to situations that are different from those studied in class.

Many students think that they understand things when they do not. The following tips may help you to see if you truly understand.

a)   State what you have read, heard, or done in your own words. (If you cannot do this, you likely do not understand the material.)

b)   Think of an application or example of the idea you have just learned.

c)   Make up a test question about the material.

d)   Try to explain the idea to someone else.

Some kitchen devices that use magnets.

Activity 18-1:   Effects Produced by Magnets

Magnets have certain properties similar to those of the electrically-charged particles that you studied in Chapter 16. In this activity you will study the effects of magnets on a variety of materials (in Part A) and on other magnets (in Part B).

The compass is an instrument that uses the properties of magnetism to indicate direction. It is basically a magnet used to detect the presence of another magnet. A simple compass consists of a long thin magnet, called a compass needle, which is mounted on a pivot. When placed near another magnet, one of the ends of the compass needle will point towards it.

a)

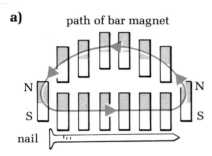

b)

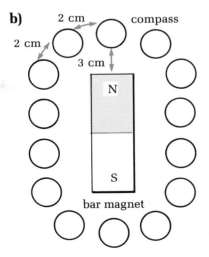

Figure 18-1. Draw a circle around the compass, and then draw an arrow in the circle to show the direction of the compass needle.

Materials

2 bar magnets

various substances and objects for Part A

soft iron nail

iron tacks

sheet of paper

compass

evaporating dish (plasticine)

Procedure

Part A: The Effect of Magnets on Different Substances

1. Hold a magnet near each material to be tested. List those that are attracted to the magnet under the heading "magnetic" and the others under the heading "nonmagnetic".

2. Dip the nail into a pile of tacks, and then lift it out. Record what happens.

3. Place the nail on your desk, and rub it with the S-pole of the magnet, as shown in Figure 18-1a). Do this 15 times, and then repeat step 2.

4. Tap the nail sharply on a hard object several times, and then repeat step 2. (Do not tap the magnet.)

Part B: The Effect of Magnets on Other Magnets

5. Place a magnet on a sheet of paper on a desktop. Draw a line around the outside of the magnet. Slowly move the compass around the magnet, as shown in Figure 18-1b), at a distance of about 3 cm. Draw arrows on the paper to indicate the direction in which the compass needle points in each new position.

6. Hold the compass in your hand at a distance of 1 m from the magnet, and observe the direction in which the needle points.

7. Place a magnet on an evaporating dish, and observe the direction in which it points. (Make sure the magnet is not near any metallic objects.)

8. Hold one end of the second magnet near one end of the magnet on the evaporating dish. Record what happens.

9. Hold the same end of the hand-held magnet near the other end of the magnet on the evaporating dish. Record what happens.

10. Reverse the ends of the hand-held magnet and repeat steps 8 and 9.

Discussion

Part A

1. a) List the metals that show strong magnetic effects.
   b) List the nonmetals that show strong magnetic effects.
2. How could you set up an activity to test if liquids and gases are strongly magnetic?
3. Suggest an explanation for what happened to the iron nail in steps 2 to 4.

Part B

4. From your observations, what can you infer about the strength of the magnetic forces exerted by the bar magnet at different points around its circumference?
5. What is significant about the direction in which the compass needle and the magnet point in steps 6 and 7? Why does this happen?
6. What similarities and differences can you infer concerning the magnetic forces exerted by the two ends of a bar magnet?
7. Write a statement summarizing what happens when the ends of the magnets are brought near one another in steps 8 to 10.

Magnetic Substances

Strong effects due to magnetism are noticeable in only a few substances. These substances are said to be **magnetic**. All other substances are **nonmagnetic**. Magnets themselves are made from magnetic substances. Only two groups of magnetic substances can be made into strong, long-lasting magnets.

Ferromagnetic Substances

One group of strongly magnetic substances consists of four elements: iron, nickel, cobalt, and gadolinium, a rare metal. These elements are said to be **ferromagnetic** (from the Latin word "ferrum" for iron). The first artificial magnets were made from iron. Alloys (solid solutions) of the ferromagnetic elements can produce two basic kinds of magnets. One kind can be easily magnetized and demagnetized. These **temporary magnets** are used in doorbells, electric motors, generators, and transformers. The other kind, **permanent magnets**, are difficult to magnetize and demagnetize.

HERMAN®

"You say you spent five years at the North Pole?"

The so-called nonmagnetic substances *do* show two different, but very weak, magnetic effects when placed near a magnet. One group of nonmagnetic substances is very slightly attracted to the magnet; these substances are said to be paramagnetic. Examples are aluminium, manganese, oxygen, platinum, and many metallic salts. The other group is weakly repelled by magnets; these substances are said to be diamagnetic or antimagnetic. Examples are zinc, copper, silver, gold, lead, and some types of glass.

The test for superconductivity, called the Meissner effect, is based on diamagnetism. A superconductor is perfectly diamagnetic. A magnet placed near a superconductor will be repelled by it.

Some common devices that use ferrimagnets.

Ferrimagnetic Substances

The other group of substances used to make strong magnets consists of the oxides of certain metals. These substances are called **ferrimagnets**, or **ferrites**. One ferrimagnetic substance, magnetite, is a naturally-occurring magnetic ore. Magnetite is a compound of iron oxide (Fe_3O_4). Unlike metal magnets, ferrites do not usually conduct electricity; most are considered to be insulators. Ferrites are often used in radio aerials and in loudspeakers. When you play an audio tape, use the telephone, or store information on a computer disc, you may be using ferrimagnets. Some examples of ferrimagnets are shown in the photograph.

Table 18-1

Uses for Magnets

magnetic tape	magnetic marks on cheques and books
computer discs	labels on cans at stores
magnetic screwdriver	stud finder
pin holder	display board magnets
loudspeaker	preprogrammed calculators
aerials	rotation rates for car engines
compasses	refrigerator door seals
magnets for cow's stomach	magnetic hockey goal posts
magnetic locks	key box

Magnetism and Electricity

Magnets can affect moving electrical charges, such as the stream of electrons inside a television tube. This effect can be observed when a strong magnet is placed near a television screen. The magnetic forces change the path of the electrons, causing the image on the screen to distort near the magnet. Magnets can also affect the flow of electrons moving through the wires of an electric circuit. Magnetic effects produced by electricity will be discussed in Section 18.2.

Magnetic Poles

If a piece of iron is placed near a hanging bar magnet, the end of the magnet closest to the iron always turns towards it. Even if the piece of iron is placed near the middle of the magnet, one end of the magnet will still move towards the iron. The attracting force of the bar magnet is stronger at the ends than in the middle. There are always at least two regions on a magnet, no matter what its shape, in which the magnetic force is stronger than anywhere else. These two regions are called the **poles** of the magnet. They are always in a fixed position in a permanent magnet. The poles may be marked either with letters (N or S) or coloured paint. Usually the poles of a bar magnet are painted red and white.

There is a magnetic pole at each end of this bar magnet.

The Law of Magnetism

Notice what happens in Figure 18-2 when the white end (S) of a hand-held magnet is brought near the white end (S) of a hanging magnet. The two magnets push each other apart. This also happens when the two coloured ends (N) are placed near one another. It seems that the two like poles repel each other. If the coloured end (N) of the hand-held magnet is placed near the white end (S) of the hanging magnet, they attract one another. Whenever magnets are brought close to one another, the magnetic poles always behave in a predictable way. The **Law of Magnetism** states that:

Like magnetic poles repel one another. Unlike magnetic poles attract one another.

This simple law is basic to the design of many common electrical and magnetic devices. The operation of all electrical generators and motors depends on the attracting and repelling forces between sets of magnets.

Figure 18-2. Like poles repel one another. Unlike poles attract one another.

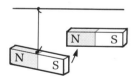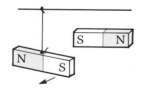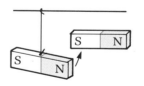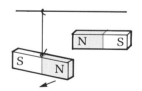
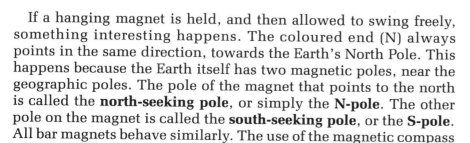

If a hanging magnet is held, and then allowed to swing freely, something interesting happens. The coloured end (N) always points in the same direction, towards the Earth's North Pole. This happens because the Earth itself has two magnetic poles, near the geographic poles. The pole of the magnet that points to the north is called the **north-seeking pole**, or simply the **N-pole**. The other pole on the magnet is called the **south-seeking pole**, or the **S-pole**. All bar magnets behave similarly. The use of the magnetic compass is based on this characteristic property of bar magnets.

The unit used to measure magnetic force (and all other kinds of force) is the newton. The symbol for the newton is N. Ensure that the newton spring scale is correctly zeroed before starting the activity.

Table 18-2

Magnetic Force (N)	Number of Pieces of Paper
	0
	1

Ensure that the bar magnet is lifted slightly from the surface of the desk before pulling on it.

Activity 18-2: Forces Exerted by Magnets

In this activity you will use a spring scale to measure the force exerted by a magnet on a piece of iron. You will study how the magnetic force changes as the distance from the magnet increases.

Materials

small flat piece of iron   bar magnet

newton spring scale   pieces of paper

tape or string

Procedure

1. Tape a small flat piece of iron onto the hook at the bottom of the spring scale. Make sure that enough of the iron is left bare to allow the end of the magnet to touch it directly.
2. Copy Table 18-2 into your notebook.
3. Lay the spring scale and the magnet flat on your desk, with one end of the magnet touching the piece of iron.
4. Hold the spring scale still, and pull on the magnet until it breaks free from the iron. Record the maximum magnetic force, in newtons, exerted by the magnet on the piece of iron.
5. Place one thickness of paper between the iron and the magnet, and repeat steps 3 and 4.
6. Repeat step 5, adding more pieces of paper, until the magnetic force is too small to be measured by the spring scale.
7. Plot a graph of magnetic force, in newtons, versus numbers of pieces of paper.

Discussion

1. Describe what happens to the strength of the magnetic force as the distance between the iron and the magnet changes.
2. Compare your results with those of other groups in the class.

The Domain Theory of Magnetism

The magnets we have used and discussed so far have all been large enough to see and handle. However, some magnets are very tiny. The magnetic tape used in an audio cassette is a brown strip, shiny on one side and dull on the other. The dull side of the tape is coated with a thin layer of magnetic iron oxide particles. Only about

0.0001 mm in diameter, each particle acts like a separate tiny magnetic needle. When sound signals are recorded on such a tape, each needle-like magnet is magnetized in a different direction. These tiny magnets remain magnetized in that direction until different information is recorded on the tape.

Something interesting to think about is the minimum size at which a magnetic particle can still behave like a magnet. Scientists have developed the **domain theory of magnetism** to explain the effects produced by all magnets, large and small. They believe that each atom of a magnetic substance behaves like a tiny magnet, and that these magnetic atoms cluster together in small groups called **domains**. When a magnet is made, domains are formed in the crystals that grow as the liquid magnetic material solidifies. The N-poles of each magnetic atom in a domain line up so that they all point in the same direction. Together they produce a domain which acts like a tiny magnet with its own N-pole and S-pole.

In an unmagnetized piece of iron, scientists believe that the domains are not arranged in any particular order (see Figure 18-3). When the piece of iron is magnetized, the domains are rearranged into a definite pattern. All the N-poles of the domains point in one direction, and all the S-poles point in the opposite direction, as

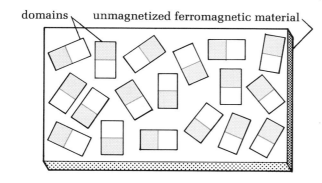

domains   unmagnetized ferromagnetic material

Figure 18-3. The domains are arranged randomly in a magnetic substance that is unmagnetized.

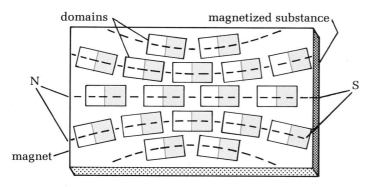

domains   magnetized substance

N   S

magnet

Figure 18-4. The domains are all lined up with one another in a magnetic substance that is strongly magnetized.

Figure 18-5. Some of the domains inside the nail are forced (induced) to face towards the S-pole of the bar magnet. The nail becomes an induced magnet.

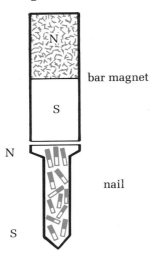

bar magnet

nail

CHALLENGER

A Perpetual Motion Machine
The perpetual motion machine shown in the diagram was proposed in the 1670s by the Bishop of Chester in England. It seems like a very simple machine. What will happen to the ball? Will this machine work? Why or why not?

Figure 18-6.

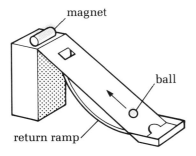

magnet

ball

return ramp

shown in Figure 18-4. The rearrangement of domains by strong magnetic forces is the principle underlying the storage of information on audio and video tapes, and on computer discs.

The domain theory can be used to explain increasing and decreasing amounts of magnetism in magnetic materials. Every time you pick up an object with a magnet, the object itself becomes another weak magnet. Figure 18-5 shows an iron nail being picked up with a magnet. Consider what happens to the domains inside the nail. When the S-pole of the magnet approaches the nail, some of the domains inside the nail line up towards the magnet. The part of the nail touching the magnet becomes a N-pole, and the other end becomes a S-pole.

This method of magnetizing an object is called **induced magnetism**. In Chapter 16 you learned that induction refers to causing an effect without direct contact. In this case the magnet is touching the nail, but has no direct contact with the individual domains *inside* the nail. Nevertheless, the magnet is able to induce, or force, the domains in the nail to line up so that the nail itself becomes a magnet. When the magnet is removed, the nail can be demagnetized by tapping it on a hard surface or by heating it; these actions disturb the arrangement of the domains.

Study Questions

1. Define the following terms: magnetic substance, magnetic pole, magnetic domain, induced magnetism.

2. a) Name the two types of magnetic substances, and list two ways in which they are different.
   b) What is the difference between a temporary magnet and a permanent magnet? State one advantage of each kind of magnet.

3. a) State the Law of Magnetism.
   b) Describe two ways to identify the poles on a magnet using a compass.

4. Describe how to measure the force exerted by a magnet.

5. a) Describe the domain theory of magnetism.
   b) Explain, with the aid of diagrams, what happens to the domains inside a piece of iron when it is magnetized by induced magnetism.

6. How could you use a magnet to find out when the Canadian Mint changed the composition of our five-cent coins?

LIVING ORGANISMS THAT USE MAGNETISM

Recent research indicates that some living organisms have probably been using magnets to help them navigate for millions of years.

While studying swamp bacteria, Dr. Richard P. Blakemore, a scientist at the University of New Hampshire, observed that one type of bacteria always swam to the north end of the microscope slide. By placing magnets in different positions near the bacteria on the slide,

Blakemore could make the bacteria swim in any direction he desired. Bacteria such as these respond to the magnetic poles of the Earth, and are called "magnetotactic".

Similar kinds of bacteria have been found in various parts of the northern hemisphere. Magnetic bacteria found in New Zealand and Tasmania, however, always move in a southerly direction.

Research showed that each bacterium contained a chain of microscopic crystals of magnetite (iron oxide) oriented along the long axis of the cell. Each ferrimagnetic crystal is a single domain between 0.04 μm and 0.12 μm long. The magnetic force

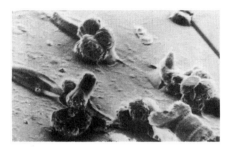

Magnetotatic bacteria move toward the Earth's magnetic pole.

seems to act as an internal compass. Scientists think that the bacteria are guided towards the magnetic pole inside the Earth, and swim to the swamp bottom, where they are better adapted to survive in a low-oxygen environment.

18.2 Electromagnetism

In 1819 Hans Christian Oersted finally discovered what scientists had long suspected. He was able to show by experiment that an electric current affects a magnet.

Activity 18-3: Electromagnets

In this activity, which is similar to Oersted's original experiment, you will study the magnetic effects produced by an electric current.

Materials

1 m copper wire	1 m cotton thread
iron filings	connecting lead
bar magnet	compass
1.5 V dry cell	sheet of paper
1 m steel wire	pencil

Hans Christian Oersted (1777-1851)

Procedure

Part A: Electromagnetism in a Single Conductor

1. Dip the piece of copper wire into a small pile of iron filings, and pull it out again. Record what happens.

2. Stroke the copper wire with the bar magnet and repeat step 1.

3. Connect the ends of the copper wire to a 1.5 V cell and repeat step 1. Disconnect the wire from the cell and record what happens.

4. Repeat steps 1 to 3 with the steel wire, cotton thread, and connecting lead.

5. Position the copper wire as shown in Figure 18-7, but do not connect the ends of the wire to the cell.

CAUTION: Do not connect any material to the dry cell for more than a few seconds at a time.

Figure 18-7.

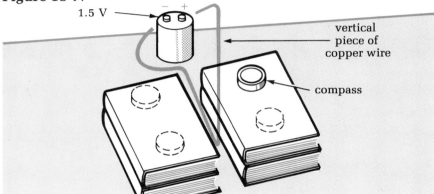

6. Place the compass in each of the four positions shown, and record what happens to the compass needle.

7. Connect the ends of the wire to the cell, and repeat step 6.

Part B: Electromagnets

8. Wind the piece of copper wire in a coil around a pencil, leaving about 15 cm of each end of the wire unwound. Remove the pencil from the coil.

9. Place the coil of copper wire on the desk, as far as possible from any ferromagnetic objects.

10. Slowly move the compass in a complete circle around the coil, and record what happens.

11. Connect the two ends of the coil to the cell. Repeat step 10.

12. Disconnect the wires from the cell, reverse them, and reconnect them again. Repeat step 10.

CAUTION: Ensure that adjacent turns of the copper wire in the coil do not touch one another.

Discussion

Part A

1. Is copper a magnetic material? Explain your answer.
2. What kinds of materials can be magnetized by means of an electric current?
3. a) From the behaviour of the compass in step 7, what can you infer about magnetic forces near the wire?
   b) Do there appear to be any magnetic poles on a straight piece of magnetized copper wire? Explain your answer.

Part B

4. Explain what happened to the compass in step 10.
5. Compare the reaction of the compass needle as it was moved around the magnetized coil to what happens near a bar magnet.
6. What happens to the magnetic effects produced when the current in the coil is reversed?
7. List the advantages and disadvantages of an electrical magnet versus a bar magnet.

Electromagnetism — Magnetism Produced by Electricity

When Oersted passed an electric current through a wire near a compass, the compass needle was deflected. This showed that an electric current could produce magnetic forces. The magnetic effect produced by an electric current can be demonstrated using a dry cell, a piece of aluminum wire, and some iron filings, as shown in the photographs below. If the aluminum wire is not connected to the dry cell when dipped into the iron filings, nothing happens. Aluminum is not a magnetic substance.

A static electric charge on a conductor does not produce a magnetic effect.

The iron filings are not attracted to the aluminum wire when it is not connected to the dry cell (left). However, the iron filings cling to the wire when it is connected to the dry cell (right).

However, if the wire is connected to the dry cell when dipped into the iron filings, something unexpected occurs. The iron filings cling to the aluminum wire as if it were a magnet. When the wire is disconnected from the dry cell, the iron filings drop off the wire. The magnetism can be switched on and off by controlling the electric current in the wire. The wire can be made from any electrical conductor. The magnetic effect produced when an electric current passes through a conductor is known as **electromagnetism.**

Although a conductor becomes magnetized when an electric current passes through it, the magnetic forces around it are quite different from those surrounding a bar magnet. The photographs below show compasses pointing at right angles to a wire in which a current is flowing. When no current is flowing, the compasses point north, as usual. If the direction of the current in the wire is reversed, the compasses point in the opposite direction. The magnetic forces seem to form in concentric rings around the entire length of the wire. Thus, a single wire carrying an electric current produces magnetic forces, but has no magnetic poles.

Compass needles point at right angles to a current-carrying wire (left) but they point to the north when there is no current flowing through the wire (right).

This electromagnet, which has a diameter of 2 m, easily hoists an estimated 3 t of scrap electric motors.

Electromagnets — Making Magnets Using Electricity

The crane in the photograph has a pie-shaped disc at the end of the cable. Hanging from the disc is a pile of scrap iron. If this disc were a permanent magnet, the load of scrap iron would not drop off when the crane operator wanted to dump it. However, the magnet hanging from the crane is controlled by an electric current. With this kind of magnet, the crane operator can turn the magnetic force on and off by simply flicking a switch.

You can easily make an electrical magnet with poles similar to a bar magnet. If a wire is wound into the form of a coil, or helix, the magnetic effect produced by the loops of wire is similar to that of a bar magnet. A current-carrying coil which produces magnetic forces is called an **electromagnet**. The compasses in the photograph show that when current is flowing through the coil, there is a N-pole at one end of the coil, and a S-pole at the other. If the current flows through the coil in the opposite direction, the magnetic poles on the coil are reversed and the compasses then point in the opposite direction. When the current is switched off, the coil becomes demagnetized, and the compasses all point towards the Earth's North Pole again.

Practical Applications of Magnetic Forces

Hundreds of technological devices use either permanent magnets or electromagnets, depending on which offers more advantages (see Table 18-3).

Table 18-3

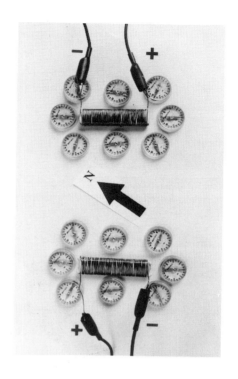

Advantages of Permanent Magnets

They need no external source of energy.

They retain magnetism for long periods of time.

They can be made extremely small.

They can be used to store information.

They can be used over a wide temperature range.

They can be used in many different environments, such as under water.

Advantages of Electromagnets

The magnetic force can be switched on and off.

The magnetic force can be increased and decreased.

The magnetic poles can be reversed.

The magnetic force can be made very large.

The magnetic forces they produce are used in four basic ways.

1. Moving Objects by Attracting or Repelling Forces

Small permanent magnets are used to hold cupboards and drawers closed, and to collect pins and needles in sewing boxes. Large electromagnets in mines separate iron, nickel, or cobalt particles from the unwanted ore. They can lift scrap metal and sort garbage. The circuit breaker in a house is really a safety switch, similar to a

Do You Know?
When new warships are launched at Norfolk Naval Base in the United States, the entire hull of the ship is wrapped with heavy cables. A large electric current is then passed through the cables to demagnetize the hull. Tests have shown that the ship travels through the water more quickly when this is done.

fuse, controlled by an electromagnet. If too large a current flows in a circuit, the current in the electromagnet produces a strong magnetic force. This magnetic force moves a piece of metal and opens the switch. Once the problem in the circuit has been corrected, the switch can be reset. Electromagnets also make objects vibrate back and forth very quickly. By reversing the current in a coil many times a second, the electromagnet in a doorbell makes a small hammer vibrate against the bell. The sounds made by a loudspeaker are produced using a similar principle. Tiny electromagnets change the magnetic domains on tapes and computer discs.

2. Rotating, Turning, or Twisting Objects

Think of all the ways electric motors are used in the home: vacuum cleaners, blenders, furnace fans, hi-fi equipment, children's electric trains, etc. The forces that turn all these electric motors are produced by magnets.

A very simple motor can be made using two bar magnets, as shown in Figure 18-8. One bar magnet is attached to the watch glass with plasticine. A second bar magnet is used to make the magnet on the watch glass turn. If the N-pole of the second magnet is brought near the magnet on the watch glass, the watch glass begins to rotate. The magnet on the watch glass turns until its S-pole is opposite the other magnet's N-pole. By flipping the hand-held magnet end over end at just the right time, it is possible to repel the S-pole and make the magnet on the watch glass continue

Some examples of electric motors.

Figure 18-8. By flipping the hand-held magnet from end to end at the right time, the magnet on the watch glass can be made to continue turning.

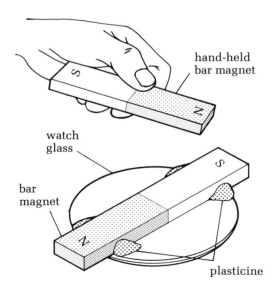

to spin. This is the basic principle of the electric motor. The motor is first made to turn by using the attracting forces between two unlike poles. It is then kept turning by changing to the repelling forces between two like poles at just the right time. This process, repeated continually, keeps the motor spinning.

A bar-magnet motor is not very practical, however, since the hand-held bar magnet must be flipped repeatedly. This problem can be solved by replacing the bar magnet with an electromagnet. The magnetic poles of an electromagnet can be changed by simply reversing the direction of the current in the coil. It is not necessary to move the coil at all. This ability to reverse the poles rapidly on an electromagnet is one of the key principles in motor design.

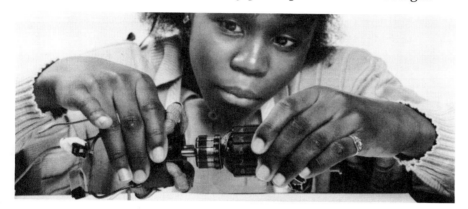

Electric motors consist of two basic parts. The part that turns in the middle is a revolving electromagnet, wound on a metal core. Built into the metal frame of the motor is another, stationary electromagnet. The changing magnetic forces between these two electromagnets make the motor turn.

3. Deflecting or Changing the Speed of Charged Particles

Every time you watch television you are using an electromagnet. The picture is produced by beams of electrons moving rapidly back and forth across the screen. An electromagnet is positioned at the back of the television tube. The current in the coil produces a magnetic field that changes the direction of the electrons as they pass by.

The electron microscope shown in the photograph is another device that uses electron beams to magnify objects about 100 000 times. The electron beams are focused using a series of electro-magnets. Nuclear scientists also use a series of electromagnets to speed up tiny particles in the particle accelerator.

4. The Production of Electrical Energy

Following Oersted's discovery that electric currents can produce magnetic forces, scientists soon found that magnetic forces can produce an electric current. What they discovered is discussed in Section 18.4.

James Hillier, co-inventor of the electron microscope, with the first commercially available model.

Study Questions

1. What is electromagnetism?

2. a) Describe how to magnetize a rod made of lead.
   b) What is unusual about the magnetic forces surrounding a current-carrying wire?

3. a) Describe how to construct an electromagnet.
   b) Draw a schematic circuit diagram showing how to connect an electromagnet that is controlled by a switch.

4. List three applications in which it would be best to use a) an electromagnet, b) a permanent magnet. Explain why in each case.

5. a) List the four basic ways in which magnetic forces are used in practical technological devices.
   b) In what basic way is a voltmeter i) similar to a motor, ii) different from a motor?

PARTICLE ACCELERATORS

Scientists and engineers have developed devices called particle accelerators to probe into the fundamental nature of matter itself. A particle accelerator speeds up particles such as protons and electrons until they are travelling close to the speed of light (300 000 km/s). Much of the progress in nuclear research has been made possible by building larger and larger accelerators to increase the energy and speed of protons.

One kind of particle accelerator, called a synchrocyclotron, uses huge electromagnets—some have masses up to 36 000 t. Because these huge electromagnets cost so much, another type of accelerator called a synchrotron has been developed, which uses many smaller electromagnets instead.

The synchrotron at the Fermi National Accelerator Laboratory (Fermilab) at Batavia, Illinois, has a circumference of more than six kilometres. There are two rings of electromagnets in this synchrotron. One ring consists of 1000 superconducting electromagnets with coils of niobium and titanium cooled to −268°C by liquid helium. Beams of particles are accelerated in opposite directions in each ring, and where the two rings intersect some of the particles collide.

The U.S. government plans to build a new particle accelerator called the Superconducting Supercollider (SSC). This new synchrotron will be 85 km in circumference, and will cost over $4 000 million. It will require more than 10 000 superconducting electromagnets to guide the protons around the huge ring.

18.3   Magnetic Force Fields

When boarding a plane at the airport, you may have to walk through a special doorway that has been installed to detect weapons. If a hijacker concealing a large piece of metal, such as a gun, walks through the doorway, an alarm bell rings. The metal in the gun affects something invisible spreading completely across the doorway. The doorway is surrounded with electromagnets, which produce an invisible magnetic force field. A magnetic force field is a region in space in which a magnetic force can be detected.

Airplane passengers step through a special electromagnetic doorway designed to detect weapons.

Research has shown that the human brain and heart both generate weak magnetic fields. In studying these magnetic fields, scientists have to make their measurements in special rooms which are screened from the Earth's magnetic field. Why is this necessary?

Activity 18-4:   Magnetic Force Fields

In this activity you will use iron filings to help visualize the patterns formed by invisible magnetic force fields. The patterns can help you infer the properties of the force fields produced by magnets. You will also compare the magnetic force fields of bar magnets and electromagnets.

Materials

bar magnet
2 cardboard sheets
iron filings
compass
small piece of iron
small piece of wood

pencil
paper plate
clamp
retort stand
1 m of insulated copper wire
6 V battery

Procedure

Part A: The Magnetic Force Field Around a Bar Magnet

1. Place a bar magnet on your desk.
2. Place a book on either side of the magnet, and lay a sheet of cardboard across the top of the books.
3. Sprinkle iron filings over the surface of the cardboard. As you do so, gently tap the cardboard.
4. Hold a compass just above one of the magnet's poles, and move it along the pattern formed by the iron filings until you return to the original position. Record what happens.
5. Draw a full-sized diagram to show the pattern formed by the iron filings on the cardboard.

6. On one side of the magnet, about 4 cm away, place a small piece of iron. Place a small piece of wood in the same position on the other side. Repeat steps 2 to 5.

Part B: The Magnetic Force Field Around a Current-Carrying Conductor

7. With a pencil, make a small hole in the middle of a paper plate. Hold the paper plate in the clamp, and attach the clamp to the retort stand.

8. Thread the copper wire through the hole in the paper plate, and sprinkle some iron filings on the plate (see Figure 18-9).

9. Attach the ends of the wire to the battery terminals. Gently tap the paper plate.

10. Draw a diagram to show the pattern formed by the iron filings around the wire.

11. Place the compass in several positions on the plate, and record in your diagram the positions of the needle.

12. Reverse the wires on the battery and repeat steps 9 to 11.

Part C: The Magnetic Force Field Around an Electromagnet

13. Wind the wire around the magnet to form the coil for the electromagnet. Leave the ends of the wire about 20 cm long.

14. Remove the magnet from the coil, and place the coil under a sheet of cardboard as in step 2.

15. Connect the wires to the battery and repeat steps 3 to 5.

16. Reverse the wires on the battery, and record what happens to the compass when it is moved around the coil.

Discussion

Part A

1. What can you infer about the magnetic force field of the magnet from the path, or lines, followed by the compass?

2. How can you infer from the pattern of iron filings where the magnetic force field is strong or weak?

3. What can you infer about the strength of the magnetic force field as the distance from the magnet increases? Explain why.

4. Are the iron filings on the paper temporary or permanent magnets? Explain your answer.

5. What evidence suggests that the magnetic field is three-dimensional?

CAUTION: Disconnect the wires from the battery as soon as the iron filings have formed into a pattern around the wire or the coil.

Figure 18-9.

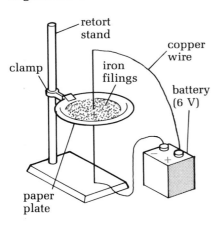

6. What effect does the presence of a) a magnetic substance, b) a nonmagnetic substance, have on the magnetic force field around a bar magnet?

7. In what ways can the magnetic field pattern of a bar magnet be compared to that of the Earth? (See Science In Action, page 551.)

8. What precautions should be taken when using a compass to indicate direction?

Part B

9. What is unusual about the magnetic field pattern around the wire magnet in Part B, compared to "normal" magnets?

10. Explain what happened to the compass needle when the wires were reversed on the battery.

11. How could the strength of the magnetic field around the wire be increased?

Part C

12. Compare the magnetic field pattern of the bar magnet in Part A to that of the electromagnet in Part C.

13. Explain what happened to the direction in which the compass pointed when the wires on the battery were reversed.

14. How were the iron filings affected when the two wires were reversed? Explain what happened to them.

15. State an advantage of an electromagnet over a permanent magnet. (Refer to evidence from this activity.)

Magnetic Force Fields

A magnetic force field, or more simply, a magnetic field, spreads invisibly in all directions around every magnet. A magnetic field exerts a force on any magnets and magnetic substances placed within it.

Scientists have developed a way to visualize the invisible magnetic fields using fine particles of iron. A two-dimensional pattern of the magnetic field around a bar magnet, for example, can be shown by covering the magnet with a sheet of cardboard and sprinkling iron filings on the cardboard. When the cardboard is tapped gently, the iron filings form a pattern around the magnet. Each iron filing becomes a tiny temporary magnet and points in the direction

The pattern of iron filings shows that a three-dimensional magnetic force field surrounds a bar magnet.

of the magnetic field. By studying such patterns, scientists have inferred the properties of magnetic fields listed in Table 18-4.

Table 18-4: Properties of Magnetic Force Fields

Observations of Patterns Formed by Iron Filings	Properties of Magnetic Fields Inferred from Observations
The iron filings on a flat plane above a magnet form a continuous pattern around it. Iron filings sprinkled on the surface of a magnet form a three-dimensional pattern.	The magnetic force field surrounds the magnet in all directions.
When a compass is moved from the N-pole of a magnet such that the needle follows the pattern of iron filings, the compass moves in a complete loop back to the N-pole.	The magnetic force field "lines" spread out in closed loops around the magnet.
The iron filings form a smooth unbroken pattern around the magnet.	The magnetic force field "lines" do not cross one another.
Many iron filings concentrate around each pole of the magnet.	The magnetic force field is stronger where the magnetic field "lines" are grouped more closely together.
As the distance from the magnet increases, the iron filings are more weakly attracted to the magnet.	The magnetic force field decreases as the distance from the magnet increases.

The magnetic field pattern around a single current-carrying conductor appears to form in concentric rings, as shown in the photograph above. When the wire is wound into a coil a different magnetic field is produced. Look closely at the bottom photograph of the magnets under the glass plate. One magnetic field is produced by an ordinary bar magnet, and the other by an electromagnet. Both types of magnets produce similar magnetic field patterns. In fact, if the magnets were covered, it might be difficult to decide which was which. The magnetic effects of an electromagnet can be made identical to those of an artificial or a natural magnet.

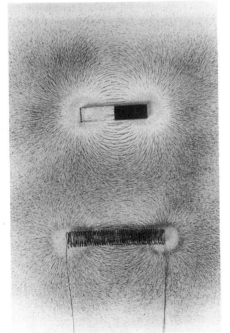

An Electron Theory of Magnetism

The domain theory explains the magnetic effects observed in magnets. As you have learned, scientific evidence suggests that a domain is made up of many atoms, all lined up in the same direction, and that each atom is itself a tiny magnet. Scientists think that the magnetic effect produced by each atom can be explained in terms of electromagnetism.

When an electric current flows in a wire, a magnetic effect is produced. An electric current is a flow of electrons, and it is the motion of the electrons through the wire that produces the magnetic effect. Think about the structure of an atom. Scientists think that electrons are constantly orbiting the nucleus in all atoms. The motion of each of these orbiting electrons produces a tiny magnetic effect. Scientists also think that each electron behaves as if it were spinning like a top as it orbits the nucleus, and that this combined motion produces the total magnetic effect for each electron.

Because there are electrons in the atoms of every substance, it would be reasonable to expect that all substances would be magnetic. In most substances, however, the magnetic effects produced by different electrons spinning as they orbit the nucleus seem to cancel each other. These substances are classified as nonmagnetic. In magnetic materials, the magnetic effects produced by several electrons in each atom combine to produce a tiny, atom-sized magnet. The magnetic field produced by the electrons is similar to that of an electromagnet. Each atom-sized magnet will always have a N-pole and a S-pole, as shown in Figure 18-10. These atom-sized magnets group together to form the magnetic domains mentioned earlier. This theory explains why every magnet always has a north and a south pole.

Ways of Changing Magnetic Fields

The magnetic field around a magnet is not fixed, but can be changed in several ways. One way is to place an unmagnetized, ferromagnetic object near the magnet. As the photograph shows, the only substances that do seem to affect a magnetic field are those that can be magnetized themselves. Nonmagnetic substances, such as air, glass, water, and paper, do not noticeably affect a magnetic field.

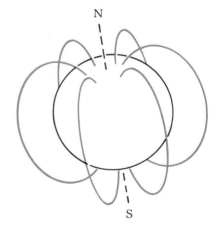

Figure 18-10. Each atom of a ferromagnetic substance behaves as if it were a tiny electromagnet, with its own N- and S-poles.

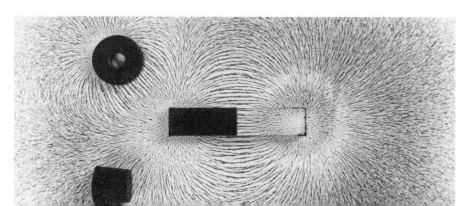

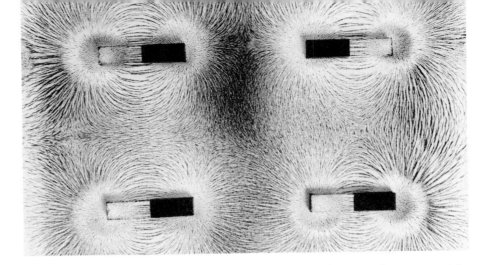

Bar magnets are usually stored in pairs, with pieces of a ferromagnetic substance called "keepers" placed across their ends. This procedure ensures that the magnetic force field is concentrated in a continuous loop, helping the magnets to retain their magnetism longer.

A second way to change the magnetic field around a magnet is to bring another magnet close to it. The magnetic field patterns around four bar magnets are shown in the photograph. When two N-poles are placed near one another, the usual smooth curves of the magnetic field pattern of the single bar magnet are distorted. Their flattened shape indicates that the two like poles of the magnets are repelling each other. In the magnetic field pattern formed when two unlike poles face one another, the pattern indicates that the magnetic lines of force form the shortest possible path between the two poles. This indicates an attracting force between the two poles.

A magnetic field can also be changed in a third way by placing within the field any electrical device that is carrying an electric current. Place a radio or a flashlight near a compass and then switch the device on and off. The compass needle will move each time the electric current changes. It is the changes in the magnetic fields caused by the current flowing in the motor's electromagnets that make electric motors rotate.

CHALLENGER

Special procedures must be followed when installing a compass in a car, boat, or snowmobile, in order to ensure that it indicates the correct direction. Study a car compass in a hardware store. What is the purpose of the objects attached to the screws you turn when adjusting the compass in the car?

Study Questions

1. a) What is a magnetic force field?
   b) List four properties of a magnetic force field.
   c) If the magnetic force field is invisible, how is it possible to identify its properties?

2. a) Describe how to show the two-dimensional pattern of the magnetic field around i) a straight wire, ii) a bar magnet, iii) an electromagnet.
   b) Draw the magnetic field pattern produced when the S-poles on two bar magnets are facing one another.

3. Explain why a magnet always has two magnetic poles, using the electron theory of magnetism.

4. a) List three ways to change a magnetic field.

   b) What precautions should be taken when using a compass to indicate direction? Explain why.

THE EARTH'S MAGNETIC FIELD

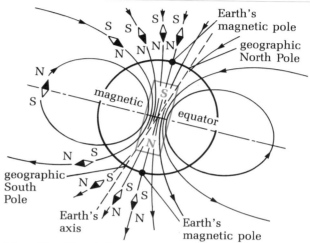

Figure 18-11. The Earth has a magnetic field similar to that of a bar magnet.

The Earth can be regarded as a huge bar magnet, with the poles of the magnet lined up with the axis on which the Earth spins (see Figure 18-11). Scientists are still not sure how this magnetic field is being produced. One theory is that the molten outer core of the Earth, which is mostly iron, is slowly swirling around in large circles, producing the same effect as a huge electromagnet.

This "magnet" inside the Earth has an enormous magnetic field stretching many thousands of kilometres into space. It is the Earth's magnetic field that exerts a force on a compass needle and makes it point towards the Earth's own magnetic poles. By convention, the end of a compass or a bar magnet that points north is considered to be a N-pole. Because opposite poles attract, the Earth's magnetic pole, near the Earth's geographic north pole, is therefore considered to be a S-pole. The Earth's magnetic S-pole is in Canada, and is about 2000 km from the geographic North Pole of the Earth. The positions of the Earth's magnetic poles are continually changing. Scientists think that each magnetic pole moves continually in small loops. Changes in position of as much as 20 km in one day have been recorded.

Evidence suggests that the two magnetic poles of the Earth have been reversed many times in the past. In the course of oceanic research activities, it was found that once-molten magnetic rocks in the ocean bed showed a series of regular reversals of the magnetic field. Scientists are still not able to explain how or why the Earth's magnetic field changes in this manner.

A geologist searches for iron ore deposits using a magnetometer.

Figure 18-12.

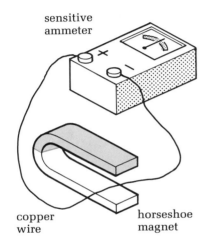

copper
wire

horseshoe
magnet

sensitive
ammeter

Figure 18-13.

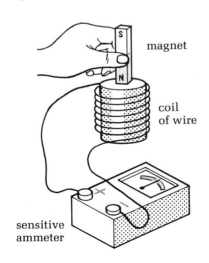

magnet

coil
of wire

sensitive
ammeter

18.4 Electromagnetic Induction

Ten years after Oersted demonstrated that an electric current can produce a magnetic effect, the English scientist Michael Faraday demonstrated that a changing magnetic field can produce an electric current. Faraday was refused funds to develop his discovery because he could not convince a government committee that it had any practical value! Today thousands of devices utilize the special relationship between electricity and magnetism discovered by Faraday.

Activity 18-5: Producing Electricity Using Magnetism

In this activity you will investigate the effects produced when conductors and magnets are moved near one another.

Materials

1 m insulated copper wire

ammeter (galvanometer)

horseshoe magnet

coil with a hollow core

bar magnet

Procedure

1. Connect the ends of the copper wire to the ammeter.
2. Hold the wire stationary between the ends of the horseshoe magnet (see Figure 18-12). Observe the ammeter.
3. Hold the wire stationary while your partner moves the horseshoe magnet back and forth. Observe the ammeter.
4. Repeat step 2, then move the wire in and out of the ends, first slowly, and then rapidly. Observe the ammeter.
5. Turn the horseshoe magnet through 180° to reverse the magnetic poles, and repeat steps 3 and 4.
6. Connect the ends of the coil to the ammeter (see Figure 18-13).
7. Quickly move the bar magnet into the coil and hold it still for 4 s, then remove it at the same rate. Observe the effect of these actions on the ammeter.
8. Reverse the poles of the bar magnet, and repeat step 7.

Discussion

1. List the inferences you can make about the relationship between magnetism and electric current, based on your observations a) in steps 2 to 5, and b) in steps 7 and 8.

2. Describe two ways to make an electric current flow through a conductor, using a magnetic force field.

3. Compare what happened in step 3 in this activity with what happened in step 7 in Activity 18-3.

4. What condition is essential for a magnet to induce an electric current in a conductor?

Producing and Controlling Electrical Energy

In all the electromagnetic devices discussed so far, electrical energy in the form of an electric current has been used to produce magnets and magnetic forces. Faraday showed that the process can be reversed. By moving magnets and their magnetic force fields, a flow of electric current can be induced in a conductor. This relationship between electricity and magnetism is one of the most fundamental in science. Whenever an electric current flows in a conductor, a magnetic field is produced. Whenever a magnet and its magnetic field move past a conductor, an electric current flows in the conductor. The production of an electric current by a changing magnetic field is called **electromagnetic induction**.

The generation of an electric current using a magnetic field can also be shown with a coil of wire, a magnet, and an ammeter. If the coil is connected to the ammeter and a magnet is pushed into the coil, the ammeter will detect a small electric current flowing through the coil. When the magnet stops moving, the current stops flowing. If the magnet is pulled out of the coil in the opposite direction, the current flows through the coil and the ammeter in the opposite direction as well. A current is induced in the coil when the magnet is moved either into or out of the coil. Whenever a conductor passes through a magnetic force field, electrons are induced to move along the conductor.

Even if a magnet is moved past the *outside* of a coil, an electric current is induced in it. A tape recorder works on this principle. When a tape is played, the magnetic particles on the tape move past the playback head on the tape recorder. Inside the playback head is a small coil of wire. As the magnetic particles on the tape move past the coil of wire, an electric current is induced in it. The induced electric current has the same pattern as that used to record the tape. This current is then amplified and flows through a loudspeaker to produce the desired sound.

There is another way to induce an electric current in a coil. The magnet can be kept still and the coil moved past it. The black lines used to code some bank cheques, price tickets, and library books

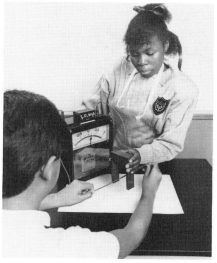

An electric current is induced in a conductor when a magnet is moved past it.

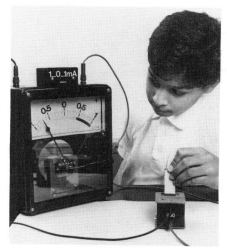

An electric current is induced in a coil of wire when a magnet moves inside the coil.

contain a magnetic compound. When a "pen" containing a small coil is moved over each coding line, a pulse of electric current is induced in the coil. It does not matter whether the coded object is kept still and the coil is moved, or the coil in the pen is kept still and the object is moved. As long as the magnetic field changes in relation to the coil, an electric current is induced in the coil.

Faraday investigated all these ways of inducing electric currents. He summarized these effects in a statement known as **Faraday's Law of Electromagnetic Induction:** Whenever the magnetic field near a conductor is moving, or changing in magnitude (size), an electric current is induced to flow through the conductor.

The photograph shows the construction of a typical electrical generator in a car. The electrical generators used in power stations are much larger versions of the car generator. However, in these large generators the permanent magnets are replaced by electromagnets.

Study Questions

1. a) What is electromagnetic induction?
   b) Draw a diagram to show how to induce an electric current in a wire.

2. What single condition is necessary for an electric current to be induced into a conductor by a magnet?

3. a) State two ways to produce an electric current using a magnet and a coil of wire.
   b) List two devices in which moving magnets are used to produce an electric current.

THE PERSONAL STEREO CASSETTE RECORDER

A personal stereo cassette recorder is a device combining most of the scientific principles presented in this unit. The source of electrical energy is a battery, made of a set of dry cells. The headphones are the major electrical loads, and the sound from the headphones is controlled by switches. Most of the conductors are fine lines of copper attached to a special "printed circuit board" inside the cassette recorder.

The design of a cassette recorder illustrates the special relationship between electricity and magnetism. When the tape is played, the magnetic particles on the tape induce an electric current in a coil of the playback head on the cassette player. This electric current is amplified, and flows through a coil of wire in the headphones. The reverse process then occurs in the headphones. The electric current flowing in the coil in the headphones produces magnetic forces that move the tiny loudspeakers in the headphones, producing the sound you hear.

Meet an Engineering Technologist— Winfield Brewster

Winfield works for the Toronto Transit Commission in the equipment department that handles all surface streetcars. His job is to give technical support to the mechanics and electricians working on streetcar repairs and maintenance.

Q. HOW WOULD YOU DESCRIBE YOUR JOB?
A. My job is simple: to keep the vehicles on the road.

Q. DID YOU KNOW WHAT YOU WANTED TO BE WHEN YOU WERE YOUNG?
A. I knew I wanted to be an electrician, and a good one, so I worked hard. Today I'm happy in my job because I did my homework. I decided where I wanted to go and I disciplined myself to get there.

Q. WHAT IS YOUR TRAINING?
A. I went to technical school in Barbados and then did a five-year apprenticeship as an electrician. I worked for two years before moving to Toronto in 1965. Here, I took the Ministry of Skills and Development exam to get certified as an electrician.

Q. HAVE YOU DONE FURTHER TRAINING IN YOUR FIELD?
A. Yes, I'm always taking courses because you have to keep upgrading. I also teach a vehicle electrician's course and give work-related courses.

Q. HOW MANY STREETCARS ARE YOU IN CHARGE OF?
A. The TTC has 155 streetcars at the Roncesvalles division. The biggest change recently has been in the development of electronic controls for the newer streetcars. We still have an older model— which is sometimes known as "the red rocket"—but we also have a newer car called the Canadian Light Rail Vehicle (CLRV). It has logic circuitry and is controlled with an electronic control unit. An even newer model is equipped with a microprocessor, which is a small computer that controls the vehicle. We will be getting 52 of these to replace the older models.

Q. WHAT IS A TYPICAL DAY LIKE IN YOUR JOB?
A. It really depends on the weather. On a bad, wintry day we might have lots of cars in the shop Snow causes problems, and in cold weather the cars also have to have proper heating. On an average day, we might have 10 cars in for a variety of things. I act as a troubleshooter. Often, I take on the jobs that aren't easily solved by the regular mechanics and electricians.

Q. HOW MANY PEOPLE DO YOU WORK WITH?
A. I work the day shift, which has about 50 people. There are three shifts, and we run 24 hours a day. Sometimes I come in at night if there's a real problem.

Q. WHAT QUALIFICATIONS DOES SOMEONE NEED FOR YOUR WORK?
A. Any of the technical schools will train someone in the technical field related to this job. We hire people mostly from the community colleges, and then train them in the vehicle specifics. I think kids should decide early on if they want to work in a technical job. There's a lot of hard work and sometimes the subject is pretty dry, but other times it can be very interesting.

Q. DOES THE FIELD CONTINUE TO INTEREST YOU?
A. Yes, because the changes in technology mean there is always something new to learn. For instance, we had one of the new streetcar models in the shop today. I will have to train on it and become an expert on how it runs.

Review Questions

A: Knowledge

1. a) What is meant by the term "ferromagnetic"?
    b) List the ferromagnetic elements.

2. Why is magnetite also called "lodestone"?

3. a) What is meant by the term "ferrite"?
    b) List three practical uses for ferrites.

4. State how to determine the position of the poles of a magnet using a) iron filings and b) a magnetic compass.

5. a) Describe an experiment that would show how the magnetic force of a magnet changes as the distance from the pole of the magnet increases.
    b) State the relationship between the magnetic force and the distance from the magnet.

6. Describe how you could show that a magnetic effect is produced when an electric current flows in a wire.

7. a) What is an electromagnet?
    b) Why is an electromagnet considered to be a temporary magnet?

8. List four practical uses for electromagnets.

9. List the kinds of motion that are produced by magnetic forces.

10. a) List ten different uses of electric motors.
    b) Why can an electric motor also be called a magnetic motor?

11. Draw a diagram to show how the domains inside a piece of iron are positioned when it is a) unmagnetized and b) magnetized.

12. Describe two demonstrations that show that the magnetic force field spreads out in all directions around a magnet.

13. List three materials that a) affect magnetic fields and b) do not affect magnetic fields.

14. List four devices in which moving magnets are used to produce an electric current.

B: Application

15. a) Explain, in terms of the domain theory, why there is very little magnetic force at the middle of a bar magnet.
    b) Draw a diagram showing the arrangement of the domains near the middle of the magnet to support your answer.

16. Explain, in terms of the domain theory, why a bar magnet broken in the middle has a N-pole and a S-pole, just like the original magnet.

17. a) What is meant by the term "induced magnetism"?
    b) Draw labelled diagrams showing how the positions of the magnetic domains change when an iron bar is touched by a bar magnet.

18. a) Describe how to magnetize an iron rod by stroking it with a magnet.
    b) Explain what happens inside the rod as it is magnetized, in terms of the magnetic domains.
    c) Draw a diagram to show how the rod is magnetized and label the magnetic poles.

19. a) Draw a labelled diagram of a compass.
    b) Explain how to determine which direction is east, using a compass.

20. How can you use a compass to distinguish between a magnet and an unmagnetized magnetic substance?

21. a) How can you retrieve pins lost in a deep crack, using a bar magnet and a steel knitting needle?
    b) Explain what happens to the knitting needle and the pin.

22. Why should a compass be kept well away from pieces of iron or steel, when it is being used to indicate direction?

23. a) Describe how to make an electromagnet.
    b) How can the magnetic poles on an electromagnet be reversed? Why does this happen?
    c) Draw a schematic circuit diagram to show how to produce an electromagnet.

24. a) List two advantages of permanent magnets compared to electromagnets.
    b) Describe two ways in which these advantages are used.

25. a) List three advantages of electromagnets compared to permanent magnets.
    b) Describe three ways in which these advantages are used.

26. List three ways of a) magnetizing a nail and b) demagnetizing a nail.

27. Which kind of magnets are most commonly used in large electric motors, electromagnets, or permanent magnets? Explain your answer.

28. Describe the correct procedure for storing permanent magnets. Explain why it is done.

29. How can you compare the strength of two magnets by studying their magnetic field patterns?

30. Why do scientists believe that the Earth's magnetic field has changed in the past?

31. a) Why does no electric current flow in a coil, when both the coil and a magnet placed next to it are not moving?
    b) What single condition is necessary for a magnetic field to induce a current in a conductor?

32. Does a magnet have to move inside or outside of a coil of wire to induce an electric current to flow in the coil? Justify your answer in terms of some devices that produce electric currents.

33. Why are electromagnets, rather than permanent magnets, used in large electrical generators?

C: Problem Solving

34. Why might problems occur if a compass is not correctly adjusted when it is installed in a car or a snowmobile? How can this problem be solved?

35. a) List the four basic ways magnetic forces are used.
    b) What factors should be considered, before you decide whether to use a permanent magnet or an electromagnet?

36. Predict and draw the magnetic field pattern that would be produced by a horseshoe magnet. Then check your prediction by experiment.

37. Electric motors and ammeters are both moved by magnetic forces. What are the basic similarities and differences in the operation of these two magnetic devices?

38. Design a table that compares the similarities and differences between electricity and magnetism.

Try This

1. **A Magnetic Ammeter**
   Some of the earliest devices for detecting an electric current, and the magnetic field it produces, consisted of a coil of wire wound around a compass. When an electric current flowed through the coil it affected the compass needle. These devices were called galvanoscopes. Make your own galvanoscope and use it to test for electric currents produced by electromagnetic induction.

2. **Electric Motors**
   Find out how to make an electric motor. Design and make a simple electric motor, using dry cells as the source of electrical energy.

3. **Three-Dimensional Magnetic Fields**
   Fill a clear glass or plastic container with salad oil. Sprinkle several spoonfuls of iron filings into the oil. Screw the lid tightly onto the container, and shake it vigorously to distribute the filings throughout the oil. Hold a magnet against the side of the container and observe the patterns produced in the oil. What happens with two magnets?

Generating Electrical Energy: What is the Cost?

The Issue: Should we continue to use nuclear energy to produce electricity in Ontario?

As the population of Ontario increases, so do the province's energy needs. Until a few decades ago, dams in the Ontario watershed provided more than enough water to generate hydroelectricity to supply these needs. Today, large amounts of thermal electricity are also required to supply the demand. This is electricity produced by fossil fuels or by nuclear reactors.

As the term "thermal electricity" suggests, large amounts of heat are used to produce steam for the steam turbines driving the electrical generators. Both the burning of fossil fuels and the use of nuclear energy release large amounts of waste heat into the atmosphere. Also, many wastes are produced by the burning fuel, and radioactive wastes and some radioactive gases are produced by nuclear reactors. The cooling systems of nuclear reactors also release large amounts of hot water into nearby lakes and rivers.

Clearly, producing electrical energy by either fossil fuels or nuclear energy pollutes the environment. The issue concerning many people is which method creates worse environmental problems. In recent years, the number of nuclear power stations being built around the world has decreased, due to public fears about the safety of nuclear reactors. The nuclear accident at Chernobyl in the Soviet Union in 1986 intensified these fears. How to dispose of the nuclear waste materials from the used fuel rods is also problematic. Some of

Pickering Nuclear Generating Station.

Disposal of nuclear waste, Douglas Point, Ontario.

these highly radioactive waste materials must be safely contained for thousands of years.

As our energy needs increase, so will the need for informed, responsible decisions about the future development of nuclear energy. In this activity you will gather and evaluate evidence relating to various aspects of the problem. Then you and your classmates will identify and clarify alternative positions on the issue, and evaluate the alternatives. Finally, you will make a personal decision as to which position seems best.

Exploring the Issue

A. Identifying Possible Positions on the Issue

As a class, carry out a brief brainstorming session to identify possible positions on the issue. Form small groups, as directed by your teacher, to investigate the issue.

B. Gathering the Evidence

1. Use both federal and provincial government documents, materials prepared by consumer awareness groups, scientific journals, reference books, magazine and newspaper articles, and library files to obtain information relevant to the issue.

2. Classify the information into scientific, technological, and societal categories wherever possible.

C. Clarifying Your Group's Position on the Issue

1. Appoint one or more students to record information during your group's discussion. Identify all the factors related to the issue and then determine the consensus of your group. Consider the viewpoints of other groups in society who would be affected by your group's position. Discuss the possible consequences of any action based on your group's position if it were carried out.

2. List reasons supporting your group's position. Select three or four of the most important reasons, and rank them in order of importance. Be prepared to justify each reason. Also list the major problems that could result from your group's position, and suggest ways of resolving them.

D. Presenting Your Group's Position on the Issue

On a sheet of chart paper, write your group's position and the list of reasons supporting it. Briefly justify each of your group's reasons in an oral presentation to the class. You may also mention any major problems related to your group's position.

E. Identifying Your Personal Position on the Issue

1. Review all the positions taken on the issue and the major reasons justifying each position. Consider major problems as well.

2. Decide which course of action you think the Ontario government should follow to resolve the issue. Identify what the following groups would have to do to achieve the position you have adopted: a) Ontario Hydro, b) the nuclear power industry, c) Ontario residents.

3. Justify your position.

Special flasks are required to transport nuclear wastes to the appropriate treatment facility.

Unit 6 Wrap-Up

Unit Summary

Electrostatics is the study of *static electric charge*. The Model for the Electrical Nature of Matter explains effects produced by static electric charges. All *atoms* contain negatively charged *electrons* and positively charged *protons*. When objects become charged, only the electrons transfer from one object to another. Like charges repel and unlike charges attract. Electroscopes detect static charges on an object.

Substances charged by friction become oppositely charged. Electric charges travel freely in *conductors*, but remain in a fixed position on *insulators*. Objects charged by *contact* receive the same charge as that on the object giving the charge. Objects charged by *induction* receive the opposite charge to that on the object giving the charge.

Most electric *circuits* consist of a source of electrical energy, an electrical *load*, a *switch*, and *connecting wires*. Electric current is measured in *amperes* using an *ammeter*. Electric *potential* (*voltage*) is measured in *volts* using a *voltmeter*.

An *electrochemical cell* converts chemical energy into electrical energy. *Primary cells*, such as a *voltaic cell* and a *dry cell*, cannot be recharged. *Secondary cells*, such as the *lead-acid cell*, can be recharged.

A *battery* consists of a number of cells connected in *series* and/or in *parallel*. When connected in series, the electric potential of the cells is added together. Cells in parallel have the same electric potential.

In a *series circuit*, electric current only flows in a single path. In a *parallel circuit*, electric current flows in several paths at the same time. If one load is disconnected in a series circuit, the current stops flowing, whereas in a parallel circuit, no other loads are affected.

Only ferromagnetic and ferrimagnetic materials can be made into strong permanent magnets. Like magnetic poles repel one another, and unlike poles attract one another. The domain theory of magnetism can be used to explain the effects produced by magnetic materials.

Electromagnetism occurs when an electric current flows through a conductor. When an electric current flows through a coil of wire, an electromagnet is formed. Magnetic forces are used to move and turn objects and to produce electricity.

A magnetic force field surrounds magnets and electromagnets. A magnetic field exerts forces on and is affected by magnets and magnetic materials placed within it. Iron filings can be used to indicate the presence of a magnetic force field.

When a magnet or electromagnet is moved past a conductor, an electric current is induced in the conductor. Electromagnetic induction occurs whenever a magnetic field moves relative to a conductor.

Key Terms

ampere	electron
circuit diagram	electroscope
conductor	electrostatics
domain	induced current
electric charge	insulator
electric circuit	magnetic force
electric current	magnetic force field
electric potential	magnetism
electrical load	negative charge
electricity	nonmagnetic
electrochemical cell	parallel circuit
electromagnet	positive charge
electromagnetic	series circuit
induction	volt

Unit Practice and Review

A: Short Answer

True or False

State whether each statement is true or false. Correct each false statement.

1. Neutral objects are attracted to charged objects.
2. A primary cell converts electrical energy into chemical energy.
3. A battery is a very large secondary cell.
4. Compasses are only affected by other magnets.
5. The magnetic field around a bar magnet is similar to that around an electromagnet.

Multiple Choice

In each question below, select the best answer.

1. An electroscope is positively charged when:
   a) it has an excess of electrons.
   b) it has a deficiency of electrons.
   c) the nuclei of its atoms are positively charged.
   d) the electrons of its atoms are positively charged.
2. The kind of circuit in which an electrical load may be disconnected without affecting other loads is called a:
   a) series circuit
   b) closed circuit
   c) open circuit
   d) parallel circuit
3. An electromagnet is produced when:
   a) an electric current flows through a straight wire.
   b) an electric current flows through a coil of wire.
   c) a magnet is pushed inside a coil of wire.
   d) a coil of wire is wound around a magnet.
4. Two light bulbs A and B are connected in a series circuit to a dry cell. The switch is closed. If bulb B is unscrewed, what will happen to the brightness of bulb A?
   a) decrease
   b) increase
   c) become zero
   d) remain the same
5. Magnetic fields do not interact with:
   a) static electric charges.
   b) moving electric charges.
   c) stationary permanent magnets.
   d) moving permanent magnets.

Complete the Statement

Complete each of the following statements with the correct word or phrase. Do not write in this book.

1. When an object is charged by ___?___ , it receives the same charge as the object giving the charge.
2. A charged particle is called a(n) ___?___ .
3. The law of magnetism states that ___?___ attract one another.
4. In a series circuit, the ___?___ is the same in all parts of the circuit.
5. When a(n) ___?___ is moved past a coil, an electric current flows in the coil.

Matching Items

Match each item in Column A with the appropriate item in Column B.

1. Column A
   i) positively charged particle
   ii) device for detecting charge
   iii) method of charge transfer when combing hair
   iv) method of charge transfer which produces sparks

   Column B
   a) friction
   b) induction
   c) proton
   d) contact
   e) electroscope
   f) electron

2. Column A
   i) device for limiting electric current
   ii) electric potential the same in all parts of circuit
   iii) disposable source of electrical energy
   iv) energy converter in an electric circuit

   Column B
   a) switch
   b) electrical load
   c) series circuit
   d) fuse
   e) parallel circuit
   f) dry cell

3. Column A
   i) magnet that is difficult to demagnetize
   ii) magnet that can be controlled by a switch
   iii) magnetic materials used to show magnetic fields
   iv) has no effect when moved past a coil of wire

Column B
   a) nonmagnetic substance
   b) temporary magnet
   c) permanent magnet
   d) electromagnet
   e) magnetic domain

B: Knowledge and Application

1. Define the following terms: insulator, conductor.

2. Describe three different ways to a) charge an object, b) discharge an object.

3. List four different kinds of applications for static electricity. Describe one application in detail.

4. Explain what happens when an atom becomes a) negatively charged, b) positively charged.

5. A balloon is attracted to both a charged glass rod (rubbed with silk) and a charged ebonite rod (rubbed with wool). What is the charge on the balloon? Explain your answer.

6. Explain what happens when you touch the ball on a positively charged metal-leaf electroscope with your finger, in terms of the movement of charged particles.

7. When cars stop at tollbooths, flexible wire brushes stick up out of the roadway and touch the sides of the cars. Why is this done?

8. Describe the function of the electrical load and the switch in an electric circuit.

9. Explain the difference(s) between a wet primary cell and a dry primary cell.

10. Why is a sharp pain experienced if a piece of aluminum foil is held between teeth in which there are fillings?

11. Why are circuit breakers used instead of fuses in many electric circuits?

12. Why must the electric potential produced by the dry cells used in calculators, wristwatches, and cameras remain constant for the life of the cell?

13. Why are series circuits containing many bulbs not in common use any more?

14. Draw a schematic circuit diagram to show three bulbs wired in parallel, which are connected to a switch, a single cell, and two bulbs wired in series.

15. If you were given a magnet with unmarked poles, describe two ways you could identify them.

16. Explain why "stroking" an iron nail with a magnet can magnetize it.

17. Why are electromagnets, rather than permanent magnets, used to lift scrap iron?

18. Describe three ways to produce an electric current, using a magnet and a coil of wire.

19. Use the domain theory to explain why:
    a) the magnetic force of a magnet is changed when a magnet is heated or hammered.
    b) a magnet that is cut in half becomes two separate magnets each with both magnetic poles.

C: Problem Solving

1. a) To measure the electric current flowing through a light bulb, should an ammeter be connected in series or in parallel with the bulb? Explain your answer.
   b) Draw a schematic circuit diagram of three cells connected in parallel that are connected to two light bulbs in series. Indicate on the circuit diagram how a voltmeter should be connected to measure the voltage across the second bulb.

2. A personal cassette recorder is operated by a 12 V battery.
   a) Determine the number of 1.5 V dry cells required to produce 12 V, and draw a schematic circuit diagram showing how the cells are connected together.
   b) What voltage would be produced by the battery if two cells were accidentally reversed?
3. Why is there an absolute limit to the maximum magnetic force that can be produced by a given permanent magnet?

D: Challengers

1. Design an electric motor that operates using static electric charges, rather than magnets. Discuss any practical problems you might have to solve if you were required to make such a motor.
2. Draw a schematic electric circuit diagram of the lighting system on a car trailer. The trailer lights should include side lights, brake lights, and turn indicator lights, as well as the red rear lights used for towing the trailer at night.
3. Place a flat copper or aluminum strip on top of two straws, so that the strip and straws will roll over a smooth surface. Hold a horseshoe magnet just above, but not touching, the metal strip and move the magnet quickly back and forth. Explain what happens.

Project Ideas

1. Name the scientists who played a major role in the development of the Rutherford-Bohr Model of the Atom, particularly in terms of its electrical nature. Write a brief paragraph on the contribution of each scientist.
2. Using local sources, develop some research data on the occurrences and effects of lightning in your area. Analyze and classify the data into useful and informative summaries.

3. Mammals that live in the water and some fish are able to generate or detect electric currents, and some can do both. What is the purpose of these electric currents and how are they generated and detected?
4. Silver-plated cutlery, bronzed baby shoes, and the chrome surfaces on cars are produced by the electroplating process. Find out how it is done and list other objects that are treated in this way.
5. At extremely low temperatures, some materials become "superconductors". Find out how these superconducting magnets are made and used.
6. Find out how the electric current flowing in the revolving electromagnet of an electric motor is continually reversed. Build a model and explain its operation to your class.

Readings

Asimov, Isaac. *How did we find out about Electricity?* New York: Walker, 1973. (The book outlines significant events and personalities related to electricity.)

Brown, Robert. *666 Science Tricks and Experiments.* Blue Ridge Summit, Pennsylvania: TAB Books, 1981. (A chapter of interesting activities on electricity and magnetism.)

Graf, Rudolf F. *Safe and Simple Electrical Experiments.* New York: Dover, 1973. (An excellent book for someone who wishes to develop an understanding of electricity and magnetism by doing many simple experiments. The materials used are commonly found in the home.)

Reuben, Gabriel. *Electricity Experiments for Children.* New York: Dover, 1968. (Good practical resource for students interested in doing experiments related to electricity and magnetism.)

VII

Waste Management

Of all living things on earth, only humans can gather resources from beyond their immediate surroundings, and then process those resources into different, more useful forms. This capacity has made it possible for us to thrive and flourish as a species. But the wastes generated and released into the environment as a result of our distinctly human activities have upset the balance of nature.

Exposure to toxic industrial by-products can cause cancer, heart and lung problems, and a score of other serious diseases. We must take responsible steps to manage our wastes and thereby protect the delicate and irreplaceable features of our world, as well as the resources needed to sustain life on this planet.

Chapter 19 Solid Wastes

Chapter 20 Liquid and Hazardous Wastes

This once pristine fishing lake in Northern Canada has become a victim of pollution.

Chapter 19
Solid Wastes

Waste is all material derived from animal and human activities that has served its original purpose and is discarded. **Solid waste** is primarily solid, as the term implies, although it may have some liquid content. If a waste is free-flowing, it is called a **liquid waste**.

Solid wastes can leave an ugly trail of visible pollution. The proper management of solid wastes is important in resource conservation, and in maintaining or upgrading environmental quality.

In this chapter you will learn about the various types of solid wastes and the most common ways to dispose of them. You will also study techniques for putting solid wastes to good use.

When you finish Chapter 19, you should be able to:

- classify solid household wastes, and describe suitable ways to dispose of them
- classify consumer products according to packaging
- list the properties of common household plastics
- describe common techniques of solid waste management
- appreciate the effort and expense required to maintain a quality environment

19.1   Municipal Solid Wastes

When wastes from residential, commercial, institutional, and industrial sources consist of materials similar to normal household waste, we use the term **municipal solid waste (MSW)**.

MSW contains food scraps, paper and newspaper, cans, glass, fireplace ashes, grass clippings, wood, worn-out appliances, tires,

Figure 19-1.   Possible sources of waste.

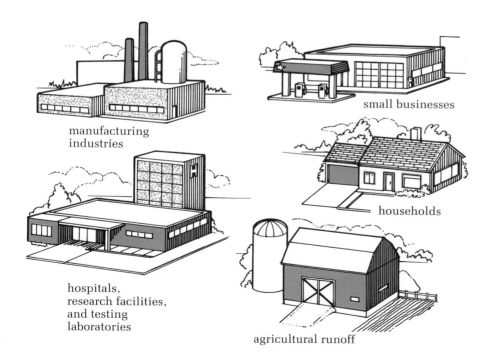

manufacturing industries

small businesses

hospitals, research facilities, and testing laboratories

households

agricultural runoff

STUDY HINT

Take a Study Break
To make sure your brain doesn't turn to jelly while you study, you need to take study breaks. Breaks can provide either a change of pace or a change of activity. If you need a change of pace, you should do something completely different for a few minutes. If you have been sitting at your desk, stand up, stretch, go for a walk around the block, or have a quick snack. Then get back to the same work. If you need a change of activity, give yourself time to unwind from one activity before beginning another. Both your body and your brain need time to adjust between activities. These breaks need be only a few minutes long, but they must be there to keep you alert and working to potential.

A **municipality** is a city, town, county, district, township, or other area, having local self-government.

furniture, broken toys, and thousands of other items. Table 19-1 shows the typical composition of municipal refuse.

Although applied generally to anything we discard, the term **garbage** usually refers to organic wastes from food products that decompose, producing putrid gases with an offensive odour. **Rubbish** refers to wastes that do not decompose to produce putrid gases; these wastes may be either combustible or noncombustible. Combustible rubbish includes paper, wood, cloth, rubber, leather, and garden wastes. Noncombustibles include metals, glass, ceramics, stones, dirt, masonry, and some chemicals.

Table 19-1: Typical Composition of Municipal Solid Waste

Physical (% by mass)		Chemical (% by mass)	
miscellaneous paper	25	water	28.0
food waste	22	carbon	25.0
yard waste	15	oxygen	21.1
newspaper	10	glass, ceramics	9.3
glass	8	metals	7.2
metals	8	ash and inert materials	5.5
other (wood, cardboard, textiles, plastics, leather, rubber)	12	hydrogen	3.3
		nitrogen	0.5
	Total = 100	sulphur	0.1
			Total = 100.0

Figure 19-2. A comparison of the quantity of solid wastes from various sources.

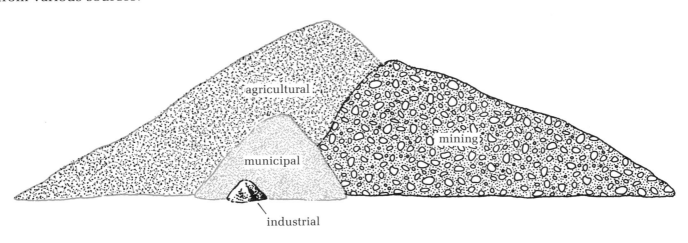

Activity 19-1:   Investigating Household Waste

We call it junk, refuse, rubbish, waste, trash, and scrap, but to most people it is just plain garbage! Latest estimates suggest that for every person living in cities and towns in Ontario, about 2 kg of MSW is produced each day.

In this activity you will sort and classify the materials in a sample of household wastes provided by your teacher. You will also calculate the cost of disposing of solid household wastes.

Materials

sample bag(s) of household wastes
   (prepared by your teacher)

balance

gloves

tongs

plastic balance cover

Procedure

Part A: What's In Your Garbage?

1. Draw the following table in your lab report.

Waste Category	Mass of Waste	Relative Volume	Percentage of Waste
paper			
plastic			
metal			
glass			
food wastes			
other			

Students sort household garbage.

2. Your teacher will provide the class with (a) bag(s) of cleaned waste that represents the amount of solid household waste produced each day by the average Canadian. You will also be given the total mass of the waste.

3. Your class will be divided into six groups, each representing one category of the household waste materials listed in the table. The groups will then sort the garbage into these categories. Wear gloves and use tongs as needed.

4. Cover the balance with a piece of plastic to protect it. Find the mass of materials in each category and record this value in your

table. Through discussions with the other groups, compare the relative volume of each of the categories of waste, and classify each volume as large, medium, or small in your table. Dispose of the waste as directed by your teacher.

5. Calculate the percentage of waste (by mass) for each category. For example:

% of paper = (mass of paper ÷ total mass of waste) × 100

Part B: Costs of Household Waste Disposal

6. Based on the total mass of waste provided in this activity and on population figures provided by your teacher, calculate the average amount of household waste generated annually in a) your household, b) your community, c) your province, d) Canada.

7. If household waste disposal costs an average of $12/t, calculate the annual average cost of waste disposal in a) your household, b) your community, c) your province, d) Canada.

Discussion

1. Which category of waste formed the largest percentage of the household waste a) by mass, b) by volume?

2. Based on this activity or on your own experience, list six items commonly found in each category of household waste.

3. If each category of household waste was compressed, which would you expect to show the greatest volume reduction? How would the density of this material change?

4. a) Which category of household waste would you expect to decompose first? Explain.
   b) Which category of waste would you expect to be most resistant to decomposition? Explain.

5. List four yard wastes from a garden or lawn that might be found in the garbage in the summer.

6. List four food wastes in your home that might be thrown out a) during meal preparation, b) after a meal.

7. a) Suggest four ways in which the person generating the waste in this activity could reduce the total waste.
   b) If a reduction of 10% could be achieved, calculate the yearly savings in waste disposal per person.
   c) Will the person generating the waste save the money? Explain.

8. Studies carried out by the Ontario Ministry of the Environment have shown wide differences in the disposal cost per tonne of waste collected in various municipalities. Give some possible reasons for these cost differences.

Why So Much Solid Waste?

During the past two decades, the quantity of solid waste collected in Canada has nearly doubled, and if predictions hold true it will double again over the next 20 years. The main reason for this phenomenal increase in solid waste in Canada and throughout the industrialized world has been the trend to the "throw-away" society. We use once-only bottles, cans, containers, diapers, medical supplies, and many other disposable items. Until producers and consumers alike realize that apparent conveniences involve less apparent inconveniences, and develop programs based on environmental responsibility, the volume of solid waste will continue to escalate.

Figure 19-3. The "disposable" society: Use it once, then throw it away.

Activity 19-2: Packaging

Packaging accounts for about 35% of municipal solid waste. In this activity you will look at the kinds, amounts, sizes, life spans, and costs of packaging.

Procedure

Part A: Renewable and Nonrenewable Resources in Packaging

Some packaging materials can be easily replaced. If you cut down a tree to make paper bags, another can be grown. Trees are a **renewable** resource. Metal cans are usually manufactured from steel or aluminum, which comes from underground ores. There is only so much ore in the earth, and we cannot create more. Metallic ores, then, are an example of a **nonrenewable** resource. Petroleum is also a nonrenewable resource used to make plastics, rubber, fabrics, etc.

While the resources used to make glass (primarily sand and soda ash) are also nonrenewable, they are in such enormous supply that their use in glass-making poses no problems in terms of resource supplies.

1. Table 19-2 lists a few grocery items. Examine Table 19-3 to see what was actually brought home after the shopping trip.

Table 19-2:   Grocery List

milk

corn flakes

tomatoes

steak

toothpaste

margarine

orange juice

Table 19-3:   Packaging From Grocery List

2 plastic grocery bags	1 piece plastic wrap (steaks)
3 L milk	100 mL toothpaste
3 small plastic bags (milk)	1 plastic tube (toothpaste)
1 large plastic bag (milk)	1 plastic lid (toothpaste)
corn flakes	1 cardboard box (toothpaste)
1 box (corn flakes)	454 g margarine
1 waxed paper bag (corn flakes)	1 cardboard sleeve (margarine)
4 tomatoes	1 plastic tub (margarine)
1 styrofoam tray (tomatoes)	1 plastic lid (margarine)
1 piece plastic wrap (tomatoes)	orange juice
2 steaks	1 glass jar (orange juice)
1 styrofoam tray (steaks)	1 metal top (orange juice)

2. The brief grocery list produced a lot of packaging. Make a table of your own, dividing the packaging materials into renewable and nonrenewable resources.

Part B: Life Spans of Packaging

3. Many packages are thrown away as we unpack our groceries.
   a) List some of these packages.
   b) List the packages that you think would still be in your home one week after the shopping trip above.

4. The box of corn flakes bought on the shopping trip arrives at the store in a large carton containing smaller individual boxes.
   a) What happens to the large carton once it is unpacked at the store?
   b) After you have finished the cereal, what happens to i) the box, ii) the waxed paper bag?

5. List some other packages that are thrown away at the store.

Part C: Disposables and Packaging

Many consumer products are made to be used once and then thrown away. Such products are called **disposables,** and the packages they come in are also designed to be thrown away. Unfortunately, many disposables are made from nonrenewable resources such as plastic and metal.

6. Make a list of a dozen disposables commonly found at home. Put an X beside any disposable items made from nonrenewable resources.

7. Suggest possible alternates to the disposables in your list.

8. Sometimes a package is too big for its product. Give an example of an unnecessarily large package for a small product, and if possible, bring the example of poor packaging to school.

Part D: Overwrapping

9. Do a survey of consumer products in your home to identify those that are overwrapped or double-wrapped. In each case, classify the wrappings as paper, cellophane, molded plastic, or other.

10. Find a product wrapped in more than three layers. Is all of this packaging needed? If not, then why was it used?

11. Visit a supermarket to find a product packaged in two different ways. Does one way use less packaging and still do the job?

Could these items do without the wrapping?

Part E: Packaging Can Be Expensive!

You have seen many examples of packaging. Do you ever think about the cost of a package? Who pays for the package? Who pays for the printing and graphics on the package? Who pays for the energy and resources used to make the package? Who pays to dispose of the package when it is thrown in the garbage?

12. We can buy soft drinks in a) cans, b) glass bottles, or c) plastic bottles. Calculate the cost per millilitre of soft drink for a), b), and c). Who pays for the three types of container? Which container gives the best value?

Discussion

1. How could we make better use of renewable resources for packaging, and thus conserve some nonrenewable resources?

2. Why are there so few packages left in your home one week after a shopping trip?

3. It has been said that you pay for a package twice. If one of the costs is for producing the package, what is the second cost for?

4. Plastics are often used for packaging. Although plastic comes from a nonrenewable resource (oil), in some cases it is the best possible packaging material. Explain why, and name two products that are best packaged in plastic.

5. Excluding beverages, name a product that comes in both disposable and refillable containers.

6. List some ways to reduce waste through wise use of packaging.

Packaging Generates Waste

Increased packaging has greatly increased solid waste over the past few decades. Each person in Ontario now produces over 260 kg of waste packaging materials annually. Why so much? The main reason has been the trend towards disposable and nonreturnable "convenience" packaging. Examples of this trend are:

1. the continuing rise in self-service merchandising, which requires eye-catching packages that help sell the product by drawing attention to themselves;

2. the use of paper and plastic packages for small items such as batteries, pens, screws, razor blades, and other merchandise that is easily and frequently shoplifted;

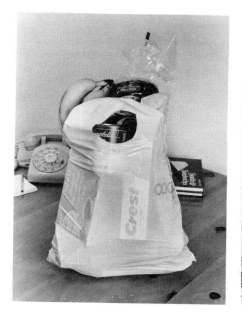 

One bag of groceries generates all of the waste on the right.

3. the increasing use of nonreturnable bottles and cans for beverages.

Many consumers want more and more convenience packaging. Others, however, are concerned about the depletion of natural resources and increased waste generation, and realize that greater packaging convenience entails a higher environmental cost.

Nonreturnable beverage containers are a special problem: each year, billions of them are made, used once, and then thrown away. Almost all manufacturers and consumers prefer nonreturnable containers. Makers of the metals, glass, and paper used in beverage containers want to keep production volumes as high as possible. Most beverage makers want to avoid the bother and expense of returning containers for cleaning and reuse. Supermarket chains and store proprietors dislike the increased handling costs and storage associated with returnable containers. As a result, effective September 1, 1987, the Ontario Ministry of the Environment introduced a new soft-drink container policy requiring 40% of soft drinks to be sold in refillable bottles.

The packaging industry insists that packaging represents only a small fraction of the total solid waste in Canada, and that picking on packaging will contribute little to a cleaner nation. That small fraction nevertheless represents not only much of the litter we see around us every day, but also a great amount of waste that could be reduced.

Figure 19-4. Some products come in a natural package.

Do You Know?
Of the individual items comprising highway litter, 59% are paper, 15% are metal, 6% are plastics, 6% are glass, and 14% are miscellaneous.

Plastics in Packaging

Packaging materials have become a significant new market for plastics, which now compete with paper, cellophane, and aluminum wrap. Of the plastics now produced in North America, 20% go into packaging materials such as the polyethylene bags used for garbage, lunches, and groceries.

Plastics constitute a major problem in solid waste management because of their durability and nondecomposing nature. But plastic packaging has also made a tremendous contribution to convenience and public health. A study of the properties of plastics can perhaps suggest a resolution of this conflict.

Figure 19-5. Packaging can be expensive.

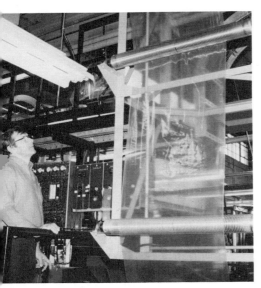

Polyethylene film is made from molten resin.

Activity 19-3:   The Properties of Plastics

As you learned in Chapter 15, plastics are a group of synthetic materials having large molecules made up of chains of atoms. For purposes of study, plastics can be conveniently grouped according to how they respond to heat. **Thermoplastics** soften when heated and harden when cooled, no matter how often the process is repeated. **Thermosets**, on the other hand, cannot be heated and reshaped once hardened by heat. Nearly all plastics can be identified by physical examination along with density tests, solvent tests, heat tests, and burn tests. In this activity you will carry out such tests on a variety of plastics.

Materials

plastic samples:
  ABS
  acrylic
  nylon
  polycarbonate
  polyethylene
  polypropylene
  polystyrene
  polyethylene terathalate
  melamine
250 mL beaker
2 100 mL beakers
graduated cylinder
water

acetone
alcohol
2 glass plates
tweezers
electric soldering iron
crucible tongs
heat-resistant ceramic pad
Bunsen burner
(Optional: sodium hydroxide,
  hydrochloric acid, and
  sulphuric acid solutions)

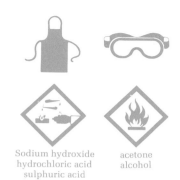

Sodium hydroxide   acetone
hydrochloric acid   alcohol
sulphuric acid

Procedure

Carry out the following tests with each plastic. Draw a table in which to record your results.

Part A: Physical Examination

1. Examine each of your plastic samples. Describe the general appearance and texture (smoothness or roughness) of each sample. Is it brittle or flexible? Can it be easily scratched? (i.e., Is it hard or soft?) Can it be stretched? (i.e., Is it elastic?)

Part B: Comparison of Density

2. Compare the density of each plastic to water. Push each sample under the surface of some water in a beaker. Record which samples float and which sink.

Part C: Solvent Tests

3. Using a graduated cylinder, place 20 mL of acetone in one small beaker and 20 mL of alcohol in another. Label the beakers and keep each one covered with a glass plate when not in use. With tweezers, dip the first plastic sample into the acetone for 10 s. Examine the sample to see whether or not the plastic has begun to dissolve. Record your findings in your table. Rinse the tweezers with water and dry. Test the other plastic samples in the same manner. Return the used solvent and plastic to your teacher for disposal.

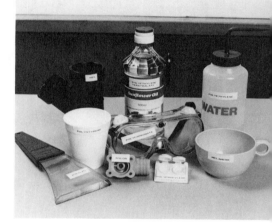

Samples of plastic.

CAUTION: Wash your hands after any contact with the solvents.

Figure 19-6. Solvent tests.

Dip each plastic sample in each of the 2 solvents for 10 s.

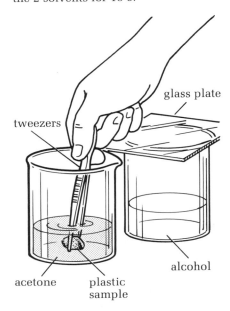

tweezers

glass plate

acetone   plastic
           sample

alcohol

CAUTION: Adequate room ventilation is required when the samples are burned. Do not burn PVC (polyvinyl chloride) because this produces toxic fumes. (PVC is commonly used to make garden hoses, wire insulation, packaging films, shower curtains, floor coverings, and pipe fittings.) Keep a beaker of water nearby to extinguish burning samples if necessary.

CAUTION: Be careful not to let hot drops of the burning sample fall into the Bunsen burner.

Optional. Your teacher will demonstrate the action of sodium hydroxide, hydrochloric acid, and sulphuric acid solutions on the plastic samples.

Part D: Heat Test (Teacher Demonstration)

4. Plug in an electric soldering iron and allow it to heat up. Press the hot tip against a plastic sample for 3 to 4 s. If the plastic melts, darkens, and becomes sticky, it is a thermoplastic. If the plastic chars but does not melt in the heated area, it is a thermoset.

Part E: Burn Test (Teacher Demonstration)

5. The burning characteristics of plastics are a good means of identifying a sample. When burning a plastic sample, hold a small piece with a pair of crucible tongs. Carry out all burn tests over a heat-resistant ceramic pad. Hold one edge of the sample over the flame for 10 s. Carefully observe how the sample burns. (Colour of flame? Size of flame? Flickering or smooth flame? Type of smoke? Does the sample melt and drip? Do the drippings burn? What kind of burning noise, if any, occurs?)

   Detect the odour of the sample *after* extinguishing the flame. Is there an odour? Is the odour sweet? Does it smell like rubber, burning wool, rancid butter, wax, or marigolds?

Figure 19-7. Step 6.

Hold one edge of the plastic sample over the flame for 10 s.

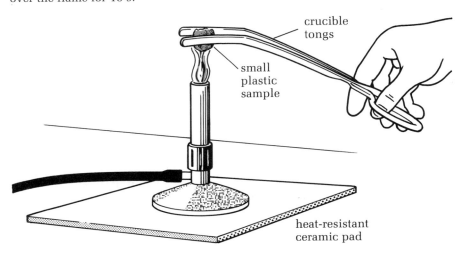

crucible
tongs

small
plastic
sample

heat-resistant
ceramic pad

Discussion

1. For each plastic sample studied, tell how its physical properties determine a possible use for the plastic.
2. Which plastics float in water and which sink?
3. Name the plastics that are soluble in both acetone and alcohol, and those that are insoluble in both solvents.
4. What is the purpose of a heat test? Use this test to classify the plastic samples.
5. What is the purpose of a burn test?
6. Suppose you are given a few unknown samples of plastic. You are told that the samples are the same as the ones used in this activity. Draw a flow chart that would enable you to identify the unknown plastics from a study of their properties.
7. Which properties explain why plastic waste is so persistent in the environment?
8. Which property of plastics provides the best clue for a possible disposal method? What problems does this method present?

Study Questions

1. a) What is municipal solid waste?
   b) What is the approximate composition of this waste?
   c) On average, how much municipal solid waste is generated each year per person in Canada?
   d) Why is there so much solid waste?
2. Distinguish among waste, garbage, and rubbish.
3. Explain the difference between each of the following, and give an example of each:

   a) renewable and nonrenewable resources
   b) disposable and refillable bottles
   c) thermoplastics and thermosets
4. a) What is the chief problem posed by the wastes we generate?
   b) What is wrong with the traditional answers to this problem?
5. List some common items formerly made from another material but now often made of plastic. Your kitchen is a good starting-point for such a list. Ask your parents to help you with this question. What advantages and disadvantages does the plastic version of the item offer compared to the original?

BIODEGRADABLE PLASTICS

Efforts to reduce the contribution of plastics to the solid waste problem and to eliminate the unsightliness of plastic wastes have focused on altering the plastic so that it becomes biodegradable. In the past, polymer chemists worked hard to find chemical stabilizers to stop plastics from breaking down, or degrading, when exposed to ultraviolet light, heat, and bacteria. Now, ironically, research is trying to modify plastic polymers so that they *will* break down in a controlled way under these same conditions. The desired degradation reaction can be achieved by one of two methods: by chemically modifying the polymer itself, or by adding suitable compounds to the plastic.

Canadian chemists were the first to develop a series of light-sensitive molecules that could be chemically incorporated into the polymer chain. These areas of the polymer then became subject to bond breakage when exposed to ultraviolet light. The degradation time can be controlled by careful modification of the polymer, or by varying the amount of light-sensitive polymer mixed with conventional plastics. This system has been successfully tested on polyethylene,

Canadians James Guillet (right) and Harvey Troth invented a crystalline material that can be used to manufacture a biodegradable plastic that disintegrates in the sun over a short period of time.

polypropylene, polystyrene, polyamide, polyester, and PVC (polyvinyl chloride). One drawback, though, is that the degrading does not continue in the absence of ultraviolet light. However, even small amounts of ultraviolet absorption tend to make the polymer brittle, allowing weathering processes to break the plastic into fragments that can then be attacked by soil microorganisms.

English scientists have developed a special additive for plastic that absorbs ultraviolet light. The resulting reaction eventually breaks down the plastic. Once initiated by light, this process continues even in the dark and degrades buried plastics.

19.2 Managing Solid Wastes

There are many aspects to the solid waste management problem. Litter on streets, highways, beaches, and other areas is a great nuisance, for example, even though only a small percentage of the population is to blame. Anti-litter advertising campaigns have not been very effective, and stiff fines for littering are difficult to enforce. Even on city streets, the accumulation of solid wastes in cans and plastic bags attracts rats and flies, stimulates bacterial growth, and creates collection problems. When large cities run out of dump space for the collected refuse, a new disposal problem is created.

Among our annual wastes are millions of tonnes of paper, metals, glass, plastics, and chemicals, all of which we worked hard to produce. Clearly something must be done about such a waste of valuable materials, and soon. We are literally throwing away our precious natural resources.

Figure 19-8. Throwing out garbage is like throwing away money. The value of the materials is lost.

Figure 19-9. Why isn't our environment littered with the bones of extinct dinosaurs?

Do You Know?
Paleontologists (scientists who study organic fossil remains) have recently unearthed more than 100 000 dinosaur and reptile bone fragments from a steep cliff in Nova Scotia, on the Bay of Fundy.

Solid Waste Cycles

For 160 million years, dinosaurs and other giant reptiles were the dominant forms of life on earth. Then, 65 million years ago, this Age of Reptiles ended with the rapid extinction of the dinosaurs and many other species. Exactly what caused this rapid demise is not known. But we do know that our landscape is not littered with huge piles of dinosaur bones or ancient vegetation. The debris from living things is reused, with the chemicals of one organism's wastes eventually forming another organism's tissues.

In the modern scenario, however, natural recycling processes are often obstructed. For example, an apple grown in the Niagara peninsula may be eaten in Ottawa, and its core then tossed into a plastic bag to be trucked to the city dump. This practice, while common, blocks natural recycling in several ways.

First, the leftover food is buried, so that it cannot be consumed by scavengers. This interrupts natural food chains, although decomposers can still act. For example, bacteria can break down the large molecules in the food and return their atoms to the soil. Other organic materials, such as paper bags, can also be broken down in this way.

The second problem is that so much of our garbage is wrapped in plastic, which is not normally biodegradable. Burning coal or petroleum recycles ancient organic matter back into the planet's ecosystem. Using these fossil fuels to make plastic, however, produces large molecules that cannot be used as food by any of the decomposers. Thus, the valuable chemicals contained in the plastic bags can neither by reused as is, nor broken down into small molecules or atoms that could be reused.

Thirdly, placing plastic bags in a dump ensures that they cannot be recycled to make other articles. There is no easy way to extract the plastic from the mixture of materials in a landfill.

The movement of matter through industrial processes, unlike the

A temporary dump site is cleared up after a strike by garbage workers.

movement through life processes, generates an increasing quantity of solid waste. Fortunately, not everything reaches a dead end. Some biodegradable industrial products, such as soaps and syndets, can be consumed by living organisms. Some wastes can be used as raw materials for other manufacturing processes. For example, the glycerol produced as a by-product in the manufacture of soap is used in cosmetics, dentifrices, candy, liqueurs, cigarettes, skin lotions, inks, and medicines. If the solid waste cycle was taken into consideration in the development of new products, many of our solid waste woes would be eliminated.

Figure 19-10. Using wastes rather than disposing of them has many advantages.

Just think — not only do we solve our garbage problem, but we also make the best hamburgers you've ever tasted!

The "Four Rs" of Waste Management

Some individuals and industries are practising four methods of waste management: reduction, reuse, recycling, and recovery. If applied to household wastes, these activities could significantly reduce the amount of waste generated in Ontario.

The four Rs of waste management are: reduce (compost heap), re-use (flea market), recycle (newspaper collection), and recover (municipal sewer sludge used as fertilizer).

1. **Reduce.**

   One way to reduce the volume of household waste is by buying products with less packaging to be discarded, such as refillable or recyclable containers. Another is to purchase higher-quality products. This means a higher initial cost, but also longer product life and less waste. Alkaline batteries, for example, cost 2 to 3 times more than regular batteries but last 5 times longer. Home-owners can compost food and yard wastes, which represent from 25 to 40% of municipal solid waste. Finally, we could avoid disposable consumer items, and buy appropriate quantities to eliminate unnecessary waste from spoilage.

2. **Reuse.**

   It seems that one person's trash is another's treasure. Garage sales, flea markets, and second-hand stores reduce waste through reuse. Glass bottles used for soft drinks and beer can be refilled an average of twenty times, and corrugated cardboard containers can be reused for shipping. At home, we can reuse empty plastic bags and containers to store all sorts of items, from food to hardware. Companies with wastes to get rid of and companies needing certain wastes can register their requirements with a "waste exchange". This increasingly popular service publishes a list of "wastes available" and "wastes wanted". The waste exchange passes on inquiries to advertisers, who then conduct their own negotiations. In such transactions, the waste generator saves on disposal costs, while the waste recipient saves on material and supply costs. Everybody wins!

3. **Recycle.**

   Waste recycling means using a waste material to replace all or part of a raw material in a manufacturing process. For example, glass containers can be recycled to produce more glass containers. Paper can be recycled for its fibre to produce more paper, insulation materials, or fuel. Some communities have recycling depots where citizens can drop off newspaper, glass, and metal cans. Other communities provide weekly curbside collection of such items separate from the trash.

4. **Recover.**

   Waste can be processed to recover either materials or energy, or both. Municipal solid waste can be converted to reusable products such as fuel or fertilizer for gardens, or it can be incinerated to produce energy. Special facilities can recover some materials from wastes. Waste motor oil, for example, is collected by some gas stations in Ontario and sent back to a refinery to be cleaned and reused.

Each of the four Rs of waste management (reduction, reuse, recycling, and recovery) offers advantages over waste disposal. Each results in a reduced quantity of waste and in the recovery of material and energy resources, which, of course, aids conservation.

While opinion polls show that the public is strongly in favour of the four Rs, actual participation levels are often below expectations, probably because of the lack of a direct benefit to the consumer. The public must be better informed about the indirect benefits of reduction, reuse, recycling, and recovery.

Current Disposal Methods

Even with full public participation in the four Rs, it will always be necessary to dispose of some wastes. In this section we will look at various options for disposing of municipal solid waste (MSW).

1. Open Dumps

The most primitive method of waste disposal, the open dump, is still used in many parts of the world. The collected waste is simply dumped in a large pile, where the organic matter rots or is consumed by insects, rats, cockroaches, mosquitoes, and other creatures. Junk dealers and individuals sometimes pick through the trash to salvage bottles, rags, knickknacks, and metal scraps. The dump is often set on fire to reduce the total volume, thus exposing more metal for salvage.

Open dumps pose serious risks. They are a potential source of diseases, especially those carried by flies and rats. The fires that ignite on their own or that are set by vandals are uncontrolled and smoky, and pollute the atmosphere. Rain carries water pollutants and disease microorganisms out of the dump. Finally, open dumps with their ugly appearance and strong stench are resented by communities.

An open garbage dump.

2. Sanitary Landfills

In sanitary landfills, the refuse is spread in thin layers that are then compacted by heavy bulldozers. For the landfill to qualify as "sanitary", a thin layer of earth must be spread over the waste at the end of each working day. This discourages insects, rodents, and other disease-carrying pests, minimizes the chances of fire, and eliminates pollution from burning, dust, and odours. Figure 19-11 shows two common types of sanitary landfills.

Inside the filled regions, much of the moist organic matter decomposes through bacterial action. If this decay occurs in the

Figure 19-11. Two types of sanitary landfills.

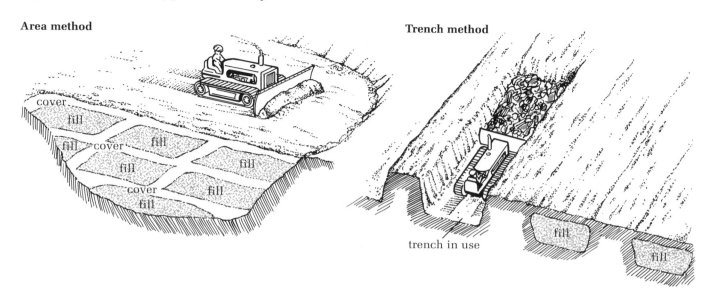

Area method

Trench method

trench in use

presence of oxygen it is called **aerobic**, while decay occurring without oxygen is called **anaerobic**. Table 19-4 lists some of the products of aerobic and anaerobic decay. Other products may also form, depending on the pH of the medium (soil, water, etc.). Note that anaerobic decay produces noxious products in each case.

Much of the decay in a landfill is caused by the slower anaerobic reaction, in which bacteria decompose the garbage, forming flammable methane, odorous hydrogen sulphide, phosphine, and ammonia gases, along with water and heat. The temperature within a landfill can rise from 20 to 70°C in just a few days from the heat produced. In aerobic reactions, the organic matter is oxidized, forming carbon dioxide and water as well as relatively harmless materials such as nitrates, phosphates, and sulphates.

Table 19-4:   Comparison of Aerobic and Anaerobic Decay

Compounds containing	Products of Aerobic decay	Products of Anaerobic decay
carbon (C)	carbon dioxide (CO_2)	methane (CH_4)
phosphorus (P)	phosphoric acid (H_3PO_4)	phosphine (PH_3)
nitrogen (N)	nitrate (NO_3^-)	ammonia (NH_3)
sulphur (S)	sulphate (SO_4^{2-})	hydrogen sulphide (H_2S)

Ideally, a landfill should be located where rain water trickling through the refuse or running off the surface will not pollute the ground water. If such drainage cannot occur naturally, piping under the landfill site must redirect the drainage water, called the **leachate**, to avoid pollution.

Other landfill site problems include the production of poisonous gases and the resultant settling of the land. With proper planning, however, landfills can reclaim spoiled land for apartment complexes, parks, playgrounds, and athletic fields.

A sanitary landfill site is converted into recreational tennis courts.

As landfill sites become filled, cities will have to transport their refuse further away; higher transportation costs will increase disposal costs. Choices of new sites may encounter stiff opposition from area landowners.

Disposal in a sanitary landfill represents a loss of materials. Food wastes which could nourish farm land, paper and wood which could be repulped, and nonrenewable supplies of metal and glass are buried forever.

3. Ocean Dumping

As coastal municipalities all over the world run out of waste disposal sites, they increasingly use the ocean for disposal. Because of damage to aquatic life, this practice is now forbidden in many areas.

4. Incineration

Incineration is a treatment method that reduces the amount of waste to be disposed of in a landfill. Waste is burned in furnaces at high temperatures, between 1350 and 1550°C, so that complete combustion of oxidizable material occurs. This method is being used more and more in urban areas. The ash, glass, metal, and other materials left behind amount to about one-fourth of the initial mass and an even smaller fraction of the original volume. The other

Figure 19-12. If you don't want something, you throw it away. But where is "away"?

Three steps in the incineration process. Garbage is dumped onto conveyers (left), which take it to the shredders (top right), where it is chopped up and tin cans are removed with a magnet. After incineration, the garbage is reduced to 5% of its original volume (bottom right) leaving easy-to-handle ash, metals, and glass.

three-quarters of the mass of garbage escapes as exhaust gases, creating potential air pollution problems.

In a modern municipal incinerator, MSW is first dumped from collection trucks into a large pit. A feeder mechanism transfers the waste to the first of a series of moving grates where hot combustion gases from the furnace dry, preheat, and ignite the waste. The waste then moves into the main combustion zone, where a grate is agitated and more hot air is blown in to ensure complete combustion. A final combustion zone completes the incineration. After the ashes are removed by a conveyor belt and cooled, any metals are salvaged by screening or magnetic separation. The remaining waste is removed to a sanitary landfill. The incinerator's furnace can heat boilers; the steam from these boilers can be sold to industry, or can produce electricity.

Incineration is more expensive than a sanitary landfill, despite the value of the steam it can produce. This is due largely to the heterogeneous nature of the refuse fuel mixture which makes it

Figure 19-13. Basic operation of a modern MSW incinerator.

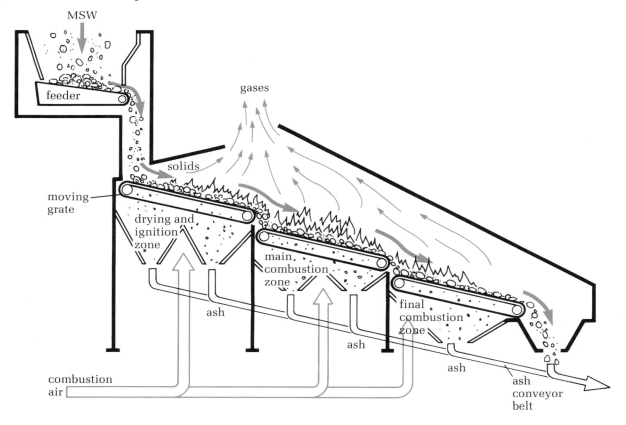

difficult to run the incinerator at high efficiency. Since plastics burn readily, they help incinerate other materials and improve the efficiency of the furnace. While plastics such as PVC produce hydrochloric acid gas (as well as water and carbon dioxide) when burned, modern incinerator technology can minimize corrosion and pollution problems. Modern incinerators also trap the black soot from plastics such as polystyrene (used in egg cartons, meat trays, and coffee cups) so that it can be fully converted to carbon dioxide. Unfortunately, many incinerators in use are not modern, and even new installations may not have all of the available pollution control devices. As well, many valuable materials such as paper, wood, plastics, textiles, and food wastes end up being burned rather than recycled.

Despite these problems, incineration offers several advantages besides the generation of steam: a) health problems associated with waste accumulation are eliminated, b) the volume of solid waste is greatly reduced, meaning less land is needed for disposal, c) no sorting of waste is required, d) the residue is odourless and easy to handle, and e) the reclaiming of certain metals from ash is easy and practical.

Study Questions

1. Define the terms reduce, reuse, recycle, and recover. Give an example of each.

2. Briefly describe four techniques for handling municipal solid waste. What are the advantages and disadvantages of each method?

3. Compare aerobic and anaerobic decay with regard to:
   a) rate of reaction
   b) oxygen required
   c) products produced
   d) desirability of reaction

4. a) Explain the meaning of the term leachate.
   b) How is leachate removed from a landfill site?

5. A proposal has been made to compact solid waste under high pressure, then dump it into trenches deep in the ocean. What are the possible advantages and disadvantages of such actions?

6. Give an example of a solid waste that can be classified as a) litter, b) biodegradable, c) refillable, d) recyclable, e) odorous, f) combustible, g) nonrenewable, h) inert (nonreactive).

OIL SPILLS
AT SEA

Between one and two billion tonnes of crude oil and oil products are moved at sea each year by 6000 to 7000 oil tankers. Also at sea the search for oil is becoming the largest exploration endeavour in the history of the petroleum industry. Both of these activities sometimes cause oil spills.

Oil spills can poison and smother marine life, cause genetic damage, and disturb the food chain. They also foul boats, fishing gear, beaches, and breakwaters, and kill or injure fish, marine mammals, and seabirds.

When oil spills into the sea, wind and waves break it up into patches. These patches are then moved by the current and spread apart by turbulence. Much of the lighter oil soon evaporates, while the heavier oil fractions mix with sea water and become more viscous. A water-in-oil emulsion then forms in which the tiny droplets of oil do not separate out but remain suspended in the water. This emulsion is called "mousse" because it is similar in consistency to the dessert of the same name.

Every attempt is made to clean up spills before the oil washes into shallower water or onto the coast, where it would cause additional damage to marine and bird life and would also pollute beaches.

Cleanup techniques include dispersing the oil chemically, mopping it up, or sinking it. Oil companies have produced a number of oil-dispersing chemicals that do not harm marine and bird life. These chemicals react with the oil to produce emulsions, which are then eaten by marine microorganisms. Straw, talc, peat, and other substances are used to soak up oil, while chalk mixtures are used to sink it.

Since ultraviolet light decomposes oil, special substances that can absorb ultraviolet light could theoretically be added to the oil before shipment. In the event of a spill, the oil would decompose more quickly. This solution is now being studied.

Clean-up crews use log booms and tugboats to contain an ocean oil spill near Vancouver.

19.3 Source Separation

Source separation means keeping recyclable wastes separate from nonrecyclable wastes at their point of generation, for future collection and recycling. Various source separation recycling programs are possible: at the office (office and computer paper, card stock); in commercial businesses (corrugated paper packaging, restaurant bottles and cans); in the home (newspaper, glass, metal cans). There are three kinds of residential source separation.

1. Householders separate recyclable materials by type and take them to a recycling centre.

2. Householders separate recyclable materials by type and leave them out in separate piles for street collection apart from the rest of their garbage.

3. Householders separate recyclable materials from their household wastes. The recyclables are left together, unsorted, for street collection. Later separation involves a combination of hand sorting and mechanical processes.

What Can Be Collected and Who Will Buy?

A source separation recycling program can only work if there is a market for the materials collected. Newspaper is the easiest material to collect and market, but some collection programs recycle glass, iron from food cans, and aluminum from beverage cans. Some materials can be sold back to the **primary industries** that produce basic commodities such as steel, aluminum, and glass. However, more often than not, they are sold to smaller **secondary industries** that modify basic commodities in some way. These include scrap dealers, detinning plants (which remove the tin coating from steel cans), and insulation and building manufacturers.

Only a small portion of MSW is suitable for recovery. Recoverable materials include newspaper, and smaller quantities of glass and metals. Who are the buyers, how stable are the prices, how much contamination is permitted, and how must these materials be prepared for recovery?

Newspapers

Buyers include paper mills, cellulose insulation manufacturers, building product manufacturers, and middlepersons who negotiate between recycling program operators and end-use buyers.

Figure 19-14. Source separation by residents is an important part of some recycling programs.

Aluminum beer and soft drink cans are dumped into a bin before being processed at a recycling plant.

Prices for recovered newspapers fluctuate with the demand for waste-paper products. Only newsprint is recyclable, thus the newspaper must be free of nonpaper items and other types of paper such as magazines. While newspaper inserts are usually acceptable, wet newspaper can be difficult to process. Paper mills accept only baled newspaper, while other markets may accept it in loose form. Waste paper may also serve as fuel. Burning this paper in kilns reduces the necessity for burning air-polluting coal.

Glass Containers

In Ontario, the main buyers are glass container manufacturing plants in Toronto, Bramalea, Hamilton, Milton, and Wallaceburg. While prices for glass containers tend to be stable, the degree of contamination can affect price. Also, higher prices can be charged for glass sorted by colour. If a load of glass has as little as 1% contamination (by ceramics or stones, for example), the glass might be rejected. If the bottles have metal caps and neck rings, the buyer must have a cleanup operation in the plant. In most cases, upgrading glass at a handling facility is not cost-efficient. Crushing simply makes contaminants more difficult to remove.

Cans

Buyers of steel and aluminum cans include scrap dealers and de-tinning plants, such as the one in Hamilton. Prices for recovered cans are fairly stable because the market is small. Lower prices are offered for cans made of a combination of metals, while higher prices are offered for aluminum cans. Excessive garbage or food residue on cans may discourage buyers. Sometimes cans are compacted or crushed, as long as the material can flow freely when agitated in scrap-processing facilities. Volume reduction of cans and bottles by crushing is justifiable only when savings in shipping costs more than offset processing costs.

Problems and Benefits

For successful source separation recycling programs, products have to be delivered to specifications, on schedule, according to the buyers' shipping requirements. Since these programs rely heavily on the voluntary support of householders, however, it is hard to predict what might be collected from week to week. This can interfere with buyers' schedules and specifications.

Nevertheless, source separation programs have several positive aspects. First, participants have the satisfaction of participating in conservation and recovery programs. Second, source separation is often the only method of resource recovery in small communities that have too little waste to justify a mechanical processing plant. Third, it is a practical way of introducing resource recovery into a community.

Activity 19-4: Can Recycling Save Energy?

Procedure

Part A: Comparison of Energy Consumption for Refillable and Throwaway Glass Beverage Bottles

(Refer to Table 19-5 for Part A.)

Table 19-5: Energy Consumption of Glass Bottle Beverages

Process	(kilojoules per litre of beverage)	
	Refillable	Throwaway
obtaining raw materials	285	1 490
container manufacture	2 155	11 320
cap manufacture and bottling	2 040	2 040
transportation, collection, and cardboard carrier	3 100	3 350
Total	7 580	18 200

1. Calculate the ratio of total kilojoules per litre for throwaway bottles to returnable bottles.

2. How many times more expensive is it to use throwaway glass bottles rather than refillable ones?

3. Calculate the ratio of container manufacture energy consumption for throwaway to refillable bottles. In light of this value:

   a) How many times more expensive is it (in terms of energy consumption per litre of beverage) to manufacture throwaway versus refillable bottles?

   b) On average, how many round trips might each refillable bottle make?

4. When bottles were first introduced for beverages, the typical soft drink bottle made about 30 round trips. Today that figure

has decreased to the value calculated in question 3 above. Suggest some possible reasons for the decline in round trips.

5. In 1958, returnable glass bottles accounted for 98% of the market share for soft drinks. Today that figure is about 40%. What types of packaging have replaced the returnable glass bottle?

Part B: Comparison of Energy Requirements for the Production of Steel, Paper, and Aluminum from Primary and Recycled Materials

(Refer to Figure 19-15 for Part B.)

6. How many millions of kilojoules per tonne of primary material is required to produce: a) steel, b) paper, c) aluminum?

7. How many millions of kilojoules per tonne of recycled material is required to produce: a) steel, b) paper, c) aluminum?

8. Producing glass from recycled material requires more energy than does glassmaking from primary material. How does this compare with steel, paper, and aluminum?

9. Calculate the ratio of energy costs for primary material to recycled material for: a) steel, b) paper, c) aluminum.

10. a) Which of the three materials generates the greatest energy saving through the use of recycled materials?
    b) Calculate the percentage of energy saving for each of the three materials, i.e., for steel,

$$\text{percentage of energy savings} = \frac{30 - 14}{30} \times 100 = ?$$

    c) In terms of energy saving during recycling, what type of container for soft drinks and beer would you recommend?

Figure 19-15.   Comparison of energy requirements for the production of steel, paper, and aluminum from primary and recycled materials.

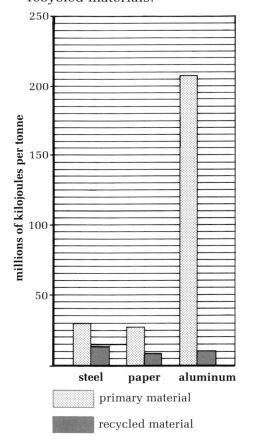

millions of kilojoules per tonne

steel   paper   aluminum

primary material

recycled material

Study Questions

1. a) What is a source separation recycling program?
   b) Describe three kinds of source separation programs.

2. a) What are the common "collectables" in a source separation program?
   b) Who are the buyers for each type of collectable?
   c) Describe the contamination restrictions for each collectable.

3. a) What problems are associated with source separation recycling programs?

   b) What are the benefits of such programs?

4. Bauxite and sand, which are the raw materials for aluminum and glass, respectively, are plentiful in the Earth's crust. Since we are in no danger of depleting these resources in the near future, why should we concern ourselves with recycling aluminum cans and glass bottles?

NYLE LUDOLPH (1927–), AMAZING RECYCLER

"I have been talking this crazy language of recycling since 1976," says Nyle Ludolph of Kitchener, Ontario. In that year he participated in a seminar on environmental issues, including recycling, and became a convert. He immediately went home and established a one-year recycling experiment in his own household. He was sold on the concept when he managed to reduce his household's landfill contribution by over 90%.

Today, Nyle Ludolph, who began his career on the back of a garbage truck, is manager of Total Recycling Systems, a subsidiary of Laidlaw Waste Systems. In September 1983, after a successful pilot project, the company purchased 35 000 blue plastic boxes, at a cost of $200 000, and gave them away to every single-family dwelling in Kitchener. Residents were invited to separate newspaper, glass, and metal cans from their other garbage. These materials were collected by Total Recycling and then sold to companies with recycling facilities. According to Ludolph, the program, which continues today, diverts 15% of the garbage that would normally end up in a landfill.

Why are four-fifths of Kitchener households willing to make the extra effort required to separate their waste? Ludolph suggests several reasons, most of which are directly related to those ever-present blue boxes with their "We Recycle" logo. He notes that because the boxes are "in the home seven days a week", they act both as an advertisement for the program and as a prod to memory. He mentions the convenience of the program, saying with a grin, "There is also the peer pressure." No one wants to be the only anti-environmentalist on the block.

As one of the most famous recycling programs in North America, Ludolph's Kitchener project has had a major impact on how other communities look at recycling. Recycling enthusiasts, environmentalists, and municipal administrators have travelled from across the continent to see first-hand how Kitchener handles its garbage. While the system is by no means the largest or even the most efficient in North America, it provides inspiration for launching similar programs across the continent.

"I like to think that recycling makes people feel good," Ludolph says. "They've got to know that they are making a difference."

19.4 Recycling and Recovery

Municipalities must dispose of wastes in a manner that protects public health. One safe disposal method is **resource recovery,** that is, the mechanical, thermal, chemical, or biological processing of waste in order to recover materials and/or energy in a form suitable for sale and reuse. If a recovery is economical, it can and does occur. Such recovery usually involves high-value metals, paper, or glass.

Some municipalities are considering the separation and sorting of municipal solid waste at the point of disposal, rather than at the point of collection. Pilot waste reclamation plants are using the physical properties of the waste constituents (density, size, mass, shape, and colour) to achieve separation by physical means such as centrifuging and shredding. This type of plant, combined with point-of-collection recovery of appropriate materials, may be the best recovery strategy for municipalities. Waste reclamation facilities cannot pay for themselves completely, but they can offset some costs through the sale of recovered materials.

Recycling may be the best way to prevent our planet from being buried in trash, while at the same time conserving valuable non-renewable resources. There are many different ways to recycle materials.

Figure 19-16. How can we prevent this from happening?

1. Composting

Humus, the partially or completely decayed plant and animal matter that adds the black colour to soil, can be produced through a process known as **composting**. Composting is the controlled and accelerated biodegradation of moist organic matter to a humuslike product that can be used as a fertilizer or a soil conditioner. Food scraps, old newspapers, straw, sawdust, grass clippings, and leaves make good compost. This material should be shredded, moistened, and loosely packed in a pile to provide maximum surface area for decomposition.

Aerobic composting is characterized by a) rapid decomposition, normally within one to ten weeks, b) high temperatures, which destroy dangerous bacteria, insect eggs, and seeds, and c) no offensive odour as long as aerobic conditions are maintained. The process begins when some bacteria oxidize compounds of carbon to carbon dioxide, thus liberating large amounts of heat. Usually the temperature of the waste reaches 45°C within two days. Other bacteria take over the next phase of decomposition, and the temperature rises to between 55 and 70°C.

Figure 19-17.   A home composter.

The layers of material must be turned over regularly to allow air in and promote aerobic decomposition.

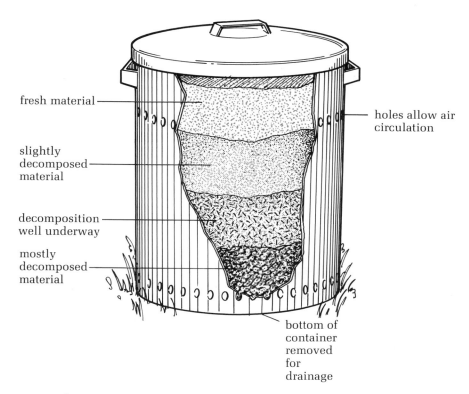

fresh material —

slightly decomposed material —

decomposition well underway —

mostly decomposed material —

— holes allow air circulation

bottom of container removed for drainage

Aerobic composting depends entirely on a suitable environment for the bacteria. Besides the nutrients contained in the wastes, adequate air and moisture are essential. Note that all municipal garbage, when collected, already contains all the organisms needed in each phase of aerobic composting.

2. Rendering

Rendering is the cooking of animal wastes, such as fat, bones, blood, and feathers, to produce a fatty product (tallow) used to make soap, and a nonfatty, high-protein product used in animal feed. A rendering plant obtains animal wastes from farms, butcher shops, poultry plants, slaughterhouses, and canneries. Without rendering, these wastes would burden municipal disposal operations. Because they produce unpleasant odours, rendering plants are unpopular with nearby communities.

Do You Know?
A species of termite found north of the Tropic of Capricorn grows to a length of 15 mm on a preferred diet of timber. It also snacks on plastic cables, paper, corn, wool, asphalt, ivory, cow dung, lead, and even billiard balls. This amazing recycler's digestion is carried out by a bacterium living in the termite's gut.

3. Recycling Paper

Any material that contains natural cellulose fibre, such as wood, cloth, and paper, can be beaten, pulped, and made into useful fibre. To reclaim this fibre, shredded waste paper is added to a large volume of water in a pulping machine. Here the scrap is stirred and beaten vigorously into a uniform mixture. Steam and de-inking chemicals added to the mixture loosen the ink, which is removed along with other impurities by a series of screen washers. The de-inked pulp is first passed through wringers to remove water, and then converted into paper by conventional methods. Ontario Paper Company's recently established de-inking plant at Thorold has expanded newspaper recycling opportunities in Canada.

The recycling process at the Ontario Paper Company's plant in Thorold. Waste paper is loaded into the pulping machine (top left) where it is converted into pulp and carried to the de-inker (top right), which removes ink and other impurities. The pulp is passed through drying cylinders (bottom left), which remove the excess water, and is finally converted into paper rolls (bottom right) ready for shipment and reuse.

Two complications in paper recycling are the damage done to the fibres during the repulping process, and the variety of synthetic materials added to paper during its manufacture. Latex and clay coatings, wet-strength resins, wax, glues and adhesives, dyes, pigments, and permanent inks are the principal contaminants normally incorporated into paper. The number of contaminants, as well as the difficulty of removing them, increases every year.

Activity 19-5:   Purification by Froth Flotation

One of the most common methods of purifying materials is called **froth flotation**. It is most commonly used to separate metal ores from rocklike impurities, and is also used to purify recycled glass and to remove ink from newspaper pulp.

In this process, the finely ground material to be separated is added to water containing complex organic oil mixtures known as frothing agents. Laboratory workers choose a frothing agent that will cling to the particles to be recovered, but not to the particles of dirt and other impurities. When air is bubbled in, the agent mixes with water to form a froth that carries the desired particles to the surface where they can be skimmed off. Because the waste particles do not cling to the frothing agent, they sink to the bottom of the water.

Malachite is an ore of copper containing cupric carbonate, sand, and rock. In this activity you will carry out a simple froth flotation to separate cupric carbonate from sand.

Materials

cupric carbonate	10% soap solution
fine sand	medicine dropper
tap water	graduated cylinder
sulphuric acid (20%)	test tube (19 mm × 180 mm)
cottonseed oil	rubber stopper
kerosene	small beaker

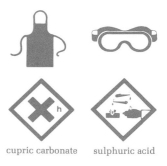

cupric carbonate   sulphuric acid

kerosene

Procedure

1. Thoroughly mix 0.5 mL of powdered cupric carbonate with 1 mL of fine sand in a test tube.

2. Add 25 mL of tap water, 3 drops of sulphuric acid, 2 mL of cottonseed oil, 5 drops of kerosene, and 10 drops of soap solution.

Figure 19-18. Step 3.

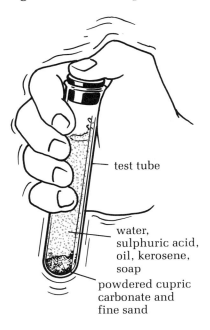

test tube

water, sulphuric acid, oil, kerosene, soap

powdered cupric carbonate and fine sand

Step 4.

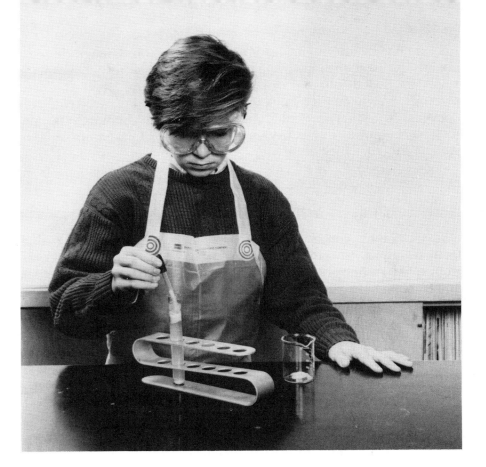

3. Stopper the test tube and shake vigorously for 2 min. Allow the tube to stand for 3 min and record your observations.

4. Use a medicine dropper to carefully remove only the top layer. Place in a small beaker. Add 1 mL of cottonseed oil to the test tube and shake as before.

5. Allow to stand as before, and again remove and place the top layer in the beaker. Record your observations.

6. Decant (pour off) and discard the solution in the test tube, while keeping the residue.

7. Examine the material recovered with the froth layer, and that left behind with the residue. Record your observations.

Discussion

1. What is the purpose of the cottonseed oil in the froth flotation?

2. What is the purpose of shaking the test tube?

3. Why was the separation performed twice in steps 4 and 5?

4. Does it appear that all the sand was removed from the recovered cupric carbonate? Estimate the percentage of the cupric carbonate not recovered from the sand.

5. Describe how froth flotation can purify a substance.

6. Ink is removed from waste newspaper pulp by froth flotation. How does this process lead to a reduction in the quantity of waste in the environment?

Recycling Junked Automobiles

Scrap automobiles are a blatant solid waste problem. Auto wreckers generally remove any parts of scrapped vehicles that can be rebuilt or reused, such as alternators, brake assemblies, radiators, lights, and batteries. A car in good condition may be kept for awhile in the auto yard, so that door and body panels, bumpers, windshields, gas tanks, and other replacement parts can be sold. Then the car is reduced to a height of about 40 cm in a mobile car flattener, and shipped to a scrap processing plant.

In less than a minute, giant shredders costing millions of dollars use enormous steel hammers to rip an automobile into fist-size pieces of scrap. The shredded scrap passes over a magnetic drum

An auto shredder reduces cars to fist-sized chunks of reclaimed metal for use by steel manufacturers.

Figure 19-19. Multiple drum-type magnetic separators are used to recover magnetic metals in a clean form.

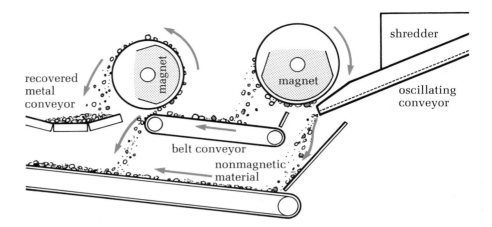

that separates the magnetic ferrous materials — iron and steel — from the nonmagnetic materials — aluminum, copper, brass, zinc, stainless steel, glass, rubber, plastics, textiles, and dirt. Of the 300 to 400 kg of residue resulting from each automobile, 20 to 30 kg is nonferrous metals, of which, on average, half is aluminum.

The ferrous components undergo **corrosion**, a chemical reaction in which first the surfaces, then the interiors, of the iron and steel are "eaten away". Air and moisture are necessary for the corrosion of iron.

The nonmagnetic residue passes through a rotating drum screen, where dirt and glass are removed before the next process, which may be wet or dry. In the dry process, nonmetallic pieces such as upholstery, plastics, and rubber are vacuumed out of the residue. In the wet process, the material is fed into a water wash system, where the less dense debris such as rubber, plastic, and textiles floats off, while the denser metals sink to the bottom. The metals then go to a "sweat furnace", where any remaining combustible materials are burned. Zinc has a lower melting point than aluminum, copper, and stainless steel, so it will melt first and run out of the furnace into moulds. The remaining aluminum, copper, and stainless steel are "sweated", and the liquified aluminum is also collected in moulds. The copper and stainless steel do not melt; recovery of these metals on a large scale is uneconomical.

Unfortunately, this multi-step recycling process is expensive. For every hour a shredder operates, one hour of maintenance is needed to repair the hammers and remove dirt. Even the cost of simply moving the car to a junkyard is often more than the car is worth. Charging new car owners a disposal fee and then using that income to strip old automobiles could defray some of the recycling costs.

The Future of Recycling

While the technology to recycle solid wastes exists, the social climate must also favour a sudden large-scale implementation of this technology. If improved efficiency in this technology can make municipal waste management profitable, private industry might develop a greater interest in recycling. We are not yet close to this stage.

One way to accelerate recycling is to pass laws which encourage reuse. Ontario laws now require all new soft drink containers to be recyclable, and at least 50% of all nonrefillable containers, including aluminum cans and the new plastic bottles, must be recycled. To encourage the use of refillable deposit bottles, retailers must provide equal or greater display space for refillable bottles as opposed to nonrefillable bottles and cans.

As our natural resources diminish, the price of raw materials will increase. Then, recycling on a large scale will become more attractive financially. But we cannot wait until our resources are almost gone before we begin to recycle. We must all work to support provincial and community recycling efforts — now.

Environmentalist Dr. John Vallentyne often wears a globe on his shoulders to impress upon his listeners that they must pay more attention to the environment.

Study Questions

1. What is resource recovery?

2. Describe each of the following recycling techniques:
   a) composting
   b) rendering
   c) recycling paper

3. Many processes are involved in the recycling of junked automobiles. Describe:
   a) the function of a mobile car flattener
   b) the function of a shredder
   c) the separation of nonmagnetic residue
   d) the problems and disadvantages of these processes

4. What conditions are necessary for the corrosion of iron? Figures indicate that iron and steel corrode more rapidly in the fogbound British Isles than in Canada. Why might this be? Suggest a way to reduce iron corrosion.

5. Suggest an efficient recycling technique for each of the following: a) sheep manure, b) old clothes, c) used oil, d) scrap lumber, e) pop cans, f) used aluminum foil, g) a burnt-out power saw, h) worn-out furniture, i) old garden tools, j) sawdust, k) chicken feathers, l) old books.

A NEW PET ON THE SCENE

A new plastic material is taking the packaging industry by storm. It's called polyethylene tetrathalate, or ''PET'' for short. PET offers great advantages in safety and convenience. From an original target market of carbonated soft drinks, PET bottles have found new applications in packaging spirits, beer, wine, perfume, and cooking oil.

PET is also on the brink of a major expansion into the food industry's heat-formed tray market. Crystallized PET trays can be taken directly from the freezer and placed into either a conventional or a microwave oven. The growth in home ownership of microwave ovens has spurred on development in this area. PET trays sectioned into compartments are now in use on several airlines. The Campbell Soup Company has pioneered the adoption of PET trays for frozen dinners in North America. According to Campbell, all of its new plastic trays are more expensive than the aluminum foil package it replaces! The cost is simply less critical than the added convenience for the consumer.

With PET replacing glass and aluminum cans in liquid packaging, an increasing proportion of MSW will consist of plastic products. Serious efforts must be made to recycle some of this material, and to educate the public to separate plastic waste from other refuse. One of the biggest metal-replacement markets, the soft-drink can, may be the next target in the PET campaign. With Ontario allowing aluminum pop cans on the market in September 1987, will PET cans be far behind? In the United States, Coca-Cola has test-marketed its product line in PET cans in some American markets—with a new twist. One of the recycling methods being studied is using vending machines that take back the can after you have finished with it.

Many brands of soft drinks are contained in PET containers.

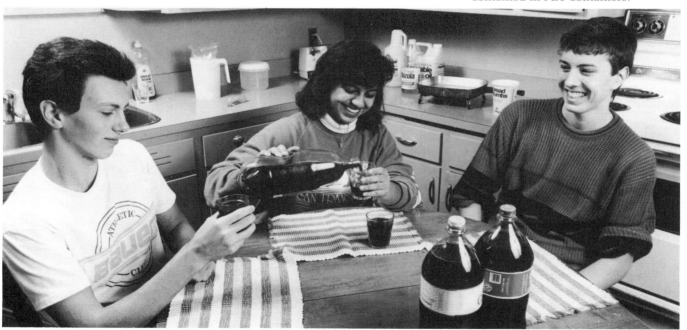

Meet a Recycling Depot Operator — Gwen Discepolo

Gwen and her husband are owners of Halton's Recycled Resources Ltd., a firm that recycles waste paper, glass, and tin collected curbside in Ontario's Halton county.

Q. WHY DID YOU BEGIN THIS BUSINESS?

A. It was really my husband's idea, because he was interested in recycling and ecology. At that time, I was involved in a program for the "hard to employ" in Hamilton, so we combined our two interests by starting a pilot project using some "hard to employ" people. After six months, we were able to rent warehouse space and start to grade paper for consumption.

Q. HOW BIG IS YOUR OPERATION NOW?

A. We have about 40 staff, including eight students who come in after school. About 30 t of paper leave our plant everyday. This is recycled into boxboard (for cereal boxes, etc.), paper towel, and toilet tissue.

Q. WHAT DO THE RESIDENTS HAVE TO DO?

A. They separate the garbage into tins, paper, and bottles, and leave it on the curb for collection. About 70 to 80% of the local residents contribute to the program. There is more awareness in Halton about recycling because we face a critical garbage situation. Our landfill site is about to close. This will be an increasing problem everywhere in the future, because nobody wants a landfill site in their backyard.

Q. IS INDUSTRY BECOMING MORE AWARE, TOO?

A. Yes, because there's been a lot of pressure from environmental groups. Industry supplies us with uses for recycled products and, in turn, we advise them on problems with recycling. For instance, we discovered that laser beam printout paper can't be de-inked because the print is burned into the paper, so it has to be downgraded for recycling. We sell it for roofing material.

Q. WHAT DO YOU DO TO RECYCLE TINS AND GLASS?

A. At the moment we simply collect them in large bins, and ship the glass to Toronto and the cans to Hamilton. We don't have the equipment to process them right now.

Q. WHAT ARE YOU MOST PROUD OF IN YOUR BUSINESS?

A. Two things. Last year the regional council signed a 10-year contract with us. That was a real breakthrough. The second thing is an educational kit on the importance of recycling that we produced for Ontario schools. I had wanted to do this kit for a long time. I feel it's really crucial to reach kids on this issue.

Q. WHAT IS A TYPICAL DAY LIKE IN YOUR JOB?

A. In the beginning I wore jeans and ran the baling machine. Now, with the growth of the operation, I mostly do administrative work and public-speaking, and meet with government and community groups. But that doesn't stop me from putting on my jeans. Quality control is very important in this business since there must not be any contaminants.

Q. CAN YOU MAKE MONEY IN THIS BUSINESS?

A. We've never made a profit. We lose money on glass, break even on cans, and need high volumes to make anything on newspaper. The equipment is expensive: our horizontal baler which compacts cardboard and newspaper cost $200 000.

Q. WHAT IS THE FUTURE OF THE RECYCLING BUSINESS?

A. It's definitely a growth industry, which has to become profitable. There will be lots of jobs in this field for young people. One way to get involved is to get your school to start a program collecting newspapers and beverage containers in your neighbourhood.

Review Questions

A: Knowledge

1. a) What is the typical composition of municipal solid waste (MSW)?
   b) Why is there so much MSW?
   c) Why has packaging become an increasing component of MSW?

2. How might the common use of polyethylene plastic garbage bags slow down the settling process in a sanitary landfill, and prevent or reduce the decomposition of the contents of the bag?

3. Why do reusable products such as beverage bottles have less impact on the environment than recyclable ones?

4. How does the movement of matter through industrial processes differ from the movement of matter through life processes? Provide examples to illustrate the difference.

5. State two advantages of each of the "Four Rs" of waste management over waste disposal.

6. What is a waste exchange? How does it operate?

7. Explain the difference between an open dump and a sanitary landfill.

8. Discuss the advantages and disadvantages of incineration as a method of waste disposal.

9. a) Why are oil spills so difficult to clean up?
   b) Describe three ways of cleaning up oil spills.

10. Why is the reuse of glass beverage bottles favoured over both recycling and the use of throwaway bottles?

11. Describe a source separation recycling program that might work in your area. Discuss the problems and benefits of your program.

12. For each of the following, describe the process, state which materials can be treated by the process, and explain how they are treated. What products result in each case?
    a) composting
    b) rendering
    c) repulping newspaper
    d) recycling junked cars

13. Explain how the froth flotation method of purification works.

B: Application

14. In your new position as junior city engineer, you are asked to report on the generation rates and the composition of solid wastes from various sources in your community. Describe how you would go about this assignment.

15. Carry out a survey of any part of your neighbourhood. Pinpoint places used for illegal dumping. Why does this happen? Is there anything you can do about it? Is there anything municipal authorities can do about it? Are there any open spaces where litter is a problem? What can be done to make the public aware of the antisocial aspects of littering?

16. Walk along a road and collect litter in two bags, one for beverage containers and one for everything else. Calculate:
    a) the number of items per kilometre
    b) the number of beverage containers per kilometre
    c) the mass of the litter per kilometre
    d) the mass of the beverage containers per kilometre
    e) percentage of beverage containers by count
    f) percentage of beverage containers by mass
    If you were the manager of a beverage company, which figure would you rather report to the press, e) or f)?

17. Using your cafeteria as a laboratory, study the prevalence of litter by counting the items in the receptacles and the items improperly disposed of. Vary the conditions as follows.
    Day 1: Normal conditions (control)
    Day 2: Remove half the receptacles.
    Day 3: Add twice the normal number of receptacles.
    If possible, run additional experiments using varying numbers of receptacles. Plot the percentage of properly disposed items compared to the number of receptacles. Discuss the implications. Note: You must obtain

authorization for your experiment, and you must tidy the cafeteria each day.

18. There have been suggestions to collect a fee (typically 5¢/kg) on all nonfood consumer items to help pay for the eventual disposal of the item. What do you think of this idea? What amount might be collected for an average automobile?

19. How is refuse collected in your area? How often does collection take place? What kinds of vehicles are used? What different types of household containers are used for the disposal of MSW? Discuss the advantages and disadvantages of the methods used.

20. How is refuse disposed of in your area? If an incinerator is used, what, in your opinion, influenced the choice of this disposal method? Discuss any ways in which you think the methods of disposal could be improved.

21. As a consulting engineer, you have been retained to develop a solid waste disposal system for a community interested in greater recovery and reuse of its solid wastes. Two alternatives are separation at home or separation at the disposal site. What factors must be considered in evaluating these alternatives?

22. Suppose you have implemented a community-wide newspaper separation and recovery program. Suddenly the price paid for waste newsprint triples. Church groups and Boy Scouts decide to raise funds by collecting newspapers on paper drives. Would you resist this type of competition? What are the implications for your newspaper recovery program?

C: Problem Solving

23. A city of 100 000 produces a daily solid waste average of 2.5 kg/person. The wastes are collected and compacted to an average density of 350 kg/m³, then buried in a sanitary landfill which can accommodate refuse only to a depth of 3.0 m. How much landfill area will be used up each year?

24. A city contracts with a private company for the collection of its solid wastes at $16.00/t. The city handles the billings and provides city land for truck maintenance facilities. The city-operated landfill receives all of the solid wastes hauled by the private company without charge, because city residents are already paying for the landfill in their property taxes. Is $16.00/t the entire cost of the system? If not, what other costs does the city incur?

25. The municipal garbage collectors in a town of 10 000 have just gone on strike. Your high school decides to accept all the city trash temporarily, and to pile it on the school football field. If all the town's residents brought their garbage to the field, how many days would the garbage collectors be on strike before the field is filled to a depth of 1 m? (Assume the field is 90 m × 100 m and the average daily solid waste production is 25 kg/person.)

26. A city of 150 000 people is evaluating the possible economic benefits of recovering materials from their solid waste. Assume that the waste contains the typical physical components shown in Table 19-1, and that the waste generation rate is 3.0 kg per person per day. The cost of processing all the waste is $18/t. The market value of the recovered materials is: ferrous metal, $30/t; aluminum, $360/t; mixed coloured glass, $24/t. If the recovery efficiency for all components is 90%, determine what revenue the city can expect from the sale of recovered materials. Are processing and recovery economical for this city? What alternatives can reduce the costs of processing and recovery?

Chapter 20
Liquid and Hazardous Wastes

Many of our society's wastes are disposed of in rivers, lakes, and seas, while some of the wastes released into the air or dumped on land eventually end up in waterways. Over the past few decades, unknown amounts of hazardous industrial wastes have been disposed of in a careless manner. Some wastes have been released into the air and some poured illegally into sewers and rivers. Some have leaked into ground and surface waters. Increased pollution, population, and leisure time have created a new awareness of the importance of water in our lives. No one wants to fish or swim in polluted waters, or to sail in water covered with oil.

In this chapter we examine water pollutants and ways to deal with them. We also look at how problems caused by hazardous wastes can be managed with maximum benefits and minimum risks.

When you finish Chapter 20, you should be able to:

- identify common water pollutants
- describe techniques used to purify water
- describe some common hazardous wastes and their routes into the environment
- identify hazardous substances in the home and the workplace
- describe techniques used to manage hazardous wastes
- consider lifestyle benefits versus environmental risks

20.1 Water Management

Cities need an adequate supply of good-quality water, and a means of disposing of waste water. The ability to bring clean water into homes and get dirty water out ranks as one of society's most successful pollution control efforts. In this section, water pollutants, the treatment of municipal water supplies, and various sewage treatment methods will be examined.

Municipal Water Supplies

Water Quality

Water is necessary to sustain all forms of life. In Canada, we require water for domestic and personal needs, for agricultural irrigation, and for industrial, commercial, and institutional uses. Because the world's supply of fresh water is not large, meeting the needs of all these users with *quality* water becomes a problem.

From your knowledge of the distinction between pure substances and mixtures, you realize that natural water is not 100% pure. If you were to drink distilled water, you would find it flat and unpleasant. The dissolved gases and minerals in natural water give it a subtle taste. When you visit a new area, the water may taste strange because of the difference in the salts dissolved in the water. In time, you adapt to the new taste.

Water quality is a broad relative term referring to the water's distinctive characteristics for specific uses: drinking, cooling, manufacturing, irrigation, food processing, washing, and recreation. Water pollution involves a change in water quality that makes the water unsuited for a particular use.

Do You Know?
To produce 1 L of gasoline, 10 L of water is needed; producing 1 t of steel requires 25 000 L of water.

The Earth's Water Supply

Salt Water

oceans	97.2%

Fresh Water

ice caps/glaciers	2.15%
ground water	0.63%
surface water	0.02%

(all lakes, rivers, ponds, puddles, rain, snow, water vapour in atmosphere, water in pipes, reservoirs, sewers, etc.)

Total = 1 360 000 000 km³
(or 1.36 Gm³)

Game fish such as trout and bass require larger amounts of oxygen than do rough fish such as carp and catfish.

Pseudomonas florescens, a common aerobic bacteria found in sewage and polluted water.

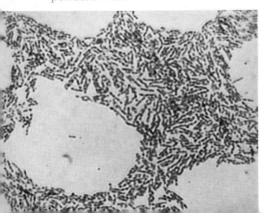

Figure 20-1. The quantity of oxygen dissolved in water is related to temperature. The higher the temperature, the lower the oxygen content of the water. Thermal pollution can lower the oxygen content below the point necessary to sustain life.

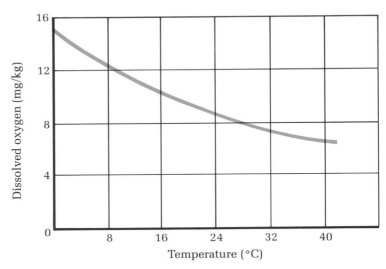

Measuring oxygen dissolved in water provides one useful indication of water quality. Water high in dissolved oxygen is desirable, as this gas is essential for the existence of fish and other aquatic life. Dissolved oxygen is also needed in the purification processes of aerobic decay normally carried out by microorganisms. Concentrations of dissolved substances can be measured in milligrams per kilogram (or litre) of water.

At 20°C, fully oxygenated water contains 9 mg of oxygen/kg of water. This value increases at lower temperatures. An oxygen level of 5 to 7 mg/kg usually indicates "healthy" water. A well-balanced fresh-water fish population requires a dissolved oxygen level of about 5 mg/kg. Areas highly polluted with sewage or other industrial wastes may have near-zero dissolved oxygen levels.

Water Pollutants

1. Sewage and Other Oxygen-demanding Wastes

If large amounts of organic matter are suddenly added to a water system, their decay places an increased demand on the amount of dissolved oxygen. Under these circumstances, the bacteria in the water use the oxygen at a much faster rate than normal. **Biochemical oxygen demand (BOD)** measures the oxygen depletion occurring in a sealed sample of water over five days. The greater the amount of sewage or other organic matter in water, the greater the

Table 20-1: Typical BOD values

(milligrams of oxygen consumed per kilogram of water)

drinking water	1
relatively unpolluted water	3
polluted water	5
municipal sewage before treatment	200-400
milk processing and canning wastes	5000-6000
wood pulping wastes	up to 15 000

amount of oxygen consumed and, thus, the larger the BOD value of the sample. Table 20-1 shows some typical BOD values.

Some pollutants increase oxygen demand much more sharply than others. For example, raw sewage is high in carbon-containing compounds, which oxygen-using aerobic bacteria consume as food. Oxidizable nitrogen — from nitrates, ammonia, and organic nitrogen compounds found in sewage and industrial waste — also uses up more oxygen. As the oxygen content of the water falls, fish are starved for oxygen and die.

2. Plant Nutrients

Plant nutrients such as nitrogen and phosphorus can stimulate the growth of aquatic plants so much that later decay produces disagreeable odours and adds to the water's BOD. The enrichment of water by plant nutrients is called "eutrophication". One common nutrient is the phosphorus that is present in detergents in the form of phosphates.

3. Exotic Organic Chemicals

These include pesticides, various industrial chemicals, the decomposition products of other organic chemicals, and certain ingredients in synthetic detergents. Concentrations of these chemicals are usually very small, and many are not biodegradable.

For pollutants not affected by bacteria, a **chemical oxygen demand** or **COD** test can be performed. This test measures the amount of oxygen needed for the oxidation of the organic matter present to form carbon dioxide and water.

4. Metallic and Other Inorganic Chemical Compounds

These pollutants, entering water supplies from municipal and industrial waste waters and from urban run-off, can kill or injure fish and other aquatic life. They can also affect the suitability of water for drinking or industrial use.

5. Sediments

Sediments are soil and mineral particles that storms and flood waters wash from croplands, unprotected forest soils, overgrazed pastures, strip mines, and bulldozed urban areas. This loosening and carrying away of sediment is called **erosion**. Studies show that for agricultural land, erosion rates are four to nine times greater than those for undeveloped land. Agriculturally productive land loses much valuable topsoil.

Most water contains some materials in solution and some in suspension. For example, the St. Lawrence River carries tonnes of soil and gravel to the ocean every year. The dissolved materials remain in the water, but the suspended solids settle to the bottom in layers. This natural settling process is called **sedimentation**.

Worldwide, an estimated nine million million tonnes of material were once washed away annually by rivers to the ocean before human intervention. Now, with increased erosion, the figure is twenty-four million million tonnes a year.

Erosion is rapidly destroying this valuable pasture land. What forces are causing this soil erosion?

6. Heat

Electric generating plants, both thermal and nuclear, use vast amounts of water for cooling purposes. The water used for cooling is discharged at a raised temperature, which has various effects on the water. The density of the water decreases, permitting solids to settle faster, while the water's evaporation rate increases. The amount of dissolved oxygen decreases as water temperature increases. Increased temperature and decreased oxygen can make the water uninhabitable for fish. A higher water temperature favours blue-green algae, which cause taste and odour problems in water and are toxic to some aquatic organisms.

An algae-infested pond.

Figure 20-2. Lethal limits of water temperature.

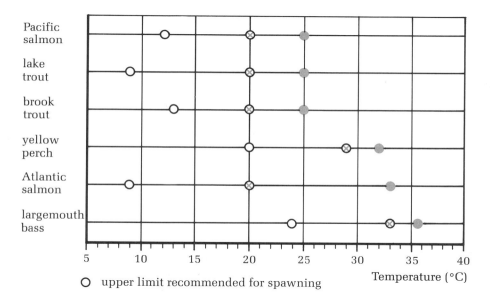

○ upper limit recommended for spawning

⊗ upper limit recommended for satisfactory growth

● upper lethal limit

7. Other Pollutants

Water can contain pathogenic microorganisms capable of causing disease in humans and animals. Infectious cholera and typhoid are transmitted through water supplies. Wastes from uranium mining and refining processes can add radioactive substances to water.

Domestic and industrial wastes contain a wide variety of pollutants. Figure 20-3 shows some of the waste substances produced during the manufacture of an automobile. Agricultural wastes include sediments, fertilizer, and farm animal wastes. Oil spills also contaminate water. Table 20-2 shows a general classification of water pollutants.

Figure 20-3. Various waste substances are produced in the manufacture of an automobile.

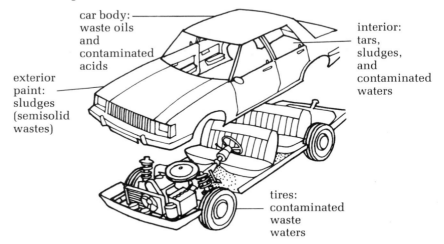

car body: waste oils and contaminated acids

interior: tars, sludges, and contaminated waters

exterior paint: sludges (semisolid wastes)

tires: contaminated waste waters

Table 20-2: Classification of Water Pollutants

Type	Examples
chemical	
organic	oil, dyes, synthetic detergents, chlorinated hydrocarbons, organic acids, carbohydrates, sugars
inorganic	acids, bases, chlorine, phosphates, nitrates, sulphates, bicarbonates, metallic salts, hydrogen sulphide, radioactive isotopes
physical	
floating matter	foam, wood, leaves, scum
suspended matter	sand, silt, gravel, metal pieces, wood chips, paper, pulp, rubber, cinders, sewage solids, animal parts
thermal effects	heat added
biological	
pathogenic (disease-causing) forms	bacteria, protozoa, algae, fungi, viruses, some parasitic worms
algae	excess growth caused by excess nutrients; eventual decay uses up oxygen
aquatic weeds	growth interferes with recreation and navigation

Activity 20-1: Separation by Coagulation and Sedimentation

The fine particles of silt and clay in muddy water can take days to settle. For most purposes, municipalities must have clear water. To achieve this, alum (aluminum potassium sulphate) and slaked lime (calcium hydroxide) are added to the water. These substances react chemically to produce many tiny jellylike particles of aluminum hydroxide. These sticky insoluble particles are called a **floc**. Impurities such as mud and silt tend to stick to these particles, forming larger particles which settle rapidly in the water. The formation of these larger particles is called **coagulation**. In this activity you will use coagulation and sedimentation to purify dirty water.

Materials

moist soil or mud

aluminum potassium sulphate (alum)

calcium hydroxide (slaked lime)

2 test tubes

2 solid rubber stoppers

test tube rack

Procedure

1. **Make a Hypothesis:** Predict what will happen to the purity of dirty water if alum and slaked lime are added to one sample of such water, but not to another.

2. Fill 2 test tubes with water to within 3 cm of the top.

3. Add 5 mL of moist soil or mud to each test tube of water.

4. To test tube 1 add alum and slaked lime, each equal in volume to the head of a match. Do not add anything to test tube 2. Label the test tubes.

5. Stopper both test tubes and shake them equally. Place them in a rack. Observe them after 30 s, 5 min, and the next day.

Discussion

1. Comment on the validity of your hypothesis.

2. Account for the layers of the sediment in terms of particle size.

3. Explain the difference in the rate of sedimentation in the two test tubes.

4. What was the purpose of the test tube to which no alum and slaked lime were added? What scientific term is applied to a test tube with this function?

Table 20-3: A Sample Water Analysis

temperature	17.8°C
dissolved oxygen	8.2 mg/kg
pH	8.0
biochemical oxygen demand	5.2 mg/kg
chemical oxygen demand	19 mg/kg
chloride	20 mg/kg
alkalinity	71 mg/kg
hardness	112 mg/kg
colour	7 (units)
turbidity	35 (units)
sulphate	70 mg/kg
phosphate	0.1 mg/kg
total dissolved solids	200 mg/kg
coliform bacteria	100 per 100 mL

Figure 20-4. What purpose does test tube 2 serve?

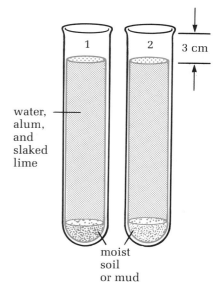

ammonia
solution

ammonia
solution
hydrochloric
acid

methyl orange
barium chloride
calcium hydroxide

ammonium
oxalate

Figure 20-5.

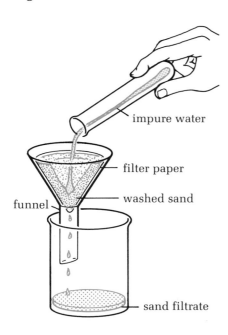

impure water

filter paper

washed sand

funnel

sand filtrate

Activity 20-2:   Water Purification

The following simple steps in water purification have been widely used for a long time. In this activity you will first prepare a sample of impure water. Then you will perform sand filter purification and powdered charcoal purification on the impure water. Finally, you will test each of the treated samples for purity.

Materials

distilled water	barium chloride solution (5%)
calcium sulphate	250 mL beakers
concentrated ammonia solution	stirring rod
powdered clay (kaolin)	filter paper
methyl orange solution	funnel
clean fine sand	large test tube (25 mm x 200 mm)
powdered animal charcoal	rubber stopper
ammonium oxalate solution (5%)	red litmus paper
hydrochloric acid solution (20%)	test tubes (19 mm × 180 mm)

Procedure

Part A: Preparing a Sample of Impure Water

1. To 100 mL of distilled water in a beaker, add
   a) 0.25 g calcium sulphate to represent dissolved solids,
   b) 4 drops of concentrated ammonia solution to represent dissolved gases,
   c) 1 g powdered clay (kaolin) to represent suspended, undissolved solids,
   d) just enough methyl orange solution to give the water a definite colour and to represent organic colouring matter.

2. Stir well. Stir again before withdrawing a sample for each of the following parts.

Part B: Sand Filter Purification

3. Wash about 20 mL of clean fine sand with 50 mL of distilled water in a beaker. Decant (pour off) the water and pour the sand into a clean filter paper in a funnel. Shape the sand to form a V-like depression as shown in Figure 20-5.

4. Filter 30 mL of the impure water prepared in Part A through the sand. Collect the filtrate in a beaker and label it "sand filtrate".

Part C: Charcoal Filter Purification

5. Add 30 mL of the impure water and 5 mL of powdered animal charcoal to a large test tube. Stopper and shake vigorously for 2 min.

6. Pour this mixture into a clean filter paper in a funnel. Collect the filtrate in a beaker and label it "charcoal filtrate".

Part D: Testing for Impurities

7. Carry out each of the following four tests on:
   i) the remaining impure water
   ii) the "sand filtrate"
   iii) the "charcoal filtrate"

Test 1:   Visual Testing
Examine each of items i) to iii) for the presence of clay (cloudiness) and methyl orange (colour).

Test 2:   Testing for Dissolved Gases
a) Check items i) to iii) above for ammonia odour.
b) (Litmus test) Ammonia is a base. Use red litmus paper to test for the presence of a base.

Test 3:   Testing for Calcium Ion
a) Pour 5 mL of each of the three samples into separate test tubes. Add 2 mL of ammonium oxalate solution to each test tube.
b) Add 4 mL of hydrochloric acid solution to each test tube. The formation of a white precipitate that *dissolves* after the addition of hydrochloric acid is a positive test for calcium ion.

Test 4:   Testing for Sulphate Ion
a) Pour 5 mL of each of the three samples into separate test tubes. Add 2 mL of barium chloride solution to each test tube.
b) Then add 4 mL of hydrochloric acid solution. The formation of a white precipitate that *remains* after the addition of hydrochloric acid is a positive test for sulphate ion.

Preparing the charcoal filtrate.

Discussion

1. Which substances were removed by the sand?
2. Which substances were removed by the charcoal?
3. What types of substances are removed by sand?
4. What types of substances are removed by charcoal?

5. Which (if any) of the techniques used in this activity removes all of the impurities? How could the water be made pure?

6. Methyl orange is a chemical indicator. Provide evidence from this activity to support this statement.

The Municipal Water Treatment Plant

Do You Know?
For each person in a community per day, water treatment plants supply 450 L of water for drinking, bathing, flushing, laundry, car washing, lawn sprinkling, and other domestic uses. At most, 10 L of this water is used for drinking.

The municipal water treatment plant is one of the major feats of modern chemistry and sanitary engineering. The plant may receive a murky liquid pumped from a muddy river polluted with bacteria. Yet it produces the clear, safe, good-tasting water of high quality that comes from our faucets. Water obtained from lakes and rivers undergoes the treatment shown in Figure 20-6. (Water obtained from wells often requires fewer treatment steps due to its higher purity.)

Figure 20-6. Water purification.

1. Take it from lakes, rivers, and wells. Screen it to keep out debris and fish.

2. Pump it to the treatment plant for purification.

3. Treat it with chemicals to remove impurities. Lime and alum together form a jellylike, sticky substance which, as it settles, carries down suspended solids and most bacteria. Charcoal absorbs dissolved organic materials.

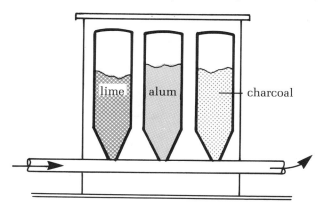

4. Settle it in huge tanks to remove suspended solids.

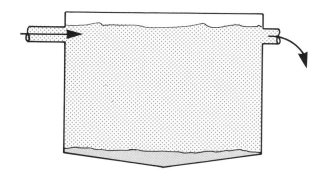

5. Filter it through sand and gravel beds to provide clear sparkling water.

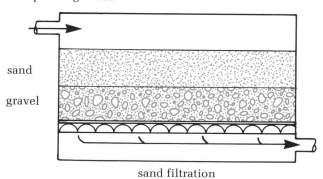

sand filtration

6. Chlorinate it to kill remaining germs and viruses. Where desired, add fluorine for tooth protection.

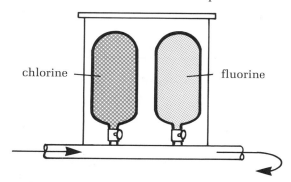

7. Analyze it to check its chemical and bacterial purity. Treat it again if necessary.

8. Distribute it to the community.

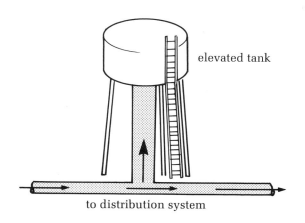

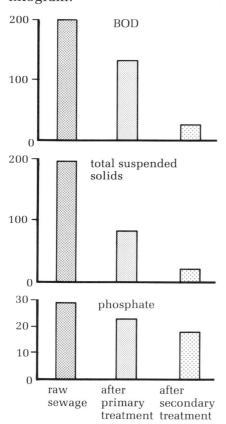

Primary clarifiers at a sewage treatment plant. The arm in the centre scrapes off floating debris while the spray of water keeps it moving towards the slot where water is separated from sludge.

Municipal Sewage

Besides the problem of getting drinking water into a city, there is the problem of getting the sewage out. **Sewage** is the waste material that drains from our sinks, bathtubs, toilets, and washing machines, as well as the waste water from industry. You might suppose that this sewage is very impure. However, the average domestic sewage is 99.9% water and only 0.1% dissolved and suspended solids. Sewage treatment removes this 0.1%. The main purpose of sewage treatment is to decompose organic matter before discharge in order to lower the oxygen demand on the receiving waters.

Three basic treatment methods are used in Ontario: "primary", "secondary", and "tertiary". In the primary stage, solids are allowed to settle, and are removed from the water as sludge. In the secondary stage, a biological process further purifies the waste water. Tertiary processes are installed only if the water requires further treatment. Recently, a chemical treatment to reduce the phosphorus content of the effluent (waste water) has been added in some places to control nuisance algae in waterways. The efficiency of each of the treatment methods is rated in terms of both the percentage removal of biochemical oxygen demand (BOD) and the percentage removal of suspended solids (SS).

Figure 20-8. Municipal sewage treatment.

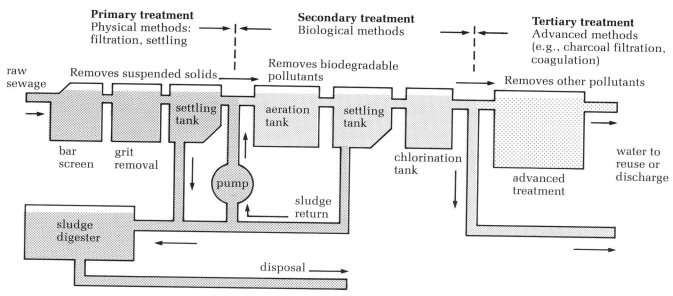

Step 1: Primary treatment
- Removes about 40% BOD.
- Removes 40-60% SS.
- Bar screen catches large debris.
- Water enters grit chamber where sand and gravel settle. Can be used as landfill as it contains little organic matter.
- Water stands in primary settling tank for about 1 h where any other suspended solids, including organic nutrients, can settle out as sludge. The sludge is removed to another treatment facility.
- No direct use of water at this stage is possible. Water may look clean but it still carries a heavy load of microorganisms and organic matter.

Step 2: Secondary treatment
- Removes another 50% BOD for a total of 90% BOD removal.
- Removes 90% SS.
- Aeration helps growth of aerobic bacteria called activated sludge. Bacteria digest the organic nutrients.
- Digestion continues as the sludge settles in the settling tank and is completed in the sludge digester. Sludge high in bacteria is recirculated to the aeration tank.
- Waste sludge is sterilized and used as landfill or fertilizer (if the metallic content is not too high). Sometimes the sludge is baked in the form of small cakes and then burned; the ash is buried in a landfill site.
- Chlorine is added to the water leaving the settling tank, to kill disease-causing organisms.
- The resulting water can be used for recreation, industrial supply, and irrigation.
- Water still contains dissolved materials, nutrients, and some types of organic materials.

Step 3: Tertiary treatment
- Most expensive treatment.
- Used where necessary to remove organic chemicals, nutrients such as phosphates, and excessive salts.
- Not widely used in Ontario where water quality after secondary treatment is usually acceptable.
- May use chemical coagulation, filtration through activated charcoal (most common in Ontario), or other processes.
- Activated charcoal with its large surface area absorbs up to 77% of organic matter.
- Phosphates are removed through chemical coagulation and sedimentation where up to 90% of the phosphates are removed.
- The resulting water can be used for all uses except drinking. It may still contain some bacteria and viruses along with organic and toxic pollutants such as PCBs.

Figure 20-9. Activated charcoal filtration.

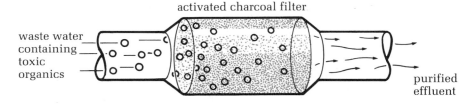

activated charcoal filter

waste water containing toxic organics

purified effluent

Effectiveness of Activated Charcoal in the Removal of Some Toxic Chlorinated Organics

Compound	Initial Concentration (μg/kg)	Concentration after Carbon Treatment (μg/kg)	Organic Reduction (%)
Aldrin*	48	<1.0	99+
Dieldrin*	19	0.05	99+
Endrin*	62	0.05	99+
DDT*	41	0.1	99+
Arochlor 1242 (PCB)	45	<0.5	99+

* These compounds are insecticides.

Sanitary and Storm Sewers

Sanitary sewer systems use gravity to transmit sewage to treatment plants. During heavy rainfall, water pressure may build up in the sanitary sewer as water from the plant backs up and as more water leaks into the sewer. To avoid backup into homes when water pressure increases, the sanitary flow is redirected to a waterway, either through a by pass tube near the treatment plant, or by means of an emergency overflow connection into the storm sewer system.

The storm sewer system is a separate facility that drains run-off from lawns and streets directly into a nearby waterway. An emergency overflow connection means that during heavy rainfall, part of the domestic sewage is diverted without treatment into waterways. Otherwise, sewage would back up into homes and overflow from toilets. Unfortunately, when untreated sewage runs directly into waterways, recreational uses, for example, swimming, must be curtailed due to the high bacterial count in the water. This is a frequent occurrence at Toronto beaches.

Do You Know?

A species of bees (*Eufriesia purpurata*) that enjoys DDT has been discovered in the Amazon region of Brazil. The bees collect DDT from houses sprayed to combat malaria-carrying mosquitoes. Some bees were found to have DDT levels in their bodies 7000 times greater than the tolerance level for normal bees (6 mg/kg).

Figure 20-10. A typical storm and sanitary sewer system.

waterway

storm sewer

storm water discharges

sanitary sewer

nonsewered runoff

street drain

emergency overflow connection

municipal wastes

storm sewer

combined sewer overflow

industrial wastes

waste water treatment plant

bypass tube

BEACH CLOSED UNSAFE FOR SWIMMING

treated effluent

Some storm sewers drain directly into a nearby waterway, and an emergency overflow connection allows both sanitary and storm sewers to drain into the waterway during high water periods.

Septic Tanks

In areas without sewers, septic tanks are used to treat the sewage from homes, schools, etc. A septic tank is buried in the ground, where it receives the wastes as shown in Figure 20-11. Anaerobic decay occurs in the tank, and the sludge sinks to the bottom. The effluent from the top of the tank passes through a drainage system to the soil where bacterial action degrades the sewage. A major environmental problem occurs, however, if the effluent reaches and contaminates ground water supplies before the wastes are completely degraded.

Study Questions

1. What is meant by "water quality"? What tests are used to measure water quality?

2. Describe the major water pollutants.

3. a) What are some processes that decrease the amount of dissolved oxygen in a stream?
   b) What are some processes that increase the amount of dissolved oxygen in a stream?
   c) Which ones are most easily subject to human control?

4. a) Describe the process used to purify water for drinking.
   b) What is the source of drinking water in your community?
   c) How is your water treated before use?

5. a) What are the industrial sources of water pollution in your area?
   b) What types of chemicals must be removed in the water treatment?

6. a) Describe the primary, secondary, and tertiary methods of sewage treatment.
   b) What methods of sewage treatment are used in your area? Where is the treated water discharged?

7. a) What problems do heavy rainfalls cause in a sewer system?
   b) What can be done to deal with these problems?

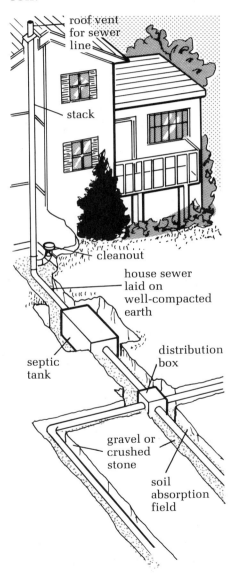

Figure 20-11. Where there are no sewer systems, septic tanks are often used. After leaving the septic tank the wastes are absorbed into the soil.

roof vent for sewer line

stack

cleanout

house sewer laid on well-compacted earth

septic tank

distribution box

gravel or crushed stone

soil absorption field

SANITARY ENGINEERING

(A Speech given by Samuel Keefer in 1889 to the Canadian Society of Civil Engineers)

It has now come to be pretty well understood as an established fact in sanitary science, that imperfect drainage of houses, badly constructed sewers, polluted drinking water, and filthy streets, are direct causes of disease and death, as to the same causes, scarlet fever, measles, diphtheria, typhus and typhoid fevers may be referred.

In the city of London [England], two centuries ago, the mortality was 80 per 1000, and it was not until the beginning of the present century that the birth rate exceeded the death rate. According to the "Bills of Mortality" there has been a steady decline in the death rate ever since, until now by a more strict attention to sanitation, London has become one of the healthiest cities in the world. . . .

It is to be deplored that we have no such progress, no corresponding results, to point to in Canada.

About a year ago there was published in the *Montreal Star* (14 Jan., 1888) a list of twenty towns and cities in Canada, shewing the populations and deaths, and the death rate per 1000. . . . We find some startling revelations. The lowest rate of mortality is found in the inland towns and cities of Ontario. These towns are Belleville, Guelph, Chatham, Galt, Peterborough, ranging from 16.50 to 19.75 per 1000. The cities are London, Kingston, Hamilton, Toronto, ranging from 18.31 to 21.50 per 1000. Halifax shews 20.52, Ottawa 28.70, Montreal 27.99, Quebec 33.57, Three Rivers 32.10, Sherbrooke 27.37, St. Hyacinthe, 41.83, and, saddest of all, Sorel 44.88 per 1000!

There is cause for serious reflection in these figures, shewing what a heavy responsibility rests with the Boards of Health in all larger cities and towns. I have gone into these details in order to prove to the Sanitary Engineer that there is in Canada plenty of important work for him to do. . . . It will be his pleasing duty to provide pure water, pure air, clean streets, and a perfect system of drainage, that shall carry off all surface water before it has time to become stagnant, and all waste from houses and yards before noxious gases are allowed to generate, and to convey the same with all possible dispatch to the proper outfall, there to be disposed of as circumstances shall dictate.

This early illustration shows how town residents cleaned up their neighbourhood in an attempt to drive the disease cholera away.

20.2 The Problems of Hazardous Wastes

What Are Hazardous Wastes?

Many sources in our society, particularly manufacturing and chemical industries, generate hazardous wastes. **Hazardous wastes** are those wastes which, due to their nature or quantity, are potentially hazardous to human health and/or the environment, and which require special disposal techniques in order to eliminate or reduce the hazard. Common hazardous wastes include acids from metal refining processes, spent bases from the pulp and paper industry, and leftovers from oil refining.

Figure 20-12. Estimated percentages of waste generated by industries in Ontario.

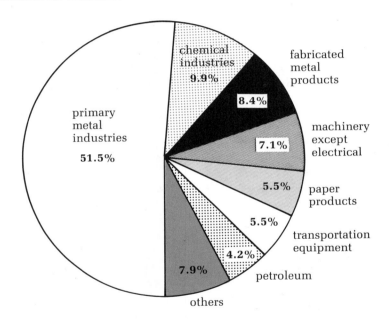

Potentially hazardous wastes come from run-off of fertilizers, pesticides, and herbicides, both agricultural and domestic. Other sources are hospital operating rooms, various types of laboratories, public utilities, and small businesses — beauty parlours, gas stations, photographic developers, electroplaters, dry cleaners, etc. Sometimes hazardous materials enter the environment through spills related to storage or transportation. We generate hazardous household wastes when we discard cleaning solvents, disinfectants, medicines, paints, and batteries.

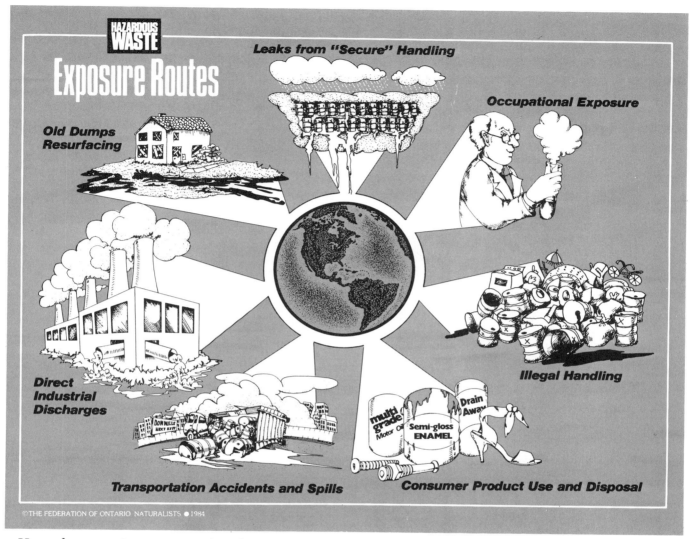

Exposure Routes

Leaks from "Secure" Handling

Occupational Exposure

Old Dumps Resurfacing

Illegal Handling

Direct Industrial Discharges

Transportation Accidents and Spills

Consumer Product Use and Disposal

©THE FEDERATION OF ONTARIO NATURALISTS ● 1984

Hazardous wastes may consist of **toxic** (poisonous) substances. Some hazardous wastes are **corrosive**, causing chemical damage to skin and matter. Other hazardous wastes are **reactive**; this means they enter readily into chemical reaction with other substances. Some wastes are so reactive they are said to be **explosive**. Still others are **volatile**, or easily vaporized at room temperature. Many are **flammable**, that is, capable of burning readily. Liquid gasoline, for example, is flammable. It is also volatile, vaporizing readily to form a gas. This gas is highly reactive and will explode if ignited by a spark. Some hazardous wastes are **infectious**, posing danger of infection from microorganisms.

Hazardous wastes are primarily liquid, ranging from very dilute to highly concentrated solutions. They can also exist in solid form, in sludge, for example, but to a lesser extent. All hazardous wastes have one property in common: existing municipal treatment facilities cannot effectively remove them. From the perspective of government regulation and control, "hazardous wastes" do not include domestic wastes, sewage system wastes, radioactive wastes, or wastes produced in small quantities by householders or waste generators.

Figure 20-13. How wastes can be hazardous.

Hazardous waste can be:

ignitible: burns at relatively low temperatures	**corrosive:** is highly acidic or alkaline	**reactive:** explodes or generates fumes
	infectious: can transmit disease	**toxic:** inflicts biological injury on plants, animals, or humans
carcinogenic: causes cancer	**mutagenic:** causes genetic damage in living organisms, with potential effects on offspring	**teratogenic:** causes birth defects

What Are The Problems?

1. Environmental and Health Concerns

The improper disposal of hazardous wastes can cause air, water, and soil pollution harmful to human, plant, and animal life. Unless properly stored and confined, wastes deposited on land sites can contaminate surface and ground water used for drinking. Chemicals in waterways may harm aquatic life.

2. Amount Produced

Less than 1% of total industrial production is waste, of which about 10% is classified as hazardous. Recent figures estimate these wastes at about 150 kg per year for every person in Canada.

3. Scarcity of Treatment and Disposal Sites

Treatment processes can reduce the danger and volume of wastes, leaving smaller amounts of less hazardous residues. However, industries that treat their own waste still need a place to dispose of the residues. Industries that cannot afford to treat their own wastes must locate treatment and disposal sites. The practice of disposing of some hazardous wastes in municipal landfill sites is now illegal; this creates an even greater demand for more treatment and disposal facilities.

Polybrominated biphenyl, PBB, is similar to PCB except that it contains bromine instead of chlorine. A Michigan chemical company that manufactured a food additive was using PBB as a fire-retardant. In 1973, PBB instead of the food additive was accidentally added to animal feed. The result: the destruction of 30 000 cattle, 1.5 million chickens and other farm animals, and $100 million in damages. Before the mistake was discovered, many of the contaminated animals, as well as their eggs and milk, had been consumed. A study found that 97% of the population of Michigan had been contaminated through the food chain. In Canada PBBs are banned.

Barrels of toxic chemicals surround a bankrupt chemical refinery in Delta, B.C. Authorities are unsure of how to dispose of this abandoned waste.

4. Illegal Disposal

Some waste generators resort to cheap illegal disposal rather than pay for approved methods. They flush their wastes into sewers and ditches, drop them off ships, explode waste-laden barges at sea, dump them into lakes and rivers, conceal them in garbage, and bury them in municipal landfills or on farmland. Spawned by the hazardous waste problem, the "midnight dumper" operates under the cover of darkness, dumping wastes illegally at prices far below those charged by legitimate disposal firms.

Two truckloads of English cucumbers
suspected of pesticide poisoning are
dumped at a suburban landfill.

Toxic Substances

When absorbed in even small quantities by a living organism, a toxic substance will affect life functions, causing adverse effects ranging from transient to fatal. Such adverse changes can be either immediately apparent or delayed. Toxic substances are classified as acute (quick-acting) and chronic (slow-acting). It is much more difficult to set standards to prevent chronic effects, because these usually result from long-term exposure to low levels of toxic substances.

Figure 20-14 The sources of Ontario's wastes.

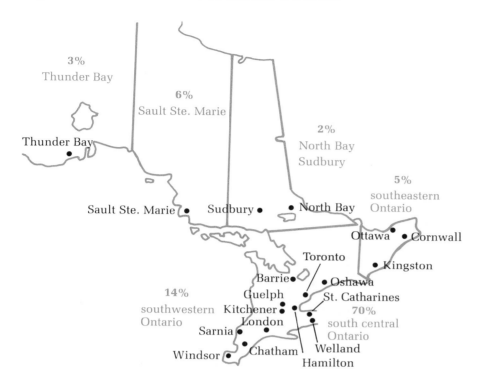

Toxicity levels are usually reported in milligrams per kilogram (parts per million). A part per million (ppm) refers to a concentration in which one unit of a substance can be found in a million units of the surrounding air or water. It is equivalent to one grain of salt in a half-cup of sugar, or one minute in two years.

During the last two decades, our analytical equipment and our ability to measure have advanced tremendously. Today micrograms per kilogram (parts per billion), or even nanograms per kilogram (parts per trillion) may be used to measure the levels of extremely toxic chemicals such as dioxins. A part per billion (ppb) is equivalent to one second in 32 years. A part per trillion (ppt) is one second in 320 centuries, or one grain of sugar in an Olympic-size swimming pool.

At present our ability to measure so precisely is better than our understanding of what consuming several parts per billion of a substance might mean over a lifetime.

What's a billion? What's a trillion?

The terms billion and trillion are no longer used in SI. They have been replaced by:

one million
= 10^6 = 1 000 000

one billion (one thousand million)
= 10^9 = 1 000 000 000

one trillion (one million million)
= 10^{12} = 1 000 000 000 000

Terms such as billion and trillion are ambiguous because of different meanings in different countries. The terms ppb and ppt are used in this text in brackets because they are still in common use. Current Canadian press accounts usually report toxic concentrations in these units, rather than in the preferred equivalents given below.

Table of Equivalents (by mass)
1 mg/kg = 1 ppm
1 μg/kg = 1 ppb
1 ng/kg* = 1 ppt

*The symbol "n" represents the prefix "nano", meaning 10^{-9}.

Figure 20-15. Toxic substances in the Great Lakes.

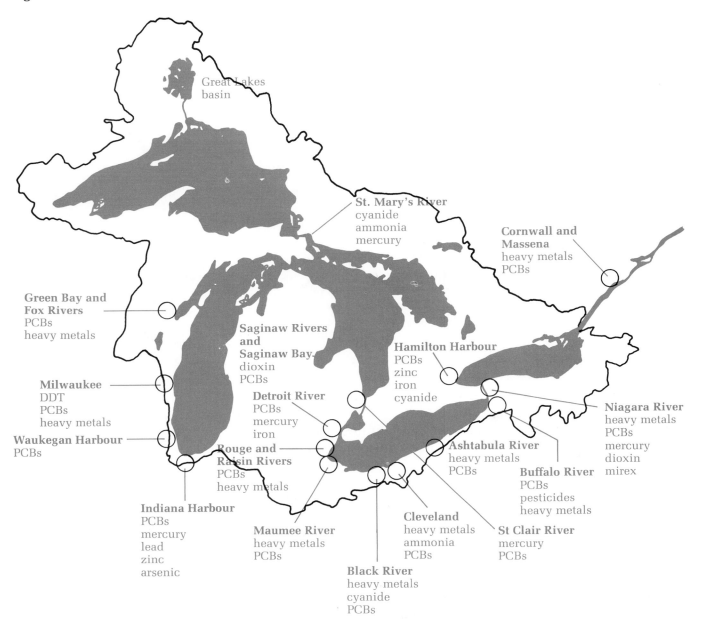

Great Lakes basin

St. Mary's River
cyanide
ammonia
mercury

Cornwall and Massena
heavy metals
PCBs

Green Bay and Fox Rivers
PCBs
heavy metals

Saginaw Rivers and Saginaw Bay
dioxin
PCBs

Hamilton Harbour
PCBs
zinc
iron
cyanide

Milwaukee
DDT
PCBs
heavy metals

Detroit River
PCBs
mercury
iron

Niagara River
heavy metals
PCBs
mercury
dioxin
mirex

Waukegan Harbour
PCBs

Rouge and Raisin Rivers
PCBs
heavy metals

Ashtabula River
heavy metals
PCBs

Buffalo River
PCBs
pesticides
heavy metals

Indiana Harbour
PCBs
mercury
lead
zinc
arsenic

Maumee River
heavy metals
PCBs

Cleveland
heavy metals
ammonia
PCBs

St Clair River
mercury
PCBs

Black River
heavy metals
cyanide
PCBs

Carcinogens

As more and more toxic substances have been found in trace amounts in our environment, some have been identified as **carcinogens**. A carcinogen is a chemical which can cause a cancer to develop. A chronic toxic problem involving carcinogens is difficult to solve because it is often not apparent for years that a problem even exists. Also, it is not certain that there is a threshold level, that is, a level below which no adverse effects can be measured. Some scientists argue that there is no safe level for a carcinogenic substance, while others disagree.

Government agencies set **tolerances**, or maximum concentrations, for pesticides and other toxic substances in food, air, and water. For example, in Canada the tolerance level of dioxin in fish for human consumption is 20 ng/kg (20 ppt). While we can measure small concentrations such as these, we cannot remove them. One of the most potent carcinogens known, alfatoxin, is produced naturally by a mould growing on peanuts, corn, and other grains. By law, a maximum alfatoxin concentration of 20 μg/kg (20 ppb) is allowed in our food. Natural carcinogens such as these are permitted in our food, not because government agencies are lax, but because if they were banned, much of our food supply would be outlawed!

What are the limits of human perception of substances present in such small concentrations? With our unaided senses, we can detect chlorine in water at a concentration of 1 mg/kg (1 ppm), and the odour of fuel oil in the air at 1 μg/kg (1 ppb). We are unable to detect 1 ng/kg (1 ppt) of *anything* without costly equipment.

Toxic Substances in the Food Chain

Oceans and lakes usually have a low concentration of pesticides. However, plants and animals can concentrate a pesticide in their fatty tissues and pass it along in complex food chains such as that shown in Figure 20-16. Food chains begin with plants as they convert carbon dioxide and water into starch in photosynthesis. Plants also absorb other nutrients and chemicals from their environment. Pesticide molecules tend to concentrate in the fatty tissues of animals who eat the plants. As the food molecules move up the chain, pesticide molecules move along with them, resulting in higher and higher pesticide concentrations. In time, if tolerance levels are reached, the plant or animal tissue is hazardous for human consumption.

Figure 20-16. An aquatic food chain.

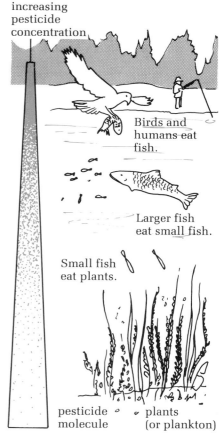

increasing pesticide concentration

Birds and humans eat fish.

Larger fish eat small fish.

Small fish eat plants.

pesticide molecule   plants (or plankton)

Biological magnification of certain pollutants can occur, causing their concentrations at the top of the chain to be thousands of times larger than in the water.

Toxicity Ratings of Household Products

Figure 20-17 categorizes household products into three main toxicity groups, ranging from slight to high toxicity. A toxicity description is also included.

The hazard symbols printed on toxic domestic products are similar to the warning symbols used in the activities in this text. By law, hazard symbols must appear on all potentially hazardous products. The level of hazard is indicated by the outline shape of the symbol as shown in Figure 20-17.

Figure 20-17. The symbolic codes for degree of hazardousness.

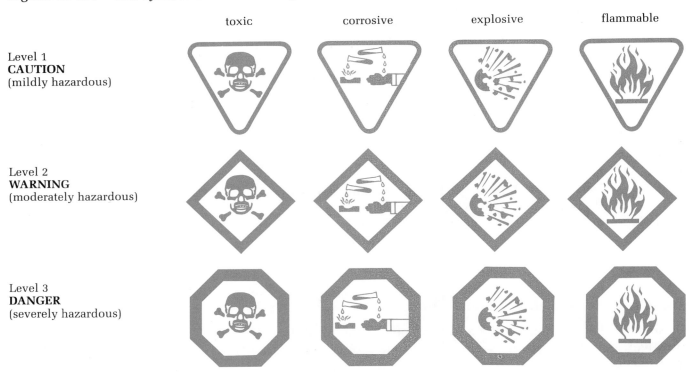

Level 1
CAUTION
(mildly hazardous)

Level 2
WARNING
(moderately hazardous)

Level 3
DANGER
(severely hazardous)

toxic   corrosive   explosive   flammable

Activity 20-3:   Survey of Hazardous Product Labels

In this activity you will do a survey of labels of hazardous domestic products. Your teacher will assign a particular type of store (grocery, hardware, garden supply, etc.) to pairs of students.

Procedure

1. Each pair of students should visit a different store to study the labels of any four hazardous products of their choice.

2. Draw a table for your survey results. For each selected product, record:

a) type of product
b) brand name
c) normal use
d) active ingredients
e) other ingredients
f) directions for use
g) precautions given
h) hazard symbols used
i) special storage instructions
j) first aid measures
k) recommended disposal option

Discussion

1. Were the hazard symbols and written warnings prominently and clearly displayed on each product? Were some products better than others in this regard? Explain.
2. Comment on the clarity of directions for use, storage, and disposal.
3. Comment on the clarity of the first aid instructions provided.
4. Select any one of your products and describe how the label could be improved.

Study Questions

1. a) What are hazardous wastes?
   b) Name some hazardous household wastes.
2. What are the main problems caused by hazardous wastes?
3. What is the difference between an acute and a chronic toxic substance?
4. a) Give an example to illustrate the meaning of i) part per million, ii) part per billion, iii) part per trillion.
   b) What are the preferred units for ppb and ppt?
   c) What are the limits of human sensory perception of substances present in small concentrations? (Use appropriate units.)
5. What is a carcinogen? Why are carcinogens sometimes difficult to identify?
6. What are tolerances? Give three examples.
7. Do you think consumers of chemical products should pay for the long-term disposal of associated waste materials when they buy the product?

SUPERBUG TO THE RESCUE

Agent Orange, the herbicide used to defoliate guerrilla-held jungles and to destroy crops in Vietnam, is a toxic compound that can remain in the environment for several decades.

Pseudomonas, a microorganism found in soil and fresh water, is a strong and hungry bacterium that makes organic compounds its basic diet. These bacteria were collected from Love Canal in New York State and from other waste-dumping sites. The microorganisms were first fed compounds that they could digest, but gradually the researchers reduced these food sources and added increasingly high concentrations of Agent Orange. The bacteria were faced with a new situation: they had to detoxify the new chemical and then try to digest it. Researchers found that in this process a new organism evolved. It not only

digested the complex compound, but also thrived and reproduced while doing so! When 1000 ppm of Agent Orange were added to soil containing 10 000 000 bacteria per gram of soil, the microorganisms could eliminate

the chemical within one week. Unlike most microorganisms, this was no picky eater! Because it could consume a wide variety of compounds, scientists called this incredible new organism a "superbug".

The effects of Agent Orange: the top photo shows a healthy mangrove forest in Vietnam; the bottom photo shows a similar area that was sprayed with Agent Orange in 1965. The trees and vegetation have been almost completely destroyed, along with the animal life they supported. Researchers are hopeful that the superbug can reverse this situation and restore this ecosystem to its former state.

20.3   Managing Hazardous Wastes

Wastes known to be hazardous are *registered* through placement on a government list of hazardous substances. In Ontario, all registered wastes require a *manifest*, that is, a detailed record of waste type, production process, quantities produced, waste properties, storage and packaging, transportation, and disposal. The photograph shows a 6-copy manifest provided by the Ontario Ministry of the Environment. This regulation is designed to prevent illegal dumping of hazardous wastes. It allows the Ministry of the Environment to control and monitor a hazardous waste from the moment of generation through to its ultimate destination, providing "cradle-to-grave" surveillance.

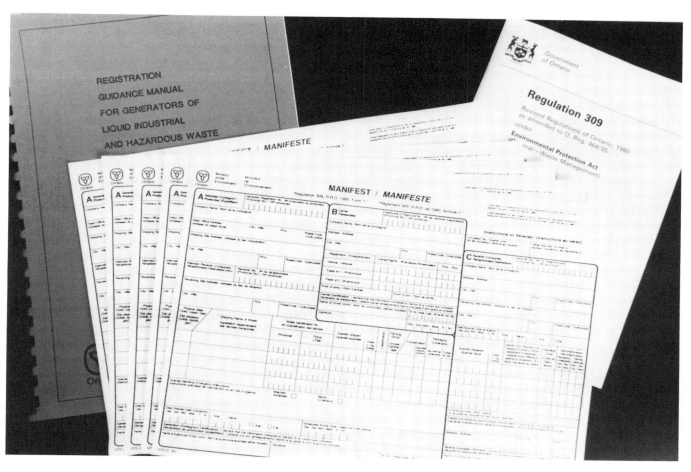

Each waste must be disposed of in a manner nonthreatening to the environment or to human health. Landfills, open dumps, and waste-water treatment plants cannot safely dispose of hazardous wastes. Waste generators, researchers, and government agencies are now searching for efficient and economic forms of hazardous waste management.

The key to effective management lies in changing such wastes to nonhazardous forms. This requires a thorough knowledge of the waste, including chemical and physical characteristics, volume, and location. Waste-management guidelines have been developed jointly by government and industry. In order of priority, these are:

1) Either don't generate, or else reduce the amount generated.

2) If you must generate, then recycle or reuse as much as possible.

3) Treat or dispose of the waste on-site.

4) Treat or dispose of the waste off-site.

Reduction

Sometimes called "source reduction" or "pollution prevention", reduction is the ideal solution, for it prohibits waste generation, emphasizes resource conservation, is legal and environmentally safe, and can save costs over time. Reduction involves modifying a process, substituting safer materials for hazardous ones, or replacing a product that creates a large quantity of hazardous waste with one that does not.

Recycling and Reuse

Recycling is recovering and treating waste by-products for use as raw materials in the same or another process. Reuse involves recovery with no need for further treatment. Reuse may also involve an **exchange** of waste materials among different industries. For example, a by-product of nylon production, acid, is sold as a raw material in manufacturing paints and solvents.

Besides reducing wastes, recovery conserves energy resources and raw materials, and lowers transportation and disposal costs. Both recycling and reuse decrease the waste generator's long-term liability for possible leaks from land burial sites.

Figure 20-18. Estimated disposal fate of current hazardous wastes in Ontario.

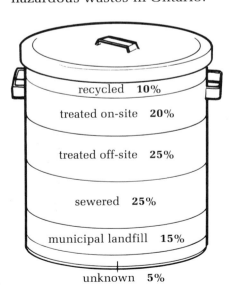

recycled 10%

treated on-site 20%

treated off-site 25%

sewered 25%

municipal landfill 15%

unknown 5%

These photos outline four steps in the treatment of organic wastes at Tricil's waste treatment facility near Sarnia, Ontario. Upon receipt (top left), the wastes are sampled, analyzed, and checked against on-file data to ensure no unknown material has been added. After pretreatment in special tanks, the wastes are loaded into the incinerator (top right), which treats and destroys over 15 000 000 t of organic wastes a year. Solid organic wastes are transported to secure chemical landfills (bottom left) and monitoring wells provide an early warning system for any contamination of groundwater from the landfill sites.

Treatment Options

Treatment is any physical, chemical, biological, or thermal process that destroys, detoxifies, or neutralizes hazardous wastes, reduces their volume, or modifies them for recovery, storage, or transport. Treatment reduces or eliminates the hazardous quality of the waste before disposal. The specific treatment used depends on the waste material and its particular properties.

Physical treatment involves physical separation and concentration of the materials in a waste stream. Typical processes include evaporation, distillation, coagulation, centrifuging, sedimentation, and filtration.

In **biological treatment**, microorganisms decompose wastes and use them as food. The digestive processes of the microorganisms break down complex organic molecules into simpler and less toxic molecules, such as water, carbon dioxide, and acids. This treatment method is often used in industrial waste streams rich in biodegradable pollutants such as starch, cellulose, fats, oils, and greases. **Landfarming** is a common form of biological treatment, in which waste is spread thinly over soil, where microorganisms decompose organic compounds as the waste infiltrates the soil. Careful controls are required to prevent run-off, and the land may be unfit for agricultural uses for many years.

Chemical treatment modifies the chemical structure of hazardous waste components. Such modifications often reduce the reactivity of the substance by forming a less hazardous product. An advantage of such treatment is that it can often be done on-site. Neutralization, for example, reduces the acidity or alkalinity of liquid wastes. As Figure 20-19 shows, fish cannot survive in acidic waters.

Figure 20-19. As the acidity of the water increases, the fish population declines.

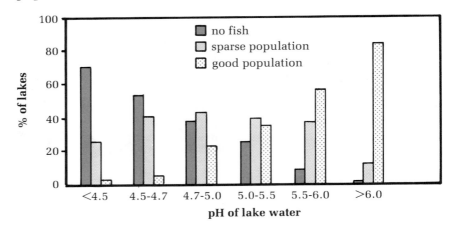

Thermal treatment destroys wastes by subjecting them to high temperatures. Although it is the most expensive treatment technique, it destroys wastes permanently, safely, and cleanly. Incineration is the most common thermal treatment; some scientists and engineers consider it the best overall treatment for hazardous wastes. During incineration, organic materials are reacted with oxygen at temperatures between 425°C and 1650°C. In theory, this oxidation process should produce nontoxic carbon dioxide and water. In practice, however, because of the complexity of the organic compounds, the combustion produces oxides, acids, ash, and gaseous vapours, and some of these raise environmental concerns. A properly designed and operated incineration facility can minimize the production of potentially harmful solids and gases, and can capture and detoxify any contaminants produced.

Fixation renders waste less hazardous by lessening the waste's ability to migrate from the disposal site. Wastes can be bound into a solid mass (solidification) and sealed in a glasslike capsule (encapsulation). This prevents the waste from leaching into the environment from a burial or storage site.

Disposal

The generation of hazardous wastes cannot always be prevented, and hazardous substances cannot always be recycled, treated, or destroyed. So, some means of final disposal is needed. "Final" disposal means placing material in a permanent storage site, never to be disturbed. Although land sites are often used, they should be avoided if at all possible.

The most favoured storage method is an **engineered landfill**, located either above or below ground in areas of heavy clay soil which can slow any movement of toxic substances into the environment. Into the site go hazardous wastes in several forms: liquid wastes stored in drums, solid wastes, and solidified sludge. These landfills contain an elaborate system of liners, tubes, and drain lines or pumps designed to monitor and remove any possible leachate before environmental damage occurs.

Figure 20-20. A below-ground engineered landfill site.

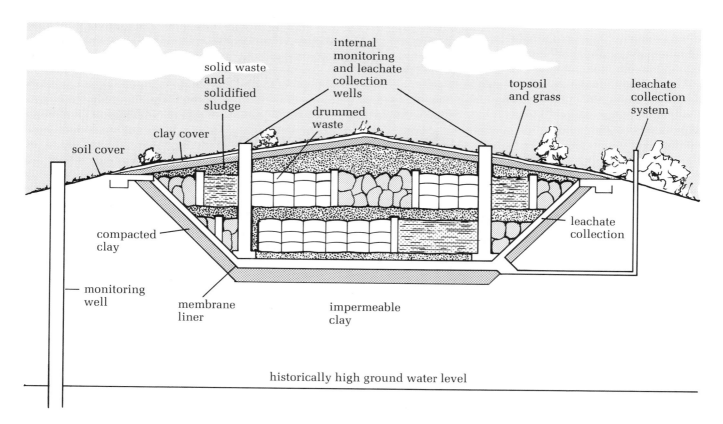

Dr. Donald Chant of the Ontario Waste Management Corporation fields questions on the siting issue during a radio talk show in London, Ontario.

Location Problems

The disposal of hazardous wastes in Canada and in many other industrialized countries is a serious technical, political, and social issue. Hazardous waste is part of our lifestyles, and so public participation is needed in the search for solutions, none of which will be simple or perfect.

Where will such wastes be dumped? Our desire for consumer products conflicts with public reluctance to locate facilities to treat, store, and dispose of the wastes resulting from the manufacture of these products. The "not-in-my-backyard" reaction to proposed locations is understandable, given the haphazard handling of such wastes in the past.

Society, however, will have to make compromises. Industry has a responsibility to the public to choose products and processes carefully in order to reduce hazardous wastes as much as possible. If the public chooses to rely on the products of modern technology, then it too must accept the responsibility of becoming informed about the wastes generated in the manufacture of those products. People must recognize that hazardous wastes are unavoidable in the manufacture of most consumer products, and facilities near generator locations must be built to handle the wastes, even if this means proximity to residential areas.

Activity 20-4:   A River Pollution Study

Concerned with water pollution in their community, a high school science class decided to carry out an investigation. The class was divided into six groups, each of which took various measurements at different sites along the river bank. The sites (A to F) are marked on the map (Figure 20-21), and the measurements made at each site are recorded in Table 20-4.

Procedure

1. Carefully study the map and the table of results, and suggest reasons for each of the following.

   a) the increase in pH between A and B with the water becoming basic

   b) the increase in temperature between B and C

   c) the large drop in pH between B and C with the water becoming acidic

   d) the increase in temperature between C and D

Figure 20-21.

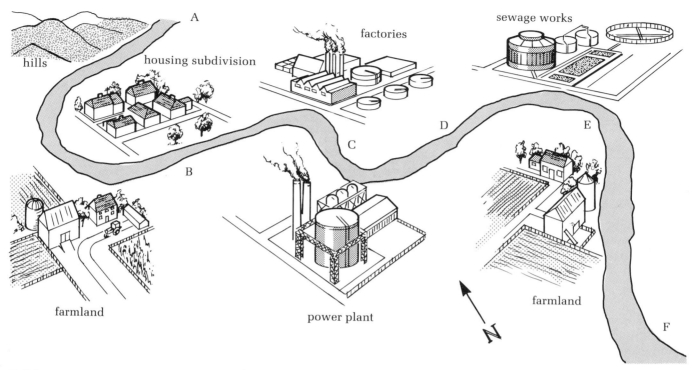

Table 20-4: River Water Survey Results

Water Samples	Site A	Site B	Site C	Site D	Site E	Site F
temperature (°C)	5	6	9	13	11	11
pH	7	9	5	5.5	6	6
dissolved oxygen (mg/kg)	12	11	9	9	4	3
existence of fish in river	yes	yes	few	few	no	no
water plant growth	normal	normal	normal	normal	above normal	very high

 e) the large drop in dissolved oxygen content between D and E

2. At E the river leaves the urban area and widens as it flows slowly through a rural farm area. The river shows above-normal plant growth at E, and has become heavily overgrown with water plants at F.

a) Suggest a reason for the above-normal river plant growth at E.

b) Suggest a pollutant that may have caused the excessive plant growth at F.

c) Which chemical element is probably responsible for the excessive plant growth?

d) How could the pollutant named in b) have entered the river?

3. Fishing is reported to be very good in the hills near A, but prospects decrease as the river flows through the town.

a) There are no fish at E. Suggest a possible reason.

b) There are no fish at F. Suggest a reason different from the one given above.

4. At F the water is turbid and has a somewhat unpleasant odour. The students assigned to this site need a small amount of drinking water. They have a small metal pot, some plastic wrap, and a small bowl, and have lit a small wood fire.

a) Describe how they could produce some distilled water.

b) Draw a sketch to illustrate your method.

c) What should the pH of the distilled water be?

d) How could the students cool the collected water to make it more suitable for drinking?

5. Later, the students wrote a report on their findings and presented it to the mayor. She asked the students for suggestions on how to improve conditions in the river.

a) Make a list of suggestions for submission to the mayor.

b) Discuss the advantages and disadvantages of each suggestion.

The Ontario Waste Management Corporation (OWMC)

The Ontario Waste Management Corporation is an agency established by the government of Ontario in 1981 to deal with liquid industrial and hazardous, nonradioactive wastes. Its first task was to determine the types and quantities of wastes in Ontario not receiving proper treatment, and the facilities necessary to manage these wastes safely. Its next tasks were to locate a suitable site for a treatment facility, to build that facility, and to find ways to encourage Ontario industries to reduce the volume of wastes requiring treatment and disposal.

Locating the Site

At least 70% of Ontario's liquid industrial waste is generated in and near the Golden Horseshoe around the western shore of Lake Ontario. This region contains excellent deposits of the type of clay soil needed for safe waste management facilities. To minimize transportation risks and costs, the search for a site centred on this area.

After extensive studies of roads, distances, soil and wind conditions, underground water movement, and agricultural and urban areas, four large candidate areas were selected. Further studies located specific potential zones within these areas. More than 60 factors were used to evaluate and compare potential sites. Finally, the OWMC selected a site in the Township of West Lincoln for the treatment plant. Before this site can be approved and a plant built, a full review and public hearings must be held under the Environmental Assessment Act. Only then can final planning and construction begin. Figure 20-22 shows an artist's conception of the proposed treatment facility.

Citizens of West Lincoln protest the siting of a waste treatment facility in their township. After reading this chapter, what arguments can you see for and against their position?

Figure 20-22. A proposed waste treatment facility.

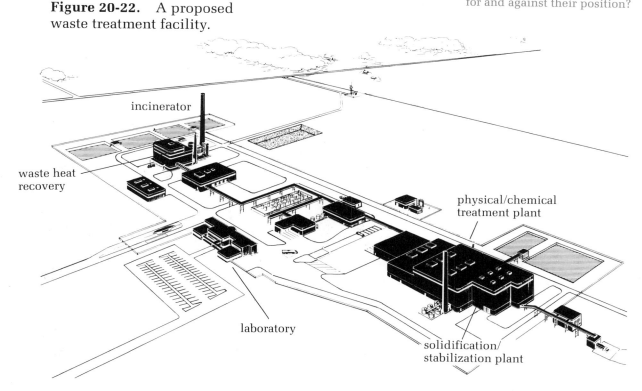

incinerator

waste heat recovery

physical/chemical treatment plant

laboratory

solidification/ stabilization plant

Study Questions

1. Describe the main strategies for hazardous waste management.
2. Describe the various treatment options in the management of hazardous wastes.
3. Regardless of the treatment used for hazardous wastes, some waste still remains for disposal. Describe:
   a) an engineered landfill
   b) the problems often encountered in siting such landfills.
4. What is the OWMC?

SCIENCE IN ACTION

LOVE CANAL

Its name—Love Canal—sounds romantic, until the horrors it conceals are described. For many years Love Canal in Niagara Falls, NY, served as the local swimming hole for neighbourhood children. In 1942, the Hooker Chemicals and Plastics Corporation used the site as an industrial landfill. About 22 000 t of chemical wastes were deposited in drums in the canal and in its banks. When the canal was almost full, a clay cap over a metre thick was placed on top to keep rain water and melting snow out of the wastes. This was considered a secure method of handling the wastes at the time.

In 1953, Hooker sold the site for $1.00 to the Niagara Falls Board of Education, which removed some of the clay cap in the construction of an elementary school—half of which was located right over the old canal.

For more than a decade the Love Canal area was a typical middle-class neighbourhood.

Then in 1976, following several years of abnormally heavy rains, the wastes leaking from their corroded drums rose to the surface and into basements to create a chemical nightmare. The neighbourhood became alarmed as the rates of miscarriages, birth defects, and liver diseases rose above normal. Investigators found more than 80 chemicals, a number of them suspected cancer-causing agents, at the site. Air samples taken from basements contained high levels of toxic vapours.

In August 1978, the State of New York closed the school and evacuated the neighbourhood. Since then, over $100 million has been spent in an effort to clean up the mess. The canal has been surrounded by a concrete wall, and leachate inside the wall is collected and detoxified. However, water moving though the contaminated soil outside the wall can still form leachate, which continues to flow into the Niagara River and from there into Lake Ontario.

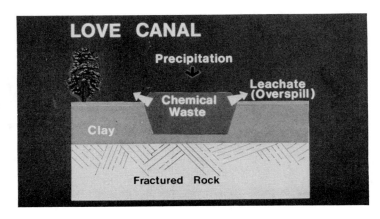

Meet a Waste Management Executive — Robert Redhead

Robert is Market Development Manager for Tricil, an Ontario-based waste management company.

Q. HAVE YOU ALWAYS BEEN AWARE OF ENVIRONMENTAL CONCERNS?
A. Not really. When I was a kid growing up in a British Columbia pulp-and-paper town, smokestacks were a sign of work. So I didn't have a childhood awareness. I always liked science, though, and did my undergraduate degree in microbiology. Later, I completed a Master's degree in business administration.

Q. HOW DO YOU DEAL WITH THE RATHER NEGATIVE IMAGE THAT HAZARDOUS WASTE HAS?

A. Our society has to recognize that we have waste to deal with. Because we want to consume, the process of producing so many goods creates hazardous wastes. Each of us generates about one tonne of municipal garbage every year, and our industries generate millions of tonnes. There's a growing awareness that the waste has to go somewhere.

Q. WHAT'S THE MOST DIFFICULT THING TO COMMUNICATE TO THE PUBLIC?
A. Nobody wants a waste disposal plant near them. Waste can be dealt with safely, but it will be impossible to do this without additional treatment centres. So I spend about 20% of my time on public awareness. We issue written material, give talks, and our trade association has produced a film.

Q. WHAT IS A TYPICAL WORK WEEK LIKE FOR YOU?
A. I coordinate the monitoring of and compliance with environmental regulations for Tricil in both the United States and Canada. Basically, I'm a negotiator who brings the companies, the regulatory bodies, and the public together. This means I travel a lot.

Q. WHAT SORT OF THINGS WOULD BE DISCUSSED WHEN YOU MEET WITH THE GOVERNMENT?
A. Right now we're discussing something new in our industry. Traditionally, we have dealt with waste by building a facility and sending the waste to it. However, companies are always looking for

ways to reduce the cost of waste disposal and governments are asking companies to produce less waste. So we've devised a solution, which is to treat the waste on site. The waste would be put through a mobile treatment facility that would travel from site to site.

Q. WHAT IS THE MOST SATISFYING ASPECT OF YOUR JOB?
A. I like being able to bring differing opinions together and to come up with a resolution. It's satisfying when people feel something positive has been achieved in a negotiation that looked impossible. I often have to persuade federal and provincial governments to agree on something. For instance, I sit on a committee that deals with the safe transportation of hazardous waste. We were able to come up with a uniform manifest for the whole country. That was satisfying.

Q. WHAT CAN STUDENTS DO TO PREPARE FOR THE KIND OF CAREER THAT YOU HAVE?
A. Studying science develops the kind of analytical mind required, but this must be combined with the ability to communicate, so English is also important. Students can investigate environmental concerns in their schools and communities, and do projects on them. This kind of involvement is important for learning how to interact with people and the skills of negotiation. Another idea is for students to encourage people from the industry, like me, to come and speak at their schools.

Review Questions

A: Knowledge

1. a) Name three sources of pollution of natural waterways.
   b) Polluted waterways are sometimes treated with oxygen. What is the purpose of the oxygen?
   c) Briefly describe the types of treatment that might be necessary to convert river water into water suitable for domestic use.

2. a) Explain the difference between a biodegradable and a nonbiodegradable material and give examples of each.
   b) What is BOD and why is it an indication of the extent of pollution of a body of water?
   c) What is a floc, and how does it help to purify water?

3. a) Why is a thick mat of blue-green algae on the surface of a lake an unhealthy sign?
   b) What can cause such algae?
   c) What will happen when the algae die?

4. It has been said that water purifies itself by running three kilometres from the source of incoming waste.
   a) What types of pollutants will be removed from the running water?
   b) How will they be removed?
   c) What types of pollutants will not be affected?

5. a) Describe the three types of sewage treatment.
   b) Explain the operation of a septic tank.

6. In some systems, untreated sewage is dumped into a waterway during heavy rainstorms.
   a) Why is this done?
   b) What problems does it cause?

7. a) Hazardous wastes may be toxic, corrosive, reactive, explosive, volatile, flammable, infectious, or carcinogenic. Explain the meaning of each of these terms.
   b) In Ontario, why are hazardous wastes registered with the Ministry of the Environment?

   c) What is a "manifest" and why does the law require that a manifest be filed for a hazardous waste?

8. Briefly describe each of the following treatment options for hazardous wastes: physical, biological, chemical, thermal, and fixation.

B: Application

9. What are some processes that decrease the amount of dissolved oxygen in a stream? What processes increase the amount of dissolved oxygen in a stream? Which ones are most readily subject to human control?

10. What is the biological importance of the fact that gases can dissolve in water? Describe how you would demonstrate that gases become less soluble in water as the temperature rises.

11. The total effect of a certain effluent on water quality will depend on factors other than the BOD. Using your community's sewage as an example, what are some other influences?

12. What is eutrophication? How can stimulation of plant growth lead to the death of a body of water?

13. Draw a flow chart showing the production, collection, and treatment of sewage in a large city. Include ways of recycling this sewage so that it may be used to advantage.

14. Explain why each of the following creates a pollution problem when its wastes are emptied into a stream.
    a) a chlorine-producing plant
    b) a steel mill
    c) an electricity-generating plant burning oil or coal
    d) an intensively cultivated agricultural area

15. Why do nonbiodegradable materials released into the environment often become more concentrated in the tissues of animals that feed at higher levels, such as carnivores (meat-eaters)?

16. The application of a single small dose of benzopyrene fails to produce a tumour in mice. Does this mean that the compound is definitely noncarcinogenic? Give a reason for your answer.

17. Two new chemicals are prepared in the lab. One is a relatively simple acid with corrosive properties. The other chemical has carcinogenic properties. Which chemical's toxic property is more likely to be discovered? Why?

18. Several operations are used in pulp and paper mills to prepare, pulp, and process wood. Usually the bark is mechanically removed and chipped in preparation for pulping. In the sulphite pulping process, solutions of sodium hydrogen sulphite and excess sulphur dioxide break down the noncellulose portions of the wood. What classes of water pollutants could result from these processes?

C: Problem Solving

19. Given that the concentration of oxygen in water is only 9 mg/L at 20°C, why should water be a last resort for the dumping of organic wastes and biodegradable chemicals? Why is the soil a more efficient medium?

20. The average person in a certain city produces 250 g of solid human wastes daily and uses 340 L of water daily, 90% of which goes into the sewers. What is the concentration of solids in the waste water (in milligrams per kilogram)?

21. A popular theory says that one of the causes of the decline of the Roman Empire was that Romans used cooking pots and serving dishes rich in lead. Discuss whether this theory is reasonable. (Note that the sale of dishes whose glaze contains lead is not permitted in Canada.)

22. Hexachlorophene is an effective germ killer put on the market in 1942. It soon found its way into aerosol deodorants, face soaps, toothpastes, hair sprays, baby powder, and cleansers. By 1972, these uses were banned when studies linked the chemical with brain damage in infants. Why can it take 30 years before such a product is removed from general use?

23. Defoliants or herbicides such as 2,4-D were used for military purposes in Vietnam by American military forces during the 1960s and 1970s. When these chemicals are highly concentrated, they not only defoliate but also kill trees. What is your reaction to their use, considering military, moral, environmental, and other points of view?

24. The use of certain pesticides such as DDT has been severely criticized in recent years. Suppose you are a legislator called upon to decide whether or not this pesticide should be banned. What would be the important pro and con arguments? How would you decide?

25. Suppose an Ontario Waste Management Corporation (OWMC) facility were to be built next door to your residence. What questions would you ask about the facility? What answers would you expect to receive before construction began?

26. Resolved: Education is the answer to problems concerning energy, pollution, and the proper use and reuse of materials. Defend or refute this statement.

Toxic Substances in the Construction Workplace

The Issue: Toxic hazards in the construction industry and how to cope with them.

Construction workers wearing gas masks remove urea formaldehyde foam insulation from the walls of a house. Over 60 000 home owners installed it in their homes before toxic hazards were linked to it.

Around the world, hundreds of thousands of construction workers are expected to die from asbestos-related cancer between now and 2010, as a result of direct exposure to asbestos in building materials installed in the 1950s. Although the dangers of the exposure have become painfully clear, there may be a whole new wave of construction deaths in the future as a result of sloppy removal practices.

Asbestos is not the only health hazard faced by construction workers on the job. Even exposure to silica dust from sandblasting or masonry can seriously impair lung function. Painters are especially vulnerable to occupational disease because they work with more than 2000 chemicals. Of these, about 150 are known or suspected carcinogens, and another 500 are known toxins that can cause brain damage. Other trades also face daily job-site exposure to an array of dangerous chemicals, including arsenic and formaldehyde (see Table 20-25). The new emphasis on toxic waste cleanups will expose workers doing the cleanups to new and possibly more deadly substances.

Exposure to chemicals is probably the greatest on-the-job hazard right now. While the construction industry and unions have made progress in striving for the welfare of workers, they have difficulty keeping up with the new chemicals and products appearing constantly. In 1983, the American Chemical Society was registering new chemicals at the rate of 70 an hour. By the time health problems surface, that new chemical may be in widespread use. New regulations require manufacturers to label products containing toxic substances, and to provide "material safety data sheets" on them. But by the time the product reaches workers, it may have changed containers or had its labelling removed. Even when contractors and owners are concerned about workers' health, they may be forced to cut corners to remain competitive.

Abroad, the level of attention paid to toxic dangers in the construction workplace varies. Japan is far ahead of Canada and

Table 20-5: Chemicals and cancer in construction.

Substance	Type of cancer known or suspected	Where found
wood dust	nasal, colon, rectal	woodworking
formaldehyde	nasal, brain	plywood, particle board, foam insulator
trichloroethylene	liver	solvents, paints, resins, varnish
vinyl chloride monomer	liver	polyvinyl chloride plastics
benzene	leukemia	solvents, glues
welding fumes, nickel, beryllium, chromates	lung, nasal	welding
asbestos	lung, mesothelioma	insulation, building products

the United States in occupational health precautions, while Europe is lagging behind. In Japan, large billboards with instructions and warnings are set up on job sites as a supervisor oversees a hazardous activity.

In Canada, efforts must be made to boost awareness of toxic substances among workers. Only when workers know the hazards can they protect themselves. Unfortunately, many workers have found the hazards of their jobs much higher than they bargained for. Workers should receive premium pay for their skills, and not for danger compensation.

Exploring The Issue

A. Selecting Concerns

Select five industries or construction activities located in your area or that are of current interest. Suggestions include: paint manufacturers, chemical suppliers, plastic producers, dry cleaning establishments, electroplating industries, machine and wood shops, building products manufacturers, welding companies, photographic developers, and sandblasting companies.

B. Gathering Information

For each choice, identify the hazardous substances in the workplace. Use fact sheets, newspaper or magazine reports, or other resources to obtain information on each chemical. For each substance:

1. Find other names or synonyms for the substance.
2. Describe the material, and state its properties.
3. Try to locate a material safety data sheet, and state the hazards and warnings given.
4. Describe how workers are exposed to the chemical.
5. Give a list of occupations in which exposure may occur.
6. State toxicity data.
7. Provide information on the possible risks to exposed workers.
8. Describe how the risks can be reduced.

C. Making a Report

As directed by your teacher, write a report, or report your findings orally to the class. Comment on the risks to workers versus the benefits of product use.

Unit 7 Wrap-Up

Unit Summary

Each of us has a great impact on the environment through the waste we produce. Participation in effective waste management is a first step in developing a responsible attitude towards the environment.

The tendency towards disposable consumer items in technologically advanced countries is the primary reason for the large increase in solid waste. Packaging increases the cost of a product and accounts for over a third of *municipal solid waste* (*MSW*). Some packaging materials, such as plastics, are not *biodegradable* and persist in the environment.

The four Rs of effective waste management are: *reduce, reuse, recycle,* and *recover*. We can reduce waste by purchasing higher-quality products in appropriate quantities, and by avoiding excessive packaging and *disposables*. Glass bottles, plastic bags and containers, and cardboard boxes can all be reused, while companies with wastes to get rid of and companies needing certain wastes can negotiate an exchange. Recycling and recovery of waste materials is accomplished through *composting, rendering,* and *recycling* items such as paper and junked automobiles. Disposal methods for MSW include *open dumps, sanitary landfills, ocean dumping,* and *incineration*.

Primary industries process raw materials to make materials for use by other industries. These *secondary industries* use the processed material to make consumer products.

Clean water is a vital resource. Pollution by industrial and hazardous waste threatens to reduce our supplies of quality water. Common pollutants include sewage, plant nutrients, organic chemicals, metallic and other inorganic chemical compounds, sediments, and heat. The municipal water treatment plant produces water free from such contaminants.

Sewage treatment plants remove most of the *suspended solids* (SS) and the *biological oxygen demand* (*BOD*) of water, making it fit for discharge into waterways.

Hazardous wastes endanger both human health and the environment. Special disposal techniques are needed to eliminate or reduce the dangers. Treatment of hazardous wastes may be physical, biological, chemical, or thermal. Hazardous wastes are especially problematic because of the amount produced and the scarcity of treatment and disposal sites.

Government agencies set tolerances, or maximum concentrations, for toxic substances in food, air, and water. If these tolerances are exceeded, the food, air, or water is declared unfit for human use.

Key Terms

aerobic decomposition	primary industry
anaerobic decomposition	reactive
biochemical oxygen demand (BOD)	recovery
	recycling
carcinogen	reduction
composting	rendering
disposables	reuse
engineered landfill	sanitary landfill
hazardous waste	secondary industry
incineration	sedimentation
leachate	sludge
municipal solid waste (MSW)	source separation
	tolerance
open dump	toxic substance
part per million (ppm)	waste management

Unit Practice and Review

A: Short Answer

True or False

State whether each statement is true or false. Correct each false statement.

1. Metal cans are made from renewable resources.
2. It is best to clean up oil spills at sea before the oil reaches the coast.

3. Composting is the biodegradation of moist organic matter to a product that can be used as a fertilizer or a soil conditioner.

4. Toxic substances are classified as chronic if they are quick-acting.

5. To produce clear water, municipalities often add slaked lime and alum to the water.

Multiple Choice

In each question below, select the best answer.

1. Which category of household waste is most resistant to decomposition in a sanitary landfill site?
   a) paper   c) metal
   b) plastic   d) food wastes

2. When a waste material is used to replace all or part of a raw material in a manufacturing process, this method of waste management is called:
   a) reduction   c) recycling
   b) reuse   d) recovery

3. Which of the following is not a method of recycling materials?
   a) incineration   c) shredding automobiles
   b) rendering   d) composting

4. The water in municipal sewage is fit to drink:
   a) after primary treatment
   b) after secondary treatment
   c) after tertiary treatment
   d) none of the above

5. The process by which wastes are bound into a solid mass and sealed in a glass-like capsule is called:
   a) biological treatment   c) fixation
   b) thermal treatment   d) landfarming

Complete the Statement

Complete each of the following statements with the correct word or phrase. Do not write in this book.

1. In Ontario, wastes known to be hazardous are ___?___ through placement on a government list of hazardous substances.

2. ___?___ is any physical, chemical, biological, or thermal process that destroys, detoxifies, or neutralizes hazardous wastes, reduces their volume, or modifies them for recovery, storage, or transport.

3. The best storage method for hazardous wastes is a(n) ___?___ landfill site.

4. Consumer products intended to be used once and then thrown away are called ___?___ .

5. ___?___ decomposition occurs in the presence of oxygen, while ___?___ occurs without oxygen.

Matching Items

Match each item in Column A with the appropriate item in Column B.

1. Column A
   i) newspaper
   ii) garage sale or flea market
   iii) waste motor oil
   iv) avoidance of disposable items

   Column B
   a) refill
   b) reduce
   c) reuse
   d) recycle
   e) recover

2. Column A
   i) coastal method of waste disposal
   ii) mass reduced about 75%
   iii) most primitive disposal method
   iv) waste covered daily with earth

   Column B
   a) open dump
   b) sanitary landfill
   c) ocean dumping
   d) incineration
   e) engineered landfill

3. Column A
   i) primary sewage treatment
   ii) secondary sewage treatment
   iii) tertiary sewage treatment

   Column B
   a) removes 90% BOD and SS
   b) most expensive
   c) screen removes debris
   d) water drinkable

4. Column A
   i) poisonous substance
   ii) damages skin and matter
   iii) vaporizes easily
   iv) readily undergoes chemical reaction

   Column B
   a) corrosive
   b) volatile
   c) reactive
   d) toxic
   e) infectious

B: Knowledge and Application

1. a) Define municipal solid waste (MSW) and give examples of some of its components.
    b) Describe four ways in which municipal solid waste can be disposed.

2. Which of the following actions, if widely adopted, would reduce the amount of waste per person? Explain your answers.
    a) using solar-powered calculators instead of ones powered by batteries
    b) purchasing a take-out meal at a restaurant instead of eating at home
    c) using plastic supermarket bags, instead of purchased bags, to line home garbage containers
    d) using both sides of sheets of paper
    e) purchasing sit-down restaurant meals instead of take-out meals.

3. Suggest ways in which your school can reduce its daily waste production. What happens to the school waste? What kind of disposal site is used?

4. List all the waste produced in the preparation of one of your favourite meals at home. Indicate how you might reduce this waste.

5. During a hike, an apple core and a soft drink can are left beside a nature trail. Which of the two discarded items is "worse" for the environment? Explain.

6. List the items you discard today. Which will decompose in the environment? Which will persist?

7. Where would the decomposition of food wastes occur most rapidly: in a compost heap, an open dump, or a sanitary landfill? Explain.

8. In a sanitary landfill site, heavy bulldozers level and compact the waste delivered to the site each day. In the process, sealed plastic garbage bags often break open. Why is this important?

9. Why is recycling an important process? What are the three other "Rs" of waste management, and why is each important?

10. An ice cream cone is an almost perfect container. Comment on this statement.

11. Why is it important to remove organic waste from water before the water is returned to a natural source?

12. In 1972 Canada and the United States signed an agreement to reduce the pollution of the Great Lakes. One of the first actions implemented was the mandatory reduction of the phosphates in detergents. Why was this action important, given the fact that the phosphorus in detergents is a nutrient rather than a toxic substance?

13. a) Briefly describe the treatment that might be necessary to convert river water into water suitable for drinking.
    b) Describe three sources of pollution of natural waterways.
    c) Stretches of polluted waterways are sometimes treated with oxygen. What is the purpose of such treatment?

14. Oil and products made from oil can cause environmental problems. Explain why each of the following pollutes the environment.
    a) the incomplete combustion of gasoline in an automobile engine
    b) discarding plastic bags in fields and along roadsides
    c) discharging detergents into a river
    d) pouring oil down sewers

C: Problem Solving

1. Laws governing municipal refuse collection usually impose controls on the generator of the waste. These controls take the form of rules which each household must follow if city trucks are to pick up household waste. If you were asked by a municipal council to develop a set of "household rules", what controls would you include? Be sure to emphasize public health concerns, resource recovery considerations, and how to minimize collection costs.

2. How does each of the following affect the composition of municipal solid waste?
    a) a garbage grinder
    b) a large number of waste compactors
    c) non-returnable beverage containers
    d) a newspaper strike

3. A power plant uses about 1 150 000 L of river water each minute to cool its generators. The water is then pumped back into the river through a discharge canal. During a hot spell one summer, the water entered the power plant at a temperature of 22 °C and returned to the river at 32 °C. A few days later, thousands of dead fish were found downstream from the plant.
   a) Calculate the heat, in kilojoules, that the power plant added to the river water each minute. How much heat was added in a day?
   b) Use Figure 20-2 to predict which fish were probably killed in the area downstream from the power plant.
   c) Examine Figure 20-1. As the temperature of the river rises, what happens to the level of dissolved oxygen? What is the dissolved oxygen content of the water at 32 °C?
   d) The preferred dissolved oxygen ranges (milligrams per kilogram, or parts per million) for various fish are: 10 ppm and up for perch, bass, herring, and salmon; 7 ppm and up for shad; 2 ppm and up for carp. Which of these fish would be harmed by the dissolved oxygen level near the mouth of the discharge canal? Which type of fish would thrive in this area?

D: Challengers

1. Typically, each human breathes in 15 m³ of air per day. If the average lead content of the air in an urban area is 2.3 $\mu g/m^3$, how much lead would a person inhale each day? (Actually, a person probably would not continually breathe air with this lead content for 24 h, and much of the inhaled lead would be exhaled.)

2. In many sanitary landfill sites, a one-to-four cover ratio is common. In other words, it takes 30 cm of soil to cover 120 cm of compacted wastes. What volume of soil is required to cover a 10 m × 30 m area of compacted wastes?

Project Ideas

1. Aquatic life cannot survive without sufficient oxygen dissolved in the water. Therefore, dissolved oxygen (DO) can be used as an index of water quality. The methylene blue test is a simple procedure used to determine the amount of DO in water. In oxygen-rich water, methylene blue retains its dark blue colour, while in oxygen-poor water, methylene blue becomes light blue or colourless. To a 10 mL sample of water, add 2 mL of methylene blue indicator solution. Record the time required for the colour to change to light blue or clear. Repeat for a variety of water samples and make comparisons. The faster the colour change occurs, the less oxygen is present. There are probably more carbon dioxide and bacteria in oxygen-poor water. Try to explain your results.

2. For a long time, the oceans have been regarded as a bottomless pit into which the world's solid wastes can be dumped. Engineers, scientists, and politicians are divided on the issue: Should ocean dumping be banned? Develop arguments for and against ocean dumping.

Readings

Fawcett, Howard H. *Hazardous and Toxic Materials: Safe Handling and Disposal.* New York: John Wiley & Sons, 1984. (Current scientific information about hazardous and toxic materials.)

Gough, Michael. *Dioxin, Agent Orange: The Facts.* New York: Plenum Publishing, 1986. (A balanced account that reads like a detective novel.)

Ottoboni, Alice M. *The Dose Makes the Poison.* Berkeley, California: Vincente Books, 1984. (An explanation of what makes chemicals harmful.)

Astronomy

Curiosity compels humans to ask questions, to search for answers, and to explore unfamiliar territory. The skies above us contain many intriguing objects: a blazing daytime Sun and at night an ever-changing Moon and thousands of stars. **Astronomy** is the science that studies these and all other objects in the universe beyond the Earth's atmosphere. Most sciences advance by means of experiments that test certain hypotheses. In astronomy, direct experiments are either difficult or impossible, since scientists observe objects at great distances. Consequently, professional astronomers spend much of their time interpreting data received from observatories and space probes.

Because many events in the universe occur without warning, amateur astronomers are often the first to notice them. Each year, many comets are named after amateurs. In 1987, a supernova (exploding star) was discovered by a Canadian, Ian Shelton, who happened to be watching the sky at an opportune moment from an observatory in Chile. Not all of us can make important discoveries, but we can make some remarkable observations for ourselves. This unit will show you how to observe objects that are truly out of this world.

Chapter 21 Observing the Sun, Moon, and Stars

Chapter 22 Exploring the Solar System and Beyond

The Canada-France-Hawaii telescope, the sixth largest reflector in the world, is located atop an extinct volcano on the island of Hawaii.

Chapter 21   Observing the Sun, Moon, and Stars

Professional astronomers build huge telescopes in observatories on high mountain peaks such as this observatory in Hawaii shown in the photograph. The remote location and high elevation (4200 m) situate this telescope well above the clouds and beyond the glow of city lights, so that it has the clearest possible view of the heavens. The telescope's optical (viewing) system allows it to observe stars so far away that their light can take millions of years to reach the Earth.

This installation was sponsored by three countries: Canada, France, and the United States. Telescopes this big are so expensive that only large organizations can afford them, and few amateur astronomers can travel the great distances involved to visit such facilities. However, there is much that the beginning astronomy student can learn from observing the skies right at home. Many of the observations suggested in this chapter can be made with the unaided eye or with a pair of binoculars. As well, many worthwhile observations can be made during daylight hours.

When you finish Chapter 21, you should be able to:

- set up and use a log book for astronomical observations
- observe and describe the surface of the Sun
- construct a simple, temporary sundial
- observe and describe the surface features of the Moon, and explain its phases
- locate specific stars and constellations using a simple star map
- observe and understand the motions of the Earth, Sun, Moon, and stars
- understand the basics of some instruments with which astronomers gather information

21.1 Watching the Sky

Viewing the night sky from within a city would frustrate a professional astronomer. By necessity, cities are well lit at night. As the light from cities floods into the sky, it bounces off particles of dust, smoke, and water vapour, changing the night sky from black to light grey and drowning out the light from faint stars. For beginners this effect offers a great advantage. When only bright objects shine through, it is easier to identify certain stars, to find some planets, and to become familiar with star groupings.

▶ **How to Construct a Log Book for Astronomical Observations**

Astronomical changes generally occur very slowly. To be of value, observations must be precisely recorded so that they can be referred to later. Many astronomical discoveries have been made using previously recorded observations. The following instructions show you how to construct a log book in which to record all the astronomical observations you will make in this unit. Keep the log book separate from your class notes.

Figure 21-1. Sample page from a log book.

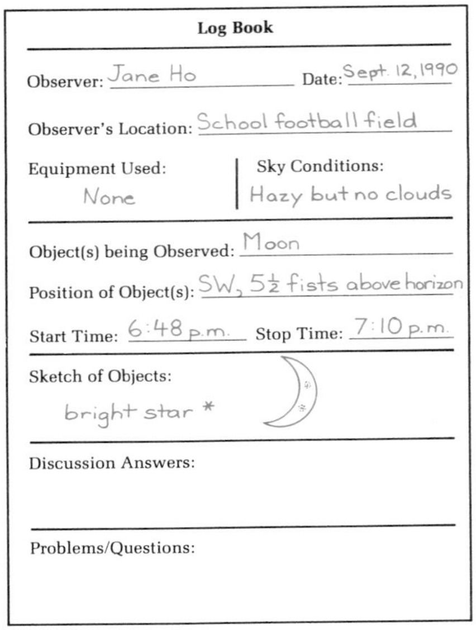

```
                Log Book
_____

Observer: Jane Ho        Date: Sept. 12, 1990

Observer's Location: School football field

Equipment Used:      | Sky Conditions:
    None             |  Hazy but no clouds

Object(s) being Observed: Moon

Position of Object(s): SW, 5½ fists above horizon

Start Time: 6:48 p.m.   Stop Time: 7:10 p.m.

Sketch of Objects:
    bright star *            ☽

Discussion Answers:
_____

Problems/Questions:
```

Figure 21-2. How to measure a celestial object in "fists".

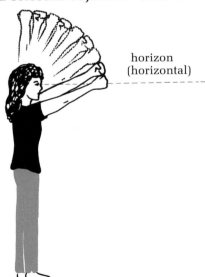

horizon (horizontal)

There are approximately nine "fists" between the horizontal and vertical positions. How many degrees does each "fist" represent?

1. Figure 21-1 shows a sample page from a log book. Obtain several blank copies of this page from your teacher and put them into a suitable binder.

2. Study the entries in Figure 21-1. Note the function of each section of the log. In particular, note how the object's position is described. In the next activity, you will learn a method to determine the position of objects in the sky.

Activity 21-1: Making Observations

In Part A you will practise filling out the log book. In Part B you will make an astronomical observation, and record the observation in your log book.

Materials

log book

(wooden) stake

hammer

2 pencils or other markers

clock or watch

Procedure

Part A: Describing the Positions of Objects at a Distance

1. Your teacher will indicate which direction is north in your classroom. Four objects labelled A, B, C, and D will be placed on the walls and ceiling of the classroom. In your log book, describe the direction of object A according to its compass direction from your desk.

2. Now study Figure 21-2. Determine the height of object A according to its height above the horizon (horizontal), measured in "fists". Describe object A's height in your log book.

3. In your log book, describe the positions of objects B, C, and D. For each, record a) its compass direction, and b) its height above the horizon in "fists".

Part B: Observing the Daytime Sky

4. In a sunny location, hammer a stake into the ground and mark the end of its shadow with a pencil stuck into the ground.

5. Record the start time in your log book.

6. Stand in the shadow of a nearby object so that the Sun is *just* hidden, as shown in Figure 21-3. In your log book, describe the position of the Sun using the method outlined in Part A.

Figure 21-3.

To measure the Sun's height safely, stand in the shadow of a large object, such as your school.

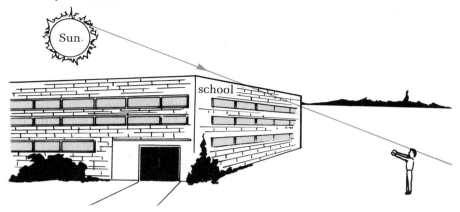

7. After at least 10 min, return to the stake and mark the top of the stake's shadow with another pencil.

8. Record the stop time in your log book.

9. Sketch the two different shadow positions in your log book.

Discussion

1. What can observing shadows in this way tell you about the Sun? Is this direct or indirect evidence? Explain.

2. Write a summary statement that describes the Sun's apparent daily motion through the sky.

3. From your observations, estimate the Sun's position a) when it rose, b) at noon, and c) when it sets.

4. How could the Sun be used to tell the time of day?

Motion in the Sky

Because the Sun is the Earth's closest star, it dominates the daytime sky. Although the Sun's rising and setting points vary from season to season, it always appears to move from east to west. Do other stars that we see at night "move" in the same way? Ancient astronomers and navigators observed that stars did seem to change position, except for one: the North Star. They relied on that star in order to find directions at night. Campers, hikers, and amateur astronomers can still rely on the North Star to indicate the direction of true north.

Earth is dependent on the Sun to warm us, to provide light for our daily activities, and to enable plants to provide food and oxygen.

Activity 21-2: Navigation by Night

In Part A of this activity, you will learn how to find the North Star.
Astronomers call the North Star "Polaris". It is located in a recognizable group of stars called the Little Dipper. Because the stars in
the Little Dipper are dim, a brighter group of stars called the Big
Dipper is used as a guide in locating the North Star. Carry out steps
1 and 2 of the procedure before going outside.

In Part B, you will trace the movements of some stars.

Materials

log book

star map showing Big Dipper and Little Dipper

(optional) flashlight covered with tissue paper to assist recording
    information

clock or watch

tracing paper

Part A: Finding Polaris

Procedure

1. Study the star map shown in Figure 21-4. Note that the line from
   Merak to Dubhe points towards Polaris. Note also that the distance between Dubhe and Polaris is about 5 times the distance
   between Merak and Dubhe. This represents a separation of about
   3 fists.

Figure 21-4. The Big Dipper
and Little Dipper.

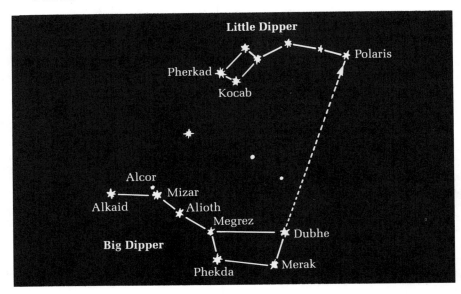

2. Turn the chart around and study it from several perspectives so that you can recognize both constellations from any orientation.

3. On a clear night, choose a viewing spot as free as possible from obstacles such as trees or buildings. Record the date, location, equipment, etc., in your log book. Then record the start time.

4. Scan the northern sky for the Big Dipper. In your log book, record its position by determining its direction and its height in fists above the horizon. Record also its length measured in fists.

5. Follow the line from Merak to Dubhe until you come to Polaris. Record the position of Polaris.

6. Find the other stars in the Little Dipper if possible, and sketch their positions as well.

7. In your log book, sketch the appearance of the two star groups and indicate the horizon line. Rank the stars in each group according to their brightness. Record the stop time.

8. (Optional) Once a month for several months, repeat your observations from the same location.

An ancient eyesight test involved trying to see a particular star, Alcor, located very close to the star Mizar at the bend in the handle of the Big Dipper. You can still test your eyesight by searching for this star.

Discussion

1. Which is the brightest star in a) the Big Dipper, and b) the Little Dipper?

2. How does the brightness of Polaris compare with the brightness of other stars in a) the Little Dipper, and b) the Big Dipper?

3. Must a navigator be able to see the Little Dipper in order to locate Polaris? Explain.

Part B: Observing Star Motions

Procedure

1. Study the three photographs on the next page. In each photograph, identify the Big Dipper, Polaris, and the reference object.

2. Place tracing paper on the first diagram and trace the positions of the Big Dipper, Polaris, and the reference object.

3. Place the tracing paper on the second picture so that the reference object overlaps, and sketch the new positions of the stars.

4. Repeat step 3 for the third picture.

5. Remove the tracing paper. Use arrows to show the paths travelled by the stars through the sky.

Figure 21-5.

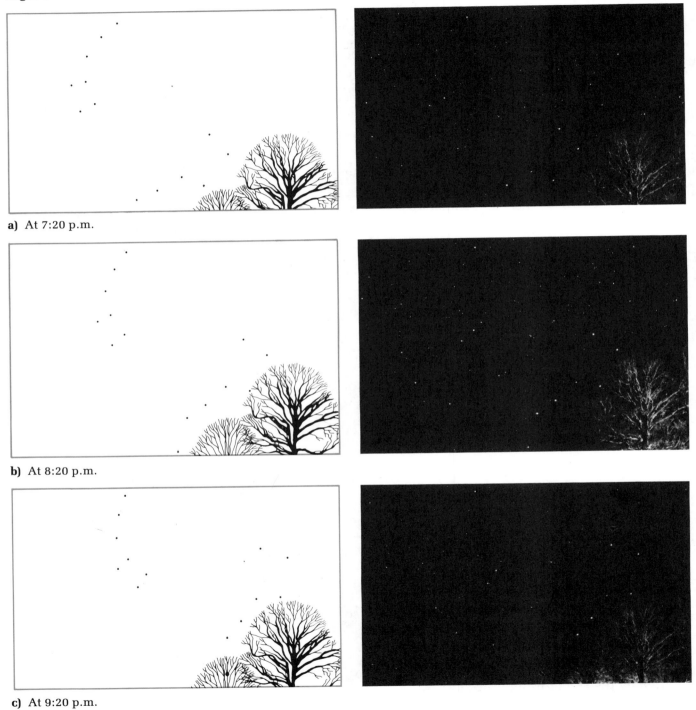

a) At 7:20 p.m.

b) At 8:20 p.m.

c) At 9:20 p.m.

Discussion

1. Did all the stars in the Big Dipper move? Did they all move
   a) the same distance, and b) in the same direction? Did Polaris move?

2. a) Judging by how far the stars moved in 2 h, how far do you think they would move in 24 h? State your reasons.
   b) How far does the Sun move in 24 h?
   c) What connection do you think exists between a) and b)? Explain.

3. Using the pictures on the opposite page, predict when you could observe the Big Dipper and the Little Dipper.

Navigation by the Sun and Stars

While the Sun appears to circle the Earth, the stars appear to circle Polaris. Some early observers suspected that these motions might be caused by the Earth rotating, but these observers had to rely on indirect evidence.

Do You Know?
True north, as determined by using the Sun or Polaris, may differ significantly from magnetic north, as determined with a compass. The Earth's north magnetic pole is not located at the geographical, or true, North Pole. Navigators using a compass require tables showing how much magnetic north differs from true north for every location on the surface of the Earth. Navigators using the Sun or Polaris, however, can locate true north directly without having to use tables.

A time-exposure photograph of Polaris. The Earth's rotation causes the stars to appear to move, leaving trails on the photograph.

Every 24 h we experience day and night as the Earth's **rotation** turns us first towards, and then away from, the Sun. This motion makes the Sun appear to move through the sky. At night the Earth's rotation makes the stars appear to move about Polaris in a circle, while Polaris itself appears stationary. Figure 21-6 illustrates why. The Earth rotates about its **axis**, an imaginary line drawn between the South Pole and the North Pole. This axis happens to point towards Polaris (which is also called the "pole star"). Therefore, in the northern hemisphere Polaris appears as the only fixed point in the sky; hence its usefulness to early sailors.

Figure 21-6. Relative orientations of the Sun, the Earth, and Polaris.

A spinning top tilted to one side will move about a circle as it spins. The Earth behaves in the same way since it is tilted 23.5° to its orbital path around the Sun. In the case of the Earth, this circular motion takes about 25 800 years to complete one cycle. During this time the star directly over the north pole will change. Currently, Polaris is about 1° from being directly over the North Pole. In 2800 B.C., Thuban was the pole star.

CHALLENGER

For any observer who can see it, Polaris indicates the north direction. The altitude of Polaris above the horizon can also determine the observer's latitude. When Polaris appears 42° above the horizon, determine the latitude at which the observation was made.

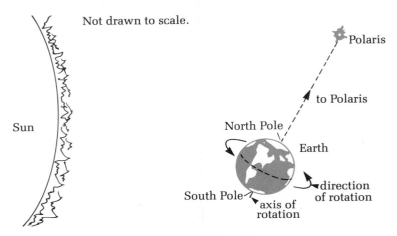

Not drawn to scale.

Study Questions

1. Define the following terms: astronomy, the North Star, rotation (of the Earth).

2. How does an astronomer's method of gathering information differ from that of other scientists?

3. What is the essential difference between observing the sky from within a city and observing it from a viewing point in the country?

4. Describe how to find the North Star.

5. a) State two reasons why it is important to keep a log book of astronomical observations.
   b) What information must be gathered in order to locate the position of an object in the sky?

6. a) Describe the *apparent* motion of the Sun as seen from the Earth.
   b) What is the actual motion?

THE FOUCAULT PENDULUM

Does the Earth remain still while the Sun circles it, or does the Earth itself rotate? Early astronomers argued this point for centuries, but they could not travel into space to make direct observations. The argument was finally resolved through indirect evidence obtained by the French physicist Jean Foucault in 1851. Using only a swinging pendulum, he established indirectly that the Earth does indeed rotate.

Once any pendulum is set in motion, it will continue to swing back and forth along the same plane, or path, as long as there are no air currents. Foucault asked some other scientists to consider the hypothetical case of a pendulum set up at the North Pole. If the Earth does *not* rotate, Foucault argued, an observer floating above the North Pole would see no change in either the pendulum's swing or the pattern of the Earth's features underneath the pendulum. To an Earthbound observer, the pendulum's swing would also appear unchanged.

On the other hand, if the Earth does rotate, an observer floating above the North Pole would see the pendulum continue to swing in the same plane while the Earth's features circled beneath it. An Earthbound observer, however, would not be aware of this latter motion. To an observer

Jean Foucault uses his swinging pendulum to provide indirect evidence that the Earth rotates.

on Earth, it would appear that the pendulum's plane of swing was changing.

Foucault carried out his experiment in Paris, not at the North Pole, but he obtained similar results. He suspended a 28 kg cannonball from the end of a wire 61 m long. The cannonball was pulled aside with a cord, which was burned to release the ball and let it swing. With every swing, a pointer on the bottom of the cannonball made a mark in a ring of sand on the floor. After several hours, the marks in the sand showed clearly that the pendulum was no longer swinging in the same direction relative to the Earth as when it started. Foucault and the other

observers concluded, therefore, that the Earth must rotate.

A Foucault pendulum at the Ontario Science Centre.

21.2 Observing the Sun

The ancient Greeks thought that the Sun was a ball of burning gas. Now we know that the Sun's "burning" is actually a nuclear reaction. The gases involved in this reaction are hydrogen (70% of the Sun's mass) and helium (20% of the Sun's mass). The nuclear reaction within the Sun is similar to that in the hydrogen bomb. At very high temperatures and pressures, atoms of hydrogen fuse, or stick together, producing helium atoms. This process releases tremendous amounts of energy, some in the form of visible light, the rest in other forms of radiation.

Figure 21-7. The electromagnetic spectrum.

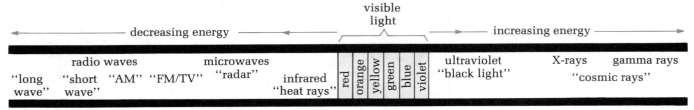

Visible light is only one of many kinds of radiation given off by the Sun.

Figure 21-8. Layers of the Sun.

Unlike the other layers, the Sun's corona has no definite outer boundary.

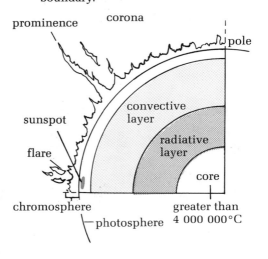

The Sun's Structure

The nuclear reaction occurs in the Sun's core, where temperatures reach over 4 000 000°C (see Figure 21-8). The energy produced in the core is transferred outward until it reaches the first visible layer of the Sun's atmosphere. This layer, called the **photosphere**, produces the sunlight that we see on Earth. The next layer, the **chromosphere**, gets its faint pinkish colour from the light produced by hydrogen gas. The Sun's outermost layer, called the **corona**, has no definite boundary. The corona is made up of charged particles — electrons and protons — released from inside the Sun. As this stream of particles moves outward into the solar system, it forms what is known as the **solar wind**. Particles of the solar wind have been detected passing the Earth at speeds of 400 to 700 km/s.

Physical Features of the Sun

Physical features found on Earth include oceans, mountains, and ice caps. The Sun has physical features too, but we cannot observe these features directly.

1. Sunspots

The photosphere is marked from time to time with darker areas called **sunspots**. These spots occur in pairs or groups of pairs which may last from a few hours to several months. Their apparent motion across the disc of the Sun indicates that the photosphere rotates faster at the Sun's equator than at its poles. Current theories suggest that sunspots result from distortions in the Sun's magnetic field caused by this difference in rotational speed. Centuries of observation have revealed that the number of spots increases regularly to a maximum every 11 years.

Figure 21-9. Sunspot cycles.

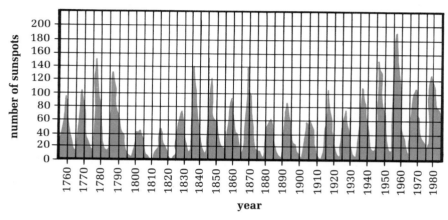

Sunspots.

Increases in solar activity can release energy and particles into space, disrupting shortwave communications, telephone circuits, power stations, and all airlines that fly over the North Pole between Europe and North America.

2. Flares

As a sunspot group ages, nearby magnetic distortions may suddenly produce a violent outburst called a **flare**. Flares release energy in the forms of visible light and high-speed particles that join the solar wind. As these particles approach the Earth, our magnetic field pulls them towards the poles. Interactions between the particles and the Earth's atmosphere produce a brilliant display of coloured light called an **aurora**. In our hemisphere this display is called the aurora borealis, or northern lights. These interactions also disturb the Earth's magnetic field, and thus interfere with radio communication.

3. Prominences

Spectacular eruptions of gases into the Sun's corona are called **prominences**. Some prominences erupt straight up and fall back along the same path. Others form loops that arc high above the Sun's surface. At present, astronomers do not know what causes these eruptions, but research continues.

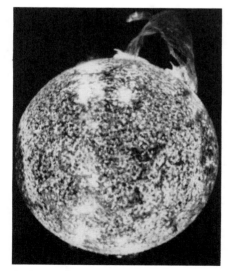

A giant solar prominence.

Activity 21-3: Projecting an Image of the Sun

In this activity you will indirectly observe the Sun's physical features by using binoculars to project light from the Sun to form an image that is safe to look at. If binoculars and a tripod are not available, your teacher can suggest other safe ways to form an image of the Sun.

Materials

binoculars

camera tripod

mounting bracket (or masking tape)

screen (e.g., a sheet of paper clipped to a piece of cardboard)

camera tripod

Bristol board (0.25 sheet)

scissors

log book

clock or watch

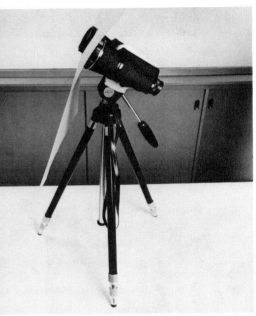

Binoculars can be used to safely project an image of the Sun.

Procedure

1. Mount the binoculars on the tripod. (If no mounting bracket is available, fasten with masking tape.)
2. To see the image produced by this method, you must shade the screen from the direct rays of the Sun. Cut an opening in the Bristol board to fit over the larger end of the binoculars.
3. Record the start time in your log book.
4. Without looking directly at the Sun, aim the binoculars at the Sun, and place the screen below the eyepiece of the binoculars.
5. Getting a satisfactory image on the screen will require repeated adjustments. Alternate between changing the focus of the binoculars and changing the position of the screen until you have the clearest possible image.
6. In your log book, sketch or trace the image seen on the screen, trying to place all surface features accurately. Record the stop time.
7. Identify and label any physical features that you recorded in your sketch or tracing.

Discussion

1. Why did you mount the binoculars on a tripod?
2. How is the Sun's image affected by:
   a) moving the screen closer to the binoculars?
   b) moving the screen farther away?

3. a) The Sun's physical features are sometimes called surface features. Why?
   b) Which of the Sun's surface features could you observe?
4. a) How could the surface features of the Sun be used to prove that the Sun rotates?
   b) How could you determine the time it takes for the Sun to rotate once?
5. a) What happened to the position of the Sun's image after a few minutes? Explain.
   b) How could you compensate for this?

Solar Time

Even the earliest civilizations used the Sun's regular motions to mark the passage of time. The time when the Sun reaches its highest point in the sky is called **noon**. The amount of time from noon on one day to noon on the following day is referred to as one **solar day**. Each solar day is divided into 24 equal hours. The sundial is an ancient time-keeping device that uses a shadow to mark off daylight hours. The modern sundial shown in the photograph has a numbered dial inscribed on a flat base. An angled upper piece called the **gnomon** casts the shadow.

Do You Know?
Canada has become a world leader in time-keeping technology. Four cesium-based atomic clocks are located at Ottawa's National Research Council. Two identical clocks are kept in Germany, and all six are linked by satellite to the international time bureau in Paris, which monitors any differences among them. Within a few years the "exact" time will be available by phone from the NRC.

This garden-type sundial is only one of many possible designs that use the Sun to indicate the time of day.

Activity 21-4: Making a Sundial

In this activity you will build, install, and calibrate a temporary sundial that can be used to determine local Sun time.

Materials

Bristol board
ruler
scissors
marking pen
atlas or local topographical map

protractor
glue
chalk
clock or watch

Procedure

Part A: Building the Sundial

1. Cut a square of Bristol board, 30 cm by 30 cm. Label this piece the "base".
2. Cut a second piece of Bristol board, 20 cm by 35 cm. Label this piece the "gnomon".
3. As shown in Figure 21-10, mark off a 3 cm wide strip along the 20 cm side of the gnomon. Label this strip the "glue strip".
4. Using an atlas or a local topographical map, obtain the latitude of your location. With the protractor, mark this angle on the gnomon.
5. Cut the Bristol board along the cut line.
6. Fold the glue strip perpendicular to the gnomon and glue onto the middle of the base, as shown in Figure 21-11.

Your teacher can give you suggestions for making a permanent garden sundial.

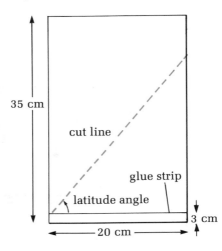

Figure 21-10. The gnomon.

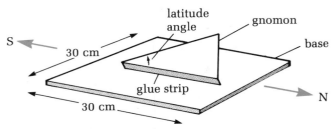

Figure 21-11. The finished sundial.

Part B: Installing the Sundial

7. Choose a location that is not shaded by buildings or trees.
8. Place the sundial on level ground with the high end of the gnomon pointing towards true north. (Your teacher will indicate the true north direction.) Mark where the sundial is placed with a piece of chalk.

Part C: Calibrating the Sundial

9. This step must be carried out when the Sun has reached its highest point in the sky. You will be able to tell when this happens because the gnomon will cast the shortest thin-line shadow pointing towards true north. Mark a line on the base of the sundial to correspond with this shadow. Label the line "12".

10. At the same instant, read and record the time shown on your watch. (*Note:* The time on your watch may be up to 30 min away from 12 noon.)

11. Exactly 60 min later, mark a line on the sundial's base to correspond with the shadow of the gnomon's sloping side. Label the line "1".

12. Continue to mark off the afternoon hours at 60 min intervals.

13. Plan a schedule for marking the next day's morning hours, and verify it with your teacher. Follow this schedule the next morning to complete the calibration. (*Note:* The sundial must be placed in the identical position to that of the previous day.)

14. Over the next week, use your sundial as a timepiece whenever possible, comparing it with your watch.

Discussion

1. Describe two different ways you could use to determine true north for the placing of your sundial.

2. To mark off the morning hours, why is it necessary to have the sundial in the identical position to the previous day?

3. a) What advantages of the sundial made it a popular timepiece for hundreds of years?
   b) What disadvantages of the sundial led inventors to design other kinds of time-keeping devices?

Study Questions

1. Name six features of the Sun, and define them.

2. Describe how the Sun can be used to indicate the time of day.

3. a) What evidence exists to show that the Earth rotates?
   b) What observable event is caused by the Earth's rotation?

4. Explain how the aurora borealis is caused.

CHALLENGER

In the thermonuclear process, the Sun converts mass into energy at a rate calculated by Einstein's equation $E = mc^2$. At the current rate, the Sun is converting about four thousand million kilograms of material per second into light! What percentage of the Sun's total mass would be converted in one day? How long would it take to "use up" the Sun in this way, if there were enough hydrogen?

SEASONAL CALENDARS

The Earth's motion around the Sun is called a **revolution**. One revolution of the Earth is called **one year**, or one Earth year. Various civilizations have divided the year into smaller parts, some based on seasons, some based on months corresponding to the cycles of the Moon. All such plans for subdividing the year are called **calendars**.

During the year, many parts of the Earth experience different **seasons**. The reason that seasons occur is because the Earth's axis is not perpendicular to the Sun's direction but, rather, pointed towards Polaris. As the Earth revolves around the Sun, the angle of the Sun's rays hitting the Earth's surface changes. In Bracebridge, Ontario, for example, the angle of the noon sun above the horizon varies from 68.5° in June to only 21.5° in December. These differences in the angles of the Sun's rays cause the regular changes in average temperature known as the seasons.

Figure 21-12 shows a detailed view of seasonal change in the northern hemisphere. When the Earth is in its **summer solstice** position on June 21, the North Pole leans towards the Sun. The Sun's rays shine from a high angle, therefore, and light up more than half of the northern

Figure 21-12. The Earth's orbit around the Sun.

a) Side view.

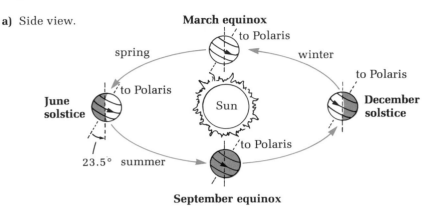

b) Top view.

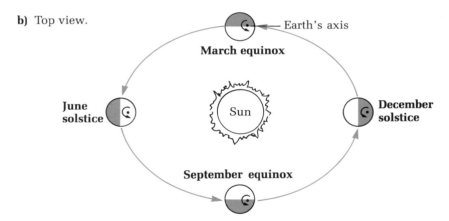

hemisphere at one time. Temperatures are moderate, days are long, and nights are short. By December 22, the Earth has moved to the other side of the Sun. The North Pole now leans away from the Sun. Rays of sunlight shine from a low angle and light up less than half of the northern hemisphere. This is the **winter solstice**. The Sun is low, temperatures are low, days are short, and nights are long. In the

southern hemisphere, the seasons are reversed.

Twice a year, around March 22 and September 23, the Earth moves to a point called the **equinox**. At this time the Sun's rays shine on exactly half of the northern hemisphere. In both cases, hours of daylight and darkness are equal, and temperatures in spring and autumn lie between those of summer and winter.

21.3 Observing the Moon

As the Earth's closest neighbour, the Moon has figured in myths and legends for thousands of years. Throughout the past few centuries, many early scientists turned their attention to learning about the Moon's surface and its phases. They found that the best place to see detail on the lunar surface is along the **terminator:** the line separating the Moon's night from its day. There, objects extending above the Moon's surface are brightly lit on one side, while depressions are hidden in darkness. Always, however, the observations of early scientists were limited by the Moon's great distance from Earth. Table 21-1 shows that much was learned by indirect methods, but eventually the desire for direct evidence led to an active program of Moon exploration.

Table 21-1:   Facts About the Moon

Period of rotation	27.3 Earth days
Length of one Moon day	2 Earth weeks
Length of one Moon night	2 Earth weeks
Surface temperature (daytime high)	100°C
Surface temperature (nighttime low)	−170°C
Lunar mass	$\frac{1}{81}$ of Earth's mass
Lunar diameter	$\frac{1}{4}$ of Earth's diameter
Atmosphere	none
Colour of daytime sky	black

Exploring the Moon's Surface Features

Over two dozen spacecraft have visited the Moon, and a dozen astronaut-scientists have walked on its surface. Their research has produced a wealth of detailed Moon photos and other data that could not have been obtained from observations from the Earth. Photographs taken on the Moon show a surface covered with a fine, compacted dust that makes the surface appear grey and lifeless. Scattered about are rocks ranging in size from several centimetres to several tens of metres in diameter. Craters are the most prominent lunar feature. Most craters are surrounded by ridges or mountains, while some have rays of material radiating outwards. The large, flat areas on the Moon are called **maria**, the Latin name for seas. The Moon also has highland areas, which are older and rougher than the maria.

Do You Know?
Both the United States and the Soviet Union have been active in Moon exploration. The Moon's first visitor from Earth was Luna 2, an unpiloted Soviet spacecraft which crash-landed in 1959. Luna 3 sent back the first photographs of the Moon's dark side in 1959. The first human visitors arrived in 1968 aboard the Eagle, an American spacecraft. Since then, vehicles have been driven on the Moon's surface, and samples of lunar material have been returned to the Earth for study. Although there have been no piloted lunar missions since 1972, equipment was left behind to collect data and to carry out remote-controlled experiments.

Flat areas on the surface of the Moon look darker and are called seas, or maria.

The experiments carried out by Apollo astronauts remained behind on the lunar surface.

Based on information and samples obtained from lunar missions, scientists have established that most of the craters were formed by the impacts of chunks of material during the early formation of the solar system. These impacts also formed the Moon's mountains and rays. Volcanic activity brought lava to the Moon's surface, where it filled some craters and "flooded" large areas, thus forming the maria.

Phases of the Moon

No other object in the sky changes as dramatically as the Moon does. Sometimes it rises at sunset and shines throughout the night. At other times, it sets with the Sun. It changes from a thin crescent to a completely illuminated disc, then back to a crescent, before completely disappearing from view. These changes, called the Moon's **phases**, are shown in the photos. Some phases of the Moon occur during daylight hours, while other phases can only be viewed at night. Ancient civilizations observed that the Moon's phases followed a regularly repeated pattern.

The appearance of the Moon changes over the course of a month.
a) The new moon can produce a solar eclipse. c) The first quarter.
e) Almost full moon. g) Just past the last quarter. i) The last crescent.

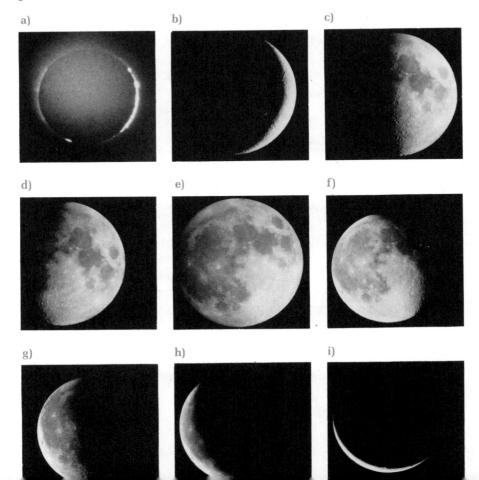

Activity 21-5: Phases and Features of the Moon

In this activity you will observe the Moon at various times of the day and night over a period of one month. You will keep a record of the Moon's phases and observe various surface features. If poor weather forces you to miss a set of observations, you may make them when the weather improves, or during the same period the next month.

Materials

log book

binoculars (optional)

map of Moon

Procedure

1. Obtain the dates of the phases of the Moon from your teacher. Record the dates and all your observations of the Moon in your log book.

2. Two or three days before the date of the first quarter, look for the Moon about noon, to the east of the Sun (6 to 9 fists). Avoid looking directly at the Sun. Repeat each day until you see the Moon. Carefully record its position and sketch its appearance in your log book.

3. The next day, observe from the same location, about one hour later. Record the position of the Moon and sketch its appearance.

4. In your log book, sketch the major visible features on the Moon's surface either on or near the first-quarter phase. Label these features.

5. Keep watching for the Moon each clear day. Record the time and the Moon's position each day.

6. **Make a Hypothesis:** From the data you have gathered so far, predict the rising time of the full Moon. Test your prediction two ways: by observation and by consulting astronomical tables.

7. On or near the appearance of the full Moon, record its position and sketch the major surface features. Use the map shown in Figure 21-13 to label the features.

8. Determine the Moon's rising times for several days after the full phase, including the rising time of the last quarter.

Figure 21-13. A map of the Moon.

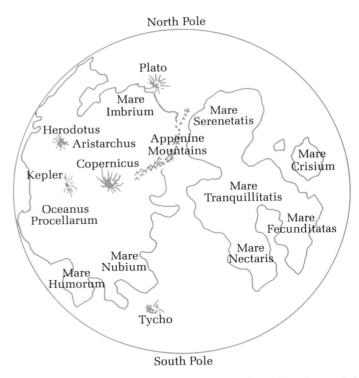

North Pole

Plato

Mare Imbrium

Mare Serenetatis

Herodotus

Aristarchus

Appenine Mountains

Copernicus

Mare Crisium

Kepler

Mare Tranquillitatis

Oceanus Procellarum

Mare Fecunditatas

Mare Nectaris

Mare Nubium

Mare Humorum

Tycho

South Pole

9. Sketch the Moon's appearance on or before the date of the last quarter.

10. Several days after the last quarter, look for the Moon in the western sky early in the morning. Record the time and the Moon's position.

11. Continue to observe the Moon until the phases begin to repeat. Record all your observations in your log book.

Discussion

1. During which phase would you expect to see the Moon:
   a) in the mid-afternoon?
   b) rising as the Sun sets?
   c) rising about 11 p.m. (23:00)?
   d) setting at 10 a.m. (10:00)?

2. a) State the map names of the Moon's surface features that you observed.
   b) Classify each of the features you named in a) according to type: crater, mountain range, or maria.

3. Which phase(s) provided the best opportunity to see the Moon's surface detail? Explain.

4. Calculate the average number of days between phases of the Moon (i.e., between the new Moon and the first quarter, the first quarter and the full Moon, etc.).

5. Approximately how many days does it take for the phases to repeat (e.g., from one full Moon to the next)?

6. a) Compare the rising times of the Moon on successive days.
   b) If the Moon sets at 8:30 p.m. on one day, estimate the setting time on the next day.

7. Design a chart to summarize your observations in this activity. How does such a chart help to clarify data?

Explaining the Moon's Phases

The Moon is visible because it reflects sunlight, but only half of the Moon's surface can be illuminated at any one time. Since the relative positions of the Earth, the Moon, and the Sun change over the period of one month, the amount of the Moon's surface that can be seen from the Earth varies. Figure 21-14 shows how the Moon will appear from Earth during each of the Moon's positions.

Figure 21-14. Various positions of the Moon relative to the Earth and the Sun.

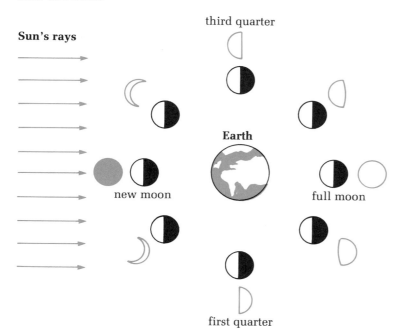

This view from above the North Pole shows the relative positions of the Earth, the Moon, and the Sun during the lunar phases. The outer circle of figures shows what an observer on Earth would see for each of the positions.

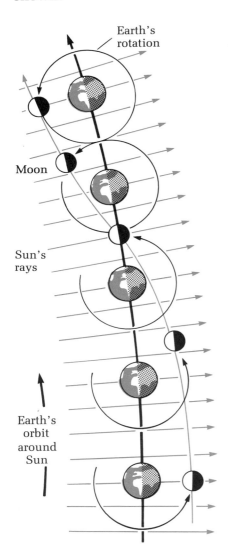

Motions of the Moon

The Moon appears to rise in the east and set in the west. Just as in the case of the Sun, this apparent motion of the Moon is caused by the rotation of the Earth. Each day, as the Moon moves further east, the Earth must rotate slightly longer before the Moon appears over the horizon. This causes the Moon to rise, on average, about 50 min later each day. Thus, the Moon takes about 29.5 d to repeat its phases.

The plane of the Moon's orbit varies, so that the new moon sometimes comes directly between the Sun and the Earth. If part of the Earth enters the Moon's shadow, the light of the Sun will be blocked for several minutes. The result is a **solar eclipse**.

If the full moon enters the Earth's shadow, a **lunar eclipse** results. Lunar eclipses last several hours as the Moon slowly enters and leaves the Earth's shadow.

Figure 21-16. Compare the positions of the Earth, the Moon, and the Sun in a solar eclipse and a lunar eclipse.

a) A solar eclipse.   **b)** A lunar eclipse.

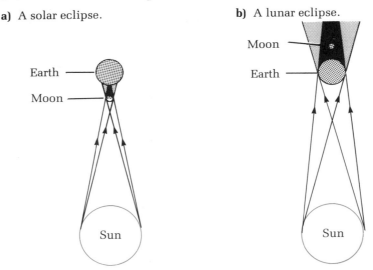

The regular cycle of the Moon's phases provided ancient societies with a natural time unit between the day and the year. Problems arose, however, in establishing a yearly calendar based on the four seasons and on lunar months, since there are approximately 12.5 lunar cycles in one year. Adjustments to the number of days in a given month were adopted to solve the problem. Another lunar time unit, the number of days between phases, is thought to have been the basis for the week.

Study Questions

1. Why is the terminator important when observing features on the surface of the Moon?

2. a) Name three types of surface features of the Moon.
   b) Describe how each type appears to an observer on the Moon's surface.

3. a) Name, in order, the phases of the Moon.
   b) What motions cause the phases of the Moon?

4. Which object causes the shadow in a) a lunar eclipse and b) a solar eclipse?

21.4 Constellations

Constellations are groups of stars that form recognizable patterns in the night sky. The pattern of stars making up a constellation remains the same, night after night. Ursa Major is the best known of all constellations seen from the northern hemisphere, where it is always above the horizon.

Each civilization has named the constellations after important people or objects. Our modern naming system originates from Greek and Roman mythology. For example, Ursa Major means Greater Bear, while Ursa Minor means Lesser Bear. The Big Dipper in Ursa Major has been known by a variety of names, such as the Wagon and the Drinking Gourd. In our culture, the number and the names of the constellations have been fixed by the International Astronomical Union (I.A.U.).

Astronomers have drawn maps of the sky which indicate the relative positions of the stars as seen from the Earth. These maps, or **star charts**, have been drawn as if all stars were the same distance away, embedded in a huge sphere surrounding the Earth. Astronomers locate the position of each star on this sphere by a grid system similar to latitude and longitude. However, we shall use stars of known constellations to "point" to new ones.

Stars such as Merak and Polaris have been given proper names, but this is not true for all stars. In each constellation, however, the stars are generally ranked in order of brightness using letters from the Greek alphabet. Using this system, the brightest star in Ursa Major is called α Ursae Majoris, the second brightest star is β Ursae Majoris, and so on.

The Moon shows phases partly because of its movement between the Sun and the Earth. What other objects seen from the Earth would show phases? What phases would we probably see, and how would they be produced?

Seventeenth-century astronomers.

When the stars of a constellation are ranked using Greek letters, the genitive case of the name is used. Thus, Dubhe in Ursa Major is known as α Ursae Majoris.

The first ten letters of the Greek alphabet are:

α alpha	ζ zeta
β beta	η eta
γ gamma	θ theta
δ delta	ι iota
ϵ epsilon	κ kappa

As the Earth revolves around the Sun in the course of a year, its night side faces toward different parts of space from season to season. As a result, the stars seen in winter are different from those seen in summer. Similarly, the view in the southern hemisphere differs from that in the northern hemisphere. Astronomers have made up star charts for both hemispheres and for every month of the year. Simplified star charts are shown on pages 686 to 687. More detailed star charts can be obtained from reference books in most libraries.

Table 21-2:   Some Constellations in the Northern Hemisphere

Constellation	English Name or Description	Constellation	English Name or Description
Andromeda	Princess of Ethiopia	Gemini	Twins
Aquila	Eagle	Hercules	Hercules, son of Zeus
Aries	Ram	Hydra	Sea serpent
Auriga	Charioteer	Leo	Lion
Bootes	Herdsman	Libra	Balance
Cancer	Crab	Lynx	Lynx
Canis Major	Big dog	Ophiuchus	Holder of serpent
Capricornus	Sea goat	Orion	Orion, the hunter
Cassiopeia	Queen of Ethiopia	Pegasus	Pegasus, the winged horse
Cepheus	King of Ethiopia	Pisces	Fishes
Cetus	Sea monster (whale)	Sagittarius	Archer
Coma Berenices	Berenice's hair	Scorpius	Scorpion
Corona	Crown	Serpens	Serpent
Corvus	Crow	Taurus	Bull
Cygnus	Swan	Ursa Minor	Little bear
Delphinus	Porpoise	Ursa Major	Big bear
Draco	Dragon	Virgo	Maiden
Eridanus	River		

Activity 21-6:   Observing Stars and Constellations

In this activity you will use pointer stars in constellations you already know to find other stars and constellations. The two constellations most commonly used for this purpose are Ursa Major and Cassiopeia. Record all observations in your log book.

Materials

blank star charts

log book

(optional) flashlight covered with tissue paper to aid vision

Procedure

1. Read the entire Procedure. As you read, study the star charts on pages 686 to 687, so that you can locate each star or constellation.

2. Follow the instructions outlined in steps 3 to 12 to find each star or constellation outdoors. Sketch them on a blank star chart.

3. Locate the Big Dipper and Little Dipper (see Activity 21-2).

4. *Cassiopeia* (a W or M shape). Using a line from γ Ursae Majoris to Polaris as a pointer, continue for a distance of about 3 or 4 fists to locate the β Cassiopeiae. Record the position of the constellation and sketch its bright stars in your log book.

5. *Cygnus* (also known as the Northern or Summer Cross). Using δ Cassiopeiae and β Cassiopeiae as pointer stars, continue for about 3 or 4 fists until you come to the cross shape. Deneb, or α Cygni, is a blue-white star at the top of the cross. Locate the rest of the stars making up the cross shape. Record the positions and make a sketch of the bright stars in your log book.

6. *Lyra.* There are no convenient pointer stars indicating this constellation. It lies next to Cygnus on the side opposite Cassiopeia. The bright, blue-white star, Vega (α Lyrae), is easily found about 2 or 3 fists from Deneb. The constellation is composed of two parts: a) a triangle with Vega as a vertex, and b) a parallelogram with one corner also forming a vertex of the triangle. Locate the stars in Lyra. Record the position of the constellation and sketch it in your log book.

7. *Aquila.* The constellation Aquila does not have an easily recognized shape. Using Vega and γ Lyrae as pointer stars, continue for about 4 fists until you come to a white star named Altair. Record the position of Altair in your log book.

8. *Bootes* (a kite shape). Use the curve from δ Ursae Majoris to η Ursae Majoris as a pointer. Follow this curve to a bright orange-red star named Arcturus. Find the rest of the stars that make up Bootes. Record their positions and sketch.

9. *Pegasus* (a large box shape, about 1.5 fists square). Use γ Cassiopeiae and α Cassiopeiae as pointers. Move about 4 fists towards the southern horizon; this is the middle of the "great square" in Pegasus. Locate the four stars that make up the constellation. Record their positions and sketch.

10. *Orion* (an hourglass shape). Use γ Cassiopeiae and δ Cassiopeiae as pointers (these two stars are about 8 fists from Orion).

Figure 21-17. The night sky in October (49° latitude).

To obtain greater detail or to view star charts for other months, check with a reference book in the library. The constellations will exhibit a monthly shift, generally towards the west.

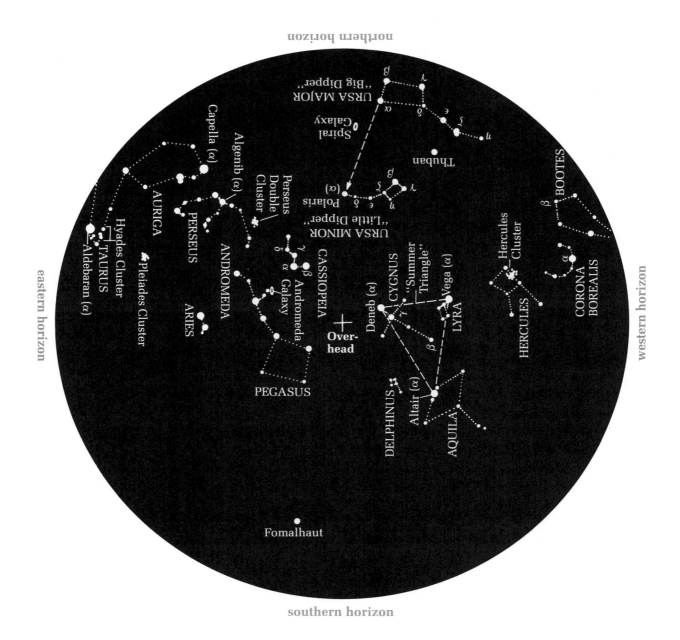

Figure 21-18. The night sky in April (49° latitude).

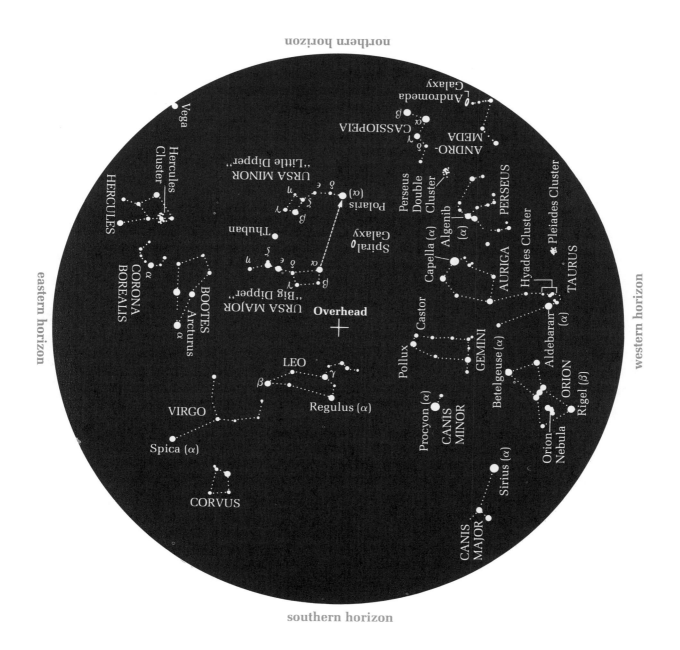

Move across the sky towards the south until you come to Betel-geuse (α Orionis) at the upper-left corner of the constellation. In the middle, locate the three bright stars that make up Orion's belt. At the lower-right corner is the blue-white star Rigel (β Orionis). Record Orion's position and sketch.

11. *Sirius* (the brightest star in the sky). Use the three belt stars in Orion as pointers to locate Sirius (α Canis Majoris) in the south. Record its position in your log book.

12. *Leo* (a right-angled triangle and a reversed question mark). There are no convenient pointer stars to this constellation. It lies below the Big Dipper. Follow the line from α Ursae Majoris to β Ursae Majoris about 4 fists. Look for a blue-white star called Regulus (α Leonis). Locate the other major stars in Leo, record its position, and sketch it in your log book.

13. To become familiar with the stars and constellations, repeat this activity over several different nights. Each time you go out, review how to find the stars and constellations that you found on previous occasions. Check with your teacher, as some of the stars or constellations may not be visible at all times throughout the school year.

Discussion

1. Which of the constellations listed above were you unable to view?

2. Which of these constellations do you think you might have been able to see:
   a) at another time of night? (State the best viewing time.)
   b) at another time of year? (State the best viewing months.)
   c) from a location with less light pollution? (State the best location nearby.)

3. List any difficulties you encountered in viewing constellations, other than those indicated in question 2.

Star Motions and Distances

Star maps assume that all stars lie at the same distance from Earth. However, the stars in a particular constellation may look close together only because of the direction from which we view them. For example, Ursa Major has the easily recognized pattern of seven stars that make up the Big Dipper. Figure 21-19 shows that these stars actually lie at different distances from the Earth. It is only our viewing point from the Earth that gives these stars a familiar pattern. If our Sun were located in a different part of the galaxy, we would see a different pattern of stars.

Each night, the stars appear to move together, maintaining the same distance from each other. If we could speed up star motion over thousands of years, we would see that stars do move with respect to each other. Each of the stars in the Big Dipper has its own particular motion. One hundred thousand years ago, the pattern as seen from the Earth would have looked different from that seen today (see Figure 21-20). One hundred thousand years from now, the pattern will have changed again.

Figure 21-19. The stars that make up the Big Dipper are located at different distances from the Earth.

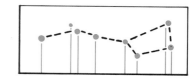

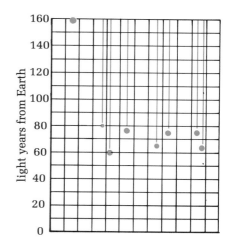

Figure 21-20. The position of the stars in the Big Dipper.

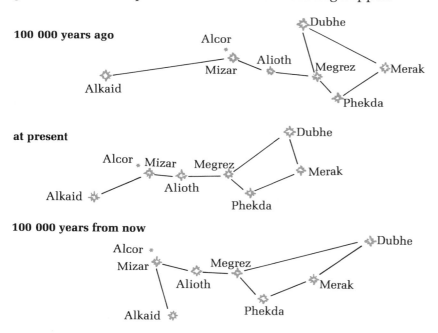

As early astronomers collected data for their star maps, they observed that some bright objects moved at different rates and in different directions from the stars. These objects were called **planets**, after the Greek word meaning "wanderers". The ancients identified five planets and named them after Greek gods: Mercury, Venus, Mars, Jupiter, and Saturn. Regular observation of planetary

Figure 21-21. The retrograde motion of Saturn, as it appears in the night sky.

Figure 21-22. A refracting telescope.

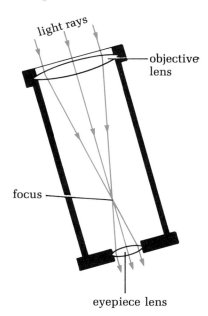

motion showed that Mars, Jupiter, and Saturn sometimes reversed direction as they wandered around the fixed star map. This effect became known as **retrograde motion**, but why it occurred was unknown. Early astronomers watched the sky without visual aids. They could not see any clear difference between the planets and the stars, except for their motion. Better astronomical instruments were needed before the real significance of these objects and their motions could be discovered.

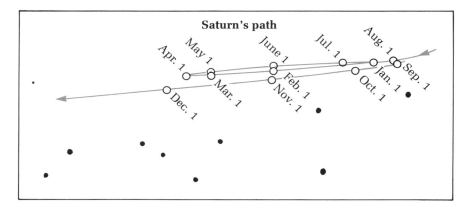

Astronomical Instruments

The science of astronomy is based on extracting the greatest possible amount of information from the radiation given off by celestial objects. However, the light from planets and stars is very dim by the time it reaches the Earth. Modern astronomers rely on a variety of specialized instruments for observing, collecting, and analyzing radiation from the sky.

An important instrument used by some astronomers is the **telescope**. A telescope collects light over a large area and concentrates it to form a brighter image. The larger the collector on a telescope, the greater the amount of light it can collect. As a result, telescopes are referred to in terms of the light collector's diameter. An eyepiece, which can vary in magnification, is used to magnify the image being viewed.

There are two different kinds of optical telescopes. A **refracting telescope**, or refractor, uses glass lenses to collect radiation. The maximum practical size of refractors is limited by two factors. The first is the problem of coloured halos around objects, which increases with the diameter of the lens. The second difficulty arises from the sheer mass of glass in a large diameter lens. Not only do many lenses crack as they cool during manufacture, but since they can only be supported at the edges, mounting the large pieces of glass in moveable assemblies above the eyepiece is very difficult.

The world's largest telescopes are **reflecting telescopes** (reflectors). These telescopes use a curved mirror to collect the light and do not suffer from coloured halos as refractors do. After cooling, huge blocks of glass are ground and polished to the correct shape. Because the image produced by a reflector is very sensitive to irregularities in mirror shape, grinding and polishing can take years to complete. A thin layer of aluminum reflects the light but requires reapplication every few years due to the effects of oxygen in the atmosphere. Although the mirror can be supported all along the back side, sizes larger than 6 m in diameter contain so much glass that they sometimes bend out of shape under their own weight.

Visible light is only one form of radiation given off by the Sun and other stars. Most celestial objects, in fact, emit many other types of radiation. The Earth's atmosphere blocks out a great deal of this radiation, allowing only visible light and some radio waves to reach the Earth's surface. Astronomers use large antennas, known as **radio telescopes**, to collect radio waves from space. While radio signals do not produce a visible picture, they can be analyzed to reveal useful information, such as the temperature of an object. The strongest sources of radio signals are the Sun, the planet Jupiter, some star remnants, and certain star groups.

To detect other radiation given off by celestial objects, it is necessary to get above the atmosphere. This is done by means of telescopes and other instruments carried aboard rockets and Earth-orbiting satellites. By detecting sources of infrared (heat) radiation, X-rays, and gamma rays, these instruments have increased our scientific understanding of the objects in our solar system and beyond. We have even gathered evidence that stars such as Vega and Fomalhaut have material orbiting them. Perhaps someday we will find evidence of a star similar to our Sun with planets similar to ours in orbit around it.

Figure 21-23. A reflecting telescope.

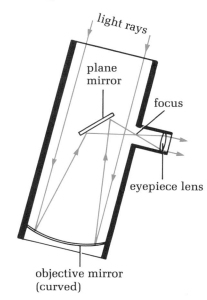

The Royal Astronomical Society of Canada (RASC)
The RASC, which has centres across Canada, offers a variety of astronomy-related activities designed for both its members and the general public. The society's regular meetings provide up-to-date information on current topics. Some centres organize observation opportunities during astronomical events such as sunspots and meteor showers. Members of the society may also be involved in astrophotography or telescope-making.

The National Research Council radio telescope at Victoria, B.C.

Astrophotography

When a camera is coupled with a telescope, a magnified image can be recorded. If the telescope is equipped with a motor drive, it can track an object as the Earth rotates. Astronomical photographs can be used to detect changes in an object over a long period of time. They can be used to assist in the hunt for planets or comets among the stars. Perhaps most importantly, long-exposure photographs can be used to record images too faint to be seen using any other method.

Study Questions

1. How do the distances from the Earth to the stars in a constellation compare with one another?
2. a) How do the stars in a constellation move relative to one another?
   b) What effect does this have on a constellation's appearance?
3. Why do we see different constellations in the night sky at different times of the year?
4. a) What determines the amount of light that a telescope can collect?
   b) How does this affect a telescope's usefulness?
5. Define a) refracting telescope and b) reflecting telescope, and describe their role in astronomy.
6. a) How does the Earth's atmosphere affect the different types of radiation emitted from stars and planets?
   b) Describe the instruments astronomers use to collect the different types of radiation.

THE McLAUGHLIN PLANETARIUM

In the countryside, the sky may appear filled with thousands of stars. Due to interference from lights, however, viewing the stars from a city may be a disappointing experience. However, that view in the country can be reproduced in a special building called a *planetarium*, while the viewers sit in comfort.

In a planetarium, a special type of computer-controlled projector is located in the centre of a large room with a ceiling shaped like the inside of a sphere. The ceiling serves as a screen on which the projector imposes an image of the night sky, complete with stars, planets, meteors, comets, and the aurora. Unaffected by bad weather or by lights from the city, projected images of motions in the sky can be sped up so that a night seems to pass in minutes. Images of planetary motions for an entire year can be speeded up in the same way. Sky scenes from the distant past can be recreated, and views from the future can be predicted.

There are 30 planetariums in Canada, six of which are open to the general public. The McLaughlin Planetarium, part of the Royal Ontario Museum in Toronto, offers a variety of programs. Some are designed to educate non-astronomers about astronomical events and concepts. Special series designed for children, students, and the

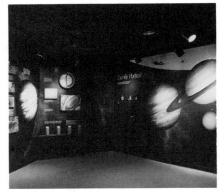

Display area in the McLaughlin Planetarium.

general public are presented several times a year. The planetarium also offers evening courses to help amateur astronomers become better acquainted with the night skies. Other events, such as musical light shows, are intended as pure entertainment.

Meet an Engineering Technician— Frank Hawker

Frank works as a technician at the David Dunlap Observatory of the University of Toronto.

Q. WHAT WERE YOUR INTERESTS AS A CHILD?

A. I tinkered in the basement and made my own fireworks, so I always thought I'd go into chemistry. Then I had a math teacher in Grade 11 who talked about astronomy in class. I was interested, so he lent me a classic text on astronomy. Soon afterwards, I found out about the Dunlap Observatory and started coming as a visitor on Saturday nights.

Q. HOW DID YOU GET YOUR JOB?

A. One Saturday night I saw a notice that said the observatory wanted a junior technician. I applied and got the job, even though my only experience was in machine shop at high school. I quit school in Grade 12 and started working here full-time. That was in 1951, and I'm still here.

Q. WHO USES THIS OBSERVATORY?

A. As part of the astronomy department of the university, it is used by undergraduate and graduate students. But one of our primary functions is to foster interest in astronomy in the public at large. We are open to the public at certain times, and we have many school tours as well.

Q. WHAT DOES YOUR JOB INVOLVE?

A. A variety of things. I work on developing photometer systems with professors and maintaining existing equipment. I interface astronomical instrumentation to microprocessors or microcomputers. I maintain a short-wave communication with the university's observatory in Chile. I'm also in charge of aluminizing all of our observatory mirrors.

Q. WHAT DOES ALUMINIZING THE MIRRORS INVOLVE?

A. Astronomical mirrors are different from ordinary mirrors. With ordinary mirrors you look through a layer of glass at your image on the aluminum coating on the back. With astronomical mirrors, the aluminum is on the front and the surface of the mirror is slightly concave for optical reasons. The aluminum gets dirty and deteriorates from exposure to outside elements, so it has to be renewed.

Q. HOW OFTEN IS THIS DONE?

A. Usually once a year. The small mirrors can be done in a small chamber, but the big job is aluminizing the 1.88-m mirror, the largest telescope in Canada. It takes a whole day in a specially built chamber, and several of us work together.

Q. WHAT IS THE MOST INTERESTING TASK YOU'VE DONE ON YOUR JOB?

A. I worked with a professor to develop a twin telescope system. It has two telescopes which are not identical and two photometers which are. One telescope is directed at a standard star and the other at the star you're studying.

Q. WHAT IS THE PURPOSE OF THIS SYSTEM?

A. It eliminates sky problems— haziness, clouds, and so forth— almost completely. It allows you to get very accurate results in less-than-perfect weather conditions, which you couldn't do with only one telescope. This sort of system wouldn't be necessary in good climates.

Q. WHAT DO YOU LIKE BEST ABOUT YOUR JOB?

A. I work with a good group of people. The work is interesting and varied, and I'm rarely bored.

Review Questions

A: Knowledge

1. a) Define the term "astronomy".
   b) Why do astronomers not use experiments as a major source of information?

2. a) How many fists are there between the horizon and the vertical?
   b) About how large is a fist in degrees?
   c) If a star is five fists above the horizon, how much is that in degrees?

3. Why are records so important to astronomers?

4. Two observers wish to view the Little Dipper, one from a medium-sized city and the other from 50 km outside the city. Which one would get the better view, and why?

5. Why was Polaris important to early sea navigation?

6. a) What astronomical observations can be made by studying shadows?
   b) How did these observations mislead early astronomers?
   c) How were the true motions finally determined?

7. a) Make a labelled sketch of the Sun, including the inner regions.
   b) In what part of the Sun does each of the following occur?
      i) sunspots
      ii) the nuclear reaction
      iii) flares
      iv) prominences
      v) energy transferred by moving gases
      vi) the production of light observed from Earth

8. a) Why should you not look directly at the Sun?
   b) Why is it even more hazardous to look at the Sun through an optical instrument?

9. Define constellation, and name five constellations.

10. List some surface features of the Moon.

11. List at least four ways astronomers can collect data about sky objects.

12. Why is it not possible to carry out X-ray astronomy from the surface of the Earth?

13. What evidence has been found to indicate that other stars might have planets orbiting them?

B: Application

14. Using the following information, complete a page in your log book.

    At 21:30 on Labour Day, two students, Sasha and John, went into their backyard to observe the Moon. The sky was partially overcast, but the full Moon was visible in the southeast sky about 40° above the horizon. A bright star was visible about one fist directly below the Moon, while another, fainter star could be seen two fists to the west of the Moon. Using binoculars with a magnification of $10\times$, they observed that the bright object was, in fact, Jupiter. By 21:45, the area had become overcast, and the two students returned to the house.

15. A student takes a picture of the Big Dipper by setting the camera on a tripod and leaving the shutter open for five minutes. Describe and make a sketch of the result.

16. Explain how you could locate the "South Star", if one exists.

17. A flare is seen erupting on the surface of the Sun. Approximately how long will it take for the effects of this flare to be noticed on Earth?

18. Describe the Sun's motion in the northern hemisphere on:
    a) the summer solstice date
    b) the vernal equinox date near March 22
    c) the winter solstice date
    d) the autumnal equinox date near September 23

19. In Australia, summer is in December and winter is in July. Explain, with the aid of diagrams, why the seasons are opposite from those in the northern hemisphere.

20. If a tall mountain was situated on the terminator on the surface of the Moon, describe how it would look from Earth.

21. Which phase of the Moon is the most difficult to observe? Explain why.

22. a) The word maria means "seas". Is this word an accurate description of the regions on the Moon that are so named?
    b) Explain why these regions are called maria.

23. What factor determines if a star is considered a member of a certain constellation?

24. a) State two advantages of using a planetarium to study objects seen in the sky.
    b) State two disadvantages of using a planetarium to study sky objects.

C: Problem Solving

25. a) Sketch the positions of the Sun and Earth during the time of the midnight sun in the Arctic.
    b) When would the midnight sun appear in Antarctica?

26. Suggest a reason why the Moon shows evidence of many impact craters, while planets like Earth and Mars do not.

27. The apparent motion of the Moon across the Earth's sky is familiar to us. Describe the apparent motion of the Earth across the Moon's sky over the period of one Earth month.

28. Suppose a telescope, with a mirror diameter of 80 mm, can collect a certain amount of light, I, from a particular star. Determine the amount of light that a 24-cm telescope could collect from the same star under the same conditions. Explain your assumptions and show all calculations.

29. A radio astronomer discovers a star at a certain location in the sky. Another astronomer uses an optical telescope to search for the star in the same location, but cannot find the star. Suggest several reasons why this might happen.

Try This

The Astrolabe
The astrolabe is a simple device that measures the altitude of an object. One can easily be constructed, using a protractor, a large soda straw, some thread, and a heavy object such as a washer (see the diagram below).

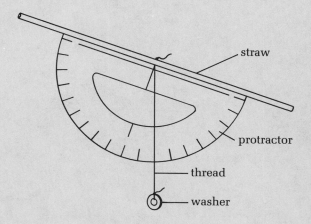

a) Determine how to use the astrolabe, and write an "instruction manual" on how to use it. Remember to include a warning about not looking directly at the Sun.

b) Carry out a series of observations with the astrolabe to:
   i) determine the altitudes of the Moon over the course of an evening. Is there any connection between altitude and phase? Is there any change in altitude from month to month?
   ii) measure the altitude of a particular star at the same time of night every second week over a period of several months. Interpret your results.

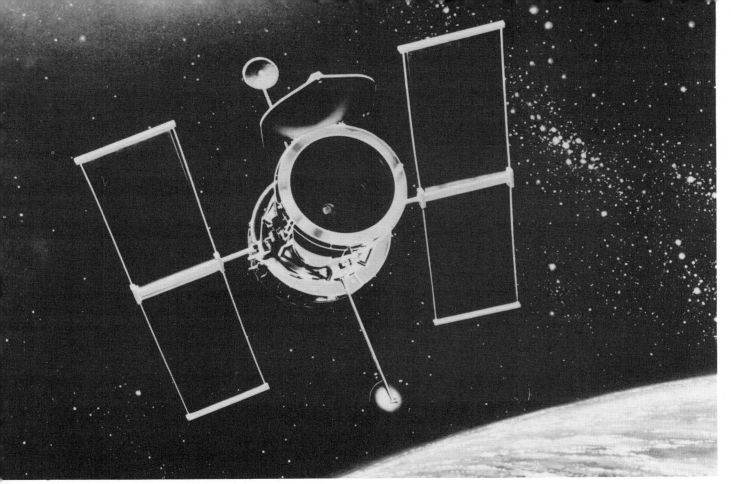

Located above the Earth's protective atmosphere, NASA's space telescope, when launched, will allow astronomers to view objects seven times more distant than ground-based telescopes.

Chapter 22 Exploring the Solar System and Beyond

Astronomy is the oldest science, and over the centuries it has built constantly on the work of early investigators. Ancient astronomers kept meticulously precise records of everything they saw, including events they did not understand. Having access to thousands of years of records has enabled modern astronomers to explain things that mystified their predecessors.

One such mystery involved the planets. These bright objects confused the ancients by wandering around the heavens and contradicting star maps. Once the telescope showed that planets were different from stars and moved as if they were closer, astronomers could develop an explanation to fit the observed facts. This explanation states that the planets are bodies like Earth, and that all planets orbit the Sun at distances much closer than the next nearest star. The Sun and its planets move through space as a group. This group has been named the solar system.

In this chapter, we examine the solar system and its planets in some detail. We then discuss the stars that lie beyond the solar system, and finally we consider the universe as a whole.

When you finish Chapter 22, you should be able to:

- describe the distribution of planets in the solar system
- list the major characteristics of planets
- identify other types of objects found in the solar system
- identify various types of star groupings

22.1 A Journey through the Solar System

Our **solar system** includes the Sun, nine known planets, their satellites (or moons), and a variety of other, smaller objects. The largest object in the solar system is the Sun, containing about 99.86% of the total mass of the solar system. The **planets** are much smaller, solid objects that revolve around the Sun and are held in their orbits by gravity. Including Earth, the planets make up only 0.135% of the solar system's mass. The **satellites**, or moons, are still smaller solid objects that revolve around the planets. Each satellite is held in orbit by gravity, and is pulled along as the planet orbits the Sun.

Figure 22-1. Our solar system.

Planetary Distances from the Sun

Every planet in our solar system has an orbit shaped like the ellipse in Figure 22-2. This means that each planet's distance from the Sun changes constantly as the planet revolves around the Sun. For convenience, astronomers refer to average distances. For example, the average distance from the Sun to Pluto is about six million million kilometres. Because planetary distances are so great, astronomers sometimes base measurements on the average distance between the Earth and the Sun. This average distance, called the **astronomical unit** (**A.U.**), equals 1.5×10^8 km. In this system of measurement, Jupiter's distance from Earth can be expressed as follows:

$$\text{Number of A.U.} = \frac{\text{distance of Jupiter's closest approach to Earth}}{\text{distance in 1 A.U.}}$$

$$= \frac{588\ 800\ 000 \text{ km}}{150\ 000\ 000 \text{ km}}$$

$$= 3.9$$

Thus, Jupiter's minimum distance from Earth is 3.9 A.U.

Another method commonly used to express vast distances involves the speed of light, which equals 300 000 km/s. Using this method, Jupiter's distance is expressed in terms of the time needed for light to travel from the Sun. This time (t) can be calculated as follows:

$$t_{\text{Sun to Jupiter}} = \frac{\text{distance of Jupiter's closest approach to Sun}}{\text{speed of light}}$$

$$= \frac{740\ 900\ 000 \text{ km}}{300\ 000 \text{ km/s}}$$

$$= 2470 \text{ s, or } 41.2 \text{ min}$$

The unit used to express distances to the stars is the **light year**. This is the distance that light can travel in one year: approximately ten million million kilometres, or 10^{13} km.

Activity 22-1:   Astronomical Distances

In this activity you will calculate the distances of the planets from the Sun, both in terms of astronomical units and in terms of the travel time of light.

Materials

planetary data from Table 22-1

Figure 22-2.   A planet's distance from the Sun varies as the planet follows its elliptical orbit.

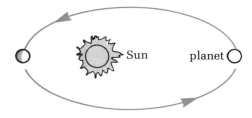

Since radio communications with space probes also travel at the speed of light, messages are received some time after being sent. From a probe 15 000 000 km away, a radio signal would take 50 s to reach Earth. Scientists must take these delays into account when planning missions.

The distance light travels in one year is calculated as follows:
300 000 km/s
$\times$ 60 s/min
$\times$ 60 min/h
$\times$ 24 h/d
$\times$ 365 d/a
$= 9.5 \times 10^{12}$ km/a
Therefore, one light year is almost ten million million kilometres.

Table 22-1: Planetary Data

	Mercury	Venus	Earth
Maximum distance from Sun	69 700 000 km	109 000 000 km	152 100 000 km
Minimum distance from Sun	45 900 000 km	107 400 000 km	147 100 000 km
Average distance from Sun	57 800 000 km	108 200 000 km	149 600 000 km
Revolution period	87.969 d	224.701 d	365.256 d
Rotation period	58.6461 d	243.16 d	23 h 56 min 4 s
Mean orbital velocity	47.7 km/s	35.02 km/s	29.79 km/s
Density (water = 1)	5.5	5.25	5.517
Mass (Earth = 1)	0.055	0.815	1
Volume (Earth = 1)	0.056	0.86	1
Escape velocity	4.3 km/s	10.36 km/s	11.18 km/s
Surface gravity (Earth = 1)	0.38	0.903	1
Mean surface temperature	350°C to −170°C	480°C	22°C
Average diameter	4878 km	12 104 km	12 750 km
Known satellites	none	none	1
Ring system	none	none	none

	Mars	Jupiter	Saturn
Maximum distance from Sun	249 100 000 km	815 700 000 km	1 507 000 km
Minimum distance from Sun	206 700 000 km	740 900 000 km	1 347 000 000 km
Average distance from Sun	227 900 000 km	778 300 000 km	1 427 000 000 km
Revolution period	687.96 d	4332.59 d	10 759.20 d
Rotation period	24 h 37 min 22.6 s	9 h 50 min 30 s (equatorial)	10 h 39.4 min
Mean orbital velocity	24.1 km/s	13.06 km/s	9.6 km/s
Density (water = 1)	3.94	1.33	0.71
Mass (Earth = 1)	0.107	318.95	95.17
Volume (Earth = 1)	0.150	1338	800
Escape velocity	5.03 km/s	60.22 km/s	32.26 km/s
Surface gravity (Earth = 1)	0.380	2.64	1.16
Mean surface temperature	−23°C	−150°C	−180°C
Average diameter	6787 km	142 800 km	120 660 km
Known satellites	2	16	17
Ring system	none	faint rings	many rings

(cont'd)

Table 22-1:   Planetary Data (cont'd)

	Uranus	Neptune	Pluto
Maximum distance from Sun	3 004 000 000 km	4 537 000 000 km	7 375 000 000 km
Minimum distance from Sun	2 735 000 000 km	4 456 000 000 km	4 425 000 000 km
Average distance from Sun	2 870 000 000 km	4 497 000 000 km	5 900 000 000 km
Revolution period	30 684.9 d	60 190.3 d	90 465 d
Rotation period	17.24 h	18 h 12 min	6 d 9 h 17 min
Mean orbital velocity	6.80 km/s	5.43 km/s	4.7 km/s
Density (water = 1)	1.7	2.25	1
Mass (Earth = 1)	14.6	17.2	0.002
Volume (Earth = 1)	67	57	0.77
Escape velocity	22.5 km/s	23.9 km/s	?
Surface gravity (Earth = 1)	1.17	1.2	?
Mean surface temperature	−210°C	−220°C	−230°C
Average diameter	50 800 km	48 600 km	2300 km(?)
Known satellites	15	2	1
Ring system	many narrow rings	?	?

Procedure

1. Copy the following chart into your notebook.

Planet	Average Distance from Sun (km)	Average Distance from Sun (A.U.)	Average Time for Light to Travel from Sun
Mercury			
Venus			
Earth			
Mars			
Jupiter			
Saturn			
Uranus			
Neptune			
Pluto			

2. Using the planetary data in Table 22-1, fill in the average distance in kilometres of each planet from the Sun.

3. Calculate these average distances in astronomical units, correct to one decimal place.

4. Using a convenient unit of time, calculate the time required for light from the Sun to travel each of these distances. Include units in your answers.

Discussion

1. How many times is the average distance between the Sun and Saturn greater than the average distance between the Sun and Earth?

2. How long would it take sunlight to reach Pluto?

3. How many times longer does it take for sunlight to reach Pluto than to reach Earth?

4. a) If you made a scale model of the solar system, with Earth placed 1 m from the Sun, how far away should you place the other planets?
   b) If Earth were placed 3 cm from the Sun in your scale model, how far away should you place Uranus?

5. The nearest star is approximately 4.3×10^{13} km from Earth. Calculate its distance in light years.

The Orbits of the Planets

Figure 22-3 shows that all planetary orbits except Pluto's can be drawn approximately on the same flat surface, or plane. For any pair of planets, the distance across this plane can vary considerably.

Figure 22-3. All of the planets' orbits, except Pluto's, lie on the same plane.

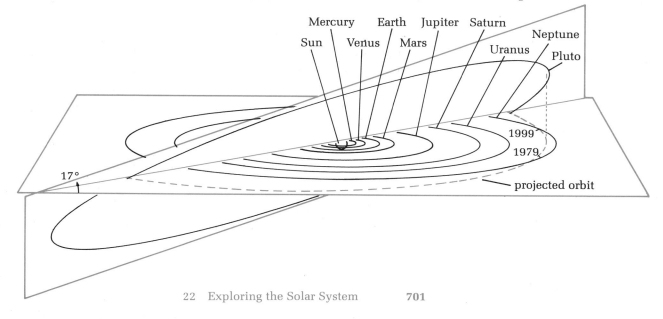

When the two planets are on opposite sides of the Sun, the distance between them is greatest. When both planets are on the same side of the Sun, the distance between them is smallest. In the next activity, we will assume that all planets are lined up on the same side of the Sun (a rare event), so that the distances between them are at a minimum.

Activity 22-2: A Scale Model of the Solar System

A scale model helps us to understand the sizes and distances in the solar system in terms of more familiar dimensions.

Materials

Table 22-1 (pages 699 to 700)   measuring tape

Bristol board   blank (unlined) sheets of paper

geometry compasses   ruler

Part A: Using a Common Scale for Diameter and Distance

In Part A, you will construct a model of the solar system using the same scale for both planet diameters and planet distances.

Procedure

1. Draw a chart with the following headings: *Object*, *Actual Average Distance from Sun*, *Scale Distance from Sun*, *Actual Diameter of Object*, and *Scale Diameter of Object*.

2. In the first column, list the Sun and the planets in order of increasing distance from the Sun.

3. Enter the actual diameter of the Sun (1 392 000 km) into the chart.

4. From Table 22-1, fill in the actual values for the average distance from the Sun and the diameter of each planet.

5. Using a scale of 100 000 km = 1 cm, determine the scale distances and the scale diameters of the planets, correct to one decimal place. Enter these scale values into your chart. For example,

$$\text{scale diameter of Sun} = \frac{1\ 392\ 000\ \text{km}}{100\ 000\ \text{km/cm}}$$

$$= 13.9\ \text{cm}$$

6. Your teacher will divide the class into ten groups. Each group will be responsible for one object in the solar system, including the Sun.

7. On a piece of Bristol board, draw and label the object assigned to your group.

8. In a large outdoor area, such as the football field of your school, position as many of the objects as possible according to the scale distance values. For each planet you cannot place in the field, estimate its position in the scale model by referring to familiar objects in your school neighbourhood.

Discussion

1. How much of this scale model of the solar system would fit inside your classroom?

2. What problems did your class have in positioning the planets outdoors?

3. a) Once it escapes Earth's gravity, the fastest modern space vehicle can travel about 1 000 000 km per day. How many centimetres on this scale model would represent one day's travel?

    b) Assuming that interplanetary distances are at a minimum, calculate the time needed to travel from:
       i) the Sun to Mercury   iv) the Sun to Pluto
       ii) the Sun to Earth   v) Earth to Mars
       iii) the Sun to Jupiter

4. What do your answers to question 3 suggest about using piloted vehicles to explore the solar system?

Part B: Using Separate Scales for Diameter and Distance

Despite its accuracy, the scale model in Part A is not as useful as a model should be. For example, it is difficult to see the entire model at once. However, if the model were "shrunk", it might then be difficult to see the planets at all. When scientists encounter this type of problem, they often use two different scales in the same model.

Procedure

1. Draw a new chart with the following headings: *Object, New Scale Distance from the Sun,* and *New Scale Diameter of Object.*

2. Using the data from the chart you made in Part A, divide all the previous scale distance values by 20, and enter the new values in your new chart.

3. Multiply all the previous scale diameter values by 10, and enter the new values in your new chart.

4. Print the title "New Scale Distances" on a blank sheet of paper. Draw a diagonal line and label one end "Sun". Measure, mark off, and label the new scale distance from the Sun to Earth. Repeat for as many of the other planets as possible.

5. Print the title "New Scale Diameters" on another blank sheet. Use the new scale diameter values to draw as many of the objects as possible.

Discussion

1. a) Were you able to place all new scale distances on one sheet of paper?
   b) Are the new scale distances more suitable for a model than the ones you used in Part A? Why or why not?

2. a) Were you able to place all objects on one sheet of paper using the new scale diameters? Explain.
   b) Are the new scale diameters more suitable for a model than the ones you used in Part A? Why or why not?

3. If you were to classify the planets into two groups based on size,
   a) which planets would belong to the large group? Explain.
   b) which planets would belong to the small group? Explain.

4. If you were to classify the planets into two groups based on distance from the Sun,
   a) which planets would belong to the "inner planet" group? Explain.
   b) Which planets would belong to the "outer planet" group? Explain.

Figure 22-4. The sizes of the planets relative to the Sun.

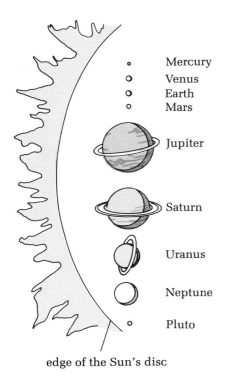

edge of the Sun's disc

Study Questions

1. Define: solar system, planet, satellite, astronomical unit, light year.

2. Draw a simple sketch to show how the solar system is held together by gravity.

3. Describe the orbits of the planets according to:
   a) their shape, b) their position in space.

4. Figure 22-4 shows the Sun and all nine known planets.
   a) What is the advantage of drawing the solar system this way?
   b) What is the disadvantage of drawing the solar system this way?

5. Explain why it is impractical to construct a model of the solar system using the same scale for both planet diameters and planet distances.

6. a) Why is it not yet practical to send piloted spacecraft to other planets?

   b) What factors do you think must be considered before sending piloted spacecraft to other planets?

22.2   Observing the Solar System

The great distances between the planets in our solar system present formidable challenges to astronomers. Even when the most sophisticated telescopes are used, observing planets from Earth provides very limited data. On the other hand, human exploration is not yet practical (see Table 22-2). Instead, robot space probes are sent to explore the planets.

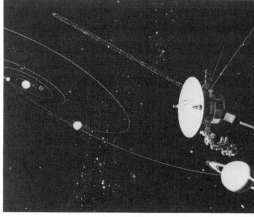

An artist's conception of Voyager 1's encounter with Saturn.

Table 22-2:   Travel Time to the Planets by Modern Spacecraft

Planet	Average Distance from Earth (km)	Minimum Time to Reach Planet*
Mercury	91 800 000	96 d
Venus	41 400 000	43 d
Mars	78 300 000	82 d
Jupiter	628 700 000	1.8 a
Saturn	1 277 400 000	3.6 a
Uranus	2 720 400 000	7.8 a
Neptune	4 347 400 000	12.4 a
Pluto	5 750 400 000	16.4 a

*Time is based on a craft travelling at 40 000 km/h, about the current velocity of the NASA Space Shuttle.

Some probes pass by a planet, collect information with many instruments, and send the data by radio to observers on Earth. Other probes land on a planet's surface to take close-up photographs, measure temperatures, and analyze samples of soil and atmospheric gases. Each successive probe is designed to expand the kind and amount of data that can be collected.

Our understanding of the solar system, therefore, is constantly changing. Each new piece of information answers some old questions, but may also create many new ones.

Do You Know?
Voyager 2's long journey should bring it near Neptune in August 1989. Although it will not land on the planet, the probe will take photographs and analyze radiations. Other missions planned, but not yet launched, include: a second Earth-orbiting space telescope, a robot probe to the moons of Jupiter, and a piloted expedition to Mars in the next century.

Activity 22-3: Describing the Planets

This activity is a library research project. The planetary information provided in this chapter is a starting point for your investigation. Since exploration of the solar system is ongoing, you should realize that some information presented in books and articles may have changed. You should check the publication date of each source you use to ensure that the information is up-to-date.

Procedure

1. Draw a chart with the following headings: *Average Distance from the Sun*, *Mass of Planet*, *Radius of Planet*, and *Density of Planet*.
2. Under "Average Distance from the Sun", list the planets in order of increasing distance.
3. Under "Mass of Planet", rank the planets from 1 (largest) to 9 (smallest), in order of decreasing mass.
4. Repeat step 3 for "Radius of Planet" and "Density of Planet".
5. Determine your approximate weight compared to Earth on the surface of a) Mercury, b) Mars, and c) Uranus.
6. Determine your age in Earth days by multiplying your age in Earth years by 365. Then calculate your age in Mercurian years, Martian years, and Jovian years.
7. For each of the planets, write a short description of a) its appearance from nearby space, and b) its surface conditions.

Discussion

1. a) Where are the largest planets in the solar system located?
   b) What could this pattern of location signify?
2. a) Which is the least dense planet? the densest?
   b) Where are the densest planets in the solar system located?
3. a) In general, how do the inner planets differ from the outer planets?
   b) What might have caused these differences?
4. a) State and explain two advantages of using robot space probes instead of piloted spacecraft to explore the planets.
   b) State and explain two disadvantages.
5. Which planets in the solar system would be most suitable for colonization by humans? Explain.

The planet Jupiter was named after the king of the gods in ancient Roman mythology. Because this god is sometimes known as Jove, the term "Jovian" is often used when referring to Jupiter. Jupiter's moons, for example, are called the Jovian moons.

The Solid Planets: Mercury, Venus, Earth, and Mars

These four planets have solid surfaces. Mars and Venus have been closely examined by robot probes landing on each planet's surface. Humans have directly examined Earth extensively.

Mercury   Three close passes by the U.S. spacecraft Mariner 10 during 1974-5 contributed a great deal to our knowledge of this planet. Since Mercury has no atmosphere to erode surface features, craters formed during the planet's early existence are still visible.

An observer on Mercury's hot, dusty, grey surface would see the Sun rise in the east, move slowly across a black sky, and set in the west 88 Earth days later.

Venus   This planet has been the object of intensive investigations. Radar from Earth has mapped its surface. Nineteen Soviet and five American missions visited the planet from 1961 to 1985. The 1985 Soviet mission dropped balloons into the upper atmosphere to sample conditions as they drifted down. Early robot probes which landed on Venus were quickly destroyed by chemical corrosion and by the extreme pressures in the turbulent, sulphur dioxide-laden atmosphere.

Venus's atmosphere also contains large amounts of carbon dioxide, which increases absorption of heat from the Sun but prevents the heat from reradiating into space. Combined with the planet's

The surface of Venus is hidden from view by a continuous cloud cover.

Mercury looks much like the Earth's moon. The inset reveals more detail in the craters on the planet's surface.

proximity to the Sun, this effect results in surface temperatures so hot that rocks simply soften and flatten out like pieces of chocolate left in the Sun. Another result is that the planet is surrounded by a perpetual cloud layer. An observer on the surface of Venus would be unable to see the Sun rising in the west and setting in the east 58 Earth days later.

Earth When seen from space, Earth's predominantly blue surface immediately sets it apart from the rest of the planets. Earth is able to sustain life because of its abundant supplies of liquid water, and because of an atmosphere, low in carbon dioxide, that can admit sufficient sunlight without trapping too much heat.

Mars Between 1963 and 1976, nine Soviet and six American probes landed on the surface of Mars. Soil sampling failed to find any evidence of life. The atmosphere of Mars is mostly carbon dioxide, with small amounts of nitrogen, argon, and oxygen. The atmosphere is so thin, however, that it captures and retains little of the heat radiation that reaches it.

When the Sun rises in the east, the Martian sky appears blue, but changes to salmon-pink as atmospheric heating creates strong winds that disturb the red, iron-rich surface dust. Violent spring dust storms may completely obscure the planet, giving it a reddish colour when viewed from Earth.

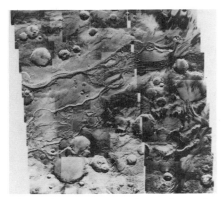

Channels cutting into the surface of Mars suggest that large amounts of water must have been present on the planet in the past.

Weather satellites photograph the Earth from an altitude of 37 000 km. The island of Madagascar and parts of Africa and Antarctica can be seen in this photo.

Mars, as photographed by a Viking spacecraft approaching the planet.

The Gas Giants: Jupiter and Saturn

Jupiter and Saturn each have a small dense core surrounded by a deep gaseous atmosphere, composed mainly of hydrogen and helium.

Jupiter   Because of its size, many of this planet's features can be examined from Earth. Even a low-powered telescope will sight four moons and Jupiter's most prominent surface feature, the Great Red Spot. This feature mystified astronomers until recent space probes revealed its nature.

Four American vehicles passed by Jupiter between 1973 and 1979. Their observations showed that the Great Red Spot is a giant storm which has been raging on Jupiter for at least 300 years. The planet's atmosphere moves constantly, partly because the equator spins faster than the poles. Also, Jupiter radiates about twice as much heat as it receives from the Sun. This extra energy provides some of the driving force behind the many storms in the planet's atmosphere.

The U.S. space probes provided close-up pictures of Jupiter's moons, and detected a thin double ring of material in orbit around the planet.

Saturn   Only when viewed through a telescope is this planet's impressive structure revealed. The last planet to be recognized in ancient times, Saturn was thought initially to have six rings. However, a close-up view by three American space probes between 1979 and 1981 revealed thousands of distinct bands surrounding the

Jupiter, a giant gas planet, shows its most prominent feature, the Great Red Spot (lower centre). The longest dimension of the Great Red Spot is about three times the diameter of the Earth.

Do You Know?
Stars are made from atoms of hydrogen and helium. Jupiter is just short of the gaseous mass required to create a star. Large gravitational forces pulling particles together are needed to create enough heat for nuclear fusion. If either Saturn or Jupiter had had a slightly larger mass, one of these two gas giants might have begun to glow. In that case, our Sun would have been part of a binary star system.

Three of Saturn's icy moons can be seen in this photograph taken by Voyager 2. A shadow of one moon is visible on Saturn's surface.

A close-up view of Saturn's ring system.

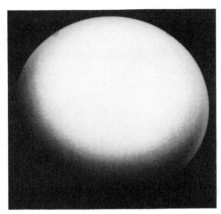

The opaque atmosphere of Uranus reveals no surface detail.

planet. Although 274 000 km in diameter, these rings are estimated to be less than 1 km thick. They are probably composed of ice and other solid matter, derived either from Saturn's formation or from a broken-up moon. Saturn's surface appears to be similar to that of Jupiter.

The Ice Worlds: Uranus and Neptune

Like the gas giants, Uranus and Neptune are believed to have solid cores and to contain gaseous hydrogen and helium. Because these planets are so far from the Sun, however, a solid surface layer has formed, consisting mainly of frozen water, methane, and ammonia ice.

Uranus Because methane gas in its atmosphere absorbs red light, the surface of Uranus appears blue-green. This planet was first observed in 1781, and its rings were discovered from Earth in 1977. Several thousand kilometres apart, these thin rings are made up of boulders, ice chunks, and pebbles, no larger than a metre in diameter. The American space probe Voyager 2 passed by Uranus in 1986. This probe detected, among other details, a sheet of small particles between the known rings, slowly spiralling down towards the planet's surface.

Neptune This planet's existence was predicted in 1821 because its gravity was influencing the orbit of Uranus. First observed in 1846, Neptune is believed to have a solid core, surrounded by a liquid mantle of methane, ammonia, and water. Its atmosphere contains hydrogen and helium. More information will be available after Voyager 2 passes by Neptune in 1989.

Pluto and Planet X

Pluto was discovered in 1930 after its existence had been predicted from variations in Neptune's orbit. Figure 22-3 on page 701 shows some unusual features of Pluto's orbit around the Sun. In 1979, the planet moved inside the orbit of Neptune. In 1999, Pluto will once again move outside Neptune's orbit, and resume its usual place as the outermost planet.

Because of Pluto's small size and extreme distance from Earth, even the world's best telescopes have been unable to provide a clear picture of it. Estimates of Pluto's mass suggest that it alone cannot be responsible for the irregularities observed in the motions of Neptune's orbit. It has been suggested that a tenth planet, Planet X, might also be exerting a gravitational influence on Neptune. Perhaps future Earth-orbiting telescopes will search for this suspected new planet.

Pluto is not a typical solid planet, nor does it seem to be related to the gas giants. Furthermore, its unusual orbit is both tilted and oddly shaped.

The planet Pluto is indicated by the arrows. How can astronomers use photos like these to identify the planet?

Asteroids, Comets, and Meteors

The solar system also contains thousands of solid objects much smaller than planets. These objects can be classified into three groups according to their motions and origins.

Asteroids   Like the planets, asteroids move in elliptical orbits that stay inside the boundaries of the solar system. Asteroids are cold, rocklike bodies that can only be seen by reflected sunlight. Only the largest ones are named. Ceres, for example, is 1000 km in diameter; Pallas and Vesta are about 500 km. Most asteroids, however, are nameless and very small. The total number of asteroids is unknown; their total mass is estimated at less than that of Earth's moon.

Some asteroids have orbits that cross those of the planets. In 1937, a small asteroid passed Earth at a distance twice that of the Moon. Although collisions are unlikely, planet-crossers might someday be the target of a space mission to learn more about the materials from which they are made.

Figure 22-5.   This diagram shows the location of the asteroid belt and the orbit of Halley's Comet.

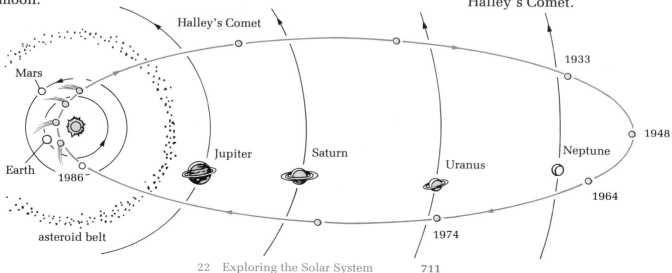

Most asteroids follow an orbit between Mars and Jupiter. Some, the Trojan asteroids, move in the same orbit as Jupiter itself. As more asteroids are discovered, astronomers are regarding their origins and compositions as important links in understanding the origin and history of our solar system.

Comets Comets are mixtures of frozen gases and solid matter moving in orbits travelling far beyond Pluto. They appear to originate in a collection of matter lying about one light year from the Sun, called Oort's Cloud.

Comets are much too small to be seen by reflected sunlight. Only as a comet approaches the Sun does it become visible. Once the Sun's heat vaporizes some of its outer layers, a halolike coma appears. Dust reflects the sunlight, while the gases absorb solar radiation and re-emit visible light. The solar wind pushes the bright coma away, forming a long, brilliant tail like that shown in the photograph.

Some comets are seen only once, while others can be seen on a regular, predictable basis. Halley's Comet, the best known of the short-period comets, has an elliptical orbit which brings it back near the Sun, on average, every 76 years. For long-period comets, the return time may be 1000 years or longer. Comets are of great interest to astronomers because the material they contain has remained unaltered since the solar system was formed.

The gas tail of Halley's Comet is visible in this 1986 photo taken from Australia.

Meteors The solar system contains a great deal of debris: remnants left from its own formation, charged particles from the Sun, and dust from passing comets. As Earth orbits the Sun, some of this debris is trapped by the planet's gravity. Pieces that fall towards Earth are called **meteors**. As meteors enter Earth's atmosphere, they begin to glow from the heat of friction.

On average, you can expect to see about 40 meteors a night. Many more can be seen, however, when Earth moves through a comet orbit. These events, called meteor showers, occur at predictable times during the year (see Table 22-3). Meteor showers are named after the constellations in which they appear to originate.

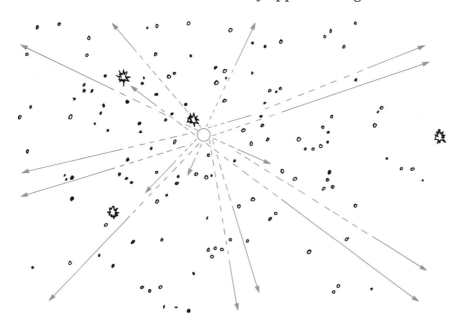

Figure 22-6. A meteor shower gets its name from the constellation (here, Lyra) in which it appears to originate.

Table 22-3:   Main Annual Meteor Showers

Name of Meteor Shower	Date			Maximum Number per Hour	Partial Description
	Start	Peak	End		
Quadrantids	Jan. 1	Jan. 3	Jan. 4	40	short maximum
Lyrids	Apr. 19	Apr. 21	Apr. 24	12	swift meteors
Eta Aquarids	May 2	May 4	May 7	20	swift; long trails
Delta Aquarids	Jul. 15	Jul. 28	Aug. 15	10	
Perseids	Jul. 25	Aug. 12	Aug. 18	50	very consistent
Orionids	Oct. 16	Oct. 20	Oct. 26	25	
Taurids	Oct. 15	Nov. 10	Nov. 30	5	slow meteors
Leonids	Nov. 14	Nov. 16	Nov. 20	variable	occasionally brilliant
Geminids	Dec. 7	Dec. 14	Dec. 15	50	rich; fairly swift
Ursids	Dec. 17	Dec. 22	Dec. 24	12	radiant in Ursa Minor

This meteorite, which has a mass of almost 3 t, is the second largest ever recovered in the U.S. It was discovered about 300 km east of Los Angeles.

Most meteors burn up before reaching the ground. Those that do land, often then disintegrating, are called **meteorites**. Astronomers study solar system formation by analyzing the remnants found in the craters created by the impacts. In 1908, a sizable impact occurred in Siberia. It flattened trees for 50 km and was heard 1000 km away. Although no solid remains were located, substances found in the crater are common to comets. Astronomers can learn a great deal about matter in the solar system by analyzing meteorites but, unfortunately, few large ones survive their journey to Earth.

Study Questions

1. a) How are robot space probes used to explore the planets?
   b) What kind of data can be collected by these probes? State specific examples.
2. a) Divide the planets into three groups based on i) distance from the Sun, ii) size, and iii) type of surface.
   b) Discuss any similarities or differences in groupings i), ii), and iii).
3. Consider the following terms: asteroid, comet, meteor. For each, describe a) what it is made of, b) what path or orbit it follows, c) how it can be observed from Earth.
4. What happens when a comet approaches the Sun?
5. a) What causes a meteor shower?
   b) How does a meteor differ from a meteorite?

EXPLORATION OF THE SOLAR SYSTEM

Active exploration of the solar system began in 1962, when the U.S. space probe Mariner 2 passed by the planet Venus, giving astronomers their first close look at another world. When a robot space probe travels past a planet, it can collect information for only a short time. To prolong the information-gathering time, some probes are designed to be captured by the planet's gravity, thus going into permanent orbit. In 1971, the U.S. Mariner 9 went into orbit around Mars. In 1975, the Soviet Venera 9 and 10 went into orbit around Venus. All of these probes collected large amounts of information about surface features and atmospheric conditions, using everything from optical cameras to radar mapping.

Placing a craft directly on the surface of another planet was first accomplished in 1967, when the Soviet probe Venera 4 made a controlled landing on Venus. Although the conditions on the surface of Venus destroyed the instruments almost immediately, astronomers could briefly receive direct information about the planet's surface conditions.

In 1976, the U.S. Viking spacecraft landed the first mobile laboratory on Mars. It was programmed to carry out a series of tests on soil samples in a search for life that proved unsuccessful. Future landers may be designed to collect materials and to lift off again in an ambitious attempt to bring soil samples back to Earth.

Detailed space probe studies have involved only Venus and Mars. Exploration of the more distant planets has progressed only to the "flyby" stage. The most ambitious of these probes, the U.S. Voyagers 1 and 2, were launched in 1977. These probes will have gathered data from six flybys by the time their missions are completed. Voyager 1 flew past Jupiter and Saturn before heading out of the solar system, while Voyager 2 was designed to fly past four outer planets. Future missions will become increasingly more elaborate as astronomers seek new information about other worlds in our solar system.

The surface of Venus is finally revealed in this photo taken by the Soviet Venera 4 Lander in 1982.

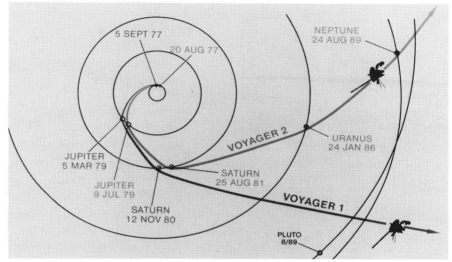

Figure 22-7. The paths of Voyager 1 and Voyager 2.

22.3   Beyond the Solar System: The Stars

In general, a **star** is a hot gaseous mass that gives off radiant energy produced by a nuclear reaction in its core. Thus, most stars are much like our Sun. By observing the Sun, astronomers have increased their understanding of other stars. By observing other stars, astronomers hope to increase their understanding of our Sun's origins and future.

Star Systems

Although some of the bright objects in the night sky are single stars like our Sun, close observation reveals that many others are actually groups called **star systems**. The most commonly seen grouping is the **double** or **binary star system**. An easily observed example is

Although most stars maintain the same brightness for hundreds of years, two types of variable stars have been observed. One type varies because of external changes. Binary stars are of this type. True variable stars, however, fluctuate due to internal changes. Many variable stars are predictable, but much remains to be learned about what causes them.

Globular clusters which consist primarily of old stars, are found around many galaxies.

The Ring Nebula (left), in the constellation Lyra, is the remains of a gas shell ejected from the central star. The Horsehead Nebula (right) is created by interstellar dust obscuring light from a gas cloud.

the binary star called ζ Ursae Majoris (Mizar in the Big Dipper). A grouping of four stars or more is called a **multiple star system**.

Sometimes star systems show variable brightness. In double stars, for example, a dimming effect may occur when one of the two stars moves in front of the other.

Unlike the stars in a constellation, all members of a **star cluster** occupy the same region of space. They stay near each other and move as a group. **Open clusters** contain at most a few hundred loosely grouped, younger stars. **Globular clusters** contain thousands of closely grouped, older stars. When viewed without a telescope, most star clusters look hazy.

Star Dust and Star Remnants

Many objects in the sky do not fit precisely the definition of a star. Some objects do not give off visible light, while others do not give off any radiation at all.

Nebulae   Some of the hazy-looking objects in the night sky are **nebulae**: large collections of dust and gas that lie scattered among the stars. Some nebulae shine by reflected starlight. Others absorb light from nearby stars and then reradiate it. A third type, the dark nebulae, do not shine at all. They can only be detected because they block light from stars beyond them. Some nebulae are halo-like. These ring nebulae consist of a shell glowing by the light of the star which ejected the material.

Supernovas   A much brighter object than a nebula is the **supernova**. Astronomers believe a supernova results when a giant star explodes so violently that its brightness increases enormously, by as much as one million times. This is a **true variable star**, one in which changes in brightness are caused by changes inside the star.

A super-bright supernova occurred in 1572. Before it exploded, the original star could be seen only through a telescope. After the explosion, the supernova grew bright enough to be seen in broad daylight, and remained visible for over a year. Most supernovas remain bright for only a few weeks.

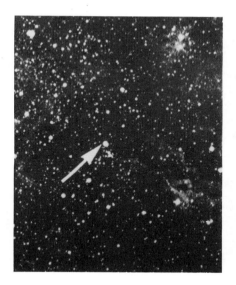

Before and after photographs of the star that became Supernova Shelton 1987A (see page 728).

Pulsars   Not all sky objects emit visible light, so scientists also use radio telescopes to search the sky. This method was used to detect **pulsars**, starlike objects that emit rapid, regular, radio pulses. Astronomers have concluded that these pulses originate from the rapidly rotating remains of old supernovas. Some pulsars reveal that their rotation is slowing as the pulsing rate decreases.

Black Holes   The collapsed remnants of giant stars are called **black holes**. They possess a gravitational field so strong that no light or other radiation can escape. Black holes cannot be observed directly, but their presence can be detected by their effect on nearby matter. For example, some black holes are part of binary star systems. In such a system, matter from the visible companion gives off unusually intense X-rays as it is pulled towards the black hole.

Pulsars are also called neutron stars. Although only 20 km across, a neutron star still contains much of the supernova's original mass, and is unimaginably dense. Astronomers think a single spoonful of the material in a neutron star would have a mass of several million tonnes.

Most astronomers now accept black holes as the best available explanation for the X-rays observed coming from certain stars. Most astronomers are also keeping an open mind. If new evidence is found that does not support current theory, new observations will be made. This is the nature of all scientific inquiry. Theories last only as long as they continue to explain the observed facts.

Stellar Distances

For nearby stars, astronomers determine distances using the method of parallax shown in Figure 22-8. If the same star is viewed from position A in the spring, and again in the fall from position B, its position on the star map will seem to have shifted slightly.

Figure 22-8. How stellar distances are determined using the parallax method.

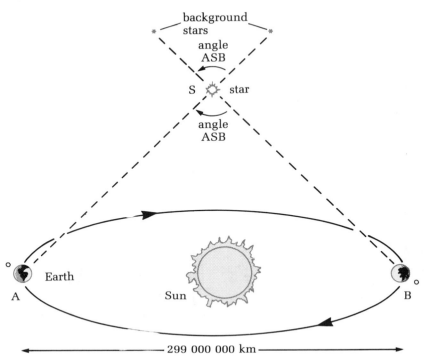

You can observe the parallax effect by holding a finger upright in front of your nose and viewing a distant wall. If you look first through your left eye and then through your right, the finger appears to move relative to the wall. The farther the finger is held from your nose, the smaller the apparent move. This is why the parallax method cannot be used to measure large stellar distances: the star's position will not shift enough to be seen.

The distance AB is equal to the width of Earth's orbit. Angle ASB is determined by using background stars to measure the apparent shift in the star's position. Once angle ASB is known, the stellar distance AS can be calculated.

Table 22-4 shows some of the 10 000 stellar distances that have been measured by this method. Other, less accurate, methods must be used for stars more than 100 light years away.

Star Properties

Many properties of stars can be determined by analyzing their radiations. Visible light is especially useful for this purpose.

Brightness   A star's brightness, or magnitude, is measured by comparison with the rating scale shown in Table 22-5. Brightness as seen from Earth is called **apparent magnitude**. This differs from true brightness because star distances vary. Astronomers therefore refer to **absolute magnitude**, which is the brightness as seen from a standard distance of 33 light years.

Table 22-4:   Stellar Distances of the 20 Closest Stars

Name	Constellation	Distance (in light years)
Proxima Centauri	Centaurus	4.22
α Centauri A	Centaurus	4.35
α Centauri B	Centaurus	4.35
Barnard's star	Ophiucus	5.90
Wolf 359	Leo	7.60
Lalande 21185	Ursa Major	8.12
Sirius A	Canis Major	8.64
Sirius B	Canis Major	8.64
UV Ceti A	Cetus	8.87
UV Ceti B	Cetus	8.87
Ross 154	Sagittarius	9.45
Ross 248	Andromeda	10.27
ε Eridani	Eridanus	10.76
Luyten 789-6	Aquarius	10.76
Ross 128	Virgo	10.82
61 Cygni A	Cygnus	11.08
61 Cygni B	Cygnus	11.08
ε Indi	Indus	11.21
Procyon A	Canis Minor	11.41
Procyon B	Canis Minor	11.41

Table 22-5:   The Magnitude of Some Stars

Apparent Magnitude	Object	Absolute Magnitude
-28	Sun	4.83
-13	full Moon	—
-1	Sirius	1
0	Rigel	-7
1	Betelgeuse	-5

A change of one in magnitude indicates a change in brightness of 2.5 times.

Table 22-6:   The Six Largest Stars

Name	Constellation	Diameter (expressed in solar diameters)
ε Aurigae	Auriga	2700
VV Cephei	Cepheus	1200
Rosalgheti	Hercules	800
Antares	Scorpio	500
Mira Ceti	Cetus	460
Betelgeuse	Orion	400

Mass   The masses of binary star systems can be determined by observing how long it takes the stars to revolve around one another. Other stellar masses can be determined from the star's brightness and distance from Earth. Generally, the least massive stars are the least bright.

Temperature   The colour of a star reveals its surface temperature. Orange and orange-red stars are coolest, yellow stars (like the Sun) are hotter, and white and bluish stars are hottest.

Chemical Composition and Age   The nuclear process that "powers" a star proceeds by stages. Astronomers know the rate at which a star's hydrogen is converted to helium, carbon, and finally, iron. Analysis of starlight with an instrument called a spectroscope indicates the kinds and amounts of materials present. The star's composition can then be used to estimate its age.

Size   Stars are too far away to measure their diameters using a telescope. However, methods involving analysis of the star's composition, brightness, and temperature can give an indication of the star's size (see Table 22-6).

The Life Cycle of Stars

An extra-terrestrial looking at photographs of many hundreds of humans could probably recognize the progression from young to old, from baby to grandparent. In much the same way, astronomers have hypothesized a life cycle to explain their observations of the stars. A simplified view of this life cycle is shown in Figure 22-9.

Figure 22-9. The life cycle of a star.

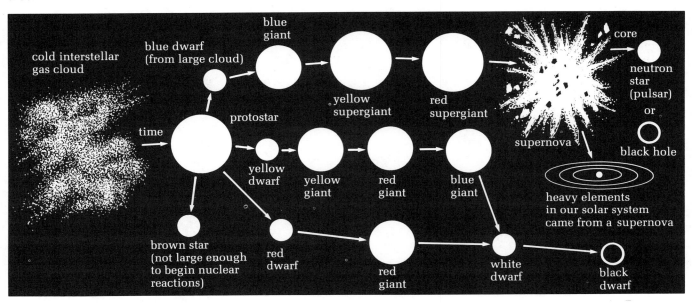

Formation of the Solar System

Supernova Shelton 1987 A has not followed exactly the current theory on the life cycle of stars shown in Figure 22-9. Continued study will be required to determine if this theory needs modification.

Do You Know?
In 1936 a new star suddenly appeared in the Orion Nebula. The birth of a star lasts for such a short time that few births have been observed.

Based on what they have learned about the life cycles of the Sun and other stars, astronomers have suggested a chain of events that could have led to the formation of our solar system. According to this theory, the process began with the exploded remains of a supernova, containing hydrogen, helium, and small amounts of solid matter. As the force of gravity acted to draw these particles together, pressures and temperatures rose high enough to create a nuclear reaction.

When the Sun first flared to life, some of the lighter gases were flung far beyond the young star, leaving the heavier elements behind. Gravity gathered the distant gas particles to form the gas giants. As solar activity diminished, gravity collected the heavier chunks and particles to form the inner planets. It is thought that asteroids, comets, and meteors are chunks that were never collected.

Figure 22-10. How the solar system was formed.

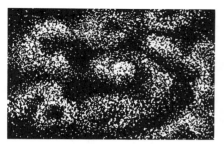 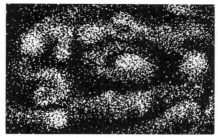 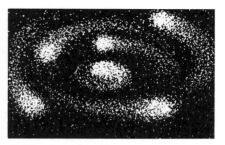

a) Exploded remains of a supernova in motion.

b) Gravity begins to draw material together.

c) Clumps of matter sweep up more of the exploded remains.

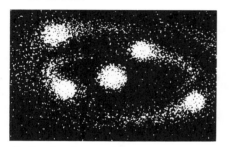 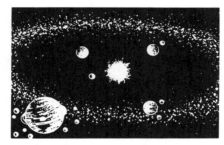

d) Sun begins nuclear reaction; lighter elements are flung outwards.

e) The solar system today.

Because this process takes millions of years, no human will ever see a solar system form from a supernova remnant. However, astronomers have recently discovered some stars with chunks and particles orbiting them. As astronomical instruments improve, we may one day discover a fully developed planetary system like our own.

Table 22-7: Stars with Orbiting Material

Star	Discovered By	Year
Fomalhaut	orbiting infrared telescope (IRAS)	1983
Vega	orbiting infrared telescope (IRAS)	1983
Beta Pictoris	orbiting infrared telescope (IRAS)	1983
Van Biesbroeck 8B	Kitt Peak Observatory, Univ. of Arizona	1983
Giclas 29-38	NASA infrared telescope in Hawaii	1987

Study Questions

1. Define: star, star system, binary star system, multiple star system, star cluster, pulsar.

2. For each pair of terms listed below, explain how the two are related and how they differ.
   a) nebula and supernova
   b) dark nebula and black hole
   c) open cluster and globular cluster
   d) variable star and true variable star
   e) apparent magnitude and absolute magnitude

3. a) List six properties of stars.
   b) Describe briefly how each property listed in a) can be determined from Earth.

4. Describe briefly the life cycle of a star the size of our Sun.

5. How do astronomers think our solar system was formed? Explain briefly how the formation of a solar system is linked to the life cycle of a star.

22.4   Galaxies of Stars

It is difficult for human minds to grasp the meaning of extremely large numbers. It may help to think of one thousand million as the number of seconds in just over 3000 years.

Many of the bright objects we see at night are **galaxies**. These are vast star collections that may contain as many as a million million stars. All of the stars in a galaxy stay in the same region of space and move together in a predictable way. The galaxy nearest to Earth is the one we live in; it is called the **Milky Way** because much of it appears as a milky-looking band of light in the sky.

The Milky Way Galaxy

When this milky band of light is viewed with a telescope, it can be seen to consist of numerous individual stars. Most stars seen with the unaided eye also belong to the Milky Way. Figure 22-11 shows how the Milky Way's one hundred thousand million stars would appear if viewed from space. Our Sun is located in one of the galaxy's spiral arms, about 33 000 light years from the galactic centre. The entire galaxy is about 100 000 light years across and is rotating very slowly, so that the Sun revolves around the galactic centre once every 225 000 000 years. When we view the Milky Way we see it "edge-on", looking towards the centre of the galaxy. Because of gas, dust, and numerous stars along this line of sight,

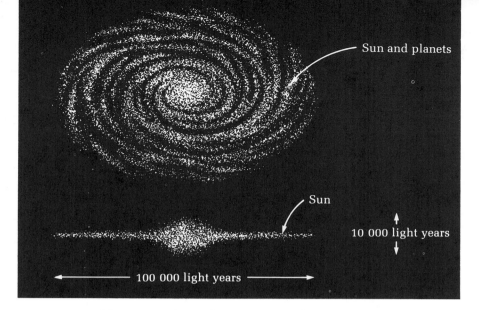

Figure 22-11. The Milky Way galaxy.

Sun and planets

Sun

10 000 light years

100 000 light years

it is impossible to see the galaxy's centre with optical telescopes. Infrared observations, however, reveal many older, cooler stars located in this region.

Open star clusters are distributed throughout the Milky Way. They rotate with the galaxy, and will eventually be dispersed as the gravitational pulls of other stars scatter them. Globular clusters survive longer because they are outside the main galaxy, and thus are influenced by fewer gravitational pulls.

Star clusters are much smaller than galaxies, although both may appear as misty patches in the sky. The largest globular clusters contain only hundreds of thousands of stars.

Other Galaxies of Stars

Many other galaxies have been observed; some appear spiral-shaped like the Milky Way, some elliptical, and some irregular. Observations show that galaxies are moving away from one another, with the farthest moving away the fastest.

As we look at these distant objects or their photographs, we must remember that we are not seeing them as they are now, but as they appeared when the light left them — thousands, millions, or perhaps a thousand million years ago.

a) The Andromeda Galaxy and two companion galaxies. **b)** The Whirlpool Galaxy. **c)** A barred spiral galaxy in the constellation Eridanus.

a)

b)

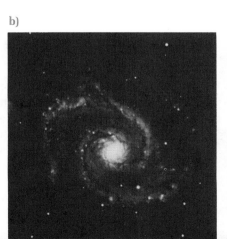

c)

Table 22-8:   Some Star Clusters, Nebulae, and Galaxies

Name	Constellation	Distance (light years)	Appearance
The Pleiades (M45) Cluster	between Cassiopeia and Orion near Taurus	415	Cluster of seven stars, easily seen with the unaided eye. Binoculars reveal many more of the estimated 250 total. There is a nebula around Merope which might be visible with binoculars or a small telescope.
The Hyades Cluster	Taurus around Aldebaran	150	Scattered cluster, best seen with binoculars. It appears in a direct line of sight, around the red star Aldebaran (distance 68 light years). The cluster is quite large and is best seen through binoculars.
Perseus Double Cluster	Perseus	7300	Two clusters containing about 650 stars. Covers an area about twice the size of the full Moon. Best seen with binoculars.
Orion Nebula (M42)	Orion	1300	Located in the lower chain of three stars in the constellation. It may be visible to the unaided eye as a hazy cloud. Best seen with binoculars.
Andromeda Galaxy (M31)	Andromeda	2.2 million	May be visible with the unaided eye as a small diffuse patch of light. A pair of binoculars or a small telescope should reveal its elliptical shape.
Hercules Globular Cluster (M13)	Hercules	22 500	This older cluster contains an estimated 300 000 stars packed closely together, and should be visible with binoculars or a small telescope.
Spiral Galaxy (M81)	Ursa Major	18 million	Located one-third of the way from α Ursae Majoris to Polaris. It is visible in a small telescope as a roundish, softly glowing patch of light that grows noticeably brighter towards the centre.

Activity 22-4:   Observing Star Clusters, Nebulae, and Galaxies

Except for the Pleiades (an easily seen star cluster), these objects must be observed with an optical device from a location unaffected by city lights. Consult your teacher for observing suggestions or for more detailed star maps. Record all observations in your log book.

Materials

star charts (pages 686 to 687)

(optional) flashlight covered with tissue paper

log book

binoculars

Procedure

Table 22-8 lists the objects you will be looking for.

1. Before going outside, familiarize yourself with the positions of the objects on the star charts.
2. Locate each of the objects listed in Table 22-8 in the sky.
3. Sketch or describe the appearance of each object.

Discussion

1. a) Which of the objects listed in the table were you able to observe?
   b) Did the objects you observed seem to fit the definitions in the table for each type of object? Explain.
2. a) What difficulties did you encounter in attempting to observe these objects?
   b) How could these difficulties be overcome?

Figure 22-12.

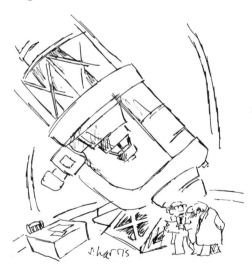

"The only part of the universe which *isn't* expanding is the budget for this place."

Clusters of Galaxies

Observations have shown that the galaxies themselves are grouped into clusters. Our Milky Way is the second largest member of a group called the **local cluster**. This cluster contains more than two dozen members. The largest member is the Andromeda Galaxy, 2 000 000 light years away. The nearest member, at 200 000 light years, consists of two small galaxies called the Large and Small Magellanic Clouds. There are probably other galaxies as well, either too faint to be observed or obscured by dust.

In addition to galaxies being grouped by their nearness to one another, they can be grouped by their types and their motion relative to each other. Recent observations show that clusters of galaxies can be grouped into **superclusters** and **supercluster complexes**. The supercluster complex to which our Milky Way belongs is thought to include millions of galaxies, stretching across 10% of observable space.

Understanding the Universe

The **universe** includes all matter, energy, and space in existence anywhere. But where did the universe come from? How did it start? Will it continue forever? If not, how will it end? The answers to these questions belong to the realm of **cosmology**. This branch of astronomy attempts to describe the formation, structure, and development of the universe. Cosmology is based on observing the positions and movements of matter in the universe.

Many theories have been suggested to explain how the universe began, but only two have been supported by observations so far. The Big Bang Theory suggests that the universe began around fifteen thousand million years ago. Space, time, and matter came into being simultaneously during a gigantic explosion. As shown in Figure 22-13, matter was propelled in all directions, eventually forming the stars and all other observable objects.

The Oscillating Universe Theory is based on the "big bang" idea. It suggests that the universe first expands after a big bang, and then contracts. Figure 22-14 shows that after the contraction is complete, another big bang spreads the materials apart again in a repeating cycle.

At present, astronomers have not gathered enough evidence to make one theory appear more likely than another. Even if future observations clarify this issue, no theory answers the fundamental questions of where the matter and energy came from in the first place, and what will happen to it eventually. The oldest science still has plenty of unanswered questions for future astronomers to ponder.

Figure 22-13. The Big Bang Theory.

According to this theory, **a)** a big ball of hydrogen exploded, **b)** galaxies were formed where parts of the expanding hydrogen cloud condensed, and **c)** the galaxies continued to move outward.

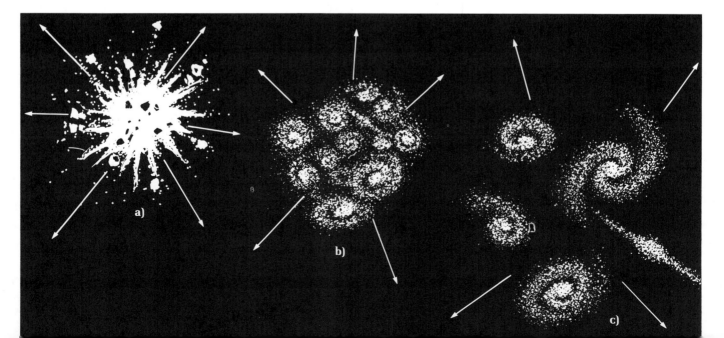

Figure 22-14. The Oscillating Universe Theory.

a) Big Bang. **b)** Galaxies form.
c) Galaxies move outward (present).
d) Galaxies halt (future). **e)** Galaxies fall inward. **f)** Big Bang cycle begins again.

Study Questions

1. a) Define: galaxy, Milky Way, universe, cosmology.
   b) Explain how the terms in a) are related to each other.

2. Draw a labelled sketch of the Milky Way Galaxy, indicating a) the position of the Sun, and b) the motion of the Sun.

3. a) How do galaxies (other than the Milky Way) appear when seen with the unaided eye? through a telescope?
   b) For what other bright objects might a galaxy be mistaken? Explain how you could tell the difference.

4. a) How are the galaxies moving relative to one another?
   b) "We look back in time when we look at other galaxies." Explain what is meant by this statement.

5. a) What is meant by the "local cluster" of galaxies?
   b) Describe how the local cluster is related to still larger structures in the universe.

6. a) Explain how the Oscillating Universe Theory is linked to the Big Bang Theory.
   b) Explain how the theories differ.

IAN SHELTON
(1958-   )

Ian Shelton, one of the discoverers of Supernova Shelton 1987A (see photos on page 717), grew up in a Winnipeg suburb, where he began his astronomy career by building an observatory in his backyard. After obtaining an undergraduate degree, he twice tried graduate school but dropped out both times.

Eventually, his keen interest in astronomy and his mechanical ability in repairing telescopes led to a job with the University of Toronto observatory at Las Campanas in central Chile. There, on a windswept Andes peak 2400 m above sea level, he was responsible for maintaining a 60-cm telescope. Although previous technicians had lasted on the mountain for only a year, Shelton spent a total of four years there before his discovery. In his spare time, he had repaired an old 1905 photographic telescope that recorded pictures on glass plates 36 cm square.

On the night of February 23-24, 1987, Shelton had planned to test the telescope by photographing a neighbouring galaxy called the Large Magellanic Cloud. When the plate was developed, an unusually bright object could be seen in the galaxy. After comparing the new plate with a photograph from the previous night, Shelton realized that the

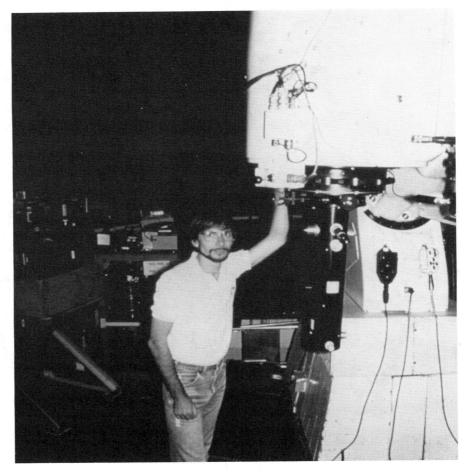

Ian Shelton and the main telescope at the University of Toronto's La Campanas Observatory.

bright object was new. He then went outside, and was able to observe the object with the unaided eye.

In a science which is chiefly based on observations rather than experiments, astronomers must wait for events such as this to happen before they can be studied. And the professionals are not always on hand. The other two discoverers of the supernova, Oscar Dunhalde (a

night assistant at the observatory) and Albert Jones (an Australian) are both regarded as amateurs, as is Shelton himself. Although he lacks the doctoral degree held by most professional astronomers, Shelton's discovery of this supernova proves that astronomy is still a science in which amateurs can make tremendous contributions.

Meet a Research Assistant in Radio Astronomy— Laura Carriere

Laura has a Bachelor of Science in astronomy and works in the Department of Astronomy at the University of Toronto.

Q. WHAT IS RADIO ASTRONOMY?
A. It is the branch of astronomy that monitors radio emission from celestial objects. Radio waves are like light waves but have a longer wavelength. Some objects can be studied more easily with radio emission than with visible light. Compared to optical astronomy, which has been around since Galileo's time, radio astronomy is quite new— the first radio telescope was built in the 1930s.

Q. WHAT KIND OF INSTRU-MENTS ARE USED?
A. Radio telescopes, which are like large dish antennas. Canada has two radio telescope sites, one in British Columbia, the other in Algonquin Park, Ontario. Most professors who work in radio astronomy apply for some time at the National Radio Astronomy Observatory in New Mexico. It has linear arrays of radio antennas distributed over a very large area of the countryside.

Q. WHAT KIND OF WORK ARE YOU DOING?
A. One of our main projects is studying Galaxy M82. In a galaxy, which is a group of stars bound together by gravity, things are constantly evolving—new stars are being created and old ones are dying. We have found an area in the centre of this galaxy where new stars are being created at a great rate. These can be detected by the radio waves they give off.

Q. WHAT ROLE DO YOU PLAY IN THIS PROJECT?
A. My professor has been observing the galaxy since 1981. Once or twice a year he goes to New Mexico to gather data, which I put into our computer system in Toronto. I first make maps by running a number of computer programs on the data. Once a map is produced, I can display it on a screen. We measure the strength of each radio source, and compare that to our last observations. With this information we make a graph plotting the strength of the source versus time.

Q. WERE YOU INTERESTED IN ASTRONOMY AS A CHILD?
A. Yes, when I was little I had a telescope. I also remember being one of the few people in high school who enjoyed going to physics classes.

Q. WHEN DID YOU START WORKING?
A. After I graduated from university. Most people who study astronomy go on to do graduate work. But I was pleased to get this job because it combined astronomy and working with computers.

Q. HOW DID YOU BECOME INVOLVED WITH COMPUTERS?
A. I became interested in computers while I was at university because I've always loved problem-solving. I can apply that skill to computer work. I spend about 50% of my time on computers.

Q. WHAT DO YOU LIKE ABOUT YOUR JOB?
A. I like the combination of computers and astronomy. The university environment is great, and I like the people I work with. Sometimes astronomy can be all-consuming—it attracts people who want to do nothing else. I think the most interesting people in this field are the ones who have outside interests.

Review Questions

A: Knowledge

1. In what units are distances commonly measured in the solar system?

2. a) What is the largest object in the solar system?
   b) Name, in order, the five largest planets in the solar system.
   c) How many planets do not have satellites? Name them.
   d) Which planets are believed to have solid surfaces?
   e) Which planets are believed to have some sort of gaseous atmosphere?
   f) Which planets have been explored by i) fly-bys, ii) landers, iii) human explorers?

3. Why have some astronomers suggested that there might be a tenth planet in the solar system?

4. How would the appearance of a planet in the sky differ from that of a star?

5. a) What is parallax?
   b) Describe an example of parallax.
   c) How is parallax useful to astronomers?

6. What is the difference between apparent magnitude and absolute magnitude of a star?

7. What information can the colour of a star reveal?

8. a) What is the Milky Way Galaxy?
   b) Name some nearby galaxies.
   c) How are galaxies classified?

9. a) What is the "Big Bang" Theory?
   b) What evidence has been found to support this theory?

B: Application

10. What is the difference between a satellite and a planet?

11. The Earth is one astronomical unit from the Sun. How many astronomical units from the Sun is the closest star?

12. a) Explain why some data is missing in Table 22-1 for the planet Pluto.
    b) What could be done to fill in this missing information? Be specific.

13. Describe the technological developments in the 1960s that contributed significant astronomical information to our observations from Earth. List several recent projects that have further increased our knowledge.

14. What is the difference between asteroids and planets?

15. What is the difference between comets and meteorites?

16. In 1979 a meteorite, which scientists believe came from the planet Mars, was found in Antarctica. Suggest possible ways that scientists could test this hypothesis.

17. Generally, more meteors are visible after midnight than before. Explain how this might relate to the motion of the Earth around the Sun.

18. Describe how parallax could be used to determine the distance of a nearby star.

19. a) List, in order, the five stars closest to Earth.
    b) Classify each star according to the type of star system in which it is located.

20. Astronomers use two systems of magnitude to measure the brightness of a star. Which system would be more useful in comparing how two stars appear in the sky? Explain why.

21. Material has been discovered orbiting around the star Vega. Describe how this material might eventually form a solar system with planets.

22. Why is the discovery of a supernova like Shelton 1987A important to astronomers?

23. a) In what ways is astronomy predictable?
    b) In what ways is astronomy unpredictable?

24. State, as completely as possible, your address in the universe.

C: Problem Solving

25. State two differences among the orbits of the planets in the solar system.

26. What problems would humans face if they tried to explore the solar system on spaceships? Base your answer on present technology.

27. A solar day is 24 h, while the time taken for the Earth to rotate once on its axis is 23 h 56 min 4 s. Considering the motions involved, how can the difference of 3 min 56 s be explained?

28. Some planets, when viewed from the Earth, exhibit retrograde motion. Explain, considering the motions of the two planets involved, how retrograde motion is produced. List the planets that you would expect to exhibit this motion.

29. Suppose you are trying to prove to a friend that the Moon is closer to us than the stars. Describe an experiment that could be used as evidence.

30. Because comet hunting does not require powerful instruments, many comets are discovered each year by amateurs. Describe how you might go about conducting a comet search. In what direction(s) should you look? What might a comet look like, near or far away from the Sun? How could you prove a starlike object might be a comet?

31. Every year, there are many serious reports of unidentified flying objects (UFOs). What objects in the sky might be mistaken for UFOs? As an investigator, describe how you could collect data to determine whether an object was astronomical.

Try This

1. **Meteor Showers**
   On a clear dark night, preferably in the country away from city lights, position yourself comfortably to watch an area of the sky and count the number of meteorites seen within a given time. Usually the count will average about one meteorite every 15 min. Check with Table 22-3 for the date of a well-known meteor shower, and perform a similar count. Compare your two counts.

2. **Planet Sightings**
   The planets Venus, Mars, Jupiter, and Saturn are easily visible to the unaided eye. Consult an astronomical almanac for each planet's current location, and locate as many as possible. If you have access to binoculars or a small telescope, observe and record the unique appearance of each planet.

Space Exploration

The Issue: Should countries continue to spend large sums of money to explore and develop space?

Since 1957, when the Soviet Union launched Sputnik 1, nations have sent into space over 3000 craft, both manned and unmanned. Plans for the next thirty years include the launching and supplying of an orbiting space station, the development of settlements on the Moon, and manned flights to Mars. These activities will require great energy and expertise as well as abundant materials and money. The Apollo program to the Moon, for example, cost about $17 000 million (in 1985 dollars), while replacing the lost Challenger Orbiter will cost $3000 million, and estimates for the Mars mission run to $40 000 million.

Since space exploration began, some people have questioned the cost and effort involved. Most money for the space programs comes from taxes collected by governments. Opponents of the programs ask whether the benefits to humanity are worth the costs. They argue that using the same money and scientific expertise to deal with problems on Earth might be more beneficial. The amount spent by Canada for foreign aid development in 1986 in over 70 countries was $2200 million, far less than the budget for space exploration.

Defenders of the space programs argue that the important short- and long-term benefits justify the high costs. Orbiting satellites, for example, are used in telecommunications, weather forecasting, predicting crop yields, monitoring pollution, finding mineral resources, and other areas of broad social benefit. Space exploration has stimulated discoveries that have increased our knowledge about the structure and behaviour of the universe, and the Earth and its atmosphere. Many of these discoveries, such as the discovery of solar winds and electric fields in space, required sending craft into space.

There are indirect as well as direct benefits that come from applying the knowledge gained from space programs to other areas of science and technology. Many materials and techniques designed for space programs have been used in areas, including medicine and computer technology, food packaging, wheelchair design, and the design of better ball-point pens. However, some people believe that it would be less expensive to research these spin-off benefits directly. Furthermore, much

Should more money be spent to send astronauts like Canada's Marc Garneau (left) into space?

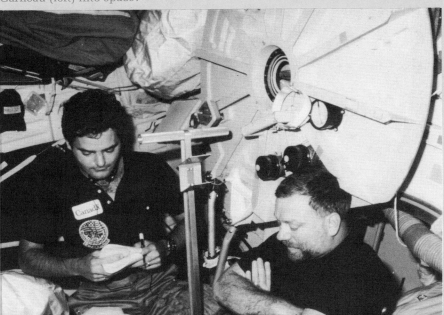

present space-program funding relates to the military use of space, and not to scientific research or exploration.

In this activity, you will develop a list of the possible benefits of continued space exploration, and a list of alternative uses on which the same money could be spent. Your group will then consider these lists and decide how they would relate the issue described above.

Exploring the Issue

A. Brainstorming

This is an activity designed to generate ideas. You should not, at this point, worry about the value of each idea, no matter how ridiculous it may seem. You will judge the merit of each suggestion later.

Form groups of about six students each. Have one student record on a large sheet of paper all the ideas suggested. Try to produce ideas related to the following questions: "What benefits are there to continuing space exploration?" and "In what alternative ways could we spend this money?"

B. Gathering the Evidence

1. Obtain from your teacher or librarian lists of magazines, scientific journals, audiovisual titles, and clipping files that are available in the school or community library.

2. From the above lists, check off possible sources of information on this topic. Based on your brainstorming activity, you may also want to contact various organizations to gather information on alternative ways of spending the money for space exploration.

3. Divide the sources among the members of your group.

4. Each student should be responsible for gathering five or six pieces of information. In your search, you should look for possible ways of reducing the cost of space exploration. Look also for information comparing the costs of space exploration with those of other government activities.

C. Discussing the Issue

1. In a class discussion, each group should present its answers to the two questions. Tabulate the suggestions on the blackboard.

2. Each student should make a copy of the suggestions. For each question, number the suggestions in order of importance. When deciding the importance of a suggestion, you should bear in mind the associated problems, the overall value of the suggestion, and its potential for success.

3. Compare your order of importance with the others in your group. Come to a group decision on the issue.

4. Compare your group's response with that of other groups.

D. Making a Recommendation

Based on the conclusions of the groups in your class, draw up a recommendation about the future of space exploration.

Unit 8 Wrap-Up
Unit Summary

Astronomers gather information by observing objects and events in the skies. They record their observations, for example, the position and appearance of an object, in a log book. Records of observations helped astronomers to realize that the apparent motion of the Sun and the stars is due to the Earth's *rotation*. At night the Earth's rotation makes the stars in the northern hemisphere appear to move about *Polaris* (the *North Star*) in a circle, while Polaris itself remains stationary. Because Polaris appears as the only fixed point in the sky, it is important to navigation.

The *Sun* is a star that produces energy by a nuclear reaction. Physical features of the Sun include *sunspots*, *flares*, and *prominences*. Sunspots can be viewed on the Sun's surface indirectly, by *projection*. The apparent motion of the Sun can be used to mark the passage of time.

Maria ("seas"), *craters*, *mountains*, and *rays* can be observed on the surface of the *Moon*. Because of its position relative to the Sun and the Earth, the Moon goes through a series of *phases* each month. Sometimes the Moon's position produces a solar or lunar *eclipse*.

The positions of *stars* are recorded on star charts. In a *constellation* (a recognizable group of stars), a brighter or unusual star often has a particular name, while other stars are designated by Greek letters. Despite appearances to the contrary, stars lie at different distances from the Earth, and move with respect to each other. These changes occur slowly, however, and are difficult to observe. Starlike objects wandering about the sky became known as *planets*.

Astronomers use optical as well as radio *telescopes* to gather information about sky objects. Artificial *satellites* orbiting the Earth collect additional information.

The *solar system* is made up of nine planets moving in *elliptical orbits* around the Sun. All except Pluto have orbits lying approximately on the same plane.

Satellites orbit many of the planets. *Comets*, *asteroids*, and *meteors*—solid objects much smaller than planets—also move throughout the solar system.

It is impossible to make a scale model of the solar system using the same scale for planet diameters and distances from the Sun, because the solar system is so vast. Astronomers use robot probes to carry out initial explorations of the planets.

In studying the stars, astronomers have succeeded in measuring *distance*, *brightness*, *mass*, *temperature*, *chemical composition*, *age*, and *size*. This knowledge has revealed a life cycle of stars, which has furthered our knowledge of the formation of the Sun and the planets.

In the course of studying other *galaxies* and the objects they contain, astronomers have suggested two theories to explain the formation, structure, and development of the *universe*: the *Big Bang Theory* and the *Oscillating Universe Theory*.

Key Terms

asteroid	planet
astronomical unit	reflecting telescope
astronomy	refracting telescope
comet	revolution
constellation	rotation
galaxy	satellite
meteor	star
meteorite	star charts
nebula	star cluster
phases	universe

Unit Practice and Review

A: Short Answer

True or False

State whether each statement is true or false. Correct each false statement.

1. The position of an object in the sky is determined by measuring the height of the object above the horizon in "fists".

2. The Moon is visible at some time during the day or night in every phase, except, the new Moon.

3. Most of the information about the universe that astronomers collect from the surface of the Earth is transmitted by light and some radio waves.

4. Most asteroids follow an orbit between Mars and Jupiter.

5. The Sun is located in one of the spiral arms of the Milky Way Galaxy.

Multiple Choice

In each question below, select the best answer.

1. A spectacular eruption of gas from the surface of the Sun is called a:
   - a) sunspot
   - b) prominence
   - c) corona
   - d) flare

2. Which of the following is not a surface feature of the Moon?
   - a) terminator
   - b) rays
   - c) maria
   - d) mountains

3. The Big Dipper is part of the constellation:
   - a) Cassiopeia
   - b) Ursa Minor
   - c) Ursa Major
   - d) Canis Major

4. A nebula is:
   - a) a cloud of gas reflecting the light of a star or stars.
   - b) a cloud of gas absorbing lignt from stars and then reradiating it.
   - c) a cloud of dust blocking the light from other stars.
   - d) all of the above.

5. The most distant object in the following list is:
   - a) the Sun
   - b) the Andromeda Galaxy
   - c) Phekda
   - d) α Centauri

Complete the Statement

Complete each of the following statements with the correct word or phrase. Do not write in this book.

1. A recognizable group of stars, such as Ursa Minor, is called a ___?___ .

2. A telescope that collects light by means of a large glass lens is called a ___?___ telescope.

3. Rocklike objects that enter the Earth's atmosphere and reach the ground before burning up are called ___?___ .

4. Stars that change in brightness due to internal changes are called ___?___ .

5. Planetary distances in our solar system are measured in ___?___ .

Matching Items

Match each item in Column A with the appropriate item in Column B.

1. *Column A*
   - i) the planet that appears most similar to the Moon
   - ii) the planet whose surface is always obscured by clouds
   - iii) the planet with the greatest mass
   - iv) the most distant planet from the Sun
   - v) the planet with the most visible ring system

   Column B
   - a) Jupiter
   - b) Mars
   - c) Mercury
   - d) Neptune
   - e) Pluto
   - f) Saturn
   - g) Venus

2. *Column A*
   - i) a collection of loosely grouped, younger stars
   - ii) a collection of many millions of stars
   - iii) a collection of closely grouped older stars
   - iv) a collection of stars occupying the same region of space
   - v) a group of stars whose position can be used to find other stars

   Column B
   - a) galaxy
   - b) star cluster
   - c) binary stars
   - d) open cluster
   - e) globular cluster
   - f) pointer stars
   - g) multiple stars

3. Column A

   i) glows from the heat
     of friction

   ii) held in place by a
     planet's gravitational
     force

   iii) can absorb, reflect,
     and reradiate light

   iv) causes craters on some
     planets

   v) principal source of light
     in our solar system

Column B

a) meteorite
b) satellite
c) asteroid
d) comet
e) meteor
f) star
g) supernova

B: Knowledge and Application

1. What is the difference between the rotation and the revolution of a planet?

2. Classify each of the following motions as rotation or revolution:
   a) the motion of Pluto around the Sun
   b) the spinning of the Earth about its axis
   c) the motion of the Sun in the Milky Way Galaxy
   d) the motion of a comet in the solar system
   e) the equator of Jupiter moving faster than the polar region
   f) the movement of sunspots on the Sun

3. State the similarities and the differences between refracting and reflecting telescopes.

4. List at least five ways by which astronomers obtain information about distant objects.

5. Draw a sketch of the Earth and another planet in circular orbits around the Sun, so that the Earth and the other planet are:
   a) at their greatest distance from each other;
   b) closest to each other.

6. Summarize how the motions and apparent motions of the Earth, Moon, Sun, and stars have contributed to time-keeping. Identify each actual motion and each apparent motion.

7. List five properties that can be discovered about a distant star by analyzing the light that reaches the Earth.

8. State an approximate length of time for each of the following events:
   a) the Moon goes from first quarter to full Moon
   b) Mars moves around the Sun
   c) the solar system moves around the galaxy
   d) light from the Sun reaches Pluto
   e) a star rises in the east and sets in the west

9. a) Sketch the appearance of the Moon:
      i) at first quarter phase
      ii) at last quarter phase
      iii) between new Moon and first quarter phase
      iv) between last quarter and new Moon phase

   b) Sketch the relative positions of the Sun, the Moon, and the Earth during each of these phases.

10. Describe one way in which you would be able to recognize the difference between:
   a) a star and a planet
   b) a nebula and a galaxy
   c) a comet and a meteorite
   d) a constellation and a star cluster
   e) Ursa Major and Ursa Minor
   f) a variable star and a true variable star

C: Problem Solving

1. What is the main reason that solar eclipses are shorter than lunar eclipses? List several other factors that might affect the duration of each type of eclipse.

2. Which planet(s) in the solar system might humans colonize one day? Which factors would affect the choice of planet(s)? What additional information would we need before attempting to colonize a planet?

3. Jupiter and Venus have appeared adjacent to one another in the night sky. Sketch their positions, relative to the Earth and the Sun, that produce this view. What other unique arrangements produce the same results?

D: Challengers

1. Why is the discovery of material orbiting other stars important to our understanding of the formation of our solar system? What things might we look for in such discoveries?

2. List the planets in the solar system that have satellites, the number of satellites each planet has, and the satellites' relative sizes. Is there any pattern in your findings? Suggest a possible theory to explain your results. What additional information would you need to test your theory?

3. At noon solar time, the shadow of an object points directly north. Devise a method, using only a watch and an object's shadow, to determine the north direction at any time of day.

Project Ideas

1. Consult an astronomical calendar to determine which planets can be seen at your location at this time of year. Decide which observations you will make regularly over two months. For example, watch for changes in brightness by comparing a planet with known stars, or log the planet's position relative to the background stars. Write a report summarizing your observations and your results. Suggest ways of increasing the number and the type of observations that an amateur astronomer could make.

2. Many people and organizations have contributed to our knowledge and understanding of astronomy. Write a report on the contributions of any one of the following:
   a) Eratosthenes of Cyrene, Copernicus, Galileo, Newton, Brahe, Kepler, Hershell, Einstein, Lovell, Hawking, Sagan, Shelton, or a scientist of your own choice.
   b) The International Astronomy Union (I.A.U.), the S.E.T.I. (Search for Extraterrestrial Intelligence) Program, the Canadian Space Agency, NASA, the Royal Astronomical Society, the Planetary Society, or an astronomical agency of your own choice.

3. The Moon looks larger near the horizon than when it is high in the sky. Design and build a simple instrument to determine if this is an optical illusion.

4. Composer Gustav Holst wrote his "Planet Suite" between 1914 and 1918. Research this piece of music and write a report summarizing your findings. Include how the knowledge and experiences of that period influenced music.

Readings

Covington, Michael. *Astrophotography for the Amateur.* New York: Cambridge University Press, 1985. (Contains instructions on how to take pictures of sky objects, using equipment and materials readily available to the hobbyist.)

McAleer, Neil. *The Cosmic Mind-Boggling Book.* New York: Warner Books Inc., 1982. (A treasure-trove of statistics about the universe, translated into easily understood terms.)

Moore, Patrick. *Travellers in Space and Time.* Garden City, New York: Doubleday and Company, Inc., 1984. (This account of the travels of an imaginary being from the Andromeda Galaxy provides a good perspective on sizes and distances, as well as current techniques used to gather information about the universe.)

Moore, Patrick. *Stargazing: Astronomy Without a Telescope.* New York: Barron's Educational Series, Inc., 1985. (A practical guide to identifying stars, constellations, and planets, and how to follow their motions through the sky.)

Preiss, Byron, ed. *The Planets.* New York: Bantam Books Inc., 1985. (A collection of essays and science fiction stories about the planets and other objects in our solar system.)

IX

the EFFECTS
of PULL on HEAT
ABSORPTION

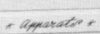

* Purpose *   * Apparatus *

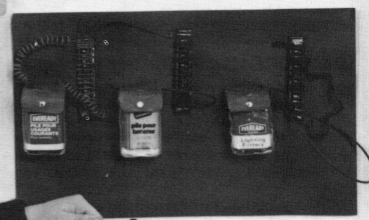

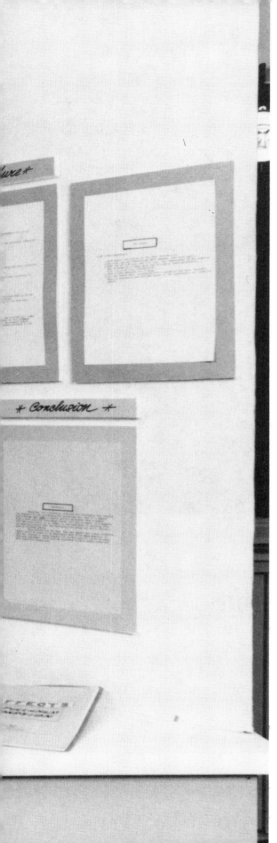

Science Project

A science project enables you to use the scientific skills you have learned in this course—observing, hypothesizing, experimenting, and using controls and variables—on a subject of your own choosing. A science project allows you to explore—in more depth than is possible in the classroom—a scientific field, question, or process that you find interesting. Instead of being told what to do, *you* decide what to study, what questions to ask, and how to design the procedure. This unit deals with how to plan, research, and carry out a successful science project.

Chapter 23 Science Project

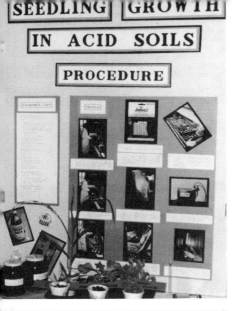

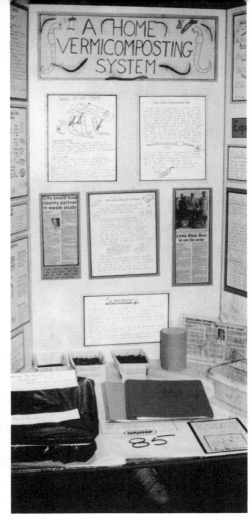

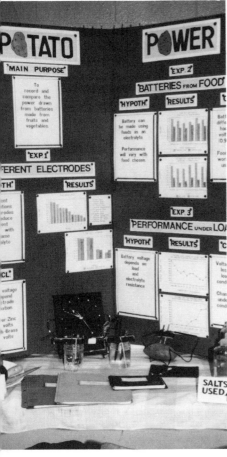

Chapter 23
Science Project

23.1 Planning a Science Project

What is a Science Project?

A science project is any scientific study that you plan and carry out yourself. It could be a survey of the opinions of people towards a particular science-related topic — for instance, the energy "crisis". It could be a collection of some sort, a comparison of computer software programs, or a study of the accuracy of calculators. It could be a model of the human heart or of a future space station. A science project can also be an experiment. In fact, an experiment is an excellent type of project to undertake, since it involves all stages of the scientific approach.

When you finish this section, you should be able to:
- identify and write good questions to investigate
- make a hypothesis linking the independent and dependent variables
- identify and classify the variables of an experiment
- design and perform a controlled experiment

Choosing the Project Idea

The first step in planning a science project is to choose a topic. Sometimes this is easy, but if you have no idea what you want to investigate, then some research is necessary. At the end of this chapter is a list of 50 project ideas. Some additional places to look for project ideas are shown in the margin.

Hobbies and sports can also suggest project ideas. You could look around your home for ideas, such as comparing the life of various brands and types of batteries. Ideas for possible project topics are endless. Whatever topic you finally choose, have a genuine interest in it. It will be much easier to devote the time and effort necessary if you are enthusiastic about the project.

Keeping a Science Project Notebook

It is a good idea to keep a notebook specially for your science project. When doing research, you should write down the sources of your information. If, say, you find a helpful article in a magazine, write down the name of the article, the author, the name of the magazine, the issue number (or date of issue), and the pages on which the article begins and ends. If you are talking to a teacher or other knowledgeable person about your subject, note down the person's name, the date of your conversation, and what you talked about. Following this practice will enable you to refer back to the original sources at later stages of the project, instead of trying to remember where the information came from. You will also need this information to do the **List of Sources (Bibliography)** that must be included with your project report.

Sources for Topics

science magazines (*Discover, Youth Science News,* etc.)

nature and science-related magazines (*Equinox, Canadian Geographic*)

newspapers

science books

textbooks and lab manuals

science television programs ("The Nature of Things", "Vista", "Owl/TV")

library vertical files

encyclopedias (under subject headings)

teachers, parents, professionals, etc.

A page from a student's science project notebook.

Asking a Good Question

Asking good questions is the key to good experimenting. Without a good question or problem, you may have difficulty knowing what to focus on in an experiment. A good question has three characteristics.

1. **It is simple and specific**. The question "Which bubblegum is better?" is difficult to answer. What is meant by better? More enjoyable taste, longer lasting flavour, or the capacity to produce larger bubbles? The word "better" can mean different things to different people. Rather, a good question focuses on a particular quality or characteristic, such as "Which brand of bubblegum will produce the largest bubbles?"

2. **It suggests an experiment that you can do yourself**. You can easily chew bubblegum, blow bubbles, and use a centimetre ruler to measure the size of the bubbles produced. Questions such as "What is the effect of aerosol sprays on the ozone layer of the atmosphere?" are important questions for scientists who have the appropriate equipment and the means to answer the question. Your question should lead to an experiment that you have the ability and the means to perform yourself.

3. **It compares one thing or situation to another**. You might compare plant growth using fresh and salt water, or the viscosity of oil at different temperatures. You might compare the sizes of bubbles produced when the same amount of different brands of bubblegum is chewed. Note that the question does not ask *why* the brands are different. "Why" questions are generally very difficult to answer. Try to avoid using the word "why" in your questions.

Using the Scientific Approach

Now that you have selected a topic and asked an appropriate question, the next step is to apply the scientific approach to the experiment.

Hypothesizing

A good hypothesis depends on a good question. A question can give rise to several hypotheses. If the reasoning behind your hypothesis is sensible, then your hypothesis is acceptable.

When you have chosen a topic or an idea, you may wish to do further research in order to come up with a good question for an experiment. It is also possible, after you have done more research, that you would like to modify your original idea, or change it altogether.

Identifying Variables

There are three kinds of variables in an experiment. They are:

1. *The Independent Variable (IV).* This is the variable that the experimenter changes. In an experiment to determine whether plants grow faster when they receive more fertilizer, the amount of fertilizer used is the independent variable. Sometimes, the independent variable is the item that is being experimented with. When different bubblegums are compared, the independent variable is the brand of bubblegum. The values of the independent variable are determined by the experimenter.

2. *The Dependent Variable (DV).* This variable is the outcome or result variable. It depends upon or responds to the change made in the independent variable. In the experiment comparing plant growth, the dependent variable is the rate of growth of the plants. In the bubblegum experiment, the bubble size is the dependent variable.

3. *The Controlled Variable (CV).* Controlled variables are used to keep an experiment "fair". If one plant in the fertilizer experiment gets more sun than the others, its growth cannot be fairly compared to that of the other plants. If more pieces of one brand of bubblegum are chewed than the other, this too is not a fair test when comparing the bubble size of the two brands. Also, each brand should be chewed by the same person and chewed for the same length of time. It often takes considerable thought and effort to identify all of the controlled variables in an experiment and to make sure that they *are* controlled.

Example of a good question

What effect does hard running have on the human pulse rate?
This is a good question because i) it is simple and direct, ii) it suggests an experiment you can do, iii) it compares one thing to another.

Hypothesis: If different distances are run at an all-out pace, then the pulse rate will increase with distance.

Independent variable: distance run

Dependent variable: pulse rate (beats per minute)

Controlled variables: same track, similar weather conditions, same runner, same equipment worn, same time of day, completely rested before each trial. (These are only some of the controlled variables.)

Activity 23-1:   Identifying Questions and Variables

Procedure

1. Write down each of the following questions. Beside each one, explain whether the question is a good one for a project.

   Which brand of paper towel absorbs the most water?

   Why are feathers light?

   What effect does temperature have on the rate of plant growth?

   How does a ship float?

   Why do people have different fingerprints?

   How strong are nylon fishing lines?

2. For each question you rated as good, write two different, clearly stated hypotheses.

3. For each good question, identify the independent variable, the dependent variable, and at least two controlled variables.

Figure 23-1.

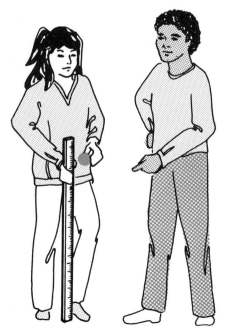

Activity 23-2:   Foot Reaction Time

In this activity you will design and carry out a simple experiment. You will compare your ability to anticipate a ball falling onto your foot from varying heights both when you concentrate on the task and when you are distracted. (Reaction time can be taken as the lowest height above your foot from which a ball can be dropped and the foot moved so that the ball does not touch the foot.)

Materials

metre stick   ping pong ball

Procedure

1. Your teacher will provide each group of students with a ping pong ball and a metre stick.

2. *Ask the Question*: Determine a good question (involving the metre stick and the ping pong ball, concentration and distraction) that you can investigate.

3. *Make a Hypothesis*: Write a hypothesis that relates to your question.

4. *Identify the Variables*: Identify the independent variable, the dependent variable, and some controlled variables.

5. *Design the Procedure*: Describe how you will carry out an experiment to answer your question. At what height will you start dropping the ping pong ball? How many times will you test your partner at each height? By how much will you decrease the height for different sets of trials? When you repeat the experiment trying to distract your partner, what questions will you ask? (You could ask your partner to give the three characteristics of a good question.) Explain how you plan to control some variables.

6. *Collect the Data*: Before beginning the experiment, draw a table in which to record your data. Then carry out your experiment.

7. *Interpret the Results*: Do your results agree with your hypothesis? State a conclusion.

Activity 23-3:   Melting Ice

Now that you have had experience in designing and carrying out a simple experiment, you should be able to conduct a controlled scientific experiment. In this experiment you will investigate the effect of the amount of water on the melting time of an ice cube.

Materials

ice cubes

beakers of varying sizes

thermometers

100 mL graduated cylinder

timer with second hand

Figure 23-2.

Procedure

1. *Ask the Question*: Write a good question to be investigated.

2. *Make a Hypothesis*: Write a hypothesis based on your question.

3. *Identify the Variables*: Draw a table with the following headings: *Type of Variable, Variable, How Variable is Measured.* Fill in the variables. Leave the last column for step 4.

4. *Design the Procedure*: Describe the experiment you will carry out to test your hypothesis. What amounts of water should be added? What should the water temperature be? Should the ice cubes be the same size? Should the water in the beakers be stirred? How many times will each trial be repeated? For each variable fill in the last column of the table.

5. *Collect the Data*: Draw a table for your results. Plot a graph of melting time versus the volume of water. Be sure to label both axes.

6. *Interpret the Results*:
   a) Comment on the validity of your hypothesis. Describe any problems encountered during the experiment.
   b) Examine your graph and make a statement which describes the relationship between the independent variable and the dependent variable.
   c) How can you explain the statement in 6b)?

Activity 23-4: Designing a Controlled Experiment

You should now be able to design a controlled experiment.

Procedure

1. Select a suitable question. You can use one of your own, one provided by your teacher, or the following one: How is the depth to which an object sinks in water affected by its mass?

2. Make a hypothesis, identify the variables, design the experiment procedure, perform the procedure, collect data, interpret the results, and state a conclusion.

Study Questions

1. For each of the following questions:

   i) explain why the question is a good one;

   ii) write a hypothesis for the question;

   iii) list the independent variable, the dependent variable, and at least two controlled variables.

   a) Do all seeds germinate at the same rate?

   b) How does the viscosity (thickness) of multigrade motor oil vary with temperature?

   c) For paper airplanes, how does the distance flown depend on wing area?

2. Make up three good questions of your own and explain why each is a good question for a science project. Write a hypothesis for each question and identify all variables.

CHALLENGER

Design an experiment to find out why cans of diet pop float and why cans of all nondiet drinks sink.

The sealed aluminum cans of diet soft drinks float, but the old standards sink in a tank of water.

23.2 Carrying Out Your Science Project

It is important to plan your project carefully so that you have all the materials ready when you need them and can complete the experiment in the available time. A badly organized project can lead to delays due to lack of materials, rushed or sloppy observations, inaccurate measurements, and erroneous conclusions.

When you finish this section, you should be able to:

- design and perform a controlled experiment
- organize and analyze the results
- state the conclusions reached
- write a science project report

Doing the Experiment

Obtaining the Materials

Make a list of all the materials and equipment you will need for your experiment. Use common and inexpensive items whenever possible. If your school does not have a necessary piece of equipment, you or your teacher could perhaps arrange to borrow it from a nearby university. If you need to order an item from a supply company, be sure to tell your teacher well in advance of when you start the experiment. He or she may be willing to order it for you.

Keeping Notes

You may find it helpful to make checklists of procedures or things to do. Each item can be ticked off as it is completed. Table 23-1 shows a Project Checklist. When actually performing the experiment, you may find it helpful to keep a daily log of your procedures and observations.

Identifying Variables and Planning Controls

The experiment that you perform should be a controlled experiment. First list all of the possible variables. Then determine how to change the independent variable, and how to control the variables that should be controlled.

Writing Out Your Procedure

It is a good idea to outline your experimental procedure, step by step, before you begin. For experiments that take place over several days or weeks, each step should be preceded by the date on which it is to be performed.

Checking Your Project

Have your teacher check over your procedure first before you start it. Often, he or she may be able to point out something you may have overlooked. Use the Safety Checklist (Table 23-2) prepared for science fairs to make sure that your experiment is safe.

If performing the experiment at home, inform your parents and alert them to the possible hazards. Make sure you and they have worked out a safe procedure for working at home.

Making Observations

In your science project, you alone are responsible for making the proper observations. Therefore, make sure that you have the proper equipment for making the right observations. Are you using appropriate measuring instruments, and are they sensitive enough? You may wish to record some observations using a tape recorder or even a video recorder, especially if events occur very quickly or if it is not convenient to write in a notebook.

Your observations should be quantitative whenever possible. All measurements should be in SI units.

Table 23-1:   Project Checklist

A. Choosing the Project Idea
1. Does the idea interest you? ☐
2. Is the idea original? ☐
3. Will the idea fit into one of the science fair categories? (Physical Science, Life Science, Applied Science, or Mathematics and Computers) ☐
4. Does your teacher support the idea selected? ☐

B. Writing the Question
1. Is the question simple and specific? Does it compare one thing or situation to another? ☐
2. Is the question sufficiently challenging? ☐
3. Does the question suggest an experiment you can do? ☐
4. Is the necessary equipment available? ☐

C. Writing the Hypothesis and Identifying Variables
1. Is the hypothesis clearly stated? ☐
2. Does the hypothesis link the independent and dependent variables? ☐
3. Can you identify all variables? ☐

D. Research
1. Have you read up on your project idea in up-to-date sources? ☐
2. Have you made a list of references for the bibliography? ☐
3. Have you obeyed the science fair rules regarding the safe use of chemicals, heat sources, electricity, and animals? ☐

E. Designing the Experiment
1. Is the procedure well thought out? ☐
2. Have you determined how to control the necessary variables? ☐
3. Is your procedure outlined in your notes? ☐
4. Have you obtained the necessary materials and equipment? ☐
5. Have you checked your procedure with your teacher before beginning the experiment? ☐

F. Carrying Out the Procedure
1. Are you keeping dated current notes? ☐
2. Are all data and observations recorded in a logical form (tables, graphs, etc.)? ☐
3. Have you repeated the experiment to verify the results? ☐
4. Have you thoroughly analyzed the data? ☐
5. Have you stated all your conclusions? ☐

G. Writing the Report
1. Does the report have the following:

Title Page	Procedure
Project Summary	Results
Purpose	Discussion and Conclusion
Acknowledgements	List of Sources (Bibliography)
Materials	

2. Does the report have an organized and neat appearance? ☐

Table 23-2: Safety Checklist

Safety

1. No hazardous materials have been used. □
2. Hazardous materials were involved. Specify: _____ □
3. The experiments were supervised by:
   Name: _____ Qualifications: _____ □
4. Hazardous moving parts are protected. □
5. Any pressurized containers have a safety valve. □
6. No open flame is used in the display. □
7. Flammable and poisonous chemicals are simulated in the display. □

Electricity

1. Electrical power cords have three-wire grounded connections. □
2. Electrical connections are insulated. □
3. Any non-current-carrying metal parts are connected to the ground lead. □
4. Exposed live parts are at a potential of less than 36 V to ground. □
5. No voltages above 10 kV are generated. □

Radiation

1. Lasers will not be operated during public display. □
2. X-ray and other high energy radiation sources, if used, have been registered and approved by provincial authorities. □
3. Radioisotopes are present at normal background activity. □

Animal Use

1. Vertebrate animals were used. □
2. The experiments were supervised by:
   Name: _____ Qualifications: _____ □
3. Active procedures which could harm or distress the animals were not used. □

Microorganism Use

1. All microbial cultures have been sealed. □
2. No organisms pathogenic to animals are on display. □
3. No biological toxins are on display. □
4. There have been no experimental manipulations with recombinant DNA or animal viruses. □

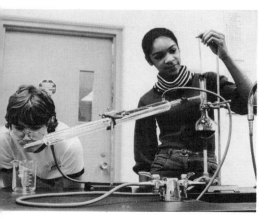

Organizing and Analyzing the Results

Organize the data you have collected in a systematic fashion, using tables and graphs as often as possible. If you are in doubt about how to organize your results, ask your teacher for help. Analyze your results by examining them for patterns.

Repeating the Experiment

Many things can go wrong in an experiment. Perhaps the conditions of the day on which you performed the experiment were not ideal. You can check your observations and results by repeating the experiment. The more times it is repeated, the more reliable your results become. The number of times you repeat the experiment depends on factors such as how much time is available and the cost involved. Your experiment should be designed in such a way that other people can duplicate it and obtain supporting data.

Drawing Conclusions

By this point, you should have completed all of your experimentation and analyzed your data. Now it is time to interpret and sum up your findings. Did your results agree with your hypothesis? If not, can you provide an explanation? Did you encounter any problems? Were you able to solve them satisfactorily? Do you suspect errors in your results? Why?

Even if your results were unsatisfactory or unexpected, they can reveal useful information, such as an inaccurate hypothesis or a fault with the experimental design. They can suggest how future experiments might be designed, or new questions to investigate. All experimenters learn as they go along. Scientific knowledge is expanded through this constant process of trial and error.

Writing the Project Report

A project report is a means of sharing your results with others. Scientists, engineers, and other researchers make their findings known through published reports. The following format is a common one for a scientific report.

Title Page

The title of your project should be centred on a full page about 10 cm from the top of the page. Your name, school, home form, science course, and date of completion of the report should be centred in the bottom third of the page.

Project Summary or Abstract

A project summary, or abstract, is a condensed version of your report. It saves time for busy scientists who can only read reports of particular interest. People read the project summary first to decide whether or not to read the entire report.

The project summary should be no longer than 200-300 words, and should fit on one side of a single page. It should consist of three brief paragraphs. The first paragraph states the purpose of your project. The second paragraph outlines the procedure you followed. The third paragraph summarizes the results you obtained and the conclusions you have made. It is a good idea to write the abstract *after* you have written the rest of the report.

Purpose

Briefly state the purpose of your experiment in one or two sentences. Your hypotheses should be stated here.

Acknowledgements

Although not required, acknowledgements are often included in scientific reports. This is because researchers often wish to thank other people for their sometimes considerable help and advice. People whom you could acknowledge include those who provided guidance (such as teachers), materials (such as a supply company), and the use of a facility (such as a university).

Materials

List the materials used in your experiment. If relevant, briefly explain where you obtained a particular item.

Procedure

Describe any preparatory work that you did. If you had to construct some equipment, describe your method in detail. Then describe the experimental procedure, step by step. If you outlined this before doing the experiment, as recommended earlier, this part of the project should not take long to write. Include a table of variables indicating how each variable was measured or controlled.

Diagrams (with titles and labels) should be placed in this section.

Results

This section consists of a written description of your observations, and charts, tables, and graphs showing the data. If you kept a log of your day-to-day activities, you may wish to include it here.

Discussion and Conclusion

This is perhaps the most important part of your report. Here you interpret your findings and discuss their significance. Arrange your points logically so that your readers can follow the discussion. State whether or not your hypothesis was supported by the results. Don't be afraid to admit your mistakes. The information gained from an experiment that went wrong can be as valuable as that gained from a smoothly-run experiment.

An important part of this section are *predictions* and *recommendations*. These predictions or recommendations show that you recognize the significance of your results. They could concern future experiments or applications beyond the laboratory. For instance, if you were comparing the effectiveness of different stain removers on identical pieces of cloth, you might predict the results using other types of cloth. You could also make recommendations about the most effective cleaner.

List of Sources (Bibliography)

List all the books, magazines, and other sources you used to research and design your project. Also include people you talked to who contributed important information to your project (especially if you made reference to their ideas in the project). Arrange the list in alphabetical order, according to surnames. Sample bibliographical entries are shown in the margin.

After finishing your report, read it several times to check for errors, and have it typed if possible. It is a good idea to ask friends or family to read and criticize the report. If you are entering the project in a science fair, have your teacher check the report.

Sample Bibliographical Entries

Beller, Joel. *So You Want to Do a Science Fair Project*. New York: Arco Publishing, Inc., 1982.

Friesen, Reg. Professor, Chemistry Department, University of Waterloo. Conversation, June 1986.

Study Questions

1. Why should you write out your experimental procedure before you begin?
2. a) What is the purpose of repeating an experiment?
   b) List four possible factors that influence how many times an experiment is repeated.
3. a) What information can be gained from an experiment that "goes wrong"?
   b) Should such an experiment be repeated? Explain why and how.
4. What is the purpose of a project report?
5. a) What is the purpose of a project summary?
   b) How should the project summary be written?
6. How does writing out your procedure before you do the experiment help you to write up the procedure for the report?
7. a) Why is the Discussion and Conclusion section perhaps the most important part of a project report?
   b) What should this section contain, besides a discussion of the experiment itself?

23.3 Entering Your Project in a Science Fair

A science fair is a public exhibition and/or contest of science projects done by students. The projects are judged for originality, scientific approach, level of difficulty, and visual presentation. In addition, participants are usually required to have an interview with the judges.

Taking part in a science fair can be an exciting and challenging prospect. It gives you the opportunity to compete with your peers in a school-wide, community-wide, or nation-wide contest. Planning and producing the project requires you to use your creative skills as well as to apply scientific discipline. The interview with the judges gives you experience in public-speaking. Finally, you are given valuable feedback on your project, regardless of whether you win a prize or not.

When you finish this section, you should be able to:

- design a project suitable for a science fair
- prepare the exhibit
- prepare for the interviews with the judges
- understand how science projects are evaluated

The Canada-Wide Science Fair

The prizes offered by science fairs can be quite substantial. The Canada-Wide Science Fair (sponsored by the Youth Science Foundation) awards prizes ranging from scholarships to trips to places in Canada and to foreign countries. There are also opportunities to work in summer jobs with research institutes such as the National Research Council in Ottawa. Your participation in the fair can also give you valuable practical experience that may be included on job résumés, and perhaps help you to decide on your future education or career plans.

Preparing the Exhibit

Care should be taken when preparing the exhibit so that your project is shown to best advantage. Before beginning your construction of the display, check the rules of the fair. The Canada-Wide Science Fair specifies that all projects must fall into one of four categories: physical science (physics or chemistry), life science, computer science and math, or applied science (engineering). Most science fairs have restrictions concerning the size of the display and the materials that can be exhibited. Figure 23-3 shows a suggested layout

The Youth Science Foundation also provides checklists, newsletters describing Science Fair winners, and information on how to set up a display.

for an exhibit, as well as the maximum dimensions allowed by the CWSF. For copies of the rules of the Canada-Wide Science Fair, write to: Youth Science Foundation, 151 Slater Street, Ottawa, Ontario, K1P 3H3.

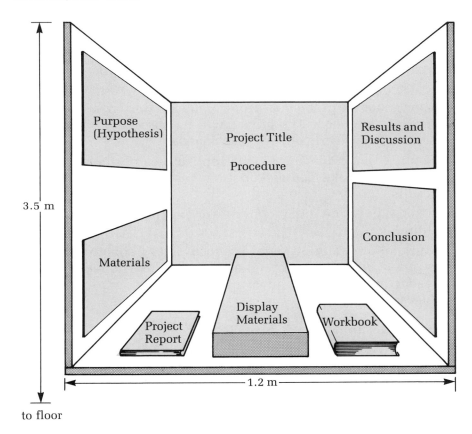

3.5 m

to floor

1.2 m

Figure 23-3. How to Set Up the Display.

For best use of space, a three-panel display board is recommended with the dimensions shown. The material should be strong yet lightweight, easy to assemble, and self-supporting.

Use attractive lettering for the title and headings to make them stand out. Check spelling, and type or print the detailed information.

Drawings, photographs, graphs, models, and slides can be used to illustrate the work done. Large items may not fit the space available, and can be replaced with models, photographs, and drawings.

Preparing for the Interviews with the Judges

Your interviews with the judges are an important part of your overall presentation. From the interview, a judge can get an idea of how well you know your topic, and can ask you questions on it.

You will likely have about ten to twenty minutes to talk to each judge assigned to your project. During this time you should be prepared to:

1. Introduce yourself to the judge, and give some personal information (your name, age, place of residence, grade level, and school).

2. Briefly describe how you became interested in the project.

3. If applicable, briefly explain where you obtained materials or what special facilities you used.

4. State your purpose and hypotheses. State the reasons why you made these particular hypotheses.

5. Describe the experimental procedure. Judges are looking for an understanding and use of variables and controls appropriate to your grade level, so you should discuss these aspects.

6. Discuss your results, pointing to charts, tables, and graphs.

7. State your conclusions, explaining how you arrived at them. Be open about the problems, errors, or unexplained results you may have experienced. The judges will be observing whether you seem to have learned from your mistakes.

8. Explain the implications and applications of your project. If applicable, make recommendations based on your experimental results.

9. Discuss how you might continue or expand your project in the future.

Your oral presentation should be focused and concise. If a judge asks you a question you cannot answer, don't try to make one up. Instead, admit that you don't have an answer and discuss the matter to the best of your ability.

Other Suggestions

You may find it useful to prepare a set of index cards to help you in your oral presentation. Write down a main point on each card, and arrange the points in the order in which you wish to discuss them. Most judges will prefer that you talk to them informally rather than give a prepared speech.

It is a good idea to practise your presentation beforehand by looking into a mirror and observing your appearance as you speak. Do you appear enthusiastic and animated? Is your presentation the right length? Taping your presentation and listening to it can also be helpful. Run through the routine before your family or friends, and use their suggestions to improve your presentation.

On the day of your interviews, dress neatly and appropriately (no jeans). It is natural to be a bit nervous, but try not to let this affect your presentation. Your index cards will focus your presentation and serve as reminders should you forget anything. Stand to one side so that the judge has an unobstructed view of your exhibit. Resist the temptation to rush through your presentation, and speak up.

When you have finished, the judge will likely ask questions and comment critically on the project. Do not be afraid of criticism, as it is meant to help you with future projects. When the interview is over, thank the judge for his or her attention.

How the Exhibits are Judged

Science fair judges are usually teachers, university professors, professionals, and sometimes senior students. Most judges are genuinely interested in the projects and enjoy discussing them with students. Judges at the Canada-Wide Science Fair use the following point system.

Scientific Thought (45 points). Problem and hypothesis clearly stated; effective planning; identification and control of variables; recognition of the limitations of the data; degree of difficulty; background research; scientific approach; data support conclusions.

Originality/Creativity (25 points). Originality of problem and approach; creative and effective procedure, design, and interpretation of data.

Skill (10 points). Effective planning of project; skillful construction of materials and display; questions answered effectively and accurately; amount of outside assistance.

Appearance of Exhibit (10 points). Logical and attractive layout; readable print and lettering; appropriate use of materials; use of multisensory approach.

Written Report (10 points). Scientific format used; logical presentation of ideas; good written expression.

Each science fair has a different system for awarding points. Ask your teacher or the fair organizers about the marking system used in the fair you plan to enter.

Interview. Clear, concise presentation; appropriate scientific vocabulary; knowledge of subject; enthusiasm; questions answered adequately; awareness of project applications and extensions.
Note: The interview is very important. The judges award many of the above points based on the interview.

When the Fair is Over

Participants at science fairs are usually given a written report of the judges' evaluation of their project. The judges try very hard to be fair. Often, they have a hard time deciding the winners among the finalists. If you disagree with the outcome, there is very little that you can do about it. Try to view the evaluation of your own project objectively and learn from the concrete suggestions for improvement. These can help you in your next science project. Even if you do not win a prize at the fair, you will have gained the satisfaction and pride that comes from doing your own project.

Study Questions

1. A good science fair project has definite characteristics. List 20 characteristics of a good science fair project.

2. Visit a school or regional science fair and select a project on display that interests you. Talk to the exhibitor(s) about the project. Write a brief report on the experience.

3. Imagine that you are a judge at a science fair. What would you look for in a project? How can this experience help you in planning your science project?

Readings

Akron-Summit County Public Library. *Science Fair Project Index 1973-1980*. Metuchen, N.J.: Scarecrow Press, 1983.

Beller, Joel. *So You Want To Do a Science Fair Project*. New York: Arco Publishing Inc., 1982. [Ideas on projects, topics, research areas, sources of information for students.]

Gutnik, Martin J. *How To Do a Science Project and Report*. New York: Franklin Watts Inc., 1980. [Intermediate level.]

Moorman, Thomas. *How To Make Your Science Project Scientific*. New York: Atheneum Publishing, 1974. [Excellent resource on scientific methods and their application to science fair projects.]

Van DeMan, Barry A. and McDonald, Ed. *Nuts and Bolts: A Matter of Fact Guide to Science Fair Projects*. Harwood Heights, Illinois: Science Man Press, 1980. [Recommended for Grade 9 and 10 students.]

This photo shows many sources of information on science fairs and project ideas.

KEN NAKAMURA: TOP PRIZE AT THE FAIR

Ken Nakamura loves fishing. Many of Ken's most enjoyable hours have been spent fishing in the North Saskatchewan River that flows through his home town of Edmonton, Alberta. Even in bad weather you may expect to see Ken out fishing with high hopes of landing that "big one".

Because of his hobby, he became interested in acid rain and its possible effects on fish. As he read about acid rain he began to realize that its impact on water life was quite complex. He was particularly interested in the effects of acidification on water plants because they play an important role in the health and beauty of aquatic environments. He was also curious about mosquitoes, because in larval form they are a basic food source for fish, while in adult form they are an annoyance and a carrier of serious diseases.

Ken decided to do a science fair project on how the acidity level of water affects mosquitoes and water plants. He carried out a preliminary experiment followed by two larger-scale investigations. With each trial he attempted to improve his experimental design and increase the reliability of his results.

He found that the larvae for one of the most common types of mosquitoes do best in a pH range of 4.5 to 5.5. At such a low pH level of water, many of the predators of the larvae are decreasing or extinct, which could lead to an increase in mosquito populations. Ken also found that water plants begin to die out at pH levels of 4.5 and lower. Since plants are the first stage in the aquatic food chain, vigorous plant life is essential in maintaining oxygen levels in the water, and in providing habitats for small fish and aquatic animals.

At the Canada-Wide Science Fair in 1986, this 13-year-old Grade 9 student won a gold medal in the Life Sciences category at the intermediate level. He also won scholarships from the Canadian Wildlife Foundation and from the Rockwell Foundation for the best project in the fair. As well, Ken was chosen by Environment Canada as the winner of the Environmental Research Award, for which he was honoured with a certificate of recognition, presented to him in Ottawa on Environment Day.

50 Project Ideas

1. How can different fabrics be compared?
2. How can large crystals of a substance be grown?
3. How does the rate of absorption of water vary with different types of paper?
4. Are all parts of the body equally sensitive?
5. Are blonde hairs thicker than brown hairs?
6. How can metals be identified by chromatography?
7. How does water quality change following its use for irrigation?
8. Is lung capacity related to cigarette consumption?
9. How does the illuminating light affect the apparent colour of objects?
10. How do detergents affect land and water plants?
11. How does the brightness of different candles compare?
12. What is the rate of diffusion through cell membranes?
13. What is the effect of excess salt water on plant growth?
14. What are the best conditions for maximum root growth from a seed?
15. What are the best conditions for maximum stem growth from a seed?
16. Do light or change in temperature affect bacteria and moulds?
17. Under what conditions do icicles form the best?
18. What are the factors affecting ice patterns on glass?
19. Do disinfectants and antiseptics destroy bacteria/moulds?
20. How does the type of light affect the colour of an object?
21. What are the characteristics of liquid crystals?
22. What are the most efficient methods for breaking down crude oil in sea water?
23. How is the drying time of various materials affected by temperature, air movement, and folding the material?
24. How does the lung capacity of different people vary?
25. How fast does the hair of different people grow?
26. How fast do the fingernails of different people grow?
27. How reliable is our sense of taste?
28. What are the optical properties of crystals?
29. How much food does a pet eat in a day?
30. What colours are in flower petals?
31. What gases are essential for plant growth?
32. Can you devise a way to investigate the truth of a manufacturer's claim for a product?
33. How does the effectiveness of commercial stain removers compare?
34. Are undamaged crystals of a substance always the same shape?
35. Does aspirin (and other similar substances) prolong the life of cut flowers?
36. What type of detergent removes the most dirt?
37. Are dyes always "fast"?
38. How can the efficiency of motors be tested?
39. Do some soft drinks hold their fizz longer than others?
40. Can eggs withstand a greater force from one direction than from others?
41. What is the best way to remove make-up?
42. How much carbon dioxide is used by different plants?
43. What is the effect of various fertilizers on the growth of a plant?
44. Do ice samples collected from various locations have the same characteristics?
45. How does electric current affect muscle cells?
46. How does your reaction time vary?
47. Can positions of artificial satellites be noted through dusk observations?
48. How can artificial stalagmites and stalactites be produced?
49. How does a shadow change with the changing position of the Sun?
50. How can plants be grown without soil?

SI Prefixes

Prefix*	Symbol for Prefix	Meaning	Scientific Notation
exa-	E	1 000 000 000 000 000 000	10^{18}
peta-	P	1 000 000 000 000 000	10^{15}
tera-	T	1 000 000 000 000	10^{12}
giga-	G	1 000 000 000	10^{9}
mega-	M	1 000 000	10^{6}
kilo-	k	1 000	10^{3}
hecto-	h	100	10^{2}
deka-	da	10	10^{1}
—	—	1	10^{0}
deci-	d	0.1	10^{-1}
centi-	c	0.01	10^{-2}
milli-	m	0.001	10^{-3}
micro-	μ	0.000 001	10^{-6}
nano-	n	0.000 000 001	10^{-9}
pico-	p	0.000 000 000 001	10^{-12}
femto-	f	0.000 000 000 000 001	10^{-15}
atto-	a	0.000 000 000 000 000 001	10^{-18}

*The more commonly used prefixes are printed in bold face.

Scientific Notation

In scientific notation, all numbers, however large or small, are expressed as values between 1.000 . . . and 9.999 . . . , multiplied by 10 raised to an appropriate power.

Example
How is the number 412.73 expressed in scientific notation?

First, the number must be expressed so that the value lies between 1.000 and 9.999.

$412.73 = 4.1273 \times 10 \times 10$

The number 4.1273 is multiplied by 10 two times (10×10). In scientific notation, 10×10 is expressed as 10^2. The superscript indicates the **power**, or **exponent**, to which 10 is raised. 10^2 is read aloud as "10 to the power of 2". Exponents may be positive or negative.

Therefore, 412.73 in scientific notation is 4.1273×10^2.

Positive Exponents

Positive exponents indicate how many times a number is multiplied by 10. For instance, 2.9×10^4 = $2.9 \times 10 \times 10 \times 10 \times 10$ = 29 000. Multiplying by tens can be done easily by moving the decimal point to the right the correct number of places.

$2.3070 \times 10^4 = 23\ 070$

$4.59 \times 10^6 = 4\ 590\ 000$

$6.02 \times 10^{23} = 602\ 000\ 000\ 000\ 000\ 000\ 000\ 000$

The last number above shows the value of scientific notation. Both very large and very small numbers can be expressed more conveniently using scientific notation than by writing them out in full.

Negative Exponents

Negative exponents indicate how many times a number is divided by 10. For example,

$$3.85 \times 10^{-3} = \frac{3.85}{10 \times 10 \times 10}$$

$$= 0.003\ 85$$

Remember that a negative exponent means that the number is **divided** by tens.

$$7.6 \times 10^{-5}$$

means "divide"

$$= \frac{7.6}{10 \times 10 \times 10 \times 10 \times 10}$$

$$= 0.000\ 076$$

Dividing by tens can be done simply by moving the decimal point to the left the correct number of places.

$4.21 \times 10^{-1} = 0.421$

$8.973 \times 10^6 = 0.000\ 008\ 973$

$3.41 \times 10^{-19} = 0.000\ 000\ 000\ 000\ 000\ 000\ 000\ 341$

To convert a number smaller than 1 into scientific notation, count the number of places the decimal has to be moved to the right to put the value between 1.000 . . . and 9.999. . . . The number of places counted is the negative exponent.

$0.000\ 145 = 1.45 \times 10^{-4}$

$0.000\ 067\ 305 = 6.7305 \times 10^{-5}$

Significant Digits

Every measurement is written with a certain number of **significant digits**, digits that are reliably known. For example, 53 cm has two significant digits, while 53.4 cm has three significant digits. When making any measurement, a person should record all of the digits that are known plus one estimated digit.

Zeroes

When zeroes are included in a measurement, the following rules can be used to determine the number of significant digits.

1. Zeroes placed before the first digit are *not* significant.
   0.0015 m has two significant digits.

2. Zeroes placed between other digits are *always* significant.
   4005 km has four significant digits.

3. Zeroes placed after other digits following a decimal are significant.
   5.30 cm has 3 significant digits.

4. Zeroes at the end of a number are significant only if so indicated by the use of scientific notation. For example, the quantity 4100 g could, depending on the type of balance that is used, have two, three, or four significant digits. There is no way of telling, just by looking at this value, how many significant digits are involved. In scientific notation, the writer is required to indicate the number of significant digits.
   4.1×10^3 g   (two significant digits)
   4.10×10^3 g   (three significant digits)
   4.100×10^3 g   (four significant digits)

Rounding Off

If the calculated answer to a problem contains more digits than are significant, the value should be rounded off, using the following rules.

1. If the digit to be dropped is less than 5, the preceding digit remains the same.

   4.523 to three significant digits becomes 4.52.

2. If the digit to be dropped is greater than 5, the preceding digit is increased by one.

   9.726 to three significant digits becomes 9.73.

   57.7457 to five significant digits becomes 57.746.

Plotting a Graph

Step 1. Laying out the axes

Use a sharp pencil when drawing on graph paper. Draw a vertical axis and a horizontal axis. Place the independent variable (e.g., time) on the horizontal axis, and the dependent variable (e.g., speed) on the vertical axis. Label the axes with the quantities to be plotted. Include the appropriate SI units.

Step 2. Choosing a scale

Choose a scale so that:
  i) all of the points you are plotting fit on the graph;
  ii) the graph fills a large part of the page;
 iii) the scale is easy to use.

For the value of one square, it is best to use numbers in multiples of 1, 2, or 5 (e.g., 0.1, 0.2, 0.3, etc.; 20, 40, 60, etc.). Add the scale to the axes. *Note:* It is not necessary to number every square on the axes.

Step 3. Plotting the points

Plot the points in pencil, making a sharp dot surrounded by a small circle. (The circle indicates that some uncertainty is associated with every measurement.) The point (0,0) is called the **origin**.

The dotted line on Figure C shows where the first point (independent variable = 2; dependent variable = 6) plotted is located.

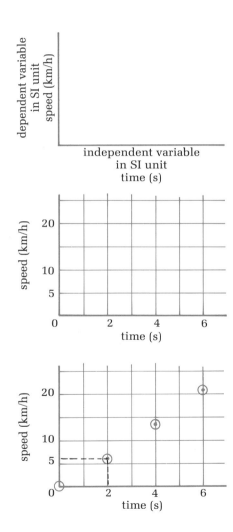

Step 4. Drawing the line or curve

Once you have plotted all the points, draw the smoothest line possible through them. Very often, the line takes the form of a curve. If it is not possible to draw through all of the points with a single line, try to draw an average line. You do this by drawing a line that has equal numbers of points on either side of it.

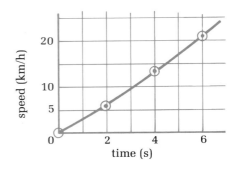

Step 5. Completing the graph

Add a neatly printed title to the graph, along with your name, grade, class, and the date.

Appendix 5

Setting Up and Caring for Your Microscope

A microscope is a delicate instrument that must be operated properly and with care. Here are the steps to follow before you use the microscope, and after you have finished using it.

Before You Use the Microscope

1. Use both hands to carry the microscope from its storage space. Hold the arm of the microscope firmly with one hand, and place your other hand under the base.

2. Place the microscope gently on the desk. Do not tip it over or place it on its side. The microscope has removable parts that may fall out and break.

3. Check the ocular and objective lenses. If they are smudged or dusty, use lens paper supplied by your teacher to *gently* clean them. Do not use paper tissues, paper towels, or other materials since they may scratch the lens surface.

4. If your microscope has a lamp as a light source, make sure that the electrical cord is not placed where someone could trip over it. If your microscope uses a mirror instead, adjust the mirror angle so that light reflects upward through the diaphragm.

5. Make sure that the low-power objective is in the viewing position. (The lens is in viewing position when it is pointing straight downwards over the microscope stage.) Also check that the body tube is at its highest position by carefully turning the coarse adjustment knob.

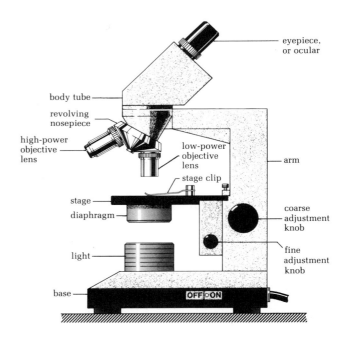

6. Look through the eyepiece. The lit-up circular area you see is called the **field of view**. Adjust the diaphragm until the field of view is bright but not glaring.

Index

The page numbers in **boldface** indicate definitions.

abiotic environment, **3**-4
absolute zero, 315-6
absorption, 224
acid-base indicators, 382-4
acid rain, 458-9, 759
acids, 372, **373**, 374, 377-80
　mineral, 378, 379
　uses of, 379, 380
adaptation
　and environment, 175-6
　and inherited variability, 177
　and learning, 183-4
　and seasonal change, 180-1
　and social structure, 182
　behavioural, **180**
　process of, 179
　structural, **180**
adaptations, **162**
aerobic, 587
Agent Orange, 638
air pressure, 174, 205
alkali, **374**
alkaloids, **394**
amber, 467
amber effect, 467
ammeter, 501
ampere, **500**
amylase, 225, **228**
anaerobic, 587
analgesics, **394**
antacids, 372, 374, 391-3
antiknock, 439
aorta, **250**
aortic arches, 249
applied chemistry, 371, 390-2, 399, 420-2
Aristotle, 116, 260
arteries, **248**
　coronary, **262**
　pulmonary, **250**
asteroids, **711**-2
astronomical unit (A.U.), **698**
astronomy, **659**, 696
atmosphere, **9**
atoms, 378, 467
atrium (pl., atria), **250**
aurora, **671**

aurora borealis, 671
autotrophs, **5**, 6, 107, 112-3
Avogadro, Count Amedeo, 285
axis, **668**

Bacon, Francis, 284
balance of nature, **33**
bases, 372, **374**, 378-81
　uses of, 379-81
battery, 495, 510
Becquerel, Henri, x
Bethune, Dr. Norman, 216
Big Bang Theory, 726
bile, **228**
bimetallic strip, 313, 314
biochemical oxygen demand (BOD), **612**, 613
biocides, **32**
bioconcentration, 33
biodegradable, **411**, 580
biomass
　pyramid of, **20**
biomes, **53**
　and natural succession, 59-64
　of North America, 54-6
　terrestrial, 53
biosphere, **9**
biotic environment, **3**-4
Black, Joseph, 283
black holes, **717**
blood, **248**
blood pressure, **261**
Boyle, Robert, 284
branch circuit, **520**, 521, 522
breakdown of food
　chemical, 224, 228
　physical, 224, 228
breathing, **201**
Brown, Robert, 285
Brownian motion, 285
bubble tower, 434

caloric fluid theory of heat, 283-4
Canada Water Act, 411
Canada-Wide Science Fair, 754-5, 759
Canadian Consumer, 400, 401
capillaries, **248**
carbon, 378
carbon cycle, 26-8
carcinogens, **635**, 652, 653
carnivores, **15**, 115
　top, **16**
Carothers, Wallace, 441
carrying capacity, **44**, 80-1

cell, 495, 510
　dry, 497, 508
　dry primary, **508**
　electrochemical, **507**
　lead-acid, **509**
　nickel-cadmium, **509**
　primary, **507**
　secondary, **507**, 509
　solar, 516
　voltaic, 505, **507**, 508
　wet primary, **507**
　zinc-copper, 508
cell respiration, 27, 167-8, **197**-8, 200
cell specialization, **202**
cells in parallel, **514**
cells in series, **515**
cellulose, 440
Celsius, Anders, 290
Charles, Jacques, 315
chemical oxygen demand (COD), **613**
chemoreception, **145**
chemosynthesis, 109
Chevreul, Michel, 412
chromosphere, **670**
cilia, 155
circuit
　branch, **520**, 521, 522
　closed, **499**
　electric, **494**, 495, 497-8
　open, **498**
　parallel, 517, **520**-3
　series, 517, 519-20, 522-3
　short, 511
circuit breaker, 541-2
circulation
　in birds and mammals, 262-3
　in earthworm, 249
　in fishes and amphibians, 261-2
　in multicellular animals, 248
　in protists, 247
circulatory fluids, 248
circulatory pump, 249
circulatory systems, 252-3
　closed, 255
　comparison of, 260-3
　of earthworm, 234
　of fish, 259
　open, 254-5
classes, **121**
classification, 115-6, 121, 122, 123
climax, **60**
climax community, **60**, 62
closed circuit, **499**
closed circulation, 255
coagulation, **617**

Answers to the Short Answer Unit Wrap-Up Questions

Unit I
True or False: F, T, T, F, T. Multiple Choice: b, d, c, a, d. Complete the Statement: food web, abiotic, carrying capacity, carbon cycle, biome. Matching Items: 1. i/d, ii/a, iii/e, iv/b; 2. i/c, ii/a, iii/d, iv/b; 3. i/e, ii/a, iii/b, iv/c; 4. i/b, ii/d, iii/a, iv/c.

Unit II
True or False: F, F, T, T, T. Multiple Choice: a, c, c, a, b. Complete the Statement: stimuli, sensory adaptation, cone/rod, the binomial nomenclature, increase. Matching Items: 1. i/a, ii/c, iii/e, iv/d, v/b, vi/e; 2. i/b, ii/c, iii/c, iv/a, v/a; 3. i/e, f, ii/d, iii/a,e, iv/b.

Unit III
True or False: F, T, T, F, T. Multiple Choice: b, c, c, a, d. Complete the Statement: septum, nephridia, bile, spiracles, surface area. Matching Items: 1. i/c, ii/d, iii/a, iv/b; 2. i/d, ii/c, iii/a, iv/b; 3. i/d, ii/a, iii/b, iv/c; 4.i/d, ii/c, iii/a, iv/b.

Unit IV
True or False: F, F, F, T, F. Multiple Choice: b, c, d, a. Complete the Statement: energy, thermal, rates of thermal expansion, specific heat of vaporization, exfiltration (air convection). Matching Items: 1. i/c, ii/f, iii/b, iv/d; 2. i/c, ii/d, iii/b, iv/a.

Unit V
True or False: F, T, T, F, T. Multiple Choice: c, c, d, b, c. Complete the Statement: hydrocarbons, fractions, polyester, hard, acid. Matching Items: 1. i/b, ii/d, iii/a, iv/c; 2. i/a, ii/d, iii/e, iv/b; 3. i/d, ii/a, iii/e, iv/c.

Unit VI
True or False: T, F, F, F, T. Multiple Choice: b, d, b, c, a. Complete the Statement: contact, ion, unlike poles, electric current, magnet (electomagnet). Matching Items: 1. i/c, ii/e, iii/a, iv/d, a; 2. i/d, ii/e, iii/f, iv/b; 3.i/c, ii/d, iii/b, iv/a.

Unit VII
True or False: F, T, T, F, T. Multiple Choice: b, c, a, d, c. Complete the Statement: registered, Treatment, engineered, disposables, Aerobic/anaerobic. Matching Items: 1. i/d, ii/c, iii/e, iv/b; 2. i/c, ii/d, iii/a, iv/b; 3. i/c, ii/a, iii/b; 4. i/d, ii/a, iii/b, iv/c.

Unit VIII
True or False: F, F, T, T, T. Multiple Choice: b, a, c, d, b. Complete the Statement: constellation, refracting, meteorities, true variable stars, astronomical units. Matching Items: 1. i/c, ii/g, iii/a, iv/d (until 1999), v/f; 2. i/d, ii/a, iii/e, iv/b, v/f; 3. i/e, ii/b, iii/d, iv/a, v/f.